MICROBIOLOGY RESEARCH ADVANCES

APPLICATIONS OF MICROBIAL GENES IN ENZYME TECHNOLOGY

MICROBIOLOGY RESEARCH ADVANCES

Additional books in this series can be found on Nova's website under the Series tab.

Additional e-books in this series can be found on Nova's website under the e-book tab.

GENETICS - RESEARCH AND ISSUES

Additional books in this series can be found on Nova's website under the Series tab.

Additional e-books in this series can be found on Nova's website under the e-book tab.

MICROBIOLOGY RESEARCH ADVANCES

APPLICATIONS OF MICROBIAL GENES IN ENZYME TECHNOLOGY

VIJAI KUMAR GUPTA
MARIA G. TUOHY
GAURI DUTT SHARMA
AND
SMRITI GAUR
EDITORS

New York

Library of Congress Cataloging-in-Publication Data

ISBN: 978-1-62417-808-5

Library of Congress Control Number: 2012956344

Published by Nova Science Publishers, Inc. † New York

Contents

Foreword

The importance of sustainability in productive activities has been widely recognized, being required the replacement of chemical processes based on non-renewable inputs for chemical or biochemical processes that use renewable inputs. It is also recognized the need for replacing the multistep chemical process for biotechnological processes more efficient. This condition favors the use of renewable raw materials through biotransformation and biocatalysis. These technologies are already being used by industry, although there is a great interest in developing new processes. Its implementation results in higher quality products, obtained by means of lower energy consumption and lower environmental impact.

In function of these tendencies and needs, it is forecasted a significant increase in consumption of enzymes worldwide. This scenario is particularly attractive because the use of enzyme catalysis allies the technological development with the utilization of renewable raw materials as well as with environmental preservation. The enzymatic technologies found applications in agriculture as biocontrol agents, in food as additive or to its production and, more recently, in biofuels production due to great interest in development a technological and economical viable process for hydrolysis of lignocellulosic or starch-rich materials for second generation ethanol production.

In this scenario, the use of microbial genes in enzyme technology is fundamental to obtain success during the developing and implementation of enzymatic process, because the use of genetic engineering employs tools that allow the selection/obtainment of more specific enzymes or to improve the its affinity to a specific substrate. These possibilities will lead to an improvement on process productivities, making it technologically and economically viable. In this sense, the book "Applications of Microbial Genes in Enzyme Technology" reports a theme in the frontier of knowledge and brings the readers with new development on genes manipulation to improve enzyme production/application.

Prof. Marcio A. Mazutti
Universidade Federal de Santa Maria - UFSM
Santa Maria – RS, Brazil

Preface

Microbes are excellent models for understanding biological interactions and evolutionary biology due to their large ecological and genetic diversity. With the advancement of biotechnology, increasing numbers of enzymes have been identified and produced before being used in various industries including medicine, agro-industry, commodity production biofuel and modern biotechnology. Microbes are ubiquitous in all ecosystems and vital for its functions. The Enzyme Technology work as to establish to identify and characterize novel enzymes with desirable characteristics by taking advantage of biodiversity, especially the hugely diverse variety of microorganisms. Microbial enzymes are economical and can be produced on large scale within the limited space and time. The amount produced depends on size of fermenter, type of microbial strain and growth conditions. It can be easily extracted and purified. Microbial diversity is one of the important resource for development of new micro-organisms and strain improvements, for several important genes and production of enzymes having high value to food and pharmaceutical and biotechnology industry. The identification of microbial resources allows the heterologous high-level overexpression of the corresponding enzymes. They used to produce broad range of hydrolytic enzymes that can break down complex biopolymers and produce chemically and structurally complex compounds with high industrial interest. A better understanding of microbial ecology may lead to the identification of novel species, functions and biomolecules for a variety of biotechnological applications. Exploitation of the valuable genetic resources that microbial diversity comprises, most often requires modern biotechnological methodology. Identifying species of organisms by short sequences of DNA has been at the center of current research. The microorganisms have specific genes introduced into their DNA through genetic engineering, so that they produce enzymes naturally made by other micro-organisms or newly developed strain of particular microbe. The research includes all aspects of enzyme biotechnology from screening of enzymes from microbial isolates and from metagenomic libraries, gene isolation, enzyme production in wild-type microbes and recombinant systems to development of enzymatic processes in industry. It means that due to presence of high genetic flexibility they can be genetically manipulated to increase the yield of enzymes within very short generation times. Since genes encode enzymes, the changes in gene certainly bring about alteration in enzyme structure, so using enzyme engineering systems and their modification of enzyme structure by alteration of gene/ modified gene it seems to be a promising technology for the production of stable enzymes by genetically engineered microbial cells in pilot scale.

This book provides an extensive survey of applications of important microbial genes and their functions in enzymes production for several industrial processes. The chapters presented in the book will cater the need of students of undergraduate, postgraduate courses and researchers across disciplines and sectors where microbial diversity and enzyme research and experimentation are undertaken. Moreover, this book covers the recent updates on important genes, their functions in microbial systems and their applications in enzyme technology. Therefore, this publication will be very useful not only to experienced researchers but also for the beginners.

Dr. Vijai Kumar Gupta, NUIG, Galway, Ireland and MITS University, India
Prof. Gauri Dutt Sharma, Assam University, India
Dr. Maria G. Tuohy, NUIG, Galway, Ireland
Dr. Smriti Gaur, JIIT, Noida, India
04th May, 2012

About the Editors

DR. VIJAI KUMAR GUPTA
FHAS, FICCB, FSAB, YSA-2009 & 2011
Molecular Glycobiotechnology Group
Department of Biochemistry
School of Natural Sciences
National University of Ireland Galway
Galway, Ireland
&
Assistant Professor of Biotechnology
Department of Science,
Faculty of Arts, Science & Commerce,
MITS University, Lakshmangarh-332311 (Sikar)
Rajasthan, India

Dr. V. K. Gupta is the Assistant Professor of Biotechnology at MITS University, Rajasthan, India. Currently, he is working as a Post Doctoral Research Scientist, at National University of Ireland Galway, Ireland. He has completed his Ph.D. in Microbiology from Dr. R.M.L. Avadh University, Faizabad, UP, India in 2009. He has been honored with several awards in his career including the prestigious Indian ICAR Senior Research Fellowship, Young Scientist Award-2009 & 2011 and Gold Medal Award-2009. Dr. Gupta is the fellow of International Society of Contemporary Biologist, Society of Applied Biotechnology and Hind Agri-Horticultural Society, India. He has submitted 29 fungal nucleotide sequences to NCBI, USA and deposited 147 fungal strains in different International/National fungal agencies/Institution *viz.* CABI, UK; NBAIM, Mau, India; IMTECH, Chadigarh, India and

ARI, Pune, India. Also, his group in NUI Galway is under process to submit 02 inventions for European patent. He is the editor and member of 9 International and 2 National journals with 38 International/National research publication and 23 book chapters in books published from highly recognized International/National publishers in his hand. He is the editor/author/internal editorial board member of books/book series from reputed publishers of International fame viz. Elsevier, The Netherlands; Science Publisher, New Hampshire, USA; Taylor and Francis, USA; Springer, USA and LAP Lambert Academic Publishing, Germany.

PROF. GAURI DUTT SHARMA
Pro-Vice-Chancellor
(Former Vice Chancellor, Nagaland University),
Assam University,
Silchar – 788 011, Assam, India

Professor G. D. Sharma has about 40 years of experience in the field of teaching and research in various central universities of India. He is Pro Vice-Chancellor and Dean School of Life Sciences, Assam University, Silchar, India. He has been Vice Chancellor of Nagaland University, India. He has supervised 30 Ph.D. and M. Phil students. He has authored/edited 10 books and published 250 research papers in journals of repute. For his research contributions certain prestigious Awards like Dr Narsimhan Medal by Indian Phytopathology Society, Birbal Sahni Award by Indian Botanical Society, Rashtriya Ratan Award by International Study center, DEED Award by Confederation of Indian Universities affiliated to UN-ECOSOC, International CCLP Honor, Vice President of Indian Mycology Society etc.Dr Sharma has visited several countries for various academic assignments. His current area of interest includes Microbial diversity, Microbial enzymes, Biocontrol, Food microbiology medicinal plants and health.

DR. MARIA G. TUOHY
Head, Molecular Glycobiotechnology Group
Department of Biochemistry

School of Natural Sciences
National University of Ireland Galway
Galway, Ireland

Dr. Maria G. Tuohy is the Head of the Molecular Glycobiotechnology Research Group, Department of Biochemistry, School of Natural Sciences, NUI Galway which has developed a strong track record in Glycobiotechnology and Enzyme Biotechnology. She has more than 20 years experience in the molecular biochemistry, genetics and biotechnology of fungi, with a special interest in thermophilic ascomycetes and the characterization of these fungi as cell factories for protein production, including novel thermostable enzymes/enzyme systems. Dr. Tuohy and her group have developed patented enzyme-based technologies for key bioenergy and biorefinery applications from terrestrial and marine biomass and wastes, including 3rd generation feedstocks. The group also investigates the use of enzymes for the recovery and selective modification of high-value biochemicals and plant carbohydrate-derived bioactives ('Glycobioengineering'). Dr. Tuohy is a PI in the Energy Research Centre, NUI, Galway and the recently funded national Bioenergy and Biorefinery Competence Centre, is a member of the EU FP7 Biofuels Platform and a national research PhytoNetwork. Dr. Tuohy has been a visiting researcher in RUGhent, Belgium and BSH Institut fur Holzchemie, Hamburg. Dr. Tuohy is author of ~132 research publications, including refereed publications, book chapters, conference papers poster/short communications. She is also a reviewer for international journals and funding agencies and several books as co-editor- Elsevier, The Netherlands, Springer Science Publisher, USA; CRC Press, Taylor and Francis, USA; Lambert, Germany; Nova Science Publisher, USA and Elsevier Press, USA (under Progress) with Dr. V. K. Gupta.

Associate Editor

DR. SMRITI GAUR
Lecturer
Department of Biotechnology
Jaypee Institute of Information Technology (Deemed University)
Noida, India

Dr. Smriti Gaur is Lecturer at Department of Biotechnology, Jaypee Institute of Information Technology (Deemed University), Noida, India. She did her graduation in Botany (Honours) and an advance certificate course of two year duration in Cell Biotechnology from Dayalbagh Educational Institute (Deemed University), Agra. She did her Masters in Applied Microbiology from Cancer Hospital and Research Institute, Jiwaji

University, Gwalior. She has done her PhD in Biotechnology in 2010, where she isolated, characterized and purified proteases from plant and microbial sources. She has been Secured second position in her graduation and master courses. She has attended many international and national conferences and presented her research work both in India and abroad. She has been awarded travel grant from Society of Industrial Microbiology and Biotechnology, USA and Department of Biotechnology, Ministry of Science and Technology, Govt of India. She is presently focused in the area of Microbial biotechnology and enzyme technology. She has submitted one bacterial strain sequences to NCBI, USA. She has 2 international research publication and 2 international book chapters in her hand.

In: Applications of Microbial Genes in Enzyme Technology ISBN: 978-1-62417-808-5
Editors: V.K.Gupta, M.G.Tuohy, G.D.Sharma et al.

Chapter 1

Use of Metagenomics for the Production of Novel Enzymes

***Tanzeem Akbar Cheema*[1]*, Radhika Singh*[2] *and Sudip Kumar Rakshit*[3*†]**

[1]Food Engineering and Bioprocess TechnologyProgram,
Asian Institute of Technology (AIT),
Klong Luang, Pathumthani, Thailand
[2]Department of Chemistry, Dayalbagh Educational Institute,
Dayalbagh, Agra, India
[3]Department of Chemical Engineering,
Lakehead University, Thunder Bay,
Ontario, Canada

Abstract

This chapter is an overview of the recent advances in metagenomics, which is a novel method of utilizing the unravelled genetic information of microorganisms which are uncuturable using classical microbial methods. With the understanding that only a small fraction (less than 1%) of infinite microbial diversity can be grown in nutrient media, the culture-independent approach of metagenomics seems to have considerable potential. The possibility of recombining the genes of useful enzymes retrieved from these "unculturable" microorganisms into the organisms, which we know to culture and genetically modify, opens up the possibility of producing a large number of enzymes with novel properties making them useful in a number of biotechnological applications. This chapter includes an example of the possibility of producing new cellulase enzymes from the metagenome of microbes which grow symbiotically in rumens of herbivores creating

* Corresponding author: Sudip Kumar Rakshit. Department of Chemical Engineering, Lakehead University, Thunder Bay, Ontario P7B 5E1, Canada, E-mail: sudip.rakshit@lakeheadu.com.

† Tanzeem Akbar Cheema: Food Engineering and Bioprocess Technology Program, Asian Institute of Technology (AIT), Klong Luang, Pathumthani, 12120, Thailand. Radhika Singh: Department of Chemistry, Dayalbagh Educational Institute, Dayalbagh, Agra – 282110, India.

breakdown of the cellulosic feed they consume. The array of methods that are used in genetic screening for novel genes, introduction of microorganisms in the phylogenetic tree, etc. are discussed.

Introduction

Enumeration of microbes in environmental samples can be done either by direct count using a microscope, or by viable count by growing diluted-samples in nutrient media. The disparity between the two was not given much importance for a long time. But recent studies have shown that we are not yet able to cultivate 99% of the microorganisms available in nature (Amann *et al.*, 1995; Streit and Schmitz, 2004), as we are not providing them the appropriate conditions for them to grow (Bull *et al.*, 2000). Many studies which explore the diversity and potential of microorganisms using classical microbial culture methods are thus certainly limited.

With the advent of genetic engineering and molecular biological methods, the possibility of using the wealth of genetic information contained in the microorganisms which we are not able to cultivate, now called unculturable microorganisms, is now promising. It is possible to mine for genetic information in these microorganisms, capable of carrying out a specific bioconversion, and reproduce them using a culturable host microorganism, such as *E. coli*. This method of using the genetic information of unculturable microorganisms is known as metagenomics.

The overall technique would then be to release all DNA from a mixture of microorganisms (e.g. from rumen fluid, or a soil sample), breakdown of the DNA into manageable fractions and then clone them into a well-studied host. Then an analysis based on functional genomics may be able to identify new catalysts, or metabolites, with characteristics better than those produced by known culturable microorganisms. Besides its practical and possible use in industrial applications, metagenomics can play a vital role in studies related to ecological diversity, phylogeny, understanding symbiosis, enriching gene families, etc.

There are many various stages in developing a metagenome. The first step is certainly sampling, like in traditional microbiology, from a source at which there is the maximum likelihood of getting the catalyst or metabolite, one is aiming to produce. It should be a representative sample from the source. The total number of microorganisms present is difficult to access as they cannot be seen. Some previous experience on the numbers involved in the sample will be helpful in this decision. Utilization of the whole sample or filtration to screen out undesirable microorganisms (e.g. viral particles from eukaryotes) is the next step. This is followed by cell lysis, extraction and shearing of metagenomic DNA. The DNA fragments are then cloned into plasmids and libraries are created. Sequencing of the clones then follows and finally alignment of the sequences is done using bioinformatics. A typical sequence procedure is to use the shotgun method, where random fragments of genetic material are cloned into plasmid vectors and amplified in quantity before being sequenced. However, more rapid and powerful methods are currently being developed and used. Assembly of the sequence information to complete DNA forms is indeed very difficult and its use in metagenomic studies to carry out partial assembly to the level of whole domains or multi-domain genes. For practical application, the most important part is then to identify useful genes. The incomplete nature of metagenomic data makes this difficult. The commonly used Basic Local Alignment Search Tool (BLAST) can be used for genes with known homologs and cannot be used to find new families and new genes. For the latter, statistical recognition methods like Morkov or hidden Morkov Models are used. A good overview of the metagenomic process methododlogy is given by Wooley *et al.* (2010). The use of enzymes in bulk requires that the enzyme can be used under conditions required for the application, rather than the other way round. The screening of thermostable enzymes used in the starch industry is a good example of this sort. Metagenomics can provide this possibility in screening enzymes which can be used in process conditions. This has resulted in a number of enzymes being under scrutiny by this method. This includes amylases (Yun *et al.*, 2004), different types of lipases (Henne *et al.*, 2000; Wei *et al.*, 2009), proteases (Lee *et al.*, 2007), cellulases (Duan *et al.*, 2009; Feng *et al.*, 2007; Voget *et al.*, 2006), xylanases (Lee *et al.*, 2006a). All these enzymes possess novel, unique, or enhanced functionality. Thus, metagenomics offers a huge potential for discovering new microbial proteins and enzymes.

Isolation of Metagenomic DNA

Metagenomic studies begin by extracting total DNA from all microorganisms living in a particular environmental sample. There could be thousands or even millions of organisms in one sample. For DNA extraction, bacteria can be lysed directly from the samples, or after separating the microbes from the other sample materials. If superior DNA integrity and purity is required, bacteria should be isolated before DNA extraction is conducted. The construction of environmentally derived DNA libraries with large inserts is often hindered because of the poor quality of the isolated DNA (Patrick *et al.*, 2005). The purity of DNA seriously affects cloning process. The contamination of purified DNA with polyphenolic compounds is the most problematic for molecular manipulation and cloning. It is not easy to sequester these compounds, and they severely affect enzymes used in DNA isolation (Streit and Schmitz, 2004). For efficient DNA extraction and its reproducibility, variations in cell lysis and purification treatments and their effects on yield and purity of DNA have been tested (Krsek and Wellington, 1999). The extraction yield improved by increasing the concentration of EDTA or monovalent ions in isolation buffers, using mechanical lysis treatments, and using ethanol precipitation in place of PEG precipitation, while purity was improved using buffers with decreasing concentration of EDTA, or by reducing the ionic strength of the buffer, and using mechanical treatments. No lytic treatment was efficient on its own. The highest purity was achieved using Crombach buffer and a combination of bead-beating with lysozyme and SDS lysis followed by potassium acetate and PEG precipitation, phenol/chloroform purification, isopropanol precipitation and spermine-HCl precipitation. Sonication sheared the DNA more efficiently than bead-beating. Lysozyme and SDS lysis without any mechanical treatments allowed isolation of larger DNA fragments (40-90 kb) (Krsek and Wellington, 1999).

Enrichment strategies have been used by others to successfully construct metagenomic libraries. Libraries constructed from cellulose-enriched samples and screened for cellulase activity had a greater number of positive clones, compared to studies without an enrichment step (Feng *et al.*, 2007; Kim *et al.*, 2008; Pang *et al.*, 2009). Enrichment cultures can be used in the laboratory to selectively enhance the isolation of genomic DNA with desired activities within environmental samples.

Metagenomic Library Construction

The extracted metagenomic DNA, consisting of millions of random fragments of DNA, can be cloned into a form capable of being maintained in cultivable laboratory bacteria. These bacteria are used to create a "metagenomic library" that includes the genomes of all the microorganisms found in a habitat, the natural environment of the organisms. These libraries are actually repositories of DNA fragments cloned into the appropriate vectors. Vectors used in construction of DNA libraries depends on insert sizes, e.g. the construction of small insert libraries (<10 kb) in a standard sequencing vector and in *Escherichia coli* as a host strain (Henne *et al.*, 1999). However, small insert libraries are not good as far as the detection of large gene clusters or operons is concerned. To overcome this limitation, investigators have been constructing large insert libraries, such as cosmid DNA libraries with insert sizes ranging from 25–35 kb (Entcheva *et al.*, 2001), and bacterial artificial chromosome (BAC) libraries with insert sizes up to almost 200 kb (Beja *et al.*, 2000a; Rondon *et al.*, 2000). The construction of fosmid libraries with inserts of 40 kb of foreign DNA has also been reported (Beja *et al.*, 2002b). *E. coli* is still the better-choice host for the cloning and expression of any metagenome-derived genes. Some other hosts, such as *Streptomyces lividans* been used to identify genes involved in the biosynthesis of novel antibiotics (Courtois *et al.*, 2003). Moreover, metagenomic libraries are currently developed in other Gram-negative hosts by several laboratories working in the field, which will become available soon. Such developments would definitely have a positive impact on screening efficiency of novel biocatalysts and other useful genes.

Metagenomic Library Screening

Two approaches have been used to investigate a metagenomic library. These include function based screening and PCR based screening.

Function-Based Screening

Function-based screening for novel genes is a way to screen out positive clones based upon their function. Such screening can help find totally new classes of genes without sequencing. Using highly sophisticated picking and pipetting robots, such function-based searches for novel genes in metagenomic libraries have often been conducted. Clones expressing a fully functional gene product can be identified for a number of specific functions (Seow *et al.*, 1997; Courtois *et al.*, 2003). Another advantage of this approach is that it does not require prior sequence knowledge, so the novel genes are detected during such searches (Brennan *et al.*, 2004). Yet there are some limitations of this approach as well. Several hundred thousand clones have often been explored to identify less than ten active clones in a single screen (Henne *et al.*, 2000; Majernik *et al.*, 2001). This is mainly due to the lack of efficient transcription of the metagenome-derived genes in the host strain. This effect might be can be further complicated by a weak translation in combination with a poor secretion of the foreign protein by the employed host strain. The possibility that the desired protein is not folded correctly because of the absence of required chaperones in the host strain can reduce numbers further. Similarly, cofactors might not be synthesized in the host strain or not inserted correctly into the recombinant metagenomic protein. The use of a different codon, could be a reason for poor protein expression and low activities as well. Several researchers are currently working on solutions for some of these problems and constructing novel vectors and strains.

PCR-Based Screening

In parallel with function-based screening, PCR-based screening is another approach frequently used in many laboratories around the world. Using appropriate primers, a PCR is conducted to amplify the desired gene from a metagenomic DNA sample. For this approach, one needs to design PCR primers based on the conserved regions of nucleotide sequences of known gene or protein families, or degenerate primers. While this is an easy approach, this is also the reason why this approach has limitations in detecting the entirely new gene, or genes. Conserved regions of ketosynthase (KS-alpha) and ACP genes, 2 CLF (KS-beta) genes from unclassified streptomycetes were used in designing PCR primers in order to conduct PCR for gene identification without isolating the parent microorganism from soil (Seow *et al.*, 1997). Similarly, conserved regions of dehydratase gene were used in designing PCR primers in order to conduct PCR to identify environmental libraries harboring dehydratase genes (Knietsch *et al.*, 2003). Dehydratase gene encoding libraries were used as starting material for revealing specific PCR product and capturing the specific clones in the library. Moreover, PCR technique was also used in screening the environmental libraries for identifying hyperthermophilic amylase gene, using degenerate PCR primers designed on the basis of sequences found at the N and C termini of the known hyperthermophilic amylase. Likewise, sequence homologues were screened from metagenomic DNA libraries by using PCR products as probes. The ultimate intent of most genetic transformation experiments is expression of recombinant protein in the expression host. To express recombinant proteins, many different expression systems are currently offered by various companies across the globe. Although most genes can be expressed in many systems, yet it is essential to ascertain which system would be more advantageous for the production of the recombinant proteins (Soresen and Mortensen, 2005). The ideal system for recombinant protein expression is that which produces most safe, biologically active material at the lowest cost. Based on the type of the host cell, currently available expression systems can conveniently be categorized into eukaryotic and prokaryotic expression systems.

Cellulose Hydrolysis and Metagenomics

Cellulose, a polymer of D-glucopyranose units linked by β-1,4-glucosidic bonds, is the most abundant renewable biomass in nature. On a world-wide basis, 1.3×10^{10} Mt (dry weight) of terrestrial plants are produced annually (Demain *et al.*, 2005). The hydrolysis of these and other cellulosic feedstuffs and their conversion to commodity products such as bioethanol has great economic potential and will impact positively on environmental conservation as it will reduce reliance on finite fossil fuels (Lynd *et al.*, 2005; Wilson, 2009).

Hydrolysis of cellulose into glucose has been studied intensively to utilize it as an alternative energy source or a starting material to convert into it various useful compounds (Jeewon, 1997; Zaldivar *et al.*, 2001). A chemical process using sulfuric acid is generally used for hydrolysis of cellulose chain into simple sugars, but it yields a large amount of strong acid as a waste product and thus burden on the environment. Hence, biological degradation of cellulose utilizing microbial cellulytic enzymes has been given attention since it is a clean and environmentally friendly process. Cellulases, which is a complex of endo-β-1,4-glucanase (EC 3.2.1.4), cellubiohydrolase (EC 3.2.1.91) and β-glucosidase (EC 3.2.1.21), can synergistically hydrolyze cellulose into glucose, which can be fermented into useful chemicals, such as ethanol–an environmentally friendly bio-fuel (Lynd *et al.*, 2002). However, in spite of major efforts of screening various fungi and bacteria for cellulase enzymes, no really effective cheap source of enzyme is available for application for large scale cellulose hydrolysis and bioethanol production.

Interest in cellulase enzymes has also accelerated in recent decades due to their important role in the global carbon cycle, as well as their use in bio-fuel production and other industries (Tomme *et al.*, 1995). Approximately 5,000 cellulase encoding genes have been identified from a wide range of culturable organisms especially bacteria and fungi (GenBank database, 2009). However, more than 90% of those microbes have not been isolated. Discovery of novel enzyme encoding genes from unculturable microorganisms is possible since a metagenomic approach is applied (Handelsman, 2004).

Considerable research had been focused on identification of the novel cellulase using various biological resources, such as termite guts (Warnecke *et al.*, 2007), human gut (Tasse *et al.*, 2010), rabbit cecum (Feng *et al.*, 2007), and ruminant digestive system (Duan *et al.*, 2009; Ferrer *et al.*, 2005). Some of these enzymes possess enhanced characteristics, although they are not ideal for industrial applications yet. Therefore, mining for more novel enzymes is still an urgent task that attracts considerable attention.

Metagenomics is a culture-independent approach that mines complex microbial communities, comprising of both culturable and non-culturable microorganisms. It has the potential to overcome the problem of culturing of microorganisms as it allows exhaustive mining of microbial communities in their natural environment (Duan and Feng, 2010). A number of cellulase genes have been cloned from uncultured microorganisms in previous reports (Feng *et al.*, 2007; Ferrer *et al.*, 2005; Healy *et al.*, 1995; Rees *et al.*, 2003: Voget *et al.*, 2003). Enzymes are favorable catalysts for the development of environmentally benign industrial processes. As most industrially relevant enzymes are of microbial origin, therefore, mining for microbial enzymes is a key step in the development of industrial bioprocesses. Uchiyama and Miyazaki (2009) reported functional metagenomics as an efficient technique for novel enzyme discovery. Using metagenomic approach, Jiang *et al.* (2010) reported biochemical characterization of two novel β-glucosidase genes, which exhibit higher activity in lower temperature and across a broad pH range (5.5–10.5) thus making them industrially important. Thus, metagenomics has emerged as a powerful tool in mining for novel biocatalysts as well as for the potential of microbes as a valuable resource for novel enzymes.

Ruminants as Potential Resource for Metagenomics

Ruminants are considered as a potential resource in the pursuit of novel cellulases using culture-independent techniques of metagenomics. They are not able to produce cellulases themselves yet their digestive tracts harbour symbiotic microorganisms that help them to digest cellulosic feed they ingest. The stomach of a ruminant, such as cow or a buffalo, consists of four compartments: the rumen, the reticulum, the omasum and the abomasums. The rumen is the most important and the largest part of their stomach, occupying 80% of the total stomach volume. Large numbers of microorganisms from the rumen have been found to be responsible for the degradation of cellulose, but more than 85% of the ruminal microorganisms have not yet been cultivated (Krause *et al.*, 2003). Therefore to exploit the genomic resources of these unculturable microorganisms, metagenomic approach is of prime importance.

Swamp buffalo (*Bubalus bubalis*) is one of the common ruminants which are able to digest a low-quality roughage feed and agricultural crop-residues. These agricultural residues consist mainly of cellulose fiber, a β-1,4-glucosidic polymer of glucose. The buffalo rumen contains a complex microbial community including bacteria, fungi and protests. PCR amplification of 16S rRNA gene libraries has shown the high genetic diversity of microbial community in buffalo rumen. Duan *et al.* (2009) provided convincing insight into the diversity and functionality of cellulases in the buffalo rumens. They isolated and partially characterized some of the novel genes encoding acidic cellulases from metagenomes of buffalo rumens.

The stomach of a buffalo is comprised of four chambers, namely the rumen, the reticulum, the omasum and the abomasum. The rumen and the reticulum are not completely separated, but have different functions. The reticulum is a flask-shaped compartment that moves ingested food (ingesta) into the rumen and the omasum. The reticulum also causes the regurgitation of ingesta during rumination, and acts as a collection compartment as well. The rumen is a large fermentation chamber (in adult cattle its volume is about 125 liters) fostering a very high population of microorganisms, particularly bacteria but also protozoa and some fungi. Rumen functions as a fermentation vessel in which slowly degrading plant materials, such as cellulose and hemicellulose, are retained long enough to be degraded by the microbes residing there (Leschine, 1995). The omasum contains numerous laminae that help grind the ingesta. These folds assist in the removal of fluid from the ingesta on their way to the abomasum, which corresponds to the stomach of the non-ruminant, and is termed as the true stomach. It secretes the gastric juices which aid in digestion. The abomasum is normally in the range of 2.0 to 2.5. This low pH facilitates initial protein breakdown, and kills the bacteria which have spilled over from the rumen.

Rumen Cellulolytic Microbes

Naturally, ruminants have developed the microbial ecosystem in the rumen. They harbour a rich community of microorganisms, assisting the animals in utilizing the cellulosic materials they ingest as their food. In fact, they exploit the symbiotic relationship with the cellulolytic microbes. There are various kinds of cellulolytic microbes, residing in the rumen, constituting a sort of rumen microbial ecosystem. The rumen microbial ecosystem includes anaerobic microbes, such as bacteria, protozoa and fungi (Kuhad and Singh, 2007). These anaerobic microbes have an excellent enzyme system to degrade cellulosic materials. Vast amounts of cellulose and hemicellulose are degraded anaerobically in the gastrointestinal tracts of herbivorous animals.

Bacteria constitute the major group of the rumen microbial ecosystem with about 200 species, and number up to 10^{12}/ml rumen liquor, of which cellulolytic bacteria number can be as high as 10^{8}/ml rumen liquor, thus reflecting their important role in degradation of fibrous feed (Agarwal, 2007). Protozoa constitute the second major group of the rumen microbial ecosystem with about 20 species, and number varying from 10^{5} to 10^{6}. As compared to bacteria though the number of protozoa is very less yet they do have significant role to play in breakdown of plant cell walls, as they secrete the enzymes required for cellulose degradation (Williams and Coleman, 1988; Agarwal *et al.*, 1991). In rumen physiology, protozoa contribute about 43% of cellulose, 53% of protease and 38% of amylase activity of the total present in the rumen liquor of buffalo (Agarwal *et al.*, 1991), while Dijkstra and Tamminga (1995) reported 17-21% contribution of protozoa in fiber degrading activity in animals fed on diet containing low levels of concentrate mixture.

Fungi constitute the third group of rumen microbial ecosystem contributing a very small fraction of rumen microbiota with 7 known species. The cellulases of the rumen fungi are the most active fibrolytic enzymes as compared to the cellulases of various other anaerobic and aerobic microbes (Trinci *et al.*, 1994) but their role in fiber degradation in rumen is still debatable.

Metagenomic Cellulases

First of all, Healy *et al.* (1995) reported the isolation of a cellulase gene from metagenomes collected from microbial consortia of an anaerobic digester maintained on lignocellulose. In their study, they identified 12 clones exhibiting CMCase activity and 11 clones exhibiting MUCase activity in the metagenome library they constructed. Further analysis indicated that four of them exhibited temperature optima (60-65°C) and pH optima (pH 6-7). By sequencing the insert, they identified one GHF5 cellulase, which showed less than 50% similarity with the known cellulases.

Considering the potential of microbes in hydrolysing cellulosic materials, the rumen has been a potential resource of novel cellulases. Several investigators focused their studies using metagenomic approaches. Ferrer *et al.* (2005) constructed a metagenomic expression library using the contents of a cow rumen. They screened it for cellulase activity and recovered seven clones exhibiting β-1,4-endoglucanase activity. After sequencing the retrieved cellulases, they found that they were entirely new as they showed only a distant phylogenetic relationship to known cellulases.

Voget *et al.* (2006) reported the first detailed characterization of a halotolrant cellulase, CelA, using a metagenomic approach from a soil sample collected from a non-extreme environment. The retrieved cellulase (CelA) exhibited a high level of stability over a broad range of pH (pH 5.5–9.0), temperature (stable at 40°C for up to 11 hours) and was highly halotolrant (being active and stable in 3M NaCl).

Duan *et al.* (2009) constructed a metagenomic library from the contents of buffalo rumen fluid. They screened it for cellulase activity, and recovered 61 clones exhibiting the cellulase activity; subcloning and sequencing analysis indicated 13 exhibiting endoglucanase and 14 MUCase activities. Further analysis of 13 recombinant cellulases revealed that they showed diverse pH optimal range from 4 to 7; seven retrieved cellulases were most active under acidic conditions with optimal pH of 5.5, or lower. One novel cellulase, C67-1, was over-expressed in *E. coli*, and the recombinant enzyme exhibited optimal activity at pH 4.5 and stability along a wide range, from pH 3.5 to 10.5. Thus, their study provided an evidence for the diversity and functionality of microbial cellulases in the rumen.

Similarly, Liu *et al.* (2009) constructed a metagenomic library from the contents of buffalo rumen fluid. Using function-based approach, they retrieved a novel cellulase gene, umcel5N, exhibiting endoglucanase activity. Sequence analysis revealed that it belongs to GH5 family of cellulases, and is related to an endoglucanase (ABN54006.1) of *Closteridium thermocellum* with 44% identity and 60% similarity.

Conclusion

The innovative field of metagenomics has maximum potential to exploit the wealth of genetic information contained in the large majority of unculturable microbial diversity in various environmental niches. It is one of the most vibrant and exciting areas of research as far as the discovery of novel biocatalysts is concerned. The biocatalysts retrieved through this route possess some useful characteristics different from those obtained from the culturable minority. In conclusion, metagenomics has become a powerful pragmatic tool that would transcend the existing conventional methods of search for novel biocatalysts in the years ahead.

References

Agarwal, N., N. Kewalramani, D. N. Kamra, D. K. Agarwal and K. Nath, 1991. Hydrolytic enzymes of buffalo rumen: Comparison of cell free rumen fluid, bacterial and protozoa fractions. *Buffalo Journal*, 7: 203–207.

Agarwal, N. 2007. Cellulose degradation in rumen: An anaerobic ecosystem. In: *Lignocellulose Biotechnology: Future prospects*. I. K. International Pvt, Ltd. Pp, 191–192.

Amann, R. L., W. Ludwig and K. H. Schleifer, 1995. Phylogenetic identification and *in situ* detection of individual microbial cells without cultivation. *Microbiol. Rev*. 59: 143–169.

Beja, O., M. T. Suzuki, E. V. Koonin, L. Aravind, A. Hadd, L. P. Ngugen, R. Villacorta, M. Amjadi, C. Garrigues, S. B. Jovanovich, R. A. Feldman and E. F. DeLong, 2000a. Construction and analysis of bacterial artificial chromosome libraries from a marine microbial assemblage. *Environ. Microbiol*. 2: 516–529.

Beja, O., L. Aravind, E. V. Koonin, M. T. Suzuki, A. Hadd, L. P. Ngugen, S. B. Jovanovich, C. M. Gates, R. A. Feldman, J. L. Spudich, A. N. Spudich and E. F. DeLong, 2000b.

Bacterial rhodopsin: evidence for a new type of phototrophy in the sea. *Science*, 289: 1902–1906.

Beja, O., E. V. Koonin, L. Aravind, L. T. Taylor, H. Seitz, J. L. Stein, D. C. Bensen, R. A. Feldman, R. V. Swanson and E. F. DeLong, 2002. Comparative genomic analysis of archaeal genotypic variants in a single population and in two different oceanic provinces. *Appl. Environ. Microbiol.* 68: 335–345.

Brennan, Y., W. N. Callen, L. Christoffersen, P. Dupree, F. Goubet, S. Healey, M. Hernandez, M. Keller, K. Li, N. Palackal *et al.* 2004. Unusual microbial xylanases from insect guts. *Appl. Environ. Microbiol.* 70: 3609–3617.

Bull, A. T., A. C. Ward and M. Goodfellow, 2000. Search and discovery strategies for biotechnology: The paradigm shift. *Microbiol. Mol. Biol. Rev*., 64: 573-606.

Courtois, S., C. M. Cappellano, M. Ball, F. X. Francou, P. Normand, G. Helynck, A. Martinez, S. J. Kolvek, J. Hopke *et al.* 2003. Recombinant environmental libraries provide access to microbial diversity for drug discovery from natural products. *Appl. Environ. Microbiol.* 69: 49–55.

Demain, A. L., M. Newcomb and J. H. D. Wu, 2005. Cellulase, *Clostridia* and Ethanol. *Microbiol. Mol. Biol. Rev.* 69: 124–154.

Dijkstra, J. and S. Tamminga, 1995. Stimulation of the effects of diet on the contribution of rumen protozoa to the degradation of fiber in the rumen. *British Journal of Nutrition*, 74: 617–634.

Duan, C. J. and J. X. Feng, 2010. Mining metagenomes for novel cellulase genes. *Biotechnol. Lett.* 32: 1765–1775.

Duan, C. J., L. Xian, G. C. Zhao, Y. Feng, H. Pang, X. L. Bai, J. L. Tang, Q. S. Ma and J. X. Feng, 2009. Isolation and partial characterization of novel genes encoding acidic cellulases from metagenomes of buffalo rumens. *J. Appl. Microbiol.* 107: 245–256.

Entcheva, P., W. Liebl, A. Johann, T. Hartsch and W. R. Streit, 2001. Direct cloning from enrichment cultures, a reliable strategy for isolation of complete operons and genes from microbial consortia. *Appl. Environ. Microbiol.* 67: 89–99.

Feng, Y., C. J. Duan, H. Pang, X. C. Mo, C. F. Wu, Y. Yu, Y. L. Hu, J. Wei, J. L. Tang and J. X. Feng, 2007. Cloning and identification of novel cellulase genes from uncultured microorganisms in rabbit cecum and characterization of the expressed cellulases. *Appl. Microbiol. Biotechnol.* 75: 319–328.

Ferrer, M., O. V. Golyshina, T. N. Chernikova, A. N. Khachane, D. Reyes-Duarte, V. A. Santos, C. Strompl *et al.* 2005. Novel hydrolase diversity retrieved from a metagenome library of bovine rumen microflora. *Environ. Microbiol.* 7: 1996–2010.

GenBank database, 2009. National Center for Biotechnology Information, US. National Library of Medicine, MD, US. http://www.ncbi.nlm.nih.gov

Handelsman, J. 2004. Metagenomics: applications of genomics to uncultured microorganisms. *Mol. Biol. Rep.* 68: 669 – 685.

Healy, F. G., R. M. Ray, H. C. Aldrich, A. C. Wilkie, L. O. Ingram and K. T. Shanmugam, 1995. Direct isolation of functional genes encoding cellulases from the microbial consortia in a thermophilic, anaerobic digester maintained on lignocellulose. *Appl. Microbiol. Biotechnol.* 43: 667–674.

Henne, A., R. Daniel, R. A. Schmitz and G. Gottschalk, 1999. Construction of environmental DNA libraries in *Escherichia coli* and screening for the presence of genes conferring utilization of 4-hydroxybutyrate. *Appl. Environ. Microbiol.* 65: 3901–3907.

Henne, A., R. A. Schmitz, M. Bomeke, G. Gottschalk and R. Daniel, 2000. Screening of environmental DNA libraries for presence of genes conferring lipolytic activity on *E. coli*. *Appl. Environ. Microbiol.* 66: 3113 -3116.

Jeewon, L. 1997. Biological conversion of lignocellulosic biomass to ethanol. *J. Biotechnol.* 56: 1– 4.

Jiang, C., Z. Y. Hao, K. Jin, S. X. Li, Z. Q. Che, G. F. Ma *et al.* 2010. Identification of a metagenome-derived β-glucosidase from bioreactor contents. *J. Mol. Catal. B: Enzym.* 63: 11–16.

Kim, S. J., C. M. Lee, B. R. Han *et al.* 2008. Characterization of a gene encoding cellulase from uncultured soil bacteria. *FEMS Microbiol. Lett.* 282: 44–51.

Knietsch, A., S. Bowien, G. Whited, G. Gottschalk and R. Daniel, 2003. Identification and characterization of coenzyme B12-dependent glycerol dehydratase–diol-dehydratase encoding genes from metagenomic DNA libraries derived from enrichment cultures. *Appl. Environ. Microbiol.* 69: 3048–3060.

Krause, D. O., S. E. Denman, R. J. Mackie, M. Morrison, A. L. Rae, G. T. Attwood and C. S. McSweeney, 2003. Opportunities to improve fiber degradation in the rumen: microbiology, ecology, and genomics. *FEMS Microbiol. Rev.* 27: 663–693.

Krsek, M. and E. M. Wellington, 1999. Comparison of different methods for the isolation and purification of total community DNA from soil. *J. Microbiol. Methods*, 39: 1-16.

Kuhad, R. C. and A. Singh, 2007. *Lignocellulose Biotechnology: Future prospects*. I. K. International Pvt, Ltd.

Lee, C. C., R. E. Kibblewhite-Accinelli, K. Wagschal, G. H. Robertson and D. W. Wong, 2006a. Cloning and characterization of a cold-active xylanase enzyme from an environmental DNA library. *Extremophiles*, 10: 295–300.

Lee, D. G., J. H. Jeon, M. K. Jang, N. Y. Kim, J. H. Lee, S. J. Kim, G. D. Kim and S. H. Lee. 2007. Screening and characterization of a novel fibrinolytic metalloprotease from a metagenomic library. *Biotechnol. Lett.* 29: 465–472.

Leschine, S. B. 1995. Cellulose degradation in anaerobic environments. *Annu. Rev. Microbiol.* 49: 399-426.

Liu, L., Y. Feng, C. J. Duan, H. Pang, J. L. Tang, and J. X. Feng, 2009. Isolation of a gene encoding endonuclease activity from uncultured microorganisms in buffalo rumen. *World J. Microbiol. Biotechnol.* 25: 1035–1042.

Lynd, L. R., W. H. van Zyl, J. E. McBride and M. Laser, 2005. Consolidated bioprocessing of cellulosic biomass: an update. *Curr. Opin. Biotechnol.* 16: 577–583.

Lynd, L. R., P. J. Weimer, W. H. van Zyl and I.S. Pretorius, 2002. Microbial cellulose utilization: fundamentals and biotechnology. *Microbiol. Mol. Biol. Rev.* 66: 506–677.

Majernik, A., G. Gottschalk and R. Daniel, 2001. Screening of environmental DNA libraries for the presence of genes conferring Na(Li)/H antiporter activity on *Escherichia coli*: characterization of the recovered genes and the corresponding gene products. *J. Bacteriol.* 183: 6645-6653.

Pang, H., P. Zhang, C. J. Duan, X. C. Mo, J. L. Tang and J. X. Feng, 2009. Identification of cellulase genes from the metagenomes of compost soils and functional characterization of one novel endoglucanase. *Curr. Microbiol.* 58: 404–408.

Patrick, D., Schloss and J. O. Handelsman, 2005. Metagenomics for studying unculturable microorganisms: cutting the Gordian knot. *Genome Biol.* 6: 229.

Rees, H. C., S. Grant, B. Jones, W. D. Grant and S. Heaphy, 2003. Detecting cellulase and esterase enzyme activities encoded by novel genes present in environmental DNA libraries. *Extremophiles*, 7: 415–421.

Rondon, M. R., P. R. August, A. D. Bettrmann, S. F. Brady, T. H. Grossman, M. R. Liles, K. A. Loiacono, B. A. Lynch *et al.* 2000. Cloning the soil metagenome: a strategy for accessing the genetic and functional diversity of uncultured microorganisms. *Appl. Environ. Microbiol.* 66: 2541–2547.

Seow, K. T., G. Meurer, M. Gerlitz, E. Wendt-Pienkowski, C. R. Hutchinson and J. Davies, 1997. A study of iterative type II polyketide synthases, using bacterial genes cloned from soil DNA: a means to access and use genes from uncultured microorganisms. *J. Bacteriol.* 179: 7360–7368.

Soresen, H. P. and K. K. Mortensen, 2005. Advanced genetic strategies for recombinant protein expression in *Escherichia coli. J. Biotechnol.* 115: 113 – 128.

Streit, W. R. and R. Schmitz, 2004. Metagenomics–the key to uncultured microbes. *Curr. Opin. Biotechnol.* 7: 492–498.

Tasse, L., J. Bercovici, S. Pizzut-Serin, P. Robe, J. Tap, C. Klopp, B. L. Cantarel, P. M. Coutinho *et al.*, 2010. Functional metagenomics to mine human gut microbe for dietary fiber catabolic enzymes. *Genome Res.* 20: 1605–1612.

Tomme, P., R. A. J. Warren and N. R. Gilkes, 1995. Cellulose hydrolysis by bacteria and fungi. *Adv. Microb. Physiol.* 37: 1–81.

Trinci, A. P. J., D. R. Davies, K. Gull, M. I. Lawrence, B. B. Nielson, A. Rickers and M. K. Theodorou, 1994. Anaerobic fungi in herbaceous animals. *Mycological Research*, 98: 129–152.

Uchiyama, T. and K. Miyazaki, 2009. Functional metagenomics for enzyme discovery: challenges to efficient screening. *Curr. Opin. Biotechnol.* 20: 616–622.

Voget, S., C. Leggewie, A. Uesbeck, C. Raasch, K. E. Jaeger and W. R. Streit, 2003. Prospecting for novel biocatalysts in a soil metagenome. *Appl. Environ. Microbiol.* 69: 6235–6242.

Voget, S., H. L. Steele and W. R. Streit, 2006. Characterization of a metagenome-derived halotolerant cellulase. *J. Biotechnol.* 126: 26–36.

Warnecke, F., P. Luginbuhl, N. Ivanova, M. Ghassemian, T. H. Richardson, J. T. Stege, M. Cayouette, A. C. Mchardy *et al.* 2007. Metagenomic and functional analysis of hindgut microbiota of a wood-feeding higher termite. *Nature*, 450: 560–565.

Wei, P., L. Bai, W. Song and G. Hao, 2009. Characterization of two soil metagenome-derived lipases with high specificity for p-nitrophenyl palmitate. *Arch. Microbiol.* 191: 233–240.

Williams, A. G. and G. S. Coleman, 1998. Rumen ciliate protozoa. In: *Rumen microbial eco-system*, Ed. Hobson, P. N. Elsevier Applied Science Publication, Amsterdam, pp 77–128.

Wilson, D. B. 2009. Cellulases and biofuels. *Curr. Opin. Biotechnol.* 20: 295–299.

Wooley, J. C., A. Godzik and I. Friedberg, 2010. A primer on metagenomics. *PLoS Computational Biology*. www.ploscompbiol.org

Yun, J. *et al.* 2004. Characterization of a novel amylolytic enzyme encoded by a gene from a soil-derived metagenomic library. *Appl. Environ. Microbiol.* 70: 7229.

Zaldivar, J., J. Nielsen and L. Olsson, 2001. Fuel ethanol production from lignocellulose: a challenge for metabolic engineering and process integration. *Appl. Microbiol. Biotechnol.* 56: 17–34.

In: Applications of Microbial Genes in Enzyme Technology ISBN: 978-1-62417-808-5
Editors: V.K.Gupta, M.G.Tuohy, G.D.Sharma et al.

Chapter 2

Chitinase and the Encoding Gene May Increase Antifungal Activity of the Antagonistic Bacteria

Chao-Ying Chen,[1*] Yi-Huei Wang[1] and Hsiao-Dao Chang[2]

[1]Department of Plant Pathology and Microbiology,
National Taiwan University,
Taipei, Taiwan

[2]Department of Safety, Health and Environmental Engineering,
Ming Chi University of Technology,
Taishan, Taipei, Taiwan

Abstract

Plant-associated non-pathogenic bacteria are common sources of biological control agents for plant health care. Membrane affecting compounds and cell wall-lytic enzymes may contribute to the antagonism toward plant pathogens.

Among cell wall-lytic enzymes, chitinases are known to act synergistically with the membrane affecting compounds against target fungi. Introduction of chitinase gene may increase antifungal activity of the host bacterium due to co-production of different molecules affecting cell integrity.

Therefore, biopesticide control of plant fungal diseases can be improved by implementation of chitinases (or its encoding gene) in combination with antagonistic bacteria, especially that affect fungal cell membrane.

* Corresponding author: Chao-Ying Chen. Department of Plant Pathology and Microbiology, National Taiwan University, No. 1, Sec. 4, Roosevelt Rd., Taipei 10617, Taiwan, R. O. C. Tel.: +886-2-336652075. E-mail: cychen@ntu.edu.tw.

Introduction

Chitin is a globally abundant biopolymer found within fungal cell walls and the exoskeletons of insects and crustaceans. Chitinases are hydrolytic enzymes that break down glycosidic bonds in chitin and present in a wide range of organisms including bacteria, fungi, virus, insects, higher plants, and animals (Felse and Panda, 1999; Flach *et al.*, 1992; Graham and Sticklen, 1994).

The majority of fungi have chitin as a constituent of the cell walls. The degradation or perturbation of this structural polymer has adverse effects on the growth and differentiation of fungi (Bartnicki-Garcia, 1969; Cohen-Kupiec and Chet, 1998). Direct antagonism by the action of diffusible or volatile antibiotic compounds is a primary mechanism of biological control (Elad, 1996; Emmert and Handelsman, 1999; O'sullivan and O'gara. 1992). Many antifungal compounds targeting fungal membrane are produced by antagonistic microorganisms and many antagonistic microorganisms produce chitinases (Chet *et al.*, 1990; El-Tarabily *et al.*, 2000; Howell, 2003; Huang *et al.*, 2005; Nielsen *et al.*, 1998; O'sullivan and O'gara. 1992).

To reduce synthetic pesticide in agriculture, the needs for biological control agents is increasing. Suitable manipulation of biological control agents would bring promising efficacy on plant health management.

Synergistic Interaction between Fungal Cell Wall Degrading Enzymes and Membrane Affecting Compounds

Good candidates for the biocontrol of plant diseases can be screened by the selection of co-production of antibiotic and endochitinase (Nielsen *et al.*, 1998). Several evidences indicate that antibiotics and hydrolytic enzymes act synergistically against fungi (Lorito *et al.*, 1996; Woo *et al.*, 2002). An antifungal chitinase from *Bacillus cereus* has synergistic interaction with a membrane affecting fungicide, tebuconazole, to inhibit spore germination of *Alternaria brassicicola*, *A. longipes*, and *Colletotrichum gloeosporiodes* (Huang and Chen, 2008; Huang *et al.*, 2005).

Trichderma species producing cell wall-degrading enzyme and antibiotics appear to be good biocontrol agents (Howell, 2003). The antibiotics and chitinases produced by *Trichoderma* biocontrol agents act synergistically against plant pathogenic fungi (Lorito *et al.*, 1994, 1996). Membrane affecting antibiotics, such as gliotoxin, are important for this synergism. On the other hand, cell wall-degrading enzymes, endochitinase and β-1,3-glucanase, produced by *Trichoderma virens* can synergistically increase the toxicity of membrane-disrupting lipodepsipeptides from *Pseudomonas* (Woo *et al.*, 2002). Thus, combining effect of membrane-affecting antibiotics with partial digestion of cell walls appears to be particularly detrimental to the fungal cells and able to reduce lethal doses of the antibiotics.

Enhancement of Antifungal Activity by Cellular Expression of Foreign Chitinase Gene Requires Suitable Bacterial Strain and Chitinase Gene

Bacteria of the genus *Pseudomonas* aggressively colonizing root surface can suppress phytopathogenic microorganisms directly or by inducing systemic disease resistance of plants (Bakker *et al.*, 2007; O'sullivan and O'gara, 1992). The biocontrol strains of *Pseudomonas* spp. could be improved on the antagonistic activity by different genetic engineering techniques. For example, *Pseudomonas putida* strain from the rhizosphere of cucumber plants was used as a host to construct biological control agent with a foreign chitinase gene carried on an expression vector. The chitinase gene originated from a marine bacterium *Alteromonas* strain increased suppressive activities of *P. putida* strain toward Rhizoctonia damping-off in cucumber (Ohno *et al.*, 2011).

A phyllosphere strain of *Pseudomonas fluorescens* was transformed with a recombinant plasmid harboring an *Aeromonas caviae* chitinase gene under control of a constitutive promoter of kanamycin resistance gene. Another recombinant plasmid carrying *Ptac-chi* was also transformed to this phyllosphere strain of *P. fluorescens*. Both modified strains showed strong chitin degradation activities but could not inhibit phytopathogenic fungi as tested (Mahk *et al.*, 2003). The *chiA* gene of *S. marcescens* was constructed in a Tn7 transposon system and introduced into a *P. fluorescens* strain as a stable integrate expressing and secreting the active chitinase enzyme. The genetically modified strain, but not the wild type strain, exhibited biocontrol activity on the phytopathogenic fungus *Rhizoctonia solani* (Koby *et al.*, 1994). Another strain of *P. fluorescens* isolated from micropropagated apple plantlets exhibited greater biocontrol activity toward *R. solani* on bean seedlings when the *chiA* gene of *S. marcescens* under control of the *tac* promoter was carried on a transferred plasmid vector or on the chromosome as an integrate (Dowing and Thomson, 2000).

We used an antagonistic bacterium *Bacillus subtilis* F29-3 originated from a potato farm in Taiwan as a host to express foreign chitinase gene from *Bacillus circulans* WL-12. The antifungal assay indicated that the *chiA* gene of *B. circulans* WL-12 with its own promoter carried on pNTU111 (Figure 1A) conducted an expression of chitinolytic enzyme in *B. subtilis* F29-3 transformants (Figure 1B) and a greater inhibition on spore germination of *Botrytis elliptica*, a fungal pathogen of lily leaf blight (Chen *et al.*, 2004). Nevertheless, the purified chitionlytic ChiA1 encoded by the *chiA* gene from a *chiA*-transformed *E. coli* strain did not exhibit antifungal activity against *B. elliptica* (Huang *et al.*, 2009). However, the chitinolytic effect of ChiA1 on fungal cell wall would facilitate the toxicity of antifungal antibiotics such as fengycin produced by *B. subtilis* F29-3 (Wei *et al.*, 2010).

When *B. subtilis* F29-3(pNTU111) carrying *chiA* gene were grown in LB medium at 28C for 2 days and the culture supernatant was mixed with nHA medium at the rate of 10%, the inhibition towards mycelial growth of *B. elliptica* increased over 10% in a plate assay as compared to that of the control strain harboring pHY300PLK. Similar phenomenon was observed when *Paecilomyces variotii* was used as a test fungus. In addition, an increased inhibition toward the growth of *R. solani* was observed, especially with addition of tetracycline for selection of the recombinant plasmid.

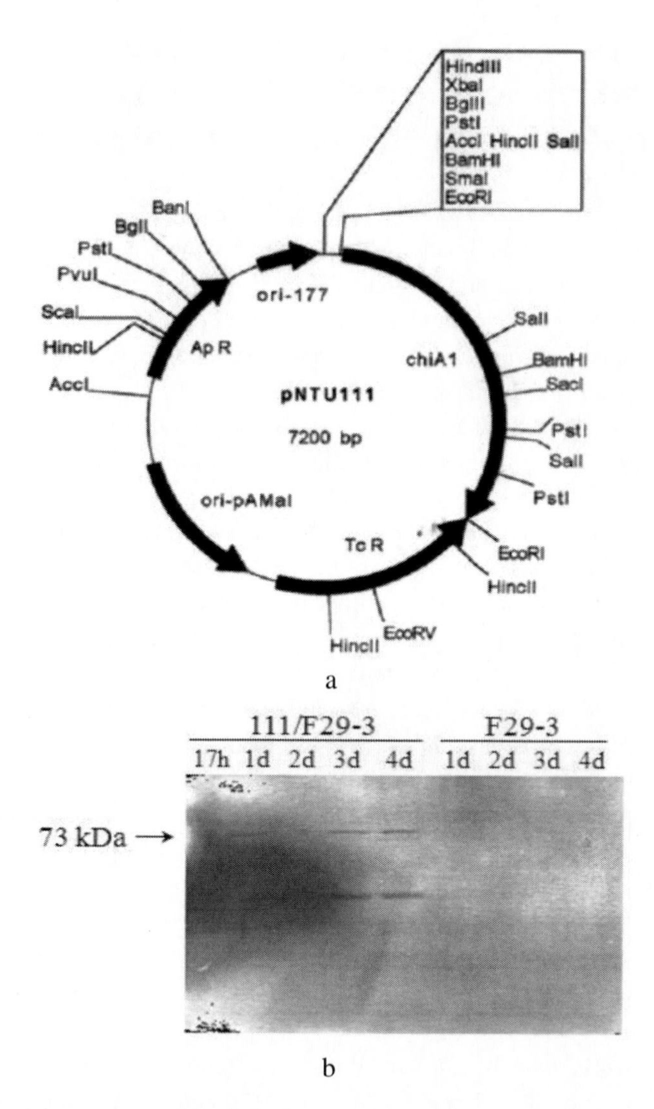

Figure 1. Plasmid pNTU111 and expression of chitinase in *Bacillus subtilis* F29-3(pNTU111). (A) Plasmid pNTU111 was constructed with *chiA* (2.4 kb) of *Bacillus circulans* WL-12 and the shuttle vector, pHY300PLK. Ap^R, ampicillin resistance gene; Tc^R, tetracycline resistance gene; *chiA*, a chitinase gene of *B. circulans* WL-12; *ori*-177, replication origin of plasmid pACYC of *Escherichia coli*; *ori*-pAMα1, replication origin of plasmid pAMα1 of *Streptococcus faecalis*. (B) Chitinase in the culture supernatant of *B. subtilis* strains growing in LB broth at 28C was detected by in-gel activity assay. The 12% running gel containing 0.01% glycol chitin was used and soaked in 100 mM acetate buffer, pH 5.0 at 37C for 1.5 h after SDS-PAGE. The gel was then stained in 0.01% Calcofluor white M2R (in 0.5% Tris-HCl, pH 8.9) for 1 h before examination on UV transilluminator.

Conclusion

Chitinases synergistically enhance antifungal activity of fungitoxic compounds as shown in the *in vitro* assay. Introduction of foreign chitinase gene conducts chitinolytic activity of the host microorganisms. The effect of chitinase on the cell wall facilitates the action of antifungal metabolites produced by the host cells. Thus, a way to reduce the impact of chemical pesticides on the environments and human health can be accomplished *via* implementation of cell wall-degrading enzymes in combination with membrane affecting compounds. On the other hand, co-production of cell wall-lytic enzymes and toxic metabolites may occur commonly in microorganisms with good antagonistic properties against fungi and worth for exploration. Development of mixture formula of biological control agents with different anti-microbial traits such as the abilities of producing chitinase and/or membrane affecting compounds would increase the efficacy of derived bioproducts.

References

Bakker, P. A. H. M., C. M. J. Pieterse and L. C. van Loon. 2007. Induced systemic resistance by fluorescent *Pseudomonas* spp. Phytopathology 97: 239-243.

Bartnicki-Garcia, S. 1969. Cell wall chemistry, morphogenesis, and taxonomy of fungi. Annu. Rev. Microbiol. 22: 87–108.

Chen, C.-Y., Y.-H. Wang and C.-J. Huang. 2004. Enhancement of the antifungal activity of *Bacillus subtilis* F29-3 by the chitinase encoded by *Bacillus circulans chiA* gene. Can. J. Microbiol. 50: 451-454.

Chet, I., A. Ordentlich, R. Shapira and A. Oppenheim. 1990. Mechanisms of biocontrol of soil-borne plant pathogens by Rhizobacteria. Plant Soil 129: 85-92.

Cohen-Kupiec, R., and I. Chet. 1998. The molecular biology of chitin digestion. Curr. Opion. Biotechnol. 9: 270–277.

Downing, K. J. and J. A. Thomson. 2000. Introduction of the *Serratia marcescens chiA* gene into an endophytic *Pseudomonas fluorescens* for the biocontrol of phytopathogenic fungi. *Can. J. Microbiol.* 46: 363-369.

Elad, Y. 1996. Mechanisms involved in the biological control of *Botrytis cinerea* incited diseases. Eur. J. Plant Pathol. 102: 719-732.

El-Tarabily, K. A., M. H. Soliman, A. H. Nassar, H. A. Al-Hassani, K. Sivasithamparam, F. McKenna and G. E. St. J. Hardy. 2000. Biological control of *Sclerotinia minor* using a chitinolytic bacterium and actinomycetes. Plant Pathol. 49: 573-583.

Emmert, E. A. B. and J. Handelsman. 1999. Biocontrol of plant disease: a (Gram-) positive perspective. FEMS Microbiol. Lett. 171: 1-9.

Felse, P. A. and T. Panda. 1999. Regulation and cloning of microbial chitinase genes. Appl. Microbiol. Biotechnol. 51: 141-151.

Flach, J., P. E. Pilet, and P. Jolles. 1992. What's new in chitinase research? Experientia 48: 701-716.

Graham, L. S. and M. B. Sticklen. 1994. Plant chitinases. Can. J. Bot. 72: 1057-1083.

Howell, C. R. 2003. Mechanisms employed by *Trichoderma* species in the biological control of plant diseases: The history and evolution of current concepts. *Plant Dis.* 87: 1-10.

Huang, C.-J. and C.-Y. Chen. 2008. Synergistic interactions between chitinase ChiCW and fungicides against plant fungal pathogens. J. Microbiol. Biotechnol. 18: 784-787.

Huang, C.-J., S.-H. Guo, S.-C. Chung, Y.-J. Lin and C.-Y. Chen. 2009. Analysis of the involvement of chitin-binding domain of ChiCW in antifungal activity, and engineering a novel chimeric chitinase with high enzyme and antifungal activities. *J. Microbiol. Biotechnol.* 19: 1169-1175.

Huang, C.J., T.-K. Wang, S.-C. Chung and C.-Y. Chen. 2005. Identification of an antifungal chitinase from a potential biocontrol agent, *Bacillus cereus* 28-9. J. Biochem. Mol. Biol. 38: 82-88

Koby, S., H. Schickler, I. Chet and A. B. Oppenheim. 1994. The chitinase encoding Tn7-based *chiA* gene endows *Pseudomonas fluorescens* with the capacity to control plant pathogens in soil. *Gene* 147: 81-83.

Lorito, M., C. Peterbauer, C. K. Hayes and G. E. Harman. 1994. Synergistic interaction between fungal cell wall degrading enzymes and different antifungal compounds enhances inhibition of spore germination. Microbiology 140: 623-629.

Lorito, M. S. L. Woo, M. D. Ambrosio, G. E. Harman, C. K. Hayes, C. P. Kubicek and F. Scala. 1996. Synergistic interaction between cell wall degrading enzymes and membrane affecting compounds. Mol. Plant- Microbe Interact. 9: 206-213.

Mahk, A., A. Suwanto, B. Tjahjono and R. Harling. 2003. Heterologous expression of a chitinase gene from *Aeromonas caviae* in *Pseudomonas fluorescens.* BIOTROPIA 20: 36-48.

Nielsen, M. N., J. Sørensen, J. Fels and H. C. Pedersen. 1998. Secondary metabolite- and endochitinase-dependent antagonism toward plant-pathogenic microfungi of *Pseudomonas fluorescens* isolates from sugar beet rhizosphere. Appl. Environ. Microbiol. 64: 3563-3569.

Ohno, M. S. Kataoka, S. Numata, K. Yamamoto-Tamura, T. Fuji, M. Nakajima, K. Akutsu and A. Hasebe. 2011. Biological control of Rhizoctonia damping-off of cucumber by a transformed *Pseudomonas putida* strain expressing a chitinase from a marine bacterium. JARQ 45: 91-98.

O'sullivan, D. J. and F. O'gara. 1992. Traits of fluorescent *Pseudomonas* spp. involved in suppression of plant-root pathogens. Microbiol. Rev. 56: 662-676.

Wei, Y.-H., L.-C. Wang, W.-C. Chen and S.-Y. Chen. 2010. Production and characterization of fengycin by indigenous *Bacillus subtilis* F29-3 originating from a potato farm. Int. J. Mol. Sci. 11: 4526-4538.

Woo, S., V. Fogliano, F. Scalal and M. Lorito. 2002. Synergism between fungal enzymes and bacterial antibiotics may enhance biocontrol. Antonie van Leeuwenhoek 81: 353–356.

In: Applications of Microbial Genes in Enzyme Technology ISBN: 978-1-62417-808-5
Editors: V.K.Gupta, M.G.Tuohy, G.D.Sharma et al.

Chapter 3

Fungal Laccase Genes

Gerardo Díaz-Godínez,[*] Maura Téllez-Téllez, Rubén Díaz and Carmen Sánchez[†]
Laboratory of Biotechnology,
Research Center for Biological Sciences,
Universidad Autónoma de Tlaxcala,
Tlaxcala, Mexico

Abstract

Laccases (EC 1.10.3.2) are glycoproteins classified as multi-copper oxidases, which catalyze one-electron oxidation of a wide range of inorganic and organic substances, coupled with reduction of oxygen to water. These enzymes are widely distributed in fungi, higher plants, bacteria and insects, however, recently evidence for distribution of laccases among archaea have been found. The most studied evidence comes from white-rot fungi. The substrates of laccases may vary from diphenols and polyphenols to diamines, aromatic amines, benzenethiols, and substituted phenols. These features are suitable for several different applications such as bioremediations, textile dye bleaching, pulp bleaching, effluent detoxification, biosensors, medical diagnostics, to degrading pesticides and explosives in soils, delignification processes in paper industries and in cosmetics formulation as additive. On the other hand, the existence of different laccase isoenzymes and multiple genes that encode them in various fungi has been reported. Laccases are regulated by several factors such as pH, temperature, ions, presence of inducers, etc. Copper has proven to be an excellent inducer, increasing the transcription of laccase genes. The different physiological functions for each of the laccase isoenzymes across the fungal life cycle could explain their presence in the genome of this organism.

[*] Corresponding author: Gerardo Díaz-Godínez. E-mail: diazgdo@hotmail.com.
[†] Laboratory of Biotechnology, Research Center for Biological Sciences, Universidad Autónoma de Tlaxcala, Tlaxcala CP 90000, Mexico.

Introduction

Laccase (benzenediol: oxygen oxidoreductases, EC 1.10.3.2) is one of the oldest enzymes reported. It was first demonstrated in the exudates of *Rhus vernicifera*, the Japanese lacquer tree (Yoshida, 1883). In 1896 laccase was demonstrated to be present in fungi for the first time by both Bertrand and Laborde (Thurston, 1994; Levine, 1965). Laccases are produced by many eukaryotes, e.g., fungi, plants, and insects (Mayer and Staples, 2002). The synthesis of laccases by prokaryotes has been reported in Gram-negative and Gram-positive bacteria (Alexandre and Zhulin, 2000; Claus, 2003). There exists a wide diversity of laccases that have very different physicochemical properties (Gianfreda *et al.*, 1999; Mayer and Staples, 2002). For example, plant laccases participate in the lignification of xylem tissues (Sterjiades *et al.*, 1992; O'Malley *et al.*, 1993; Liu *et al.*, 1994; Boudet 2000; Ranocha *et al.*, 2002; Gavnholt and Knud, 2002; Hoopes and Dean, 2004), whereas in fungi laccases probably have more roles, including morphogenesis, fungal plant-pathogen/host interaction, stress defense and lignin degradation (Thurston, 1994; Eriksson *et al.*, 1990; Zhu and Williamson, 2004). Bacterial laccases appear to have a role in morphogenesis (Sharma *et al.*, 2007), the biosynthesis of the brown spore pigment, the protection provided by the spore coat against UV light and hydrogen peroxide, and in Cu homeostasis (Roberts *et al.*, 2002; Langfelder *et al.*, 2003). The main function of the laccase-type proteins in insects is believed to be sclerotization of the cuticle in the epidermis (Andersen *et al.*, 1996; Dittmer *et al.*, 2004).

Laccases are glycoproteins with a molecular mass of 50–100 kDa. An important feature is a covalently linked carbohydrate moiety (10–45%), which may contribute to its stability (Claus, 2004). These enzymes compose one of three polyphenol oxidase groups responsible for the initial fragmentation of the plant cell wall polymer, lignin, resulting in low molecular weight breakdown products (Eriksson *et al.*, 1990; Bernards and Lewis, 1998). Laccases are classified as multi–copper oxidases, use the distinctive redox ability of Cu ions to catalyze the oxidation of a wide range of aromatic substrates concomitantly with the reduction of molecular oxygen to water (Thurston, 1994; Solomon *et al.*, 1996). Laccases catalyze the removal of a hydrogen atom from the hydroxyl group of methoxy-substituted monophenols, ortho-, and para-diphenols, and also can oxidize other substrates such as aromatic amines, syringaldazine, and non-phenolic compounds, to form free radicals (Claus, 2003). Although laccase was also called diphenol oxidase, monophenols like 2,6-dimethoxyphenol or guaiacol are often better substrates than diphenols, e.g. catechol or hydroquinone. Syringaldazine [N,N´-bis(3,5-dimethoxy-4-hydroxybenzylidene hydrazine)] is often considered to be a unique laccase substrate (Harkin *et al.*, 1973) as long as hydrogen peroxide is avoided in the reaction, as this compound is also oxidized by peroxidases. They couple the four single-electron oxidations of the reducing substrate to the four electron reductive cleavage of the dioxygen bond, using four Cu atoms distributed against three sites, defined according to their spectroscopic properties (Solomon *et al.*, 1996). Typical metal content of laccases includes one type-1 (T1) copper (Cu1), and one type-2 (T2) and two type-3 (T3) copper ions (Cu2 and Cu3), with Cu2 and Cu3 arranged in a trinuclear cluster (Giardina *et al.*, 2010), one of which gives it its characteristic blue color. Similar enzymes lacking the Cu atom responsible for the blue color are called 'yellow' or 'white' laccases, but several authors do not regard them as true laccases (Baldrian, 2006).

Laccases are useful biocatalysts for a wide range of biotechnology applications due to its high capacity and non-specific oxidation. These enzymes are increasingly tested for their oxidative properties in a variety of practical applications ranging from hair dyeing process (Onuki *et al.*, 2000; Pruche *et al.*, 2000) to the generation of wood adhesives (Peshkova *et al.*, 2003). These enzymes are used efficiently in detoxification of wastewater produced in pulp bleaching process (Bajpai, 1999), in the treatment of wastewater from industrial plants (Durán and Esposito, 2000), enzymatic modification of fibers and effluent decolorization (Abadulla *et al.*, 2000), enzymatic removal of phenolic compounds in beverages and processed fruit juices (Minussi *et al.*, 2002), as biosensors and in the production of biodiesel (Amir *et al.*, 2009). They are also used for wine clarification (removal of phenolic compounds) and drug testing (to distinguish morphine from codeine) (Mayer and Staples, 2002). Laccases have been employed to synthesize new cephalosporin antibiotics (Agematu *et al.*, 1993), and to improve the synthesis of actinocin antibiotics (Osiadacz *et al.*, 1999). Another application is in environmental remediation; the laccases have been shown capable of degrading hazardous compounds such as polycyclic aromatic hydrocarbons (PAH), pentachlorophenols (PCP), polychlorinated biphenyls (PCB), 1,1,1-trichloro-2,2-bis (4-chlorophenyl) ethane (DDT), benzene, toluene, ethylbenzene, xylene (BTEX) and trinitrotoluene (TNT). These compounds are persistent in the environment and are known to have carcinogenic and/or mutagenic effects (Desai and Nityanand, 2011).

Biotechnological and environmental applications require large amounts of enzymes. Research on regulation of laccase gene expression may be very useful for increasing the productivity of native laccases in fungi and also for unraveling the physiological role of the different isoenzymes produced by the same organism. Synthesis and secretion of laccases are strictly influenced by nutrient levels, culture conditions, developmental stage as well as the addition of a wide range of inducers to cultural media, with variations among both different fungal species and different isoenzymes in a same strain (Piscitelli *et al.*, 2011). Heterologous expression is a potential option to increase the production of laccases with significant features.

Fungal Laccases

Laccase activity has been demonstrated in many fungal species, mainly as extracellular activity, and the enzyme has already been purified and characterized from some of those species. However, there is evidence in literature of the occurrence of intracellular laccases in white-rot fungi (Schlosser *et al.*, 1997; Téllez-Téllez *et al.*, 2005). On the other hand, there are many taxonomic or physiological groups of fungi that typically do not produce significant amounts of laccase or where laccase is only produced by a few species (Baldrian, 2006). Laccase production has never been demonstrated in lower fungi, i.e. *Zygomycetes* and *Chytridiomycetes*; however, this aspect of these groups has not been studied in detail (Baldrian, 2006). Laccases have been found in Ascomycetes, Deuteromycetes and Basidiomycetes, being particularly abundant in many white-rot fungi that are involved in lignin metabolism (Bourbonnais *et al.*, 1995; Leontievsky *et al.*, 1997). Laccase was observed in some ascomycetes such as *Ophiostoma novo-ulmi* (Binz and Canevascini, 1997), *Gaeumannomyces graminis* (Edens *et al.*, 1999), *Magnaporthe grisea* (Iyer and Chattoo,

2003), *Podospora anserina* (Molitoris and Esser, 1970), *Neurospora crassa* (Froehner and Eriksson, 1974), *Monocillium indicum* (Thakker *et al.*, 1992), *Melanocarpus albomyces* (Kiiskinen *et al.*, 2002), *Mauginella sp.* (Palonen *et al.*, 2003), some species from the genera Aspergillus, Curvularia, Penicillium (Banerjee and Vohra, 1991; Rodríguez *et al.*, 1996; Scherer and Fischer, 1998), Trichoderma and the ligninolytic Bothryosphaeria (Vasconcelos *et al.*, 2000). Yeasts are a physiologically specific group of both Ascomycetes and Basidiomycetes. Until now, laccase was only purified from the human pathogen *Cryptococcus* (*Filobasidiella*) *neoformans*. This basidiomycete yeast produces a true laccase capable of oxidation of phenols and aminophenols and is unable to oxidize tyrosine (Williamson, 1994). The production of laccase was not demonstrated in ascomycetous yeasts (Baldrian, 2006). Among physiological groups of fungi, laccases are typical for the wood-rotting basidiomycetes causing white-rot and a related group of litter-decomposing saprotrophic fungi, i.e. the species causing lignin degradation including *Agaricus bisporus, Coprinus cinereus, Ganoderma lucidum, Melanocarpus albomyces Trametes* (*Coriolus*) *versicolor, Trametes hirsute, Trametes ochracea, Trametes villosa, Trametes gallica, Cerrena maxima, Phlebia radiata, Coriolopsis polyzona, Lentinus tigrinus, Pleurotus ostreatus, Pleurotus eryngii, Pycnoporus cinnabarinus* (Díaz-Godínez, 2011).

Laccase Sequences

Analysis of the essential sequence features of fungal laccases based on multiple sequence alignments of more than 100 laccases has resulted in identification of a set of four ungapped sequence regions, L1-L4, as the overall signature sequences that can be used to identify the laccases, distinguishing them within the broader class of multi-copper oxidases. The 12 amino acid residues in the enzymes serving as the Cu ligands are housed within these four identified conserved regions, of which L2 and L4 conform to the earlier reported Cu signature sequences of multi-copper oxidases while L1 and L3 are distinctive to the laccases. The mapping of regions L1-L4 on to the three-dimensional structure of the *Coprinus cinerius* laccase indicates that many of the non-copper-ligating residues of the conserved regions could be critical in maintaining a specific, more or less C-2 symmetric, protein conformational motif characterizing the active site apparatus of the enzymes (Kumar *et al.*, 2003). Larrondo *et al.* (2003b) identified four loop regions, designated loops I, II, III, and IV, which are involved in substrate binding. These loops were determined through analysis based on structural superimposition and the three-dimensional coordinates of *Trametes versicolor* laccase (Piontek *et al.*, 2002).

Laccase Induction

It has been suggested that laccase activity and the number of laccase isoenzymes are influenced by environmental factors such as temperature, pH, inducers, culture conditions, and medium composition (Giardina *et al.*, 1999; Téllez-Téllez *et al.*, 2008). The effect of these factors at the level of laccase gene transcription has been demonstrated in many fungal species (Piscitelli *et al.*, 2011). There are many studies about the effect of metal ions, aromatic compounds, carbon and/or nitrogen sources on the laccase production.

It was observed that white-rot fungi requires trace amounts of essential heavy metals such as Cu, Cd, Mn or Zn for their growth, but these metals are toxic when present in excess. Toxic heavy metals can inhibit the growth, cause morphological and physiological changes and affect the reproduction of *Basidiomycetes*. Fungal species and strains differ in their sensitivity towards metals and in the protection mechanisms involved. The toxicity of some heavy metals such as Hg, Cu or Ni has been used for the development of antifungal wood preservatives. Extracellular ligninolytic and cellulolytic enzymes are regulated by heavy metals on the level of transcription as well as during their action (Baldrian, 2003). Díaz *et al.*, (2011), reported the effect of Cu in the liquid culture medium on the laccase activity of several strains of *Pleurotus ostreatus*. In general, the maximal biomass produced was lower in those media containing Cu than without Cu, however, the maximal laccases activity was very high in presence of Cu; in particular, the strain Po83 showed 37490 and 1086 U L^{-1} with and without Cu respectively. Giardina *et al.*, (1999), obtained a laccase production of 30000 U L^{-1}, growing *Pleurotus ostreatus* (ATCC MYA-2306) in nutrient-rich medium, with addition of Cu, whereas laccase production resulted between 0.5 and 4 U L^{-1} in the presence of Cu traces. Cu has an important effect on the induction of several extracellular laccase isoenzymes in *Pleurotus ostreatus*, including phenol oxidase A1b (POXA1b), POXA2, and POXC (Palmieri *et al.*, 2000). Palmieri *et al.*, (2003), reported the production of two atypical laccase isoenzymes (POXA3a and POXA3b) from Cu supplemented *Pleurotus ostreatus* cultures. *Pleurotus pulmonarius (Fr) Quélet*, produced laccase as the main ligninolytic enzyme when cultivated on solid-state cultures using corn cob as substrate. The addition of 25.0 mM CuSO4 increased the level of laccase from 270 to 1420 U L^{-1} and the fungus showed high resistance to Cu under the conditions used in this work (Kirst *et al.*, 2006).

In *Trametes versicolor* 290, the highest laccase activity value (2500 U L^{-1}) was 18-fold higher in culture with Cu than in the absence of Cu (Collins and Dobson, 1997). Galhaup and Haltrich (2001) have studied the effect of Cu on the laccase production by different *Trametes spp*. The laccase activity of *Trametes versicolor* MB 52, *Trametes versicolor* MB 54, *Trametes suaveolens* MB 51 was induced by 1 mM Cu, reaching values of about 9000, 10000, and 7000 U L^{-1}, respectively, while none of these strains produced laccase activity when grown on culture medium without additional Cu.

The major laccase isoenzyme LAP2 was secreted by *Trametes pubescens* in response to high Cu concentrations (Galhaup *et al.*, 2002b). *Trametes pubescens* MB 89 is an excellent producer of the industrially important enzyme laccase. Extracellular laccase formation can be considerably stimulated by the addition of Cu in the millimolar range to a simple, glucose-based culture medium, under these conditions it was not necessary to add aromatic compounds that are routinely used as inducers of laccase in fungi (Galhaup *et al.*, 2002a). The effect of Cu on the laccase production of *Trametes versicolor* (CBS100.29) in cultures supplemented with 3.5 mM Cu was studied, the laccase activity was 11-fold higher than in the medium without Cu (Lorenzo *et al.*, 2006). Recently, a higher laccase production (15273 U L^{-1}) induced by Cu (1 mM) was observed by the *Trametes sp*. 48424 (Fan *et al.*, 2010). These results show the effect of Cu induction of laccase and that some strains are more sensitive to this metal than others. In the majority of fungal studied, regulation of laccase production by Cu occur at transcription level.

On the other hand, phenolic and aromatic compounds structurally related to lignin or lignin derivatives are often used to increase the fungal laccase production (De Souza *et al.*, 2004). Laccase induction by phenolic substances may represent a response developed by fungi against toxic aromatic compounds (Piscitelli *et al.*, 2011). Laccase inducer compounds have a different effect for each organism, even among strains of the same species, so that each organism should be evaluated with inducers to know the level of increase in the production of laccases.

On the other hand, the effect of phenolic and aromatic compounds on laccase production dependent on experimental conditions namely physical and chemical parameters as well as nutrient availability and inducer stimulation. An isolate of *Coriolus hirsutus* constitutively expresses substantial amounts of extracellular laccase on a defined growth medium. The most efficient inducer of extracellular laccase synthesis was syringaldazine, which increased the enzyme yield by 1000% at a concentration of 0.11 μM (Koroljova-Skorobogat'ko *et al.*, 1998). Cavallazzi *et al.*, (2005) studied the effects of two levels of N (2.6 and 26 mM) and seven levels of Cu (0, 50, 100, 150, 200, 250 and 300 μM) on the laccase activity of *Lentinula edodes*. The medium with 2.6 mM N and 250 μM Cu was found to provide the highest laccase activity. To the selected medium it was added gallic acid (1 mM), catechol (1 mM), ammonium tartrate (55 μM), hydroxybenzoic acid (1 mM) and vanillin (1 mM). The two first compounds completely inhibited laccase activity and a 30 day time course experiment was carried out with the remaining compounds. Only cultures with ammonium tartrate exhibited laccase activity higher than control cultures, reaching 251 U mL^{-1} of extract after 30 days. The effects of different inducers such as guaiacol, caffeic acid, syringaldazine and sinapinic acid on enhance laccase production by *Penicillium aculeatum*, *P. digitatum* and *P. cyclopium* were investigated. Laccase from the three *Penicillium* species was induced by all the compounds evaluated; however, sinapinic acid was the most efficient inducer of laccase biosynthesis (Hamed *et al.*, 2008). The cultivation of *Trametes versicolor* for laccase production was studied.

In order to obtain laccase induction, addition of solid lignin, lignosulphonates, veratryl alcohol, xylidine and ethanol was tested at different concentrations. To optimize laccase activity, the combined effect of inducer addition and simultaneously glucose suppression was studied. The best result for laccase induction (1240 U L^{-1}) was obtained with solid lignin, a by-product of pulp and paper industry and the higher laccase activity attained (1583 U L^{-1}) was obtained with the combined effect of xylidine addition and glucose suppression (Xavier *et al.*, 2007). 2,2'-Azino-di-(3-ethylbenzothialozin-6-sulfonic acid) (ABTS) (1 mM) was shown to be the best inducer of laccase production of *Pleurotus ostreatus* 32, reaching maximum values of about 400 U mL^{-1}. Cu (1 mM) also had a positive effect on laccase production, activity being enhanced to 360 U mL^{-1} (Hou *et al.*, 2004). Among 15 phenolic and aromatic compounds tested in *Pleurotus pulmonarius*, ferulic acid and vanillin were the most efficient inducers, increasing the production of laccase activity up to 10 times. A mixture of ferulic acid and vanillin was more efficient to induce the production of laccase than the isolated phenolics.

At least three laccase isoforms designated as lcc1, lcc2 and lcc3 were identified. The lcc1 and lcc2 isoforms were produced by non-induced cultures, while lcc3 was found only in induced-culture filtrates (De Souza *et al.*, 2004). *Trametes* sp. AH28-2 can synthesize extracellular laccase by induction in cellobiose-based liquid culture medium. Both yields and composition of laccase isoenzymes, would be quite different with induction by different small-molecule aromatic compounds, *o*-toluidine, guaiacol and 3,5-dihydroxytoluene. Higher concentrations of the three inducers could considerably increase laccase isoenzymes yields but not change the laccase composition. Laccase B isoenzyme, was selectively induced by 3,5-dihydroxytoluene (Xiao *et al.*, 2004).

Pleurotus eryngii, *P. ostreatus* and *P. pulmonarius* produced laccases. The highest levels of laccase activity were found in *P. eryngii*, under submerged fermentation conditions of dry ground mandarine peels and in *P. ostreatus*, strain No. 493, under solid-state fermentation conditions of grapevine sawdust (Stajić *et al.*, 2006). The strain of *Pleurotus ostreatus* HP-1 was studied on solid state fermentation. A maximum laccase yield was of 3952 U g^{-1} of dry wheat straw, however, enhancement in laccase activity was achieved with the use of various aromatic inducers and copper sulphate. Highest laccase activity of 14189 U g^{-1} of dry substrate was achieved using 0.28 mM copper sulphate under optimized conditions (Patel *et al.*, 2009). Lee *et al.*, (1999) found in *Trametes versicolor* that alcohol enhanced laccase activity more in comparison to xylidine.

It was postulated that the addition of ethanol to the cultivation medium caused a reduction in melanin formation. The monomers, when not polymerised to melanin, then acted as inducers for laccase production. This is a very economical way to enhance laccase production. Kinetic parameters of growth and laccase activity of five strains of *Pleurotus ostreatus* from the ATCC in submerged fermentation were evaluated. In general, the laccase activity was observed at the end of the exponential phase and during the stationary phase of growth.

It has been suggested, that laccase activity observed during the lag and exponential phases of fungal fermentation should be involved in substrate degradation, while the laccase activity detected in the stationary phase should be related to mushroom morphogenesis and pigmentation processes (Díaz *et al.*, 2011). In *Botryosphaeria rhodina* culture, highest laccase titers occurred only when the inducer was added to the nutrient medium prior to inoculation, and they decreased when the inducer was added later in the experiment (Dekker *et al.*, 2007).

On the other hand, *P. ostreatus, Rigidoporus lignosus* and *Trametes modesta* increased their laccase production when the inducer was added 2-5 days after inoculation (Vanhulle *et al.*, 2007; Nyanhongo *et al.*, 2002). *Volvariella volvacea* V14, produced multiple laccase isoenzymes in liquid culture. Enzyme synthesis was associated with the onset of secondary growth, and was positively regulated by Cu and by various aromatic compounds. In solid-state systems, only low levels of laccase are detectable during the vegetative growth phase but enzyme activity increases sharply at the onset of fruiting and during sporophore development (Shicheng *et al.*, 2003).

Laccase Gene Transcriptional Regulation

It has been suggested that synthesis and secretion of laccases laccase activity and the number of laccase isoenzymes are influenced by environmental factors such as temperature, pH, inducers, culture conditions, and medium composition (Giardina, *et al.*, 1999; Téllez-Téllez *et al.*, 2008). In many cases, the induction has been found to occur at the transcriptional level, in agreement with the finding of putative xenobiotic or metal response elements in the upstream regions of several induced laccase genes (Giardina, *et al.*, 2010).

Neurospora crassa produced laccase only in presence of cycloheximide and D-phenylalanine. De novo synthesis of laccase mRNA was followed over 96 h after induction. A fast appearance of the message, as well as its presence over a rather long period indicates a regulation on a transcriptional and maybe on a post-transcriptional level (Linden *et al.*, 1991). The expression of laccase in *Trametes versicolor* is regulated at the level of gene transcription by Cu and N (Collins and Dobson, 1997). In *Agaricus bisporus* growing on solid substrates, laccase expression has been found the level of laccase transcripts was highest in colonized compost (prior to the onset of fruiting), declined during the period of fruit body enlargement and increased again after harvesting and during the second flush of fruit body production (Ohga *et al.*, 1999). Transcript levels of genes *lcc1*, *lcc2*, and *lcc3* from basidiomycete I-62 (CECT 20197) were analyzed under four different culture conditions to study their expression patterns. Two of the laccase genes were clearly inducible by veratryl alcohol: the *lcc1* gene is inducible in early stages of growth, and the *lcc2* gene is also inducible but only when the organism reaches the stationary phase. Transcript levels for the third gene, *lcc3*, were uninduced by veratryl alcohol and repressed by glucose (Mansur *et al.*, 1998). Four laccase isoenzyme genes, Psc *lac1*, *2*, *3* and *4* have been cloned from the edible mushroom, *Pleurotus sajor-caju*. Induction of individual laccase isoenzyme genes by carbon, nitrogen, Cu, manganese and the two aromatic compounds, 2,5-xylidine and ferulic acid, occured at the level of gene transcription (Soden and Dobson, 2001). Extracellular laccase and laccase transcript levels (gene *cglcc1*) increased when *Coriolopsis gallica* was grown in the presence of tannic acid (Carbajo *et al.*, 2002). Faraco *et al.*, (2003) identified multiple putative metal-responsive elements (MRE) in the *P. ostreatus* laccase PoxC and Poxa1b gene promoter regions, which extended about 400 nt upstream of the start codon (ATG). In *Trametes villosa* the expression of lcc1 is highly induced by 2,5-xylidine, while the expression of lcc2 appears to be constitutive (Yaver *et al.*, 1996). Likewise, *lcc1* transcript titers in *Volvariella volvacea* are differentially tuned by the addition of copper sulfate, 4-hydroxybenzoic acid, veratric acid, ferulic acid, 2,5-xylidine and p-coumaric acid, whereas *lcc4* transcription is not affected by these compounds (Chen *et al.*, 2004). In the ligninolytic basidiomycetes *Trametes* sp. I62, nine structural closely related aromatic compounds (p-coumaric acid, ferulic acid, guaiacol, syringol, p-methoxyphenol, pyrocatechol, phloroglucinol, 3,5-dihydroxybenzoic acid, and syringaldazine) appear to have different effects on laccase gene expression. The three laccase isoenzyme genes in this fungus lcc1, lcc2, and lcc3 are differentially expressed in the presence of some of these aromatics with total lcc transcript levels differing markedly depending on the aromatic compound tested. Guaiacol (the best inducer of lcc gene transcription) and p-coumaric acid selectively induced expression of lcc1 and lcc2; ferulic acid induced lcc3 expression, while 3,5-dihydroxybenzoic acid had no marked effect on laccase gene transcription (Terrón *et al.*, 2004).

Laccase Promoters

In silico inspection of several laccase promoter sequences highlights the presence of many different responsive elements differentially distributed along the promoter sequences. Promoter analyses allowed a correlation between the observed regulatory effects on laccase gene transcription and the presence of specific responsive elements, and to postulate in some cases, a mechanism for their functioning. Differences in copy number, location or orientation of the putative response elements determine a complex picture of laccase regulation phenomena (Piscitelli *et al.*, 2011).

The promoter region of the laccase gene (*Cs-lcs1*) from *Ceriporiopsis subvermispora* possesses several putative MREs, as well as a putative target site responding to Cu termed ACE (Polanco *et al.*, 2002). The coding region of the genomic laccase sequence of *Pycnoporus cinnabarinus*, is preceded by the eukaryotic promoter elements TATA and CAAT. In genes of filamentous fungi, pyrimidine- rich sequences often directly precede the transcriptional start site, particularly in highly expressed genes, however, such sequences were not found in the *P. cinnabarinus* laccase promoter (Eggert *et al.*, 1998). The laccase gene *lac-1*, from *Cryphonectria parasitica* is repressed by hypoviruses, a group of virulence-attenuating mycoviruses. *lac-1* has also been shown to be transcriptionally activated by low concentrations of the translational inhibitor cycloheximide (CHX) and by the immunosuppressant cyclosporin A. Was reported a CHX responsive element within the *lac-1* promoter region. Gel-mobility shift analysis revealed a 111-bp fragment located 1.8 kb upstream of the *lac-1* transcriptional start point that exhibited protein binding activity. Insertion of this element within a basal *lac-1* promoter sequence conferred CHX responsive transcriptional activation.

Moreover, this activation was prevented by hypovirus infection. A 22-bp sequence with an imperfect dyad symmetry located within the 111-bp element was found to be essential for sequence-specific protein binding and, thus, represents a putative target for interactions between the *lac-1* promoter and proteins that are involved in mediating CHX inducible activation of *lac-1* transcription (Wang and Nuss, 1998). Promoter region analysis of laccase gene from *Pleurotus eryngii* named *pel*3, showed different consensus sequences: the TATA box, one copper-sensing sequence VTVBVGCTGW, one yeast copper-response element and two putative MREs (Rodríguez *et al.*, 2008).

The promoter regions for each of four different laccase isoenzymes were cloned from *Pleurotus sajor-caju*, using amplified flanking region-PCR (AFR-PCR). Sequences stretching 724, 214, 840 and 1740 bp upstream from the predicted start codons for lac1, lac2, lac3 and lac4, respectively, were cloned in each case and analysed for the presence of putative transcriptional response elements. A number of putative response elements including MREs, xenobiotic response elements (XRE) and antioxidant response elements appear to be present. In addition putative consensus sequences such as those for the binding of AP1, AP2, creA and NIT2 transcription factors, which are involved in nitrogen and carbon regulation in different fungi, are also present in the promoter regions of some of the isoenzymes (Soden and Dobson, 2003). The promoter region of the *lccK* laccase gene of *Pleurotus ostreatus* contains a putative TATA and inverted CAAT elements, which were localized at nucleotide positions -91 and -289, respectively, of the 5′flanking region. A putative inverted Sp1 transcription factor recognition site (GGGCGG) was found at -188. A putative heat shock element (NGAANNTTCN) was found at -142, whereas a putative metal response element (TGC(A/G)CNC) was found at -244. The positions of CAAT and TATA elements differ among fungal laccase genes (Okamoto *et al.*, 2003). Sequence analysis of 5′ nontranscribed regions of three laccase genes (*LAC1*, *LAC2*, and *LAC3*) from *Gaeumannomyces graminis*, revealed typical promoter sequences. Four putative MRE consensus sequences situated around the TATA box of the *LAC2* gene promoter and two consecutive putative MRE sequences located 751 and 690 bp upstream of the TATA box of the *LAC1* gene promoter. In addition, this promoter contains two putative ACE1 (activation of cup1 expression protein) binding sites situated between the TATA box and ATG codon (Anastasia *et al.*, 2002). An inferred TATA box and several putative CAAT, MRE, XRE and CreA consensus sequences have been identified in the *lacA*, *lacB* and *lacC* promoter regions (1881bp, 993bp and 1703bp long, respectively) of three laccase genes (*lacA*, *lacB* and *lacC*) from *Trametes sp.* AH28-2. Differences in copy number and distribution of XREs among the three genes (seven XREs in *lacA* and only two in *lacB* and *lacC*) are supposed to be responsible for their different responses to aromatic compounds: *lacA* is induced by all tested aromatic compounds, *lacB* is induced mainly by guaiacol and 3,5-dihydroxytoluene, whilst *lacC* transcript levels are not detectable in the presence of these compounds. The overlapping of one XRE element with the TATA box in the *lacC* promoter is probably responsible for the absence of induction of this gene by aromatic compounds (Xiao *et al.* 2006). The promoter regions of all *Pleurotus ostreatus* laccase genes, extending 500bp upstream of the start codon, have been analysed, revealing very little identity degree among them. *In silico* analysis allowed the identification of several putative response elements, differentially distributed along the promoter sequences. It is worth noting that the promoters of the most abundantly produced proteins (POXC and POXA3) display the highest number of signals belonging to different classes. Furthermore some characteristics are peculiar to each subfamily, i.e. the high number of antioxidant response elements, and the absence of XRE and C and N nutrient responsive element in the *poxa1b* sub-family (Piscitelli *et al.*, 2011).

Fungal Laccase Genes

The first fungal genes for laccase enzymes have been detected in ascomycetes when complementing defects in spore coloration (O´Hara and Timberlake, 1989) and the first gene and/or cDNA sequences were recorded for laccase from the Ascomycete fungus, *Neurospora crassa* (German and Lerch, 1986).

A similar methodology of screening a cDNA library with degenerate primers designed from known protein sequences lead to the discovery of a first conventional basidiomycete laccase gene from the white-rot *Trametes hirsuta* (Kojima *et al.*, 1990). It has been reported the secretion of laccase isoenzymes in many fungi (Palmieri *et al.*, 2003; Téllez-Téllez *et al.*, 2008).

Such diversity in laccase isoenzymes was first attributed to posttranslation modifications of the same gene product, but the characterization of several laccase gene families suggested that at least a part of this biochemical diversity could be the result of the multiplicity of gene in fungal genomes (Ong *et al.*, 1997). The largest taxon-level family of laccase genes so far identified (17 and 9 genes) are found in the non-lignin-degrading basidiomycetes *Coprinopsis cinerea* and *Laccaria bicolor,* repectively (Kilaru *et al.*, 2006; Courty *et al.*, 2009). White-rot fungi that have been shown to possess multiple laccase genes belong to the genera *Trametes* (Yaver and Golightly, 1996, Jönsson *et al.*, 1997, Mansur *et al.*, 1997, Necochea *et al.*, 2005) and *Pleurotus* (Soden and Dobson, 2001, Rodríguez *et al.*, 2008, Pezzella *et al.*, 2009).

The number of laccase gene sequence has increased considerably, now several hundreds of laccase gene sequences found in databases. Table 1 shows some laccase genes and their access numbers in the GenBank.

Table 1. Some laccase genes reported in the GenBank

Organism	Gene	GenBank	DNA/ cDNA	Referencias
Arthroderma gypseum CBS 118893	laccase	XM_ 003169329.1	1959 bp	The Broad Institute Genome Sequencing Platform
Coriolus hirsutus	phenoloxidase	M60560.1	2904 pb	Kojima *et al.*, 1990
Ceriporiopsis subvermispora	lcs1	AF053472.2	3032 pb	Karahanian *et al.*, 1998
Cerrera unicolor FCL 139	Lac1	JF927721.1	3608 pb	Janusz *et al.*, 2012
Flammulina velutipes	laccase	AY485826.1	2804 pb	Zhang *et al.*, 2004
Fusarium oxysporum strain 42887	Lcc1	EF990894.1	3470 pb	Cordoba-Cañero and Roncero, 2008
Fusarium oxysporum strain 42887	Lcc3	EF990899.1	4166 pb	Cordoba-Cañero and Roncero, 2008
Fusarium oxysporum strain 42887	Lcc5	EF990897.1	3229 pb	Cordoba-Cañero and Roncero, 2008
Ganoderma lucidum	laccase	AY485829.1	1766 pb	Zhang and Ma, 2012
Ganoderma tsugae 1109	lac1	DQ914874.1	1566 pb	Tai, 2012
Lentinula edodes 2 VT	LAC2	AY676426.1	1715 pb	Marabottini *et al.*, 2012
Lentinula edodes 3 VT	LAC3	AY676427.1	1790 pb	Marabottini *et al.*, 2012
Monilinia fructigena	Lcc2	EF050081.1	1934 pb	Hirschhauser and Frohlich, 2007
Sclerotinia sclerotiorum	Lcc2	EF050080.1	1896 pb	Hirschhauser and Frohlich, 2007
Polyporus grammocephalus TR16	laccase	FJ473384.2	4505 bp	Huang *et al.*, 2011
Pleurotus ostreatus	laccase	AY485827.1	1638 pb	Zhang and Ma, 2012
Pleurotus ostreatus	lccK	AB089612	2929 pb	Okamoto *et al.*, 2003
Pleurotus ostreatus	poxA1b	AJ005017	3371 pb	Giardina *et al.*, 1999
Pleurotus ostreatus	poxa3	AJ344434	3480 pb	Palmieri *et al.*, 2003
Pleurotus ostreatus	lac1 ex 1-3	AJ420179	238 pb	Luis *et al.*, 2004
Pleurotus ostreatus	lac2 ex 1-2	AJ420180	198 pb	Luis *et al.*, 2004
Pleurotus ostreatus	lac3 ex 1-3	AJ420181	238 pb	Luis *et al.*, 2004
Pleurotus ostreatus MYA-2306	sspoxa3a	AM409318	1318 pb	Giardina *et al.*, 2007

Table 1. (Continued)

Organism	Gene	GenBank	DNA/cDNA	Referencias
Pleurotus ostreatus MYA-2306	sspoxa3b	AM409319	1528 pb	Giardina *et al.*, 2007
Pleurotus ostreatus TCC:MYA-2306	pox 3 ex 1-11	FM202669	2870 pb	Pezzella *et al.*, 2009
Pleurotus ostreatus TCC:MYA-2306	pox 4 ex 1-20	FM202670	3191 pb	Pezzella *et al.*, 2009
Pleurotus ostreatus TCC:MYA-2306	pox 5 pseudogene	FM202671	2837 pb	Pezzella *et al.*, 2009
Pleurotus ostreatus	diphenol oxidase	Z22591	3155 pb	Giardina *et al.*, 1995
Pleurotus ostreatus	POX2	Z49075	3571 pb	Giardina *et al.*, 1996
Pleurotus sapidus	lac2	AJ973225.1	1734 p	Linke *et al.*, 2012
Pleurotus ostreatus ATCC 32783	lacP83	JF719064.1	2421 pb	Téllez-Téllez *et al.*, 2012
Phanerochaete flavidoalba	pfaL	EF446161.1	4589 pb	Rodríguez-Rincón *et al.*, 2010
Pycnoporus coccineus	laccase	FJ858750.1	2119 pb	Uzan *et al.*, 2010
Pycnoporus sanguineus	laccase	FJ858751.1	2125 pb	Uzan *et al.*, 2010
Pycnoporus sanguineus	laccase	AY510604.1	2154 bp	Zhao *et al.*, 2012
Pycnoporus cinnabarinus	Lcc3-1	AF025481.1	2629 pb	Eggert *et al.*, 1996; Eggert *et al.*, 1998
Pycnoporus cinnabarinus	Lcc3-2	AF123571.1	2840 pb	Temp *et al.*, 1999
Pycnoporus cinnabarinus	Lac1	AF170093.1	3331 pb	Otterbein *et al.*, 2000
Termitomyces sp.	Lcc 1-2	AB201164.1	3712 pb	Taprab *et al.*, 2005
Trametes sp. AH28-2	LacA	AY839936.1	4009 pb	Xiao *et al.*, 2006
Trametes sp. 48424	laccase	HM483869.1	1563 bp	Fan *et al.*, 2011
T. gibbosa CB-1	Laccase 1	JF906786.1	3816 pb	Zheng and Chi, 2012
Tramete gibbosa LS01	Lac1	HM243485.1	1782 pb	Zheng and Chi, 2012
Trametes pubescens	lap1A	AF414808.1	2554 pb	Galhaup *et al.*, 2002b
Trametes pubescens	lap2	AF414807.1	4996 pb	Galhaup *et al.*, 2002b
Trametes versicolor	lcc1	X84683.1	2800 pb	Jonsson *et al.*, 1995

Heterologous Expression of Fungal Laccases

Biotechnological and environmental applications require large amounts of enzymes. Laccases secreted from wild-type fungal organisms may not be suitable for commercial purposes mainly because the low yields and undesirable preparation procedures (such as presence of toxic inducers) are not economically advantageous; however recent advances in bioreactor design and culture conditions have significantly increased the production yields (Couto and Toca-Herrera, 2007). Heterologous expression should be better suited for large-scale production, because of the potential of expressing different laccases in one selected optimised host. Laccases, like other oxidative enzymes, are difficult to express in non-fungal systems (Kunamneni *et al.*, 2008).

The highest yields have been obtained in filamentous fungi, especially in *Aspergillus* spp. that are widely used in the production of industrial enzymes. Production of heterologous laccase has often been improved by varying the cultivation conditions.

For example, better production of heterologous laccase has been achieved in yeast systems by controlling the pH of the culture medium and by lowering cultivation temperatures In contrast to homologous laccase production, in which Cu addition often affects laccase gene expression, the increased laccase production by Cu addition is probably related to improved folding of the active laccase in heterologous production (Kiiskinen *et al.*, 2004). The heterologous expression of laccases has been mainly in filamentous fungi. Table 2 shows heterologous expression of some fungal laccase including the source and host for each case.

Table 2. Heterologous expression of fungal laccase

Laccase	Source	Host	Comments	Reference
PO1	*Coriolus hirsutus*	*Saccharomyces cerevisiae*	Active laccase secreted in the medium	Kojima *et al.*, 1990
PO2	*Coriolus hirsutus*	*Saccharomyces cerevisiae*	Active laccase secreted in the medium	Kojima *et al.*, 1990
PrL	*Phlebia radiata*	*Tricoderma reesei*	Laccase secreted activity of 7.7nkat ml^{-1} (ABTS). The enzyme was purified and partially characterized.	Saloheimo *et al.*, 1991
LCC1	***Rhizoctonia solani***	*Aspergillus oryzae*	Laccase activity secreted in the medium. The enzyme was purified and partially characterized	Wahleithmer *et al.*, 1996
LCC2	***Rhizoctonia solani***	*Aspergillus oryzae*	Active laccase secreted in the medium	Wahleithmer *et al.*, 1996
LCC4	***Rhizoctonia solani***	*Aspergillus oryzae*	Laccase activity secreted in the medium. The enzyme was purified and partially characterized	Wahleithmer *et al.*, 1996

Table 2. (Continued)

Laccase	Source	Host	Comments	Reference
LCC1	*Trametes villosa*	*Aspergillus oryzae*	Laccase activity secreted in the medium. The enzyme was purified and partially characterized	Yaver *et al.*, 1996
MtL	*Myceliophtora thermophila*	*Aspergillus oryzae*	Laccase secreted activity of 0.85 Uml^{-1} (SGZ). The enzyme was purified and partially characterized	Berka *et al.*, 1997
LCC1	*Trametes versicolor*	*Pichia pastoris*	Laccase activity secreted in the medium. Production yield was further optimized.	Jönsson *et al.*, 1997; O´Callaghan *et al.*, 2002
LAC1	***Cryptococcus neoformans***	*Saccharomyces cerevisiae*	Laccase activity was detected	**Williamson *et al.*, 1998**
LCC1	*Trametes versicolor*	*Saccharomyces cerevisiae*	Undetectable laccase activity in the medium	Cassland and Jönsson, 1999
LCC2	*Trametes versicolor*	*Saccharomyces cerevisiae*	Active laccase secreted in the medium. Production of ethanol from raw materials	Cassland and Jönsson, 1999; Larsson *et al.*, 2001
LAC	*Schizophyllum commune*	*Aspergillus sojae*	Laccase secreted activity of 774 U ml^{-1} (Gallic acid)	Hatamoto *et al.*, 1999
LCCI	*Trametes versicolor*	*Pichia pastoris*	Active laccase secreted in the medium. The enzyme and truncated version (LCCIa) were purified and partially characterized.	Gelo-Pujic *et al.*, 1999
LCC1	*Coprinus cinereus*	*Aspergillus oryzae*	Transformants secreted from 8.0 to 135 mg of active laccase per liter. The enzyme was purified and partially characterized.	Yaver *et al.*, 1999
LAC1	*Pycnoporus cinnabarinus*	*Pichia pastoris*	Transformants secreted 8.0 mg l^{-1} of hyperglycosylated active laccase	Otterbein *et al.*, 2000
LCCIV	*Trametes versicolor*	*Pichia pastoris*	Laccase secreted activity of 0.15 U ml^{-1} (ABTS). The enzyme was purified and partially characterized	Brown *et al.*, 2002

Laccase	*Source*	*Host*	Comments	Reference
LAC4	*Pleurotus sajor-caju*	*Pichia pastoris*	Transformants produced 4.85 mg l^{-1} of active laccase. The enzyme was purified and partially characterized	Soden *et al.*, 2002
LAC1	*Pycnoporus cinnabarinus*	*Aspergillus niger*	77-fold increased activity (7000 U ml^{-1}) (ABTS) using A. niger signal peptide. The enzyme was purified and partially characterized	Record *et al.*, 2002
LCC1	*Tramete sanguine M85-2*	*Saccharomyces cerevisiae Pichia pastoris*	Laccase activity was detected in the medium	Hoshida *et al.*, 2001
LCCI	*Trametes versicolor*	*Zea mays L.*	Laccase activity was found in the seed, and variability in the amount was seen. The highest level was 0.55% TSP (respect to Total soluble protein)	Hood *et al.*, 2003
MtL	*Myceliophthora thermophyla*	*Saccharomyces cerevisiae*	Laccase secreted activity of 0.6 U l^{-1} (ABTS). Total activity was enhanced 170-fold by directed evolution	Bulter *et al.*, 2003
LCS-1	*Ceriporiopsis subvermispora*	*Aspergillus nidulans*	Laccase secreted activity of 0.23 U ml^{-1} (ABTS). The enzyme was purified and partially characterized	Larrondo *et al.*, 2003a
LCS-1	*Ceriporiopsis subvermispora*	*Aspergillus niger*	Laccase secreted activity of 0.23 U ml^{-1} (ABTS). The enzyme was purified and partially characterized	Larrondo *et al.*, 2003a
MCO1	*Phanerochaete. chrysosporium*	*Aspergillus nidulans*	The recombinant characterized protein was not a typical laccase but rather a multi-copper oxidase with strong ferroxidase activity	Larrondo *et al.*, 2003b
LCC	*Fome lignosus*	*Pichia pastoris*	Laccase secreted activity of 5.95 U ml^{-1} (ABTS). The enzyme was purified and partially characterized	Liu *et al.*, 2003
LCCT	*Panus rudis*	*Pichia pastoris*	Laccase activity secreted in the medium	Yang *et al.*, 2003

Table 2. (Continued)

Laccase	Source	Host	Comments	Reference
LAC1	*Melanocarpus albomyces*	*Saccharomyces. cerevisiae*	200-fold increased production using α-factor signal peptide (2.8 nkat ml^{-1}) (ABTS)	Kiiskinen and Saloheimo, 2004
LAC1	*Trametes sp. strain C30*	*Saccharomyces cerevisiae*	Activity barely detectable in the medium	Klonowska *et al.*, 2005
LAC2	*Trametes sp. strain C30*	*Saccharomyces cerevisiae*	Undetectable laccase activity in the medium	Klonowska *et al.*, 2005
LAC3	*Trametes sp. strain C30*	*Saccharomyces cerevisiae*	Laccase secreted activity of 0.5 U ml^{-1} (SGZ). The enzyme was purified and partially characterized	Klonowska *et al.*, 2005
LAC1	*Pycnoporus cinnabarinus*	*Aspergillus oryzae*	Laccase secreted activity of 0.84 U ml^{-1} (ABTS). The enzyme was purified and partially characterized	Sigoillot *et al.*, 2004
LAC1	*Melanocarpus albomyces*	*Trichoderma reesei*	Laccase secreted activity of 230 mg l^{-1}. The highest production level was obtained in fed-batch culture (920 mg l^{-1}).	Kiiskinen *et al.*, 2004
LAC1	***Flammulina velutipes***	*Pichia pastoris*	Laccase activity secreted in the medium	Zhang *et al.*, 2004
LacIII	*Coriolus versicolor*	*Nicotiana tabacum*	The produced that was secreted into the rhizosphere	Sonoki *et al.* 2005
POXC	*Pleurotus ostreatus*	*Kluyveromyces lactis Saccharomyces cerevisiae*	Both trasformed host secreted recombinant active laccase	Piscitelli *et al.*, 2005
LCCPol	*Pleurotus ostreatus*	*Pichia pastoris*	Laccase activity was detected	Zhang *et al.*, 2005
LAC1	*Pycnoporus cinnabarinus*	*Yarrowia lipolytica*	Production was estimated to 20 mg l^{-1} in a bioreactor. Thus, complex metalloenzymes can be produced in *Yarrowia*, assuming some control of host physiology	Madzak *et al.*, 2005
*lac*D	*Trametes sp. 420*	*Pichia pastoris*	Laccase secreted activity of 8.3 x 10^4 U ml^{-1} (ABTS).	Hong *et al.*, 2007

Laccase	*Source*	*Host*	Comments	Reference
LCC	***Fomes lignosus***	*Saccharomyces cerevisiae*	5-fold increased production using ABTS	Hu *et al.*, 2007
*pel*3	*Pleurotus eryngii*	*Aspergillus niger*	The activity laccase was low, probably due to incomplete or incorrect folding.	Rodríguez *et al.*, 2008
MalL	*Melanocarpus albomyces*	*Oryza sativa*	The rice-produced laccase were purified and characterized	De Wilde *et al.*, 2008
	Pycnoporus cinnabarinus	*Oryza sativa*	The rice-produced laccase were purified and characterized	De Wilde *et al.*, 2008
Ery3	*Pleurotus eryngii*	*Saccharomyces cerevisiae*	Laccase activity was detected	Bleve *et al.*, 2008
GLIac1	***Ganoderma lucidum***	*Pichia pastoris*	Activity high laccase	Joo *et al.*, 2008
POXA3b	*Pleurotus ostreatus*	*Kluyveromyces lactis*	Clones expressing the large subunit alone exhibited always notably lower activity than those expressing both subunits	Faraco *et al.*, 2008
POX3	*Pleurotus ostreatus*	*Saccharomyces cerevisiae Kluyveromyces lactis*	Laccase activity was detected	Pezzella *et al.*, 2009
POX4	*Pleurotus ostreatus*	*Saccharomyces cerevisiae Kluyveromyces lactis*	Laccase activity was detected	Pezzella *et al.*, 2009
LAC	*Pycnoporus sanguineus*	*Pichia pastoris*	The recombinant enzyme was purified	Lu *et al.*, 2009
*Lac*3	*Cryphonectria parasitica*	*Saccharomyces cerevisiae*	Laccase activity secreted in the medium	Kim *et al.*, 2010
POXA1b	*Pleurotus ostreatus*	*Kluyveromyces lactis Saccharomyces cerevisiae*	Both trasformed host secreted recombinant active laccase (2,6-dimethoxyphenol)	Piscitelli *et al.*, 2005; Miele *et al.*, 2010
072 laccase	*Trametes hirsuta*	*P. canescens*	Activity of the secreted heterologous laccase in the culture liquid reaches 3 U/ml	Abyanova *et al.*, 2010
TR16	*Polyporus grammocephalus*	*Pichia pastoris*	The highest activity of the heterologously expressed laccase reached 893·3 U ml^{-1}.	Huang *et al.*, 2011
Lcc1	*Coriolus versicolor*	*Pichia pastoris*	Recombination laccase was expressed at a higher level	Li *et al.*, 2011

Conclusion

Laccase are enzymes with potential aplications in various areas, such as environmental, pharmaceutical, food, chemical, etc. However, the success of their application depends largely of the production of high levels of enzymes with catalytic properties on several substrates.

Many studies have focused on the search for laccase-producing microorganisms, as well as, production conditions such as carbon and nitrogen sources, pH and temperature, etc.

On the other hand, the use of inducers in the increased production of laccases has been successful. It has been reported many studies about the identification and characterization of laccase genes from different microorganisms, so the heterologous production in fungal hosts capable of producing high amounts of extracellular enzymes is a potential alternative.

References

Abadulla, E., T. Tzanov, S. Costa, K. H., Robra, A. Covaco-Paulo and G. M. Gübitz. 2000. Decolorization and detoxification of textile dyes with a laccase from *Trametes hirsute. Appl. Environ Microbiol.* 66: 3357-3362.

Abyanova, A. R., A. M. Chulkin, E. A. Vavilova, T. V. Fedorova, D. S. Loginov, O. V. Koroleva and S. V. Benevolensky. 2010. A heterologous production of the *Trametes hirsuta* laccase in the fungus *Penicillium canescens. Appl. Biochem. Microbiol.* 46: 313-317.

Agematu, H., K. Kominato, N. Shibamoto, T. Yoshioka, H. Nishida, R. Okamoto, T. Shin and S. Murao. 1993. Transformation of 7-(4-hydroxyphenylacetamido) cephalosporanic acid into a new cephalosporin antibiotic, 7-[1-oxaspiro(2.5) octa-6-oxo-4, 7-diene-2-carboxamido] cephalosporanic acid, by laccase. *Biosci. Biotech. Biochem.* 57:1387-1388.

Alexandre, G. and L. B. Zhulin. 2000. Laccases are widespread in bacteria. *Tibtech.* 18:41-42.

Amir, L., T. K. Tam, M. Pita, M. M. Meijler, L. Alfonta and E. Katz. 2009. Biofuel cell controlled by enzyme logic systems. *J. Am. Chem. Soc.* 131: 826-832.

Anastasia, P. L. and J. M. Henson. 2002. Cloning, Characterization, and Transcription of Three Laccase Genes from *Gaeumannomyces graminis* var. *tritici*, the Take-All Fungus. *Appl. Environ. Microbiol.* 68:1305-1311.

Andersen, O. S., M. G. Peter and P. Roepstorff. 1996. Cuticular sclerotization in insects. *Comp. Biochem. Physiol. B.* 113: 689–705.

Bajpai, P., 1999. Application of enzymes in the pulp and paper industry. *Biotechnol. Prog.* 15: 147-157.

Baldrian, P. 2003. Interactions of heavy metals with white-rot fungi. *Enzyme Microb. Technol.* 32:78–91.

Baldrian, P. 2006. Fungal laccases occurrenceand properties. *FEMS Microbiol Rev.* 30: 215-242.

Banerjee, U. C. and R. M. Vohra. 1991. Production of laccase by *Curvularia* sp. *Folia Microbiol.* 36: 343-346.

Berka, R. M., P. Schnerder, E. J. Golightly, S. H. Brown, M. Madden, K. M. Brown, T. Halkier, K. Mondorf and F. Xu. 1997. Characterization of the gene encoding an extracellular laccase of *Myceliophtora thermophila* and analysis of the recombinant enzyme expressed in *Aspergillus oryzae*. *Appl. Environ. Microbiol.* 63: 3151-3157.

Bernards, M. and N. G. Lewis. 1998. The macromolecular aromatic domain in suberized tissue: a changing paradigm. *Phytochemistry*. 47:915–933.

Binz, T. and G. Canevascini. 1997. Purification and partial characterization of the extracellular laccase from *Ophiostoma novo-ulmi*. *Curr. Microbiol.* 35: 278-281.

Bleve, G., C. Lezzi, G. Mita, P. Rampino, C. Perrotta, L. Villanova and F. Grieco. 2008. Molecular cloning and heterologous expression of a laccase gene from *Pleurotus eryngii* in free and immobilized *Saccharomyces cerevisiae* cells. *Appl. Microbiol. Biotechnol.* 79: 731-741.

Boudet, A. M. 2000. Lignins and lignification: selected issues. *Plant. Physiol. Biochem.* 38: 81-96.

Bourbonnais, R., M. G. Paice, I. D. Reid, P. Lanthier and M. Yaguchi. 1995. Lignin oxidation by laccase isozymes from *Trametes versicolor* and role of the mediator 2,29-azinobis(3-ethylbenzthiazoline-6-sulfonate) in kraft lignin depolymerization. *Appl. Eviron. Microbiol.* 61: 1876-1880.

Brown, M. A., Z. Zhao and A. G. Mauk. 2002. Expression and characterization of a recombinant multi-copper oxidase: laccase IV from *Trametes versicolor*. *Inorg. Chim. Acta* 331: 232-238.

Bulter, T., M. Alcalde, V. Sieber, P. Meinhold, C. Schlachtbauer and F. H. Arnold. 2003. Functional expression of a fungal laccase in *Saccharomyces cerevisiae* by directed evolution. *Appl. Environ. Microbiol.* 69: 987-995.

Carbajo, J. M., H. Junca, M. C. Terrón, T. González, S. Yagüe, E. Zapico and A. E. González. 2002. Tannic acid induces transcription of laccase gene *cglcc1* in the white-rot fungus *Coriolopsis gallica*. *Can. J. Microbiol.* 48: 1041-1047.

Cassland, P. and L. J. Jönsson. 1999. Characterization of a gene encoding *Trametes versicolor* laccase A and improved heterologous expression in *Saccharomyces cerevisiae* by decreased cultivation temperature. *Appl. Microbiol. Biotechnol.* 52: 393-400.

Cavallazzi, J. R. P., C. M. Kasuya and M. A. Soares. 2005. Screening of inducers for laccase production by *Lentinula edodes* in liquid medium. *Braz. J. Microbiol.* 36: 383-387.

Chen, S., W. Ge and J. A. Buswell. 2004. Molecular cloning of a new laccase from the edible straw mushroom *Volvariella volvacea*: possible involvement in fruit body development. *FEMS Microbiol. Lett.* 30:171–176.

Claus, H. 2003. Laccases and their occurrence in prokaryotes. *Archiv. Microbiol.* 179: 145-150.

Claus, H. 2004. Laccase: structure, reactions, distribution. *Micron* 35: 93–96.

Collins, P. J. and A. Dobson. 1997. Regulation of laccase gene transcription in *Trametes versicolor*. *Appl. Environ. Microbiol.* 63: 3444-3450.

Cordoba-Cañero, D. and M. I. G. Roncero. 2008. Functional analyses of laccase genes from *Fusarium oxysporum*. *Phytopathology* 98: 509-518.

Courty, P. E., P. J. Hoegger, S. Kilaru, A. Kohler, M. Buée, J. Garbaye, F. Martin and U. Kües. 2009. Phylogenetic analysis, genomic organization and expression analysis of multi-copper oxidases in the ectomycorrhizal basidiomycetes *Laccaria bicolor*. *New Phytol.* 182: 736-750.

Couto, S. R. and J. L.Toca-Herrera. 2007. Laccase production at reactor scale by filamentous fungi. *Biotechnol. Adv.* 25: 558-569.

De Souza, C. G. M., G. K. Tychanowicz, D. F. De Souza and R. M. Perlata. 2004. Production of laccase isoforms by *Pleurotus pulmonarius* in response to presence of phenolic and aromatic compounds. *J. Basic Microbiol.* 44: 129-136.

De Wilde, C., E. Uzan, Z. Zhou, K. Kruus, M. Andberg, L. Buchert, E. Record, M. Asther and A. Lomascolo. 2008. Transgenic rice as a novel production system for *Melanocarpus* and *Pynoporus* laccases. *Transgenic Res.* 17: 515-527.

Dekker, R. F. H., A. M. Barbosa, E. C. Giese, S. D. S. Godoy and L. G. Covizzi. 2007. Influence of nutrients on enhancing laccase production by *Botryosphaeria rhodina* MAMB-05. *Int. Microbiol.* 10: 177-185.

Desai, S. S. and C. Nityanand. 2011. Microbial Laccases and their Applications: A Review. *Asian J. Biotechnol.* 3: 98-124.

Díaz, R., S. Alonso, C. Sánchez, A. Tomasini, M. Bibbins-Martinez and G. Díaz-Godínez. 2011. Characterization of the growth and laccase activity of strains of *Pleurotus ostreatus* in submerged fermentation. *BioRes.* 6: 282-290.

Díaz-Godínez, G. 2011. Chapter VI: Production of Laccases by *Pleurotus ostreatus* in Solid-State and Submerged Fermentation. In: *Biotechnology of Microbial Enzymes, Ed: Vijai Kumar Gupta et al. Nova Science Publishers*, Inc. pp 1-23.

Dittmer, N. T., R. J. Suderman, H. Jiang, Y. C. Zhu, M. J. Gorman, K. J. Kramer and M. R. Kanost. 2004. Characterization of cDNAs encoding putative laccase-like multicopper oxidases and developmental expression in the tobacco hornworm, *Manduca sexta*, and the malaria mosquito, *Anopheles gambiae. Insect Biochem. Mol. Biol.* 34: 29-41.

Durán, N. and E. Esposito. 2000. Potential applications of oxidative enzymes and phenoloxidase-like compounds in wastewater and soil treatment: a review. *Appl. Catal. B-Environ.* 28: 83-99.

Edens, W. A., T. Q. Goins, D. Dooley and J. M. Henson. 1999. Purification and characterization of a secreted laccase of *Gaeumannomyces graminis* var. *tritici. Appl. Environ. Microbiol.* 65: 3071-3074.

Eggert, C., P. R. LaFayette, U. Temp, K. E. Eriksson and J. F. Dean. 1998. Molecular analysis of a laccase gene from the white rot fungus *Pycnoporus cinnabarinus. Appl. Environ. Microbiol.* 64: 1766-1772.

Eggert, C., U. Temp and K. E. Eriksson. 1996. The ligninolytic system of the white rot fungus *Pycnoporus cinnabarinus*: purification and characterization of the laccase. *Appl. Environ. Microbiol.* 62: 1151-1158.

Eriksson, K. E. L., R. A. Blanchette and P. Ander. 1990. Microbial and enzymatic degradation of wood and wood components. *Springer-Verlag, Berlin.* pp 225–333.

Fan, F., R. Zhuo, S. Sun, X. Wan, M. Jiang, X. Zhang and Y. Yang. 2011. Cloning and functional analysis of a new laccase gene from *Trametes sp.* 48424 which had the high yield of laccase and strong ability for decolorizing different dyes. *Bioresour. Technol.* 102: 3126-3137.

Fan, F., R. Zhuo, S. Sun, X. Wan, M. Jiang, X. Zhang and Y. Yang. 2010. Cloning and functional analysis of a new laccase gene from *Trametes sp.* 48424 which had the high yield of laccase and strong ability for decolorizing different dyes. *Bioresour. Technol.*102: 3126-3137.

Faraco, V., C. Ercole, G. Festa, P. Giardina, A. Piscitelli and G. Sannia. 2008. Heterologous expression of heterodimeric laccase from *Pleurotus ostreatus* in *Kluyveromyces lactis. Appl. Microbiol. Biotechnol.* 77: 1329-1335.

Faraco, V., P. Giardina and G. Sannia. 2003. Metal-responsive elements in *Pleurotus ostreatus* laccase gene promoters. *Microbiology* 149: 2155–2162.

Froehner, S. C. and K. E. Eriksson. 1974. Purification and properties of *Neurospora crassa* laccase. *J. Bacteriol.* 120: 458-465.

Galhaup, C. and D. Haltrich. 2001. Enhanced formation of laccase activity by the white-rot fungus *Trametes pubescens* in the presence of copper. *Appl. Microbiol. Biotechnol.* 56: 225-232.

Galhaup, C., H. Wagner, B. Hinterstoisser and D. Haltrich. 2002a. Increased production of laccase by the wood-degrading basidiomycetes *Trametes pubescens. Enzyme Microb. Technol.* 30: 529–536.

Galhaup, C., S. Goller, C. K. Peterbauer, J. Strauss and D. Haltrich. 2002b. Characterization of the major laccase isoenzyme from *Trametes pubescens* and regulation of its synthesis by metal ions. *Microbiology* 148: 2159-2169.

Gavnholt, B. and L. Knud. 2002. Molecular biology of plant laccases in relation to lignin formation. *Physiol. Plantarum* 116: 273–280.

Gelo-Pujic, M., H. H. Kim, N. G. Butlin and G. T. Palmore. 1999. Electrochemical studies of a truncated laccase produced in *Pichia pastori. Appl. Environ. Microbiol.* 65: 5515-5521.

German, U. A. and K. Lerch. 1986. Isolation and partial nucleotide-sequence of the laccase gene from *Neurospora crassa*: Amino acid sequence homology of the protein to human ceruloplasmin. *Proc. Natl. Acad. Sci. US 83*: 8854-8858.

Gianfreda, L., F. Xu and J. M. Bollag. 1999. Laccases. A useful group of oxidoreductive enzymes. *Bioremed. J.* 3: 1-25.

Giardina, P., F. Autore, V. Faraco, G. Festa, G. Palmieri, A. Piscitelli and G. Sannia. 2007. Structural characterization of heterodimeric laccases from *Pleurotus ostreatus. Appl. Microbiol. Biotechnol.* 75: 1293-1300.

Giardina, P., G. Palmieri, A. Scaloni, B. Fontanella, V. Faraco, G. Cennamo and G. Sannia. 1999. Protein and gene structure of a blue laccase from *Pleurotus ostreatus. Biochem. J.* 341: 655-663.

Giardina, P., R. Cannio, L. Martirani, L. Marzullo, G. Palmieri and G. Sannia. 1995. Cloning and sequencing of a laccase gene from the lignin-degrading basidiomycete *Pleurotus ostreatus. Appl. Environ. Microbiol.* 61: 2408-2413.

Giardina, P., V. Aurilia, R. Cannio, L. Marzullo, A. Amoresano, R. Siciliano, P. Pucci and G. Sannia. 1996. The gene, protein and glycan structures of laccase from *Pleurotus ostreatus. Eur. J. Biochem.* 235: 508-515.

Giardina, P., V. Faraco, C. Pezzella, A. Piscitelli, S. Vanhulle and G. Sannia. 2010. Laccases: a never-ending story. *Cell. Mol. Life Sci.* 67: 369-385.

Hamed, M., El-Shora, M. Y. Magdy and A. K. Salwa. 2008. Inducers and Inhibitors of Laccase from *Penicillium. Biotechnology.* 7: 35-42.

Harkin, J. M. and J. R. Obst. 1973. Syringaldazine: an effective reagent for detecting laccase and peroxidase in fungi. *Experientia.* 29: 381-387.

Hatamoto, O., H. Sekine, E. Nakano and K. Abe. 1999. Cloning and expression of a cDNA encoding the laccase from *Schizophyllum commune. Biosci. Biotechnol. Biochem.* 63: 58-64.

Hirschhauser, S. and J. Frohlich. 2007. Multiplex PCR for species discrimination of *Sclerotiniaceae* by novel laccase introns. *Int. J. Food Microbiol.* 118: 151-157.

Hong, Y., H. Zhou, X. Tu, J. Li and Y. Xiao. 2007. Cloning of a Laccase Gene from a Novel Basidiomycete *Trametes* sp. 420 and its heterologous expression in *Pichia pastoris. Curr. Microbiol.* 54: 260-265.

Hood, E. E., M. R. Bailey, K. Beifuss, M. Magallanes-Lundback, M. E. Horn, E. Callaway, C. Drees, D. E. Delaney, R. Clough and J. A. Howard. 2003. Criteria for high-level expression of a fungal laccase gene in transgenic maize. *Plant Biotechnol. J.* 1: 129-140.

Hoopes, J. T. and J. F. D. Dean. 2004. Ferroxidase activity in a laccase like multicopper oxidase from *Liriodendron tulipifera. Plant Physiol. Biochem.* 42: 27-33.

Hoshida, H., M. Nakao, H. Kanazawa, K. Kubo, T. Hakukawa, K. Morimasa. 2001. Isolation of five laccase gene sequences from the white-rot fungus *Tramete sanguine* by PCR, and cloning, characterization and expression of the laccase cDNA in yeast. *J. Biosci. Bioeng.* 92: 372-380.

Hou, H., J. Zhou, J. Wang, C. Du and B. Yan. 2004. Enhancement of laccase production by *Pleurotus ostreatus* and its use for the decolorization of anthraquinone dye. *Process Biochem.* 39: 1415-1419.

Hu, M. R., Y. P. Chao, G. Q. Zhang, X. Q. Yang, Z. Q. Xue and S. J. Qian. 2007. Molecular evolution of *Fomes lignosus* laccase by ethyl methane sulfonate-based ramdom mutagenesis in vitro. *Biomol. Eng.* 24: 619-624.

Huang, S. J., Z. M. Liu, X. L. Huang, L. Q. Guo and J. F. Lin. 2011. Molecular cloning and characterization of novel laccase gene from a write-rot fungus *Polyporus grammocephalus* TR16 and expression in *Pichia pastoris*. *Lett. Appl. Microbiol.* 52: 290-297.

Iyer, G. and B. B. Chattoo. 2003. Purification and characterization of laccase from the rice blast fungus, *Magnaporthe grisea. FEMS Microbiol. Lett.* 227: 121-126.

Janusz, G., A. Mazur, A. Checinska, W. Malek and J. Rogalski. 2012. Cloning and characterization of a laccase gene from the white-rot basidiomycete *Cerrena unicolor* (http://www.uniprot.org/uniprot/B8YQ97).

Jonsson, L., K. Sjostrom, I. Haggstrom and P.O. Nyman. 1995. Characterization of a laccase gene from the white-rot fungus *Trametes versicolor* and structural features of basidiomycete laccases. *Biochim. Biophys.* Acta 1251: 210-215.

Jönsson, L. J., M. Saloheimo and M. Penttila. 1997. Laccase from the write-rot fungus *Trametes versicolor*. cDNA cloning of lcc1 and expression in *Pichia pastoris*. *Curr. Genet.* 32: 425-430.

Joo, S. S., I. W. Ryu, J. K. Park, Y. M. Yoo, D. H. Lee, K. W. Hwang, H. T. Choi, C. J. Lim, D. I. Lee and K. Kim. 2008. Molecular cloning and expression of a laccase from *Ganoderma lucidum*, and its antioxidative properties. *Mol. Cells* 25: 112-118.

Karahanian, E., G. Corsini, S. Lobos and R. Vicuna. 1998. Structure and expression of a laccase gene from the ligninolytic basidiomycete *Ceriporiopsis subvermispora. Biochim. Biophys. Acta* 1443: 65-74.

Kiiskinen, L. L, K. Kruus, M. Bailey, E. Ylösmäki, M. Siika-aho and M. Saloheimo. 2004. Expression of *Melanocarpus albomyces* laccase in *Trichoderma reesei* and characterization of the purified enzyme. *Microbiology* 150: 3065–3074.

Kiiskinen, L. L. and M. Saloheimo. 2004. Molecular cloning and expression in *Saccharomyces cerevisiae* of a laccase gene from the ascomycete *Melanocarpus albomyces. Appl. Environ. Microbiol.* 70: 137-144.

Kiiskinen, L. L., L. Viikari and K. Kruus. 2002. Purification and characterization of a novel laccase from the ascomycete *Melanocarpus albomyces*. *Appl. Microbiol. Biotechnol.* 59: 198-204.

Kilaru, S., P. Hoegger and U. Kües. 2006. The laccase multi-gene family in *Corprinopsis cinerea* has seventeen different members that divide into two distinct subfamilies. *Curr. Genet.* 50: 45-60.

Kim, J. M., S. M. Park and D. H. Kim. 2010. Heterologous expression of a tannic acid-inducible laccase3 of *Cryphonectria parasitica* in *Saccharomyces cerevisiae. BMC Biotechnol.* 10: 9-18.

Kirst, T. G., D. F. De Souza, C. G. M. De Souza, M. K. Kimiko and R. M. Peralta. 2006. Copper Improves the Production of Laccase by the White-Rot Fungus *Pleurotus pulmonarius* in Solid State Fermentation. *Braz. Arch. Biol. Technol.* 49: 699-704.

Klonowska, A., C. Gaudin, M. Asso, A. Fournel, M. Reglier and T. Tron. 2005. LAC3, a new low redox potential laccase from *Trametes* sp strain C30 obtained as recombinant protein in yeast. *Enzyme Microb. Tech.* 36: 34-41.

Kojima, Y., Y. Tsukuda, Y. Kawai, A. Tsukamoto, J. Sigiura, M. Sakaino and Y. Kita. 1990. Cloning, sequence analysis, and expression of ligninolytic phenoloxidase genes of the white-rot basidiomycete *Coriolus hirsutus. J. Biol. Chem.* 265: 15224-15230.

Koroljova-Skorobogat'ko, O. V., E. V. Stepanova, *V. P.* Gavrilova, O. V. Morozova, *N. V.* Lubimova, A. N. Dzchafarova, A. I. Jaropolov and A. Makower. 1998. Purification and characterization of the constitutive form of laccase from the basidiomycete *Coriolus hirsutus* and effect of inducers on laccase synthesis. *Biotechnol. Appl. Biochem.* 28*:* 47–54.

Kumar, S. V. S., P. S. Phale, S. Durani and P. P. Wangikar. 2003. Combined sequence and structure analysis of the fungal laccase family. *Biotechnol. Bioeng*. 83: 386–394.

Kunamneni, A., S. Camarero, C. García-Burgos, F. J. Plou, A. Ballesteros and M. Alcalde. 2008. Engineering and Applications of fungal laccases for organic synthesis. *Microb. Cell Fact.* 7: 15-32.

Langfelder, K., M. Streibel, B. Jahn, G. Haase and A. A. Brakhage. 2003. Biosynthesis of fungal melanins and their importance for human pathogenic fungi. *Fungal Genet. Biol.* 38:143–158.

Larrondo, L. F., L. Salas, F. Melo, R. Vicuna and D. Cullen. 2003b. A Novel extracelular multicopper oxidase from *Phanerochaete chysosporium* with ferroxidase activity. *Appl. Environ. Microbiol*. 69: 6257-6263.

Larrondo, L. F., M. Avila, L. Salas, D. Cullen and R. Vicuna. 2003a. Heterologous expression of laccse cDNA from *Ceriporiopsis subvermispora* yields copper-activated apoprotein and complex isoform patterns. *Microbiology* 149: 1177-1182.

Lee, I. Y., K. H. Jung, C. H. Lee and Y. H. Park. 1999. Enhanced production of laccase in *Trametes vesicolor* by the addition of ethanol. *Biotechnol. Lett.* 21: 965–968.

Leontievsky, N. Myasoedova, N. Pozdnyakova and L. Golovleva. 1997. "Yellow" laccase of *Panus tigrinus* oxidizes non-phenolic substrates without electron-transfer mediators. *FEBS Lett.* 413: 446-448.

Levine, W. G. 1965. Laccase, a review, In: The biochemistry of copper. *Academic Press Inc. New York*. pp. 371-385.

Li, Y. H., B. W. Gui, L. C. Fu, G. Z. Lin and X. J. Yong. 2011. Cloning of laccase gene from *Coriolus versicolor* and optimization of culture conditions for Lcc1 expression in *Pichia pastoris*. *Adv. Mater. Res.* 236-238: 1039-1044.

Linden, R. M., B. C. Schilling, U. A. Germann and K. Lerch. 1991. Regulation of laccase synthesis in induced *Neurospora crassa* cultures. *Curr. Genet.* 19: 375-81.

Linke, D., H. Bouws, T. Peters, M. Nimtz, R. G. Berger and H. Zorn. 2012. Laccases of *Pleurotus sapidus*: Characterization, cloning, and sustainable production. NCBI (GenBank).

Liu, L., J. F. D. Dean, W. E. Friedman and K. E. L. Eriksson, 1994. Laccase like phenoloxidase is correlated with lignin biosynthesis in *Zinnia elegans* stem tissue. *Plant J.* 6: 213-224.

Liu, W., Y. Chao, S. Liu, H. Bao and S. Qian. 2003. Molecular cloning and characterization of a laccase gene from the basidiomycete *Fome lignosus* and expression in *Pichia pastoris*. *Appl. Microbiol. Biotechnol.* 63: 174-181.

Lorenzo, M., D. Moldes and M. A. Sanromán. 2006. Effect of heavy metals on the production of several laccase isoenzymes by *Trametes versicolor* and on their ability to decolourise dyes. *Chemosphere* 63: 912-917.

Lu, L., M. Zhao, S. C. Liang, L. Y. Zhao, D. B. Li and B. B. Zhang. 2009. Production and synthetic dyes decolourization capacity of recombinant laccase from *Pichia pastoris*. *J. Appl. Microbiol.* 107: 1149-1156.

Luis, P., G. Walther, H. Kellner, F. Martin and F. Buscot. 2004. Diversity of laccase genes from basidiomycetes in a forest soil. *Soil Biol. Biochem.* 36: 1025-1036.

Madzak, C., L. Otterbein, M. Chamkha, S. Moukha, M. Asther, C. Gaillardin and J. M. Beckerich. 2005. Heterologous production of a laccase from the basidiomycete *Pycnoporus cinnabarinus* in the dimorphic yeast *Yarrowia lipolytica*. *FEMS Yeast Res.* 5: 635-646.

Mansur, M., T. Suárez, J. B. Fernández-Larrea, M. A. Brizuela and A. E. González. 1997. Identification of a laccase gene family in the new lignin-degrading basidiomycete CECT 20197. *Appl. Environ. Microbiol.* 63: 2637-2646.

Mansur, M., T. Suárezand and A. E. González. 1998. Differential gene expression in the laccase gene family from basidiomycete I-62 (CECT 20197). *Appl. Environ. Microbiol.* 64: 771-774.

Marabottini, R., M. Ciaffi and A. D'Annibale. 2012. Molecular characterization of gene sequences coding for laccase in *Lentinula edodes* NRRL 22663. NCBI (GenBank).

Mayer, A. M and R. C. Staples. 2002. Laccase: new functions for an old enzyme. *Phytochemistry*. 60: 551-565.

Miele, A., P. Giardina, G. Sannia and V. Faraco. 2010. Random mutants of a *Pleurotus ostreatus* laccase as new biocatalysts for industrial effluents bioremediation. *J. Appl. Microbiol.* 108: 998-1006.

Minussi, R., G. M. Pastore and N. Duran. 2002. Potential applications of laccase in the food industry. *Trends Food Sci. Tech.* 13: 205-216.

Molitoris, H. P. and K. Esser. 1970. The phenoloxidases of the ascomycete *Podospora anserina*. V. Properties of laccase I after further purification. *Arch. Mikrobiol.* 72: 267-296.

Necochea, R., B. Valderrama, S. Díaz-Sandoval, J. L. Folch-Mallol, R. Vázquez-Duhalt and G. Iturriaga. 2005. Phylogenetic and biochemical characterization of a recombinant laccase from *Trametes versicolor*. *FEMS Microbiol. Lett.* 244: 235-241.

Nyanhongo, G. S., J. Gomez, G. Gubitz, R. Zvanya, J. S. Read and W. Steiner, 2002. Production of laccase by a newly isolated strain of *Trametes modesta*. *Bioresour. Technol.* 84: 259-263.

O´Callaghan, J., M. M. O´Brien, K. McClean and A. D. W. Dobson. 2002. Optimisation of the expression of *Trametes versicolor* laccase gene in *Pichia pastoris*. *J. Ind. Microbiol. Biotechnol.* 29: 55-59.

O´Hara, E. B. and W. E. Timberlake. 1989. Molecular characterization of the *Aspergillus nidulans yA* locus. *Genetics* 121: 249-254.

O'Malley, D., R. Whetter, W. Bao, C. Che and R. Sederhoff. 1993. The role of laccase in lignification. *Plant J.* 4: 751-757.

Ohga, S., M. Smith, C. F. Thurston and D. A. Wood. 1999. Transcriptional regulation of laccase and cellulase genes in the mycelium of *Agaricus bisporus* during fruit body development on a solid substrate. *Mycol. Res.* 103: 1557-1560.

Okamoto, K., Y. Ito, I. Shigematsu, S. O. Yanagi and H. Yanase. 2003. Cloning and characterization of a laccase gene from the white-rot basidiomycete *Pleurotus ostreatus*. *Mycoscience* 44: 11-17.

Ong, E., W. B. R. Pollock and M. Smith, 1997. Cloning and sequence analysis of two laccase complementary DNAs from the ligninolytic basidiomycete *Trametes versicolor*. *Gene* 196:113-119.

Onuki, T., M. Nogucji and J. Mitamura. 2000. Oxidative hair dye composition containing laccase. *Pat. Int. Appl. WO 0037,030. Chem. Abstr.* 133: 78994m.

Osiadacz, J., A. J. H. Al-Adhami, D. Bajraszewska, P. Fischer and W. Peczynska-Czoch. 1999. On the use of Trametes versicolor laccase for the conversion of 4-methyl-3-hydrocyanthranilic acid to actinocin chromophore. *J. Biotechnol.* 72: 141-149.

Otterbein, L., E. Record, S. Longhi, M. Asther and S. Moukha. 2000. Molecular cloning of the cDNA encoding laccase from *Pycnoporus cinnabarinus* I-937 and expression in *Pichia pastoris*. *Eur. J. Biochem.* 267: 1619-1625.

Palmieri, G., G. Cennamo, V. Faraco, A. Amoresano, G. Sannia and P. Giardina. 2003. Atypical laccase isoenzymes from copper supplemented *Pleurotus ostreatus* cultures. *Enzyme Microb. Technol.* 33: 220-230.

Palmieri, G., P. Giardina, C. Bianco, B. Fontanella and G. Sannia. 2000. Copper induction of laccase isoenzymes in the ligninolytic fungus *Pleurotus ostreatus*. *Appl. Environ. Microbiol.* 66: 920-924.

Palonen, H., M. Saloheimo, L. Viikari and K. Kruus. 2003. Purification, characterization and sequence analysis of a laccase from the ascomycete *Mauginiella* sp. *Enzyme Microb. Technol.* 33: 854-862.

Patel, H., A. Gupte and S. Gupte. 2009. Effect of different culture condition and inducers on production of laccase by a basidiomycete fungal isolate *Pleurotus ostreatus* HP-1 under solid state fermentation. *BioRes.* 4: 268-284.

Peshkova, S. and L. Kaichang. 2003. Investigation of chitosan-phenolics systems as wood adhesives. *J. Biotech.* 102: 199-207.

Pezzella, C., F. Autore, P. Giardina, A. Piscitelli, G. Sannia and V. Faraco, 2009. The *Pleurotus ostreatus* laccase multi-gene family: isolation and heterologous expression of new family members. *Curr. Genet.* 55: 45-57.

Piontek, K., M. Antorini and T. Choinowski. 2002. Crystal structure of a laccase from the fungus *Trametes versicolor* at 1.90-A resolution containing a full complement of coppers. *J. Biol. Chem.* 277: 37663-37669.

Piscitelli, A., P. Giardina, C. Mazzoni and G. Sannia. 2005. Recombinant expression of *Pleurotus ostrestus* laccases in *Kluyveromyces lactis* and *Saccharomyces cerevisiae. Appl. Microbiol. Biotechnol.* 69: 428-439.

Piscitelli, A., P. Giardina, V. Lettera, C. Pezzella, G. Sannia and V. Faraco, 2011. Induction and Transcriptional Regulation of Laccases in Fungi. *Curr. Genomics* 12: 104-112.

Polanco, R., S. Lobos and R. Vicuña. 2002. Binding of nuclear proteins to the promoter region of the laccase gene *Cs-lcs1* from the basidiomycete *Ceriporiopsis subvermispora. Enzyme Microb. Technol. 30:* 525–528.

Pruche, F., L. P. Saint and B. Bernards. 2000. Hair dye compositions containing hydroxystilbene. *Eur. Pat. Appl. EP 1013,260. Chem. Abstr.* 133: 63587g.

Ranocha, P., M. Chabannes, S. Chamayou, S. Danoun, A. Jauneau, A. M. Boudet and D. Goffner. 2002. Laccase down-regulation causes alterations in phenolic metabolism and cell wall structure in poplar. *Plant Physiol.* 129: 1-11.

Record, E., P. J. Punt, M. Chamkha, M. Labat, C. A. Van den Hondel and M. Asther. 2002. Expresión of the *Pycnoporus cinnabarinus* laccase gene in *Aspergillus niger* and characterization of the recombinante enzyme. *Eur. J. Biochem.* 269: 602-609.

Roberts, S. A., A. Weichsel, G. Grass, K. Thakali, J. T. Hazzard, G. Tollin, C. Rensing and W. R. Montfort. 2002. Crystal structure and electron transfer kinetics of CueO, a multicopper oxidase required for copper homeostasis in *Escherichia coli. Proc. Natl. Acad. Sci. US* 99: 2766-2771.

Rodríguez, A., M. A. Falcón, A. Carnicero, F. Perestelo, G. De la Fuente and Trojanowski. 1996. Laccase activities of *Penicillium chysogenum* in relation to lignin degradation. *Appl. Microbiol. Biotechnol.* 45: 399-403.

Rodríguez, E., F. J. Ruiz-Dueñas, R. Kooistra, A. Ram, Á. T. Martínez and M.J. Martínez. 2008. Isolation of two laccase genes from the white-rot fungus *Pleurotus eryngii* and heterologous expression of the *pel*3 encoded protein. *J. Biotechnol.* 134: 9-19.

Rodríguez-Rincón, F., A. Suarez, M. Lucas, L. F. Larrondo, T. De la Rubia, J. Polaina and J. Martínez. 2010. Molecular and structural modeling of the *Phanerochaete flavido-alba* extracellular laccase reveals its ferroxidase structure. *Arch. Microbiol.* 192: 883-892.

Saloheimo, M. and M.-L. Niku-Paavola. 1991. Heterologous production of a ligninolytic enzyme: expression of the *Phlebia radiata* laccase gene in *Trichoderma reesei. Bio-Technol.* 9: 987-990.

Scherer, M. and R. Fischer. 1998. Purification and characterization of laccase II of *Aspergillus nidulans. Arch. Microbiol.* 170:78-84.

Schlosser, D., R. Grey and W. Fritsche. 1997. Patterns of ligninolytic enzymes in *Trametes versicolor*. Distribution of extra- and intracellular enzyme activities during cultivation on glucose, wheat straw and beech wood. *Appl. Microbial. Biotechnol.* 47: 412-418.

Sharma, P., R. Goel and N. Capalash. 2007. Bacterial laccases. *World J. Microbiol. Biotechnol.* 23: 823-832.

Shicheng, C., M. Dengbo, G. Wei and J. A. Buswell. 2003. Induction of laccase activity in the edible straw mushroom, *Volvariella volvacea FEMS Microbiol. Lett.* 218: 143-148.

Sigoillot, C., E. Record, V. Belle, J. L. Robert, A. Levasseur, P. J. Punt, C. A. Van Den, C. A. Van Den Hondel, A. Fournel, J. C. Sigoillot and M. Asther, 2004. Natural and recombinant fungal laccases for paper pulp bleaching. *Appl. Microbiol. Biotechnol.* 64: 346-352.

Soden, D. M. and A. D. Dobson. 2001. Differential regulation of laccase gene expression in *Pleurotus sajor-caju. Microbiology* 147: 1755-1763.

Soden, D. M. and A. D. W. Dobson. 2003. The use of amplified flanking region-PCR in the isolation of laccase promoter sequences from the edible fungus *Pleurotus sajor-caju. J. Appl. Microbiol.* 95: 553-562.

Soden, D. M., M. J. O´Callaghan and A. D. Dobson. 2002. Molecular cloning of a laccase isozyme gene from *Pleurotus sajor-caju* and expression in the heterologous *Pichia pastoris* host. *Microbiology* 148: 4003-4014.

Solomon, E. I., U. M. Sundaram and T.E. Machonkin. 1996. Multicopper oxidases and oxygenases. *Chem. Rev.* 96: 2563-2605.

Sonoki, T., S. Kajita, S. Ikeda, M. Uesugi, K. Tatsumi, Y. Katayama and Y. Limura. 2005. Transgenic tabacco expressing fungal laccase promotes the detoxification of enviromental pollutants. *Appl. Microbiol. Biotecnhnol.* 67: 138-142.

Stajić, M., L. Persky, D. Friesem, Y. Hada, S. P. Wasser, E. Nevo and J. Vukojević. 2006. Effect of different carbon and nitrogen sources on laccase and peroxidases production by selected *Pleurotus* species. *Enzyme Microb. Technol.* 38: 65-73.

Sterjiades, R., J. F. D. Dean and K. E. L. Eriksson. 1992. Laccase from sycamore maple (*Acer pseudoplatanus*) polymerizes monolignols. *Plant Physiol.* 99: 1162-1168.

Tai,Y. R. 2012. Cloning, classification and heterologous expression of laccases from *Ganoderma* species. NCBI (GenBank).

Taprab, Y., T. Johjima, Y. Maeda, S. Moriya, S. Trakulnaleamsai, N. Noparatnaraporn, M. Ohkuma and T. Kudo. 2005. Symbiotic fungi produce laccases potentially involved in phenol degradation in fungus combs of fungus-growing termites in Thailand. *Appl. Environ. Microbiol.* 71: 7696-7704.

Téllez-Téllez, M., C. Sánchez, O. Loera and G. Díaz-Godínez. 2005. Differential patterns of constitutive intracellular laccases of the vegetative phase for *Pleurotus* species. *Biotechnol. Lett.* 27: 1391-1394.

Téllez-Téllez, M., G. Díaz-Godínez, M. B. Aguilar and F. J. Fernández, 2012. Description of laccase gene from *Pleurotus ostreatus* expressed under submerged fermentation conditions. *BioRes.* (in press).

Téllez-Téllez, M., J. F. Fernández, A. M. Montiel-González, C. Sánchez and G. Díaz-Godínez. 2008. Growth and laccase production by *Pleurotus ostreatus* in submerged and solid-state fermentation. *Appl. Microbiol. Biotech.* 81: 675-679.

Temp, U., U. Zierold and C. Eggert. 1999. Cloning and characterization of a second laccase gene from the lignin-degrading basidiomycete *Pycnoporus cinnabarinus*. *Gene* 236: 169-177.

Terrón, M. C., T. González, J. M. Carbajo, S. Yagüe, A. Arana-Cuenca, A. Téllez, A. D. Dobson and A. E. González. 2004. Structural close related aromatic compounds have different effects on laccase activity and on lcc gene expression in the ligninolytic fungus *Trametes sp*. I-62. *Fungal Genet. Biol.* 41: 954-962.

Thakker, G. D., C. S. Evans and K. Rao. 1992. Purification and characterization of laccase from *Monocillium indicum* Saxena. *Appl. Microbiol. Biotechnol.* 37: 321-323.

Thurston, C. F. 1994. The structure and function of fungal laccases. *Microbiol.* 140: 19-26.

Uzan, E., P. Nousiainen, V. Balland, J. Sipila, F. Piumi, D. Navarro, M. Asther, E. Record and A. Lomascolo. 2010. High redox potential laccases from the ligninolytic fungi *Pycnoporus coccineus* and *Pycnoporus sanguineus* suitable for white biotechnology: from gene cloning to enzyme characterization and applications. *J. Appl. Microbiol.* 108: 2199-2213.

Vanhulle, S., R. R. Radman, R. R. Parra, T. Cui, C. M. Bols, T. Tron, G. Sannia and T. Keshavarz. 2007. Effect of mannan oligosaccharide elicitor and ferulic acid on enhancement of laccases production in liquid cultures of basidiomycetes. *Enzyme Microb. Technol.* 40: 1712-1718.

Vasconcelos, A. F., A. M. Barbosa, R. F. H. Dekker, I. S. Scarminio and M. I. Rezende. 2000. Optimization of laccase production by *Botruospaeria* sp. In the presence of veratryl alcohol by the respose-surface method. *Proc. Biochem.* 35: 1131-1138.

Wahleithmer, J. A., F. Xu, K. M. Brown, S. H. Brown, E. J. Golightly, T. Haalkier, S. Kauppinen, A. Pederson and P. Schneider. 1996. The identification and characterization of four laccases from the plant pathogenic fungus *Rhizoctonia solani. Curr. Genet.* 29: 395-403.

Wang, P. and D. L. Nuss. 1998. Identification of a *Cryphonectria parasitica* laccase gene promoter element involved in cycloheximide-inducible, hypovirus-repressible transcriptional activation. *Gene* 210: 79-84.

Williamson, P. R. 1994. Biochemical and molecular characterization of the diphenol oxidase of *Cryptococcus neoformans*: identification as a laccase. *J. Bacteriol.* 176: 656-664.

Williamson, P. R., K. Wakamatsu and S. Ito. 1998. Melanin biosynthesis in *Cryptococcus neoformans. J. Bacteriol.* 180: 1570-1572.

Xavier, A. M. R. B. X., A. P. M. Tavares, R. Ferreira and F. Amado. 2007. *Trametes versicolor* growth and laccase induction with by-products of pulp and paper industry. *Electron J. Biotechnol.* 10: 444-451.

Xiao, Y. Z., Q. Chen, J. Hang, Y. Y. Shi, Y. Z. Xiao, J. Wu, Y. Z. Hong and Y.P. Wang. 2004. Selective induction, purification and characterization of a laccase isozyme from the basidiomycete *Trametes* sp. AH28-2. *Mycologia* 96*:* 26–35.

Xiao,Y. Z., Y. Z. Hong, J. F. Li, J. Hang, P. G. Tong, W. Fang and C. Z. Zhou. 2006. Cloning of novel laccase isozyme genes from *Trametes sp.* AH28-2 and analyses of their differential expression. *Appl. Microbiol. Biotechnol.* 71: 493-501.

Yang, J. Q., G. Y. Tang, H. M. Dai, G. Liu and H. C. Zhu. 2003. Expression and Purification of the purification of the modified gene of laccase from *Panus rudis* in *Pichia pastoris. Lett. Biotechnol.* 16: 255-258.

Yaver, D. S. and E. J. Golightly. 1996. Cloning and characterization of three laccase genes from the white-rot basidiomycete trametes villosa: genomic organization of the laccase gene family. *Gene* 181: 95-102.

Yaver, D. S., F. Xu, E. J. Golightly, S. H. Brown, M. W. Rey, P. Schneider, T. Halkier, K. Mondorf and H. Dalbøge. 1996. Purification, characterization, molecular cloning, and expression of two laccase genes from the white rot basisiomycete *Trametes villosa. Appl. Environ. Microbiol.* 62: 834-841.

Yaver, D. S., M. D. Overjero, F. Xu, B. A. Nelson, K. M. Brown, T. Halkier, S. Bernauer, S. H. Bron and S. Kauppinen. 1999. Molecular characterization of laccase genes from the basidiomycetes *Coprinus cinereus* and heterologous expression of the laccase Lcc1. *Appl. Environ. Microbiol.* 65: 4943-4948.

Yoshida, H. 1883. LXIII.—Chemistry of lacquer (Urushi). Part I. Communication from the Chemical Society of Tokio. *J. Chem. Soc. Trans.* pp 472.

Zhang, Y. and L. Ma. 2012. Cloning a laccase gene from *Ganoderma lucidum* and its expression in *Pichia pastoris.* NCBI (GenBank).

Zhang, Y. B., M. L. Jiang, X. J. Hu, G. M. Zhang and L. X. Ma. 2005. Expression of a laccase gene from *Pleurotus ostreatus* in *Pichia pastoris* and characterization of the recombinant enzyme. *Acta Microbiol. Sinica* 45: 625-629.

Zhang, Y. B., Q. Jiang, M. L. Jiang and L. X. Ma, 2004. Cloning of a laccase gene from *Flammulina velutipes* and study on its expression in *Pichia pastoris. Acta Microbiol. Sinica* 44: 775-779.

Zhao, M., X. Song and G. Liu, 2012. Cloning and characterization of laccase gene from white rot fungus, *Pycnoporus sanguineus.* NCBI (GenBank).

Zheng, M. and Y. Chi. 2012. Cloning and sequence analysis of two laccase genes from white-rot fungus *Trametes gibbosa.* NCBI (GenBank).

Zhu, X. and P. R. Williamson. 2004. Role of laccase in the biology and virulence of *Cryptococcus neoformans. FEMS Yeast Res.* 5: 1-10.

In: Applications of Microbial Genes in Enzyme Technology ISBN: 978-1-62417-808-5
Editors: V.K.Gupta, M.G.Tuohy, G.D.Sharma et al.

Chapter 4

Applications of *Pichia Pastoris* Expression System in the Microbial Production of Industrial Enzymes

Long Liu,[1,2] *Haiquan Yang,*[1,2] *Yanfeng Liu,*[1,2]
Xin Chen,[1,2] *Ningzi Guan,*[1,2] *Jianghua Li,*[1,2]
Guocheng Du[1,2] *and Jian Chen*[1,2*#]
[1]Key Laboratory of Industrial Biotechnology,
Ministry of Education, Jiangnan University, Wuxi, China
[2]School of Biotechnology, Jiangnan University, Wuxi, China

Abstract

This chapter focuses on the applications of *Pichia pastoris* expression system in the microbial production of industrial enzymes. Firstly, the features of *Pichia pastoris* expression system were systematically introduced, and then the production of important industrial enzymes with *Pichia pastoris* was overviewed. The industrial enzymes include alkaline polygalacturonate lyase, alkaline proteases, lipases, trypsin, xylanase, laccase, glucose oxidase, cyclodextrin glycosyltransferase, phytase and mannanase and so on.

Introduction

Lots of strains of *Pichia pastoris* with a wide range of genotypes are now available. The specific strain is chose by the required application. The genotype and phenotype characteristics of some useful *Pichia* transformants are summarized in Table 1. The

[*] Corresponding author: Dr. Jian Chen, School of Biotechnology, Jiangnan University, Wuxi 214122, China, Tel.: +86-510-85913661, Fax: +86-510-85910799, E-mail: jchen@ jiangnan.edu.cn.

[#] 1) Key Laboratory of Industrial Biotechnology, Ministry of Education, Jiangnan University, Wuxi 214122, China. 2) School of Biotechnology, Jiangnan University, Wuxi 214122, China.

SMD1168 and SMD1168H strains are defective in the vacuole peptidase A (pep4). These SMD1168 and SMD1168H strains are also defective in these proteases (White *et al.*, 1994). KM71, GS115 and SMD1168 strains are defective in the histidine dehydrogenase gene (*HIS4*). The transformants were selected based on their ability of growing in medium without histidine. Own to the alcohol oxidase 1 gene (AOX1), SMD1168 and GS115 strains could utilize about 85% of methanol by the alcohol oxidase enzyme. These strains have a wild-type methanol utilization phenotype designated as Mut$^+$ (Inan *et al.*, 2001). However, the KM71 strain contains a non-functional AOX1 (*aox1*) and relies on the alcohol oxidase enzyme from an alternative gene AOX2. The AOX2 enzyme has the same specific activity as AOX1. But, own to weaker promoter, the expression level is lower and methanol is lowly consumed. The phenotype of these strains are termed 'methanol utilization slow' (Mut^s) (Inan *et al.*, 2001, Cregg *et al.*, 1993). Based on the type and modification of protein, the useful competencies are provided by the screening procedures and cloning strategy, and which could be contemplated for use in discrete applications (Daly *et al.*, 2005).

There are numerous available vectors that can be commonly used to express foreign proteins in *P. pastoris* (Table 2).

Several vectors do not contain a vector-copy of a secretion signal upstream from the multiple cloning sites, which can be used for intracellular or extracellular expression by cloning the protein together with the native secretion signal.

Table 1. Types of *Pichia* transformant

Strain	Genotype	Phenotype	Reference
P. pastoris KM71	*his4, aox1*: *ARG4*; *arg4*	Mut^s, His$^-$	Romanos 1995
P. pastoris SMD1168	*His4, pep4*	Mut$^+$, His$^-$, pep4	White *et al.* 1995
P. pastoris GS115	*his4*	Mut$^+$, His$^-$	Romanos 1995, Cregg *et al.* 1985
P. pastoris SMD1165	*His4, prb 1*	Mut$^+$, His$^-$, prb	Abdulaev *et al.* 1997
P. pastoris SMD1163	*his4, prb1, pep4*	Mut$^+$, His$^-$, pep4, prb1	Abdulaev *et al.* 1997
P. pastoris MC100-3	*arg4 his4 aox1 Δ:: SARG4 aox2 Δ:: Phis4*	Mut$^-$, His	Inan *et al.* 2001, Gellissen 2000

Table 2. Commonly used *Pichia* expression vectors

Vector name	Unique cloning sites	Selection markers	References
pHIL-D2	*Eco*RI	*HIS4*	Romanos 1995
pAO815	*Eco*RI	*HIS4*	Cregg *et al.* 1993, Thill *et al.* 1990
pPIC9	*Xho*I, *Sna*BI, *Eco*RI, *Avr*II and *Not*I	*HIS4*	Scorer *et al.* 1994
pPIC9K	*Xho*I, *Sna*BI, *Eco*RI, *Avr*II and *Not*I	*HIS4* and *kan*^{r}	Scorer *et al.* 1994

On the other hand, some vectors could secrete the aim gene product because they contain a vector-copy of a signal sequence such as the alpha-mating factor pre-pro leader sequence (α-MF) prior to the cloning site. At the first, *P. pastoris* expression vector (pPIC9) generated and contained the functional histidine dehydrogenase gene (HIS4).

And HIS4 can be used as a selectable marker following transformation into *P. pastoris* (histidine dehydrogenase-deficient strain) by the integration/transformation method of choice (Daly *et al.*, 2005).

It was detected that the tandem multi-copy integration events of the expression cassette was required to obtain high protein expression levels with these His^+ transformants. And then a gene conferring resistance to GS418 (kanamycin) was added to these vectors, and the pPIC9K expression vector was constructed. It was allowed that after selection of histidine, transformants are resistant to high levels of GS418 (kanamycin), and might contain multiple copies of the expression vector.

It was considered that the culture conditions of *P. pastoris* expression systems are an important factor for improving the productivity of a correctly processed protein. Shaken-flask and small-scale expression methods are the first stage employed in optimizing protein levels and selecting culture conditions. This method could be simply used in quantitating the product (Romanos, 1995). The levels of protein obtained from shaken-flasks are commonly 10-fold lower than that achieved with fermentors (White *et al.*, 1994). And the extent of aeration is more limited (Romanos, 1995). Both Mut^+ and Mut^s strains have their advantages: Mut^+ strains are less likely to become poisoned by methanol, while Mut^s strains are less likely to become oxygen-limited. The aeration is a particularly limiting factor with Mut^+ strains in shake-flasks when air or methanol supply is no constant, and at the same time these, strains can utilize methanol rapidly. However, it was reported that Mut^s and Mut^+ strains are equally rapid (48 h) in using induction (Clare *et al.*, 1991, Sreekrishna *et al.*, 1988, Romanos *et al.*, 1991, Clare *et al.*, 1991). The small-scale expression conditions were developed, and which more closely resembled the requirements of fermentor systems by ensuring high cell densities. The cell density was generated by dramatic increases of the volume of the initial biomass generating cultures, and then resuspending this biomass into small volumes of methanol induction media (Barr *et al.*, 1992). The culture of *P. pastoris* transformants based on the AOX1 promoter can therefore be executed in two stages: the generation of biomass in a repressive media; induction with methanol (Daly *et al.*, 2005, Heyland *et al.*, 2011).

For smaller-scale expression studies, the type of culture flask is important in the experimental design. The baffles in shaken flasks can be used to increase the amount of oxygen transferred (Daly *et al.*, 2005). The components and pH of the media could make a difference to expression levels. When the pH values of media is buffered to between pH 3.0 and 6.0, the amount of proteolysis of the recombinant protein is reduced (Cregg *et al.*, 1993, Sreekrishna *et al.*, 1997). When peptone or yeast extract-based media is used, the amount of proteolysis is reduced. The addition of 1% casamino acids could also reduce proteolysis (Clare *et al.*, 1991). In the induction phase, the temperature was found to affect the amount of proteolysis and the amount of protein expressed. The higher cell viability was observed at 23°C compared with that at 30°C culture, although the biomass in each culture was equal. The lower temperature can efficiently stabilize the cell membranes and reduce the rate of protease secretion from the cells to the supernatant (Li *et al.*, 2001). The effects of low temperatures in the induction phase have been reported in other studies.

The levels of protein expression are typically much higher in fermenter cultures compared to those in shake-flask culture. Since the mineral media for *P. pastoris* (containing only glycerol or methanol, biotin, salts and trace elements) are economical and well defined, *P. pastoris* is nearly ideal for large-scale production of heterologous proteins in fermenters. The parameters such as pH, aeration and carbon source feed rate can be controlled in fermenters, and which makes it possible to achieve ultra-high cell densities (>100 g/L dry cell weight; >400 g/L wet cell weight; >500 OD600 units/ml). The fermenter culture inevitably requires considerable re-optimization of culturing conditions. However, conditions established in a small fermenter typically need little further adjustment during scale-up to large volumes, a characteristic of significant appeal to bioprocess engineers charged with this often difficult task (Cereghino *et al.*, 2002).

A three-stage process is typically utilized for the production of foreign proteins in fermenter cultures of *P. pastoris*. In the first stage, the engineered strain is batch-cultured in a simple defined medium, and carbon source such as glycerol was controlled to accumulate biomass. The second stage is a feed-batch transition phase, in which glycerol is fed to the culture at a growth-limiting rate to further increase the biomass concentration and to prepare (depress) the cells for induction. The third stage, induction phase, is started by adding methanol to the culture at a slow rate, and which facilitates the culture's acclimation to methanol and initiates the synthesis of the recombinant protein. The methanol feed rate is then adjusted upwards periodically until the desired growth rate is reached (Cereghino *et al.*, 2002).

Textile Enzymes

Alkaline Polygalacturonate Lyase

Alkaline polygalacturonate lyase (EC 4.2.2.2), which catalyzes the cleavage of a-1, 4-glycosidic bonds of polygalacturonate by a trans-eliminative reaction and generates a 4 : 5 unsaturated oligogalacturonates, has been used in the textile industry to release fibers from flax stems, as an alternative to conventional retting to resolve many problems such as environmental pollution and high-energy cost (Kalantzi *et al.*, 2008). With the emergence of new applications for pectate lyases, the demand for the commercial enzyme is increasing. Polygalacturonate lyase (PGL) is produced mainly by bacteria, and in a few fungi causing food spoilage, such as *Erwinia* (Tardy *et al.*, 1997), *Pseudomonas* (Fuchs *et al.*, 1965), *Bacillus* (Nasser *et al.*, 1990), *Thermoanaerobacter* (Chaen *et al.*, 1999), *Streptomyces* (Mitsuiki *et al.*, 2002), *Amycolata* (Bruhlmann *et al.*, 1995) and *Fusarium* (Wattad *et al.*, 1997), were reported to liberate water-soluble pectic substances by restricted degradation of water-insoluble protopectin in plant tissue (Matsumoto *et al.*, 2000).

Several bacterial PGL genes, such as those from *Erwinia, Bacillus*, *Treponema pectinovorumand Amycolata* have been cloned and expressed in *Escherichia coli*. However, expensive isopropyl thiogalactoside (IPTG) is usually required as an inducer, which is undesirable for the large-scale production. In addition, the PL titer was less than 1 U/mL, which is considerably lower compared with other pectinases (Gumma di *et al.*, 2005).

Therefore, research to improve the enzyme productivity and other properties is required to meet commercial application.

P. pastoris is a good choice for PGL secreted overexpression. However, to date only a small, amount of PGL have been expressed in *P. pastoris*, including those of *Bacillus* and *Fusarium* which are both prokaryotic microorganisms. In 1995, a new pectate lyase gene pel from *Fusarium solani f. sp. pisi* (*Nectria haematococca*, Mating Type VI) was amplified and ex-pressed in *P. pastoris* for the first time, but the activity was only 3.3 U/mL (Guo *et al.*, 1995). In the study of Zhan-Min Liu, the protopectinase-N gene form *Bacillus subtilis* XZ2 was cloned into *P. pastoris* GS115, the pPICZαA plasmid containing α-factor was used. After induction with methanl for 120 h in flasks, 20U/mL of PGL activity was achieved (Liu *et al.*, 2006). In the study of Zhuge Bin, the PGL gene was cloned from a high PGL production strain *Bacillus* sp. WSHB04-02 (Zhang, 2005), and integrated into *P. pastoris* GS115 genome with single-cross (Zhuge *et al.*, 2008). PGL activity as high as 100 U/mL was attained in the fermentation broth of *P. pastoris* GS115, The pL1 gene encoding pectate lyase 1 (PL1) from *Fusarium oxysporum f. sp. cubense* race 1 was cloned into the expression vector pPICZαA and then successfully expressed in *Pichia pastoris strains* of SMD1168 by Zhangyong Dong (Dong *et al.*, 2010). The pL gene from *Bacillus subtilis* 168 was cloned into the expression vector pHBM905a and then successfully expressed in *Pichia pastoris* GS115 by Jia Yao (Yao, 2010). After 72h culture in flasks, 26U/mL PGL activity was obtained in culture broth.

Such a level was not sufficient enough for commercial application in industry. A comprehensive list of PGL expressed in *P. pastoris* was shown in the Table1. Among the more than 300 heterologous proteins that have been expressed in *P. pastoris*, only a few bacterial genes were functionally expressed (Gellissen, 2000). The glycosylation of heterologous proteins expressed in *P. pastoris* apparently reduce the specific activity and the general use of yeast expression is restricted to non-glycosylated proteins (Gellissen, 2000). Based on available data, most of PGL expressions in *P. pastoris* are at reasonable level. The biggest hurdle seems to be generating initial success. After success at this initial stage, there are well-defined parameters that can be manipulated to optimize expression, and it is often at this stage that attractive levels of expression are achieved. Efficient and accurate monitoring of key process variables is essential for effective process control and maintenance of the conditions optimal for recombinant protein production. Factors having particular importance on the process include residual methanol concentrations, protein production rates and cell density. With the target of further increasing PGL production by *P. pastoris* GS115, a series of exploratory tests were carefully investigated.

In the study of Yun Wang, with an optimized initial cell concentration and ratio of methanol to cell density in fed-batch cultivations (exponential feeding glycerol), the PGL production was significantly increased to 430 U/mL in the recombinant *Pichia pastoris* GS115 Zhuge Bin had previously constructed (Zhuge *et al.*, 2008). The results showed that the methanol feeding strategy based on the optimal ratio of methanol to cell concentration could be effectively used for heterologous PGL expression when the cells stayed in non-growth status after applying the advanced glycerol exponential feeding (Wang *et al.*, 2009a). What's more, PGL activity could be improved significantly by decreasing the cultivation temperature. It was reached 931 U/mL with temperature lowered to 22°C at the beginning of induction phase, which were 2.1-fold and 2.9-fold increase compared to that at 30 and 26 °C (Wang *et al.*, 2009b). In order to enhance cell viability and volumetric recombinant protein productivity, sorbitol, which had been confirmed to be a non-repressive carbon source, was added together with methanol during the induction phase in the research of Zhihao Wang. The resultant PGL activity was up to 1593 U/mL, which was enhanced 1.85-fold compared to the control (863 U/mL) cultured with sorbitol added at a constant rate of 3.6 g h^{-1} L^{-1} after an induction period of 100 h. Further results revealed that an appropriate sorbitol co-feeding strategy not only decreased the cell mortality to 8.8% (the control is about 23.1%) in the end of fermentation, but also reduced the proteolytic degradation of PGL (Wang *et al.*, 2010). Further, the scaling up of fermentation was implemented according to the above research results with related principles of Biochemical Reaction Engineering. The activity of PGL could achieve 1425 U/mL, 1315 U/mL and 1305 U/mL in 30 L, 1000 L and 10000 L fermentation tank, respectively. The successful scaling up of fermentation shows the advantage and stability of overexpression PGL in *P. pastoris* (Table 3).

Leather Enzyme

Alkaline Proteases

Alkaline proteases are a class of serine proteases and are of considerable interest in view of their activity and stability at alkaline pH. Alkaline proteases are widely used in detergents, tannery industry, food processing, chemical industries, silver recovery, medical purposes, waste treatment, feed industry. As alkaline proteases account for at least 25% of the total enzyme sales, to obtain large quantities of alkaline proteases is important for both theoretical research and industrial use. Alkaline proteases produced by bacteria such as Subtilisin Carlsberg, Subtilisin BPN, and Savinase mostly available commercially (Guo and Ma, 2008). Using recombined *Pichia pastoris* as a host for alkaline proteases producing can lower the cost and obtaining large quantities of product with high cell density cultivation.

Therefore, Kim et al. explored the possibility of high level extracellular expression of TfpA, a serine protease originated from *Thermomonospora fusca* YX, in the methylotropic yeast *Pichia pastoris* X33. A 1.0-kb DNA fragment (tfpA) encoding the pro-peptide and mature protein of was cloned into expression vectors pPICZαA (inducible) and pGAPZαA (constitutive) and introduced into *P. pastoris* by electroporation.

Table 3. Heterologous PGLs Expressed in *Pichia pastoris*

Source of PGL gene	Vector	Host	PGL Activity (U/mL)	References
Fusarium solani f. sp. pisi	pHILS1	*P. pastoris*	NS	Guo *et al.* 1995
B. subtilis SO113	pPICZαA	*P. pastoris* X-33	20	Liu *et al.* 2006
Bacillus sp. WSHB04-02	pPIC9K	*P. pastoris* GS115	100	Zhuge *et al.* 2008
Fusarium oxysporum f. sp. *cubense* race 1	pPICZαA	*P. pastoris* SMD1168	NS	Dong *et al.* 2010
Bacillus subtilis 168	pHBM905a	*P. pastoris* GS115	26	Yao, 2010

Expression of r-TfpA was greater in the inducible system than in the constitutive one, producing 135 U/mL medium supernatant 6 days after methanol induction. The r-TfpA was not glycosylated (21.7 kDa), and had pH and temperature optima of 8.5 and 80°C, respectively, using azocasein as a substrate. Kim et al.' research suggests that *P. pastoris* can be used as a host to produce extracellular r-TfpA, and expression efficiency may be improved by optimizing fermentation conditions and modifying factors related to protein expression and stability (Kim and Lei, 2005).

The alkaline protease gene from *Aspergillus oryzae* was cloned into a vector pPIC9K, and it was then successfully expressed in the heterologous *Pichia pastoris* GS115 with native signal peptide or α-factor secretion signal peptide. The yield of the recombinant alkaline protease with native signal peptide was about 1.5-fold higher than that with α-factor secretion signal peptide, and the maximum yield of the recombinant alkaline protease was 513 mg/L, which was higher than other researches. The recombinant alkaline protease was purified by ammonium sulfate precipitation, ion exchange chromatography and gel filtration chromatography. The purified recombinant alkaline protease showed on SDS-PAGE as a single band with an apparent molecular weight of 34 kDa. The recombinant alkaline protease was identical to native alkaline protease from *A. oryzae* with regard to molecular weight, optimum temperature for activity, optimum pH for activity, stability to pH, and similar sensitivity to various metal ions and protease inhibitors. The native enzyme retained 61.18% of its original activity after being incubated at 50°C for 10 min, however, the recombinant enzyme retained 56.22% of its original activity with same disposal. Both optimum pH for activity and stability to optimum pH were 9.0. The alkaline protease gene from *A. oryzae* can be expressed largely in *P. pastoris* without affecting its enzyme properties and the recombinant alkaline protease could be widely used in various industrial applications (Guo and Ma, 2008). As reported, some alkaline serine proteases originated from *Streptomyces* have a high level of activity for insoluble protein substrates. Li reported the initial characterization and expression of sfp2, a gene encoding a keratinolytic serine protease from *Streptomyces fradiae* var. k11. Recombinant SFP2 was expressed in and secreted from *Pichia pastoris* SMD1168 with plasmid pPIC9k obtaining a final yield of 78 mg/L (136.2 U/mL caseinolytic activity) after 25 h of induction. The recombinant enzyme was purified using by ammonium sulfate precipitation and gel filtration chromatography to electrophoretic homogeneity, which was appropriately glycosylated and had a molecular mass of 26.0 kDa. The purified recombinant SFP2 was characterized. The optimal pH and temperatures of SFP2 for proteolysis of casein and keratin azure were pH 10.0, 60°C, and pH 9.0, 55°C, respectively. SFP2 activity was stable from pH 3.0 to pH 11.0. The enzyme activity was inhibited by Co^{2+} and Cr^{3+} and enhanced by Ni^{2+} and Cu^{2+}. The K_m of 0.45 mmol/L and V_{max} of 19.84 mmol/(min·mg) were calculated using N-succinyl-Ala-Ala-Pro-Phe-pNA as a substrate. The activity of SFP2 with soluble and insoluble substrates was tested, which indicated that SFP2 was more specific for keratinous substrates compared with proteinase K and other commercial proteases (Li *et al.*, 2007).

Lipases

Lipases are a class of enzymes which catalyse the hydrolysis of long chain triglycerides. Microbial lipases constitute an important group of biotechnologically valuable enzymes, mainly because of the versatility of their applied properties and ease of mass production. Microbial lipases are widely diversified in their enzymatic properties and substrate specificity, which make them very attractive for industrial applications in the leather, detergent, food, flavour industry, biocatalytic resolution of pharmaceuticals, esters and amino acid derivatives, making of fine chemicals, agrochemicals, use as biosensor, bioremediation and cosmetics and perfumery.

Lipases represent a more environmentally sound method of removing fat in leather industry. Degreasing is an essential stage in the processing of fatty raw materials such as small animal skins and hides from intensively fed cattle. Conventional methods use organic solvents and surfactants, which can give rise to environmental problems such as volatile organic compound (VOC) emissions. Lipase enzymes can remove fats and grease from skins and hides, particularly those with a moderate fat content. Both alkaline stable and acid active lipases can be used in skin and hide degreasing. For bovine hides, lipases allow tensides to be replaced completely. For sheepskins, which contain up to 40% fat, the use of solvents is very common and these can also be replaced with lipases and surfactants. If surfactants are used for sheepskins, they are usually not as effective and may be harmful to the environment. Maps (India) offers a range of lipases for degreasing which work in different pH conditions; Palkodegrease, lipase for degreasing in neutral to alkaline pH conditions and Palkodegrease AL, Lipase for degreasing in acidic pH conditions. The main advantages of using lipases are a more uniform colour and a cleaner appearance. Lipases also improve the production of hydrophobic (waterproof) leather; makers of leather for car upholstery have commented that 'fogging' is reduced (Hasan *et al.*, 2006).

The strong alcohol oxidase (*AOX1*) promoter and the high secretion capacity of *P. pastoris* have attracted many researchers for producing lipases in this expressing system.

Holmquist et al. reported the heterologous high-level expression of the two Geotrichum candidum lipase (GCL) isoen from strain ATCC 34614 in the methylotrophic yeast *Pichia pastoris*. The lipase cDNAs were placed under the control of the methanol-inducible alcohol oxidase promoter. The lipases expressed in *P. pastoris* were fused to the α-factor secretion signal peptide of *Saccharomyces cerevisiae* and were secreted into the culture medium. Cultures of *P. pastoris* expressing lipase accumulated active recombinant enzyme in the supernatant to levels of 60 mg/L virtually free from contaminating proteins. Recombinant GCL I and GCL II had molecular masses of 63 and 66 kDa, respectively, as determined by SDS–PAGE (Holmquist *et al.*, 1997).

In Minning et al.'s research, mature lipase of the fungus *Rhizopus oryzae* (ROL) was functionally expressed and secreted in the methylotrophic yeast *Pichia pastoris*.

In a batch cultivation, where methanol feeding was linked to the dissolved oxygen content in the cultivation solution, a lipase activity of 500 U/ mL of culture was achieved after initial glycerol feeding of the culture. Recombinant ROL lipase was purified to homogeneity by a simple two-step purification procedure and had a specific activity of 8571 U/ mg which is comparable with the purified native enzyme [45] (Minning *et al.*, 1998). Optimization of lipase production was then implemented. Combined with optimal methanol feeding strategy, dissolved oxygen feedback control, and feeding strategy introducing a transition phase, this optimized strategy resulted in the highest productivity (12 888 U/L/h), which is 13.6-fold higher than the DO-based strategy (Minning *et al.*, 2001).

In a research of Rotticci-Mulder et al., *Candida antarctica* lipase B (CALB) and *C. antarctica* lipase B fused to a cellulose-binding domain (CBD-CALB) were expressed functionally in the *Pichia pastoris* SMD1168. The recombinant proteins were secreted into the culture medium reaching levels of approximately 25 mg/L. The proteins were purified using hydrophobic interaction chromatography and gel filtration with an overall yield of 69%. Results from endoglycosidase H digestion of the proteins showed that CALB and CBD–CALB were N-glycosylated. The specific hydrolytic activities of recombinant CALB and CBD–CALB were identical to that reported for CALB isolated from its native source (Rotticci-Mulder *et al.*, 2001).

To avoid reduction of lipase production by non-universal codon, the 17 non-universal serine codons (CTG) in the *Candida rugosa* LIP2 gene have been converted into universal serine codons (TCT) by overlap extension PCR-based multiple site-directed mutagenesis in Lee et al.'s research. An active recombinant LIP2 lipase was overexpressed in *Pichia pastoris* and secreted into the culture medium. The recombinant LIP2 showed distinguishing catalytic activities when compared with recombinant LIP4 and commercial *C. rugosa* lipase. The purified enzyme showed optimum activity at pH 7 and a broad temperature optimum in the range 30-50 °C. The enzyme retained 80% of residual activity after being heated at 70 °C for 10 min. From comparative modeling analysis, it appears that several amino acid substitutions resulting in greater hydrophobicity in the substrate-binding site might play an important role in the substrate specificity of LIP2 [48] (Lee *et al.*, 2002).

To improve the expression efficiency of recombinant LIP1 in *P. pastoris*, a regional synthetic gene fragment of lip1 near the 5'- end of a transcript has been constructed to match *P. pastoris*-preferred codon usage for simple scale-up fermentation.

The present results show that the production level (152 mg/L) of coLIP1 (codon-optimized LIP1) has an overall improvement of 4.6-fold relative to that (33 mg/L) of non-codon-optimized LIP1 with only half the cultivation time of *P. pastoris* (Chang *et al.*, 2006).

The BTL2 lipase gene from *Bacillus thermocatenulatus* was subcloned into the pPICZaA vector and integrated further into the genome of *Pichia pastoris* GS115 by Quyen et al. The BTL2 lipase was produced as an extracellular protein in large quantities of 309 U/mL supernatant. The lipase was purified using butyl-Sepharose with a specific activity of 23,000 U/mg protein towards tributyrin (Quyen *et al.*, 2003).

Surribas et al. established an automated sequential injection analysis (SIA) system using stop-flow technique was developed to determine methanol concentration by means of the enzymatic reactions of alcohol oxidase and peroxidase. Its application as an on-line device for monitoring *Pichia pastoris* fermentations producing a heterologous protein was demonstrated (Surribas *et al.*, 2003). By implementation of an in-line sampling device, it is possible to robustly on-line monitor the substrate level. Its performance has been demonstrated during a complete *P. pastoris* fermentation producing a heterologous lipase from *R. oryzae*. In combination with an adequate control strategy, it will allow an automatic maintenance of the residual methanol concentration during cultures and the optimization (Surribas *et al.*, 2007).

Pfeffer et al. focuses on shedding further light on the characteristics of lipase A from *Candida antarctica* (CalA). CalA was functionally expressed in the methylotrophic yeast *Pichia pastoris*, purified and characterized. A classical fed-batch process and a semi-continuous process were developed and tested with regard to their yield capacity. Lipase concentrations of 0.88 and 0.55 g/L were obtained using the fed-batch and semi-continuous processes, respectively. The semi-continuous process reaches a total activity of 10,233,000 U and so surpasses the fed-batch process reaching 7,530,000 U. The purified enzyme showed highest activity between 50 and 70 °C, pH 7.0 and a preference for short-chain triglycerides (C4-C8) (Pfeffer *et al.*, 2006).

A systematic study of the influence of methanol set-point and sorbitol feeding rate in fed-batch operation with Mut^s phenotype was implemented by Arnau et al. Lipolytic activity, yields, productivity and specific productivity, but also specific growth, consumption and production rates were analyzed showing that the best conditions were reached when the methanol set-point was 2 g/L with a low influence of the constant specific growth tested (Arnau *et al.*, 2007).

The effect of glycerol mixed substrate on the heterologous production of a *Rhizopus oryzae* lipase in *Pichia pastoris* system was investigated. One of the key advantages of using glycerol instead of sorbitol is its higher μ (0.18 h^{-1} versus 0.02 h^{-1}) and the subsequent potential increase in the productivity of the bioprocess. However, for Mut^s phenotype this potential advantage is ineffective. When the relation μ_{Gly} per μ_{MeOH} was larger than 4, a significant decrease of ROL $Y_{P/X}$, volumetric and specific productivity was observed. The highest values of proteolytic activity found at the highest μ tested, when glycerol was used as co-substrate, was one of the factors that affected down all the productivity parameters (Arnau *et al.*, 2011). Wittrup et al. studied effects of different types of promoter on production of *Candida anarctica* lipase B fused to a cellulose binding module in *P. pastoris.* The glyceraldehyde-3-phosphate dehydrogenase (*GAP*) gene promoter was found to be suitable for protein production in both deep well, shake flask, and bioreactor scale. In shake flask cultivations the *GAP* promoter using glycerol as carbon source proved superior to the two other tested systems, yielding 37 mg lipase/L after 72 h. A 96-deep well plate format was tested using glycerol as a carbon source. This system proved to be very efficient, yielding 37 mg lipase/L in 28 h (Wittrup *et al.*, 2007).In the research of Zhao et al., the high-cell-density fermentation of *Candida rugosa* lipase in the constitutive *Pichia pastoris* expression system was scaled up from 5 to 800 L in series by optimizing the fermentation conditions at both lab scale and pilot scale. A stable lipase activity of approximately 14,000 U/mL and a cell wet weight of 500 g/L at the 800-L scale were obtained. The efficient and convenient techniques suggested in this study might facilitate further scale-up for industrial lipase production (Zhao *et al.*, 2008).

Resina et al. investigated the effect of combining two cell engineering strategies to alleviate putative bottlenecks in *Rhizopus oryzae* lipase secretion, namely the constitutive expression of the induced form of the *Saccharomyces cerevisiae* unfolded protein response transcriptional factor *Hac1* and the deletion of the *GAS1* gene encoding a β-1,3-glucanosyltransglycosylase, GPI-anchored to the outer leaflet of the plasma membrane, playing a key role in yeast cell wall assembly. The double mutant *HAC1/Δgas1* strain yielded about a 7-fold increase, reaching 298 U/mL. Overall, these results reflect the multiplicity of physiological bottlenecks at different levels/steps throughout the Rol synthesis, secretion and excretion processes in *P. pastoris* (Resina *et al.*, 2009). Yu et al. reported the cloning and expression of the lipase gene from *Rhizopus chinensis* in *Pichia pastoris* and characterization of the recombinant lipase. The lipase gene without its signal sequence were cloned downstream to the alpha-mating factor signal and expressed in *P. pastoris* GS115 under the control of *AOX1* promoter. The pH and temperature optimum of mRCL were pH 8 and 35°C, respectively. The maximum lipase activity reached 120 U/mL (Yu *et al.*, 2009). In Xu et al's research, a novel lipase gene, *lipJ08*, was cloned from *Candida rugosa* ATCC14830, along with the already reported five lipase genes (lip1–lip5). Nucleotide sequencing indicated that the *lipJ08* gene contains a 1650 bp open reading frame (ORF) without introns. The deduced amino acid sequence corresponds to 534 amino acid residues, including a putative signal sequence of 15 amino acid residues. Seventeen of the non-universal serine codons (CTG) of *lipJ08* were converted into universal serine codons (TCT) by PCR based mutagenesis. The native and codon-optimized *lipJ08* genes were expressed in *Pichia pastoris*. The hydrolytic activity of the recombinant LIPJ08 was 4.7 U/ml, whereas the activity of the recombinant wild-type lipase could not be detected (Xu *et al.*, 2010). High-level heterologous expression of an alkaline lipase gene from *Penicillium cyclopium* PG37 was investigated by Tan et al. in *Pichia pastoris.* A 777-bp cDNA fragment encoding a mature alkaline lipase (LipI) from *Penicillium cyclopium* PG37 was amplified by RT–PCR, and inserted into the expression plasmid pPIC9K. The recombinant plasmid was transformed into *Pichia pastoris* GS115 (his4, Mut^+) by electroporation. MD plate and YPD plates containing G418 were used for screening of the multi-copy *P. pastoris* transformants (His4, Mut^+). One transformant resistant to 4.0 mg/mL of G418, numbered as *P. pastoris* GSL4-7, expressing the highest recombinant LipI (rLipI) activity was chosen for optimizing expression conditions. The integration of the gene LipI into the *P. pastoris* GS115 genome was confirmed by PCR analysis using 5'- and 3'- AOX1 primers. SDS–PAGE and lipase activity assays demonstrated that the rLipI, a glycosylated protein with an apparent molecular weight of about 31.5 kDa, was extracellularly expressed in *P. pastoris*. When the *P. pastoris* GSL4-7 was cultured under the optimized conditions, the expressed rLipI activity was up to 407 U/mL, much higher than that (10.5 U/mL) expressed with standard protocol. The rLipI showed the highest activity at pH 10.5 and 25°C, and was stable at a broad pH range of 7.0-10.5 and at a temperature of 30°C or below (Tan *et al.*, 2011).

Trypsin

Trypsin is a highly valuable protease that has many industrial applications due to their high specificity that allows a controlled proteolysis. Considering that *Pichia pastoris* appears to be the most desirable microbial host in the scale-up production of trypsin, the gene of cold-adapted fish trypsins (CAFTs) was cloned. In *P. pastoris* X-33, the cunner fish trypsin (CFT) was in different *Pichia* expression vectors. The vectors were constructed targeting both internal and secreted expression and keeping the CFT native signal peptide. Western-blotting analysis confirmed the expression with evident differences for each construct, observing a major effect of the leader peptide sequence on the expression patterns. Immobilized nickel affinity chromatography yielded a partially purified recombinant CFT, which exhibited trypsin-specific activity after activation with bovine enterokinase (Macouzet *et al.*, 2005).

Paper-Making Enzyme

Xylanase

Xylanases are hydrolytic enzymes which randomly cleave the β-1,4 backbone of the complex plant cell wall polysaccharide xylan. Diverse forms of these enzymes exist, displaying varying folds, mechanisms of action, substrate specificities, hydrolytic activities (yields, rates and products) and physicochemical characteristics. Research has mainly focused on only two of the xylanase containing glycoside hydrolase families, namely families 10 and 11, yet enzymes with xylanase activity belonging to families 5, 7, 8 and 43 have also been identified and studied, albeit to a lesser extent. Driven by industrial demands for enzymes that can operate under process conditions, a number of extremophilic xylanases have been isolated, in particular those from thermophiles, alkaliphiles and acidiphiles, while little attention has been paid to cold-adapted xylanases. Xylanases have potential applications in a wide range of industrial processes, such as biobleaching of kraft pulps and bio-mechanical pulping in paper and pulp industry. Using xylanases in paper and pulp industry can reduce chlorine consumption and toxic discharges (Collins *et al.*, 2006).

Several industrial yeasts have been developed as recombinant systems for the commercial production of xylanase. These organisms combine ease of genetic manipulation with the ability to perform many eukaryotic post-translational modifications. One of the most commonly used systems is the yeast *Pichia pastoris*. This organism possesses a number of attributes that make it an attractive host for the expression and production of xylanase. Most importantly, it can be grown conveniently in a simple and inexpensive medium and it does not secrete any endogenous xylanase of its own (Deng *et al.*, 2006).

Zhang et al. cloned and expressed a xylanase gene (xyn10) from alkaliphilic *Bacillus* sp. N16-5 in *Pichia pastoris*. First, a xylanase gene xyn10 was cloned from the alkaliphilic strain *Bacillus* sp. N16-5 based on its partial genome sequence. The gene was then inserted into expression vector of *P. pastoris* pHBM905A with alcohol oxidase I (*AOX I*) gene promoter. Plasmid pHBM905A-xyn10 DNA was transformed and expressed in *Pichia pastoris* GS115. The deduced amino acid sequence has 85% identity with xylanase xyn10A from *B. halodurans* and contains two potential N-glycosylation sites. The glycosylated Xyn10 with MW 48 kDa can hydrolyze birchwood and oatspelt xylan. The enzyme had optimum activity at pH 7 and 70°C, with the specific activity of 92.5 U/mg. The Xyn10 retained over 90% residual activity at 60°C for 30 min but lost all activity at 80°C over 15 min. Most tested ions showed no or slight inhibition effects on enzyme activity (Zhang *et al.*, 2010).

Deng et al. obtained from the gene *xynB* encoding an acidophilic, endo-1,4-xylanase from *Aspergillus niger* CGMCC1067. The gene *xynB* was cloned, and then successfully expressed in *Pichia pastoris* X33 under the control of the glyceraldehyde-3-phosphate dehydrogenase (*GAP*) gene promoter. The full-length gene contained 745 bp, including an intron of 67 bp, and encoded a mature protein containing 188 amino acids. The purified, recombinant xylanase showed three bands at about 21, 30 and 35 kDa. The maximum yield of the recombinant xylanase was 62 IU/ml, which was about 50-fold higher than that obtained when *A. niger* was cultured. No cellulase or β-D-xylosidase activity was found. The optimal temperature for the recombinant xylanase enzyme was 50 °C. The enzyme displayed about 95% of peak activity in the temperature range found in the body of animals to which the enzyme might be fed. The optimal pH for the recombinant xylanase was about pH 5.0 and the enzyme retained about 76% of its activity after being incubated at pH 2.0 for 30 min at 37°C. The enzyme possessed high resistance to various metal ions and chemical reagents, with the exception of copper and iron (Deng *et al.*, 2006).

In another research of Zhang et al., a gene encoding a new xylanase, named xynZG, was cloned by the genome-walking PCR method from the nematophagous fungus *Plectosphaerella cucumerina*. The genomic DNA sequence of xynZG contains a 780 bp open reading frame separated by two introns with the sizes of 50 and 46 bp. The 684 bp cDNA was cloned into vector pHBM905B with *AOX I* gene promoter and transformed into *Pichia pastoris* GS115. The optimal secreting time was 3 days at 25°C and enzymatic activities in the culture supernatants reached the maximum level of 362 U/mL. The molecular mass of the enzyme was estimated to be 19 kDa on SDS-PAGE. The optimal pH and temperature of the purified enzyme is 6 and 40°C, respectively. The purified enzyme is stable at room temperature for at least 10 h. The K_m and V_{max} values for birchwood xylan are 2.06 mg /ml and 0.49 mmol/min/mg, respectively. The inhibitory effects of various mental ions were investigated. Cu^{2+} ion, which strongly inhibits most other xylanases studied, reduces enzyme activity by only 40%. Furthermore, enzyme activity is unaffected by EDTA even at a concentration of 5 mM (Zhang *et al.*, 2006).

Tanaka et al. obtained cDNA encoding the precursor protein (XynI) from a yeast-like fungus *Aureobasidium pullulans* var. *melanigenum* strain. The xynI was expressed in the methylotrophic yeast *Pichia pastoris* GS115 under the control of the alcohol oxidase I (*AOX I*) gene promoter. The 34 amino acid prepro-signal peptide of the A. pullulans XynI directed the efficient secretion of 178 mg of active xylanase per liter of the culture medium. The secretion level of the xylanase with its own signal peptide was comparable to that of the mature protein fused to the prepro leader from *Saccharomyces cerevisiae* α-mating factor and twofold higher than that of the mature protein fused to the pre-type signal peptide from *P. pastoris* acid phosphatase. The N-terminal amino acid sequence and the apparent Mr of 24 kDa of the secreted recombinant protein indicated the native-like processing of the *A. pullulans* XynI signal sequence in *P. pastoris*. The three-dimensional model and mutational analysis of the xynI gene product showed that Asp-73 and Glu-157 residues located at the upper and lower edges of the active site cleft, respectively, play a significant role in its low pH optimum (Tanaka *et al.*, 2004).

Cheng et al. obtained a gene (*xyl11*) encoding xylanase from *Thermobifida fusca* NTU22, which was cloned into and secretively expressed in *Pichia pastoris* KM71H under the control of the *AOX I* promoter. The xylanase productivity of the *P. pastoris* transformant (pPICαXYL) was about 67-fold higher than that of *T. fusca* NTU22 cultured in a 5-liter fermentor. The optimal pH and temperature of the purified xylanase were 7.0 and 70◦C, respectively. About 70% of original activity remained after heat treatment at 70◦C for 3 h. Various degrees of glycosylation occurred during the expression of xylanase in *P. pastoris* transformant. However, the properties of xylanase from *T. fusca* NTU22 were not greatly changed by the glycosylation in *P. pastoris* (Cheng *et al.*, 2005).

Damaso et al. achieved highly efficient production of a *Thermomyces lanuginosus* IOC-4145 β-1,4-xylanase expressed in *Pichia pastoris* GS115 under the control of the *AOX I* promoter. In the optimized medium and conditions, 148 mg of xylanase per liter was achieved. Three recombinant protein species of 21.9, 22.1, and 22.3 kDa were then detected in the mass spectrum due to variability in the amino terminus. For both enzymes, the optimum temperature was 75°C, and they retained 60% of their original activity after 80 min at 70°C or 40 min at 80°C. The high level of fully active recombinant xylanase obtained in *P. pastoris* makes this expression system attractive for fermentor growth and industrial applications (Damaso *et al.*, 2003).

Liu et al. cloned the mature peptide of *Aspergillus niger* xylanase A (AnxA), and AnxA was successfully expressed in *Pichia pastoris* GS115 at high levels under the control of *AOX*

I promoter. The recombinant AnxA (reAnxA) was secreted into culture medium. After 96 h 0.25% methanol induction, the activity of reAnxA in the culture supernatant reached the peak, 175 U/mg, which was 1.9 times as high as that of the native AnxA (92 U/mg). The optimum temperature and optimum pH of reAnxA were 50 °C and 5.0, respectively. The reAnxA was very stable in a wide pH range of 3.0-8.0. After incubation at the pH 3.0-8.0, 25°C for 1 h, all the residual activities of reAnxA were over 80%. The K_m and k_{cat} values for reAnxA were 4.8 mg/ml and 123.2 s^{-1}, respectively. Xylotriose was the main hydrolysis product of birchwood xylan and bran insoluble xylan by reAnxA (Liu *et al.*, 2006).

Ruanglek obtained a recombinant gene *XylB* (564 bp) encoding endo-1,4-β-xylanase from *Aspergillus niger* BCC14405. *XylB* was then successfully cloned and secreted as a 21 kDa in *Pichia pastoris* KM71 under the control of *AOX I* promoter. The activity of the recombinant xylanase was highest at 55◦C which was 5◦C higher than native xylanase. In addition, the recombinant xylanase was active over the range of pH 3.6-6.5 with maximal activity at pH 5 (8007 U/mg). Two-liter production of xylanase was performed with BSM medium which increased cell concentration up to 84.5 g/L via the 80% μ_{max} exponential feed strategy. This process provided maximum xylanase production (3676 U/mL) with highest specific activity (7352 U/mg protein) and volumetric productivity (22,832 U/L/h) at 3.0% (v/v) methanol induction. By far, this was the highest xylanase expression in *P. pastoris* host system being reported (Ruanglek *et al.*, 2007).

In another research of Liu et al., the mature peptide of *Bacillus licheniformis* xylanase A (BlxA) was successfully expressed in *Pichia pastoris* GS115 under the control of *AOXI* promoter. After 96 h 0.25% methanol induction, the activity of recombinant *B. licheniformis* xylanase A (reBlxA) in culture supernatant was 122.9 U/mg. Enzymatic properties assays showed that the optimum temperature and pH for reBlxA were 60°C and pH 6.0, respectively. When treated at 70°C, pH 6.0 for 2 min, the residual activities of the reBlxA were 76%. Over 80% of reBlxA activity was retained after treatment of the enzyme by preincubation over a pH range of 5.0-9.0 for 1 h at 25 °C. Studies showed that reBlxA was an endo-acting xylanase and xylobiose (X2), xylotriose, xylotetraose (X4), xylopentaose (X5), and xylohexaose (X6) could be hydrolyzed by it (Liu *et al.*, 2008).

Chantasingh et al. obtained a full-length xylanase gene, encoding 326 amino acids belonging to the fungal glycosyl hydrolase family 10, from *Aspergillus terreus* BCC129. The mature xylanase gene of 906 bp was cloned into a yeast expression vector, pPICZαA, for heterologous expression in *Pichia pastoris* KM71. A band of approximately, 33 kDa was observed after one day of methanol induction. The expressed enzyme was purified by gel Wltration chromatography. The purified recombinant xylanase demonstrated optimal activity at 60°C, pH 5.0 and a K_m of 4.8 mg/ml and a V_{max} of 757 μmol/min mg, using birchwood xylan as a substrate. Additionally, the purified enzyme demonstrated broad pH stability from 4 to 10 when incubated at 40°C for 4 h. It also showed a moderate thermal stability since it retained 90% of its activity when incubated at 50°C, 30 min, making this enzyme a potential use in pulp industries (Jeya *et al.*, 2009).

In a research of Jeya et al., a xylanase gene, xynf11a of *Aspergillus fumigatus* MKU1 was cloned and expressed in *Pichia pastoris* X33. Two exons of the xynf11a gene were amplified separately and fused by overlap extension PCR. The fused product was cloned in yeast expression vector pPICZB and expressed in *P. pastoris* under the control of the *AOX I* promoter.

Table 4. Overview of xylanase activity with different expression host under different promoter control

Expression host	Genetic source	Promoter	Xylanase activity	Optimal pH and temperature	Reference
Pichia pastoris X33	*Aspergillus niger* CGMCC1067	*GAP*	62 IU/ml	pH 5.0 50°C	Deng *et al.* 2006
Pichia pastoris GS115	*Bacillus* sp. N16-5	*AOX I*	925 U/mg	pH 7.0 70°C	Zhang *et al.* 2010
Pichia pastoris GS115	*Plectosphaerella cucumerina.*	*AOX I*	362 U/mL	pH 6.0 40°C	Zhang *et al.* 2006
Pichia pastoris GS115	*Aureobasidium pullulans* var. *melanigenum*	*AOX I*	38 U/mL	pH 2.0 40°C	Tanaka *et al.* 2004
Pichia pastoris KM71H	*Thermobifida fusca* NTU22	*AOX I*	324.2 U/mL	pH 7.0 70°C	Cheng *et al.* 2005
Pichia pastoris GS115	*Thermomyces lanuginosus*	*AOX I*	360 U/mL	7 °C	Damaso *et al.* 2003
Pichia pastoris GS115	*Aspergillus niger*	*AOX I*	175 U/mg	pH 5.0 50°C	Liu *et al.* 2006
Pichia pastoris KM71H	*Aspergillus niger* BCC14405	*AOX I*	8007 U/mg	pH 5.0 55°C	Ruanglek *et al.* 2007
Pichia pastoris GS115	*Bacillus licheniformis*	*AOX I*	122.9 U/mg	pH 6.0 60°C	Liu *et al.* 2008
Pichia pastoris KM71H	*Aspergillus terreus* BCC129	*AOX I*	533 U/mg	pH 5.0 60°C	Jeya *et al.* 2009
Pichia pastoris X33	*Aspergillus fumigatus* MKU1	*AOX I*	14 U/mL	pH 6.0 60°C	Chantasingh *et al.* 2006

GAP: glyceraldehyde-3-phosphate dehydrogenase.
AOX I: alcohol oxidase I.

P. pastoris transformants expressing recombinant xylanases were selected on xylan agar plate and their ability to produce the xylanase was evaluated in flask cultures. *P. pastoris* X33 (pZBxynf11aFP) efficiently secreted the recombinant xylanase into the medium and produced the high level of xylanase activity (14 U/mL) after 96 h of growth. The recombinant xylanase produced by *P. pastoris* showed maximum activity at pH 6.0 and temperature 60°C. The recombinant xylanase did not exhibit any cellulase activity and hence it could be potentially used for pretreatment of paper pulp before bleaching (Chantasingh *et al.*, 2006).

Overview of xylanase activity with different Expression host under different promoter control was shown in Table 4.

Laccase

Laccases, EC 1.10.3.2, p-diphenol:dioxygen oxidoreductase, are part of a larger group of enzymes termed the multicopper enzymes, which includes among others ascorbic acid oxidase and ceruloplasmin. Laccase was one of the oldest enzymes ever described. Laccases can be roughly divided into two major groups which show clear differences. The presence of laccase-like enzymes has been reported in bacteria.

The reports of molecular weights, pH optima, and substrate specificity are extremely diverse. Commercially, laccases have been used to delignify woody tissues and biological bleaching in paper and pulp industry, produce ethanol, and to distinguish between morphine and codeine.

A very wide variety of bioremediation processes employ laccase in order to protect the environment from damage caused by industrial effluents. Research in recent years has been intense, much of it elicited by the wide diversity of laccases, their utility and their very interesting enzymology (Mayer and Staples, 2002).

Industrial scale production of enzymes requires relatively high levels of expression in a producing organism that is suitable for use in large-scale fermentation. As a result the genes for many industrially important enzymes have been inserted into heterologous hosts such as *Aspergillus* and yeasts. A frequently used expression organism is the methylotropic yeast *Pichia pastoris* that can grow on methanol as a sole carbon and energy source. The methanol utilisation pathway is highly inducible; the first enzyme in the pathway, methanol oxidase, is undetectable in cells grown on glucose but comprises up to 35% of the total protein in methanol-grown cells. A number of *P. pastoris* expression vectors have been constructed using the methanol oxidase promoter to drive expression of a large number of heterologous proteins. The list of heterologous proteins expressed numbers greater than 300, including prokaryotic, eukaryotic and viral proteins (O'Callaghan *et al.*, 2002). Here we have focused on more recent reports on the heterologous expression laccase in *Pichia pastoris*.

Liu et al. obtained a cDNA encoding for a laccase from the white-rot fungus *Fome lignosus* by RT-PCR. The deduced mature protein consisted of 497 amino acids and was preceded by a signal peptide of 21 amino acids. The genomic DNA of the laccase, containing 11 introns, was cloned by PCR. The cDNA was cloned into the vectors pGAPZαA and pGAPZA, and expressed in the *Pichia pastoris* GS115 under the control of the glyceraldehyde-3-phosphate dehydrogenase (*GAP*) gene promoter. Laccase-secreting transformants were selected by their ability to oxidize the substrate 2'2-azinobis-(3-ethylbenzthiaoline-6-sufonic acid) (ABTS). The laccase activity obtained with the native signal peptide was found to be 5-fold higher than that obtained with the α-factor secretion signal peptide. The presence of 0.4 mM copper was necessary for optimal activity of the enzyme. The highest activity value reached 9.03 U/mL, and the optimal secreting time was 2-3 days at 20°C. The crude laccase was stable in a pH range from 6.0 to 10.0 and at temperatures lower than 30°C in pH 4.5 for 24 h. The molecular mass of the enzyme was estimated to be 66.5 kDa by SDS-PAGE. The optimum pH and temperature were 2.4 and 55°C. The K_m and V_{max} values for ABTS were 177 mM and 23.54 mmol/min, respectively. The extent of glycosylation of the purified enzyme was 58.6% (Liu *et al.*, 2003).

O'Callaghan obtained a laccase enzyme cDNA from a *Trametes versicolor* cDNA library. The gene was subcloned into the *Pichia pastoris* expression vector pPIC3.5 with alcohol oxidase I (*AOX I*) gene promoter and transformed into the *P. pastoris* strains KM71 and GS115. Laccase-secreting transformants were selected by their ability to oxidise the substrate ABTS. No difference in laccase activity was observed between culture supernatants from GS115 (proteolytic) and KM71 (nonproteolytic) strains. The presence of at least 200 IM copper was necessary for optimal laccase activity in the culture supernatants. During growth of *P. pastoris* on minimal medium the pH of the medium was reduced to <3.0. If alanine was added to the medium the pH reduction was not as pronounced and at alanine concentrations >0.6% w/v the pH was kept constant for >7 days. Cultures in which the pH was maintained by alanine metabolism produced higher levels of laccase activity than those grown in the absence of alanine. This study describes the development of a medium that allows convenient pH control of *P. pastoris* without the need for continuous neutralisation(O'Callaghan *et al.*, 2002).

In the research of Gelo-pujic et al., the cDNA that encodes an isoform of laccase from *Trametes versicolor* (LCCI), as well as a truncated version (LCCIa), was subcloned and expressed by using the yeast *Pichia pastoris* as the heterologous host under the control of the alcohol oxidase I (*AOX I*) gene promoter. Three strains of *P. pastoris* were used: KM71 (*arg4 his4 aox1::ARG4*), GS115 (*his4*), and SMD1168 (*his4 pep4*). The amino acid sequence of LCCIa is identical to that of LCCI except that the final 11 amino acids at the C terminus of LCCI are replaced with a single cysteine residue. This modification was introduced for the purpose of improving the kinetics of electron transfer between an electrode and the copper-containing active site of laccase. The two laccases (LCCI and LCCIa) are compared in terms of their relative activity with two substrates that have different redox potentials. Results from electrochemical studies on solutions containing LCCI and LCCIa indicate that the redox potential of the active site of LCCIa is shifted to more negative values (411 mV versus normal hydrogen electrode voltage) than that found in other fungal laccases. In addition, replacing the 11 codons at the C terminus of the laccase gene with a single cysteine codon influences the rate of heterogeneous electron transfer between an electrode and the copper-containing active site (k_{het} for LCCIa 5 1.3×10^{-4} cm s^{-1}). These results demonstrate for the first time that the rate of electron transfer between an oxidoreductase and an electrode can be enhanced by changes to the primary structure of a protein via site-directed mutagenesis (Gelo-Pujic *et al.*, 1999).

Soden et al. obtained the Psc *lac4* gene from *Pleurotus sajor-caju* has been cloned and expressed in the heterologous host *Pichia pastoris* GS115 (*his4*) and KM71 (*arg4 his4*), under the control of the *AOX1* methanol inducible promoter. The native *P. sajor-caju* laccase signal sequence was effective in directing the secretion of *lac4* expressed in *P. pastoris*. The control of media pH and temperature was found to be important in obtaining sufficient quantities of the protein to allow purification and subsequent biochemical characterization. The recombinant Psc Lac4 was purified to electrophoretic homogeneity and was shown to be immunologically related to *Pleurotus eryngii* Lac1. The purified laccase was estimated to have a molecular mass of around 59 kDa, to have a carbohydrate content of approximately 7% and a calculated pI of 4<38. The enzyme oxidized the substrates 2,2-azinobis- (3-ethylbenzthiazoline-6-sulphonate) (ABTS), 2,6-dimethoxyphenol, syringaldazine and guaiacol, exhibiting optimal pHs of 3<3, 6, 6<5 and 7 respectively. With ABTS as substrate the enzyme displayed optimal activity at 35°C and pH 3<5. The enzyme was strongly inhibited by sodium azide and thioglycolic acid but not by EDTA (Soden *et al.*, 1999).

Jönsson et al. obtained a cDNA coding for laccase isolated from the ligninolytic fungus *Trametes versicolor* by RNA-PCR. The cDNA corresponds to the gene *lcc1*, which encodes a laccase isoenzyme of 498 amino-acid residues preceded by a 22-residue signal peptide. The *lcc1* cDNA was cloned into the vector pHIL-D2 for expression in *Pichia pastoris* under the control of the *AOX1* promoter. Transformants were found to secrete active recombinant enzyme after induction with methanol. The use of growth medium buffered to pH 6.0 and control of pH during cultivation were found to be important, or even necessary, for obtaining activity in liquid cultures. The effect of exchanging the native secretion signal for the *Saccharomyces cerevisiae* α-factor pre-pro secretion signal was studied by cloning the portion encoding the mature enzyme into the vector pPIC9. The activity obtained for the construct encoding the native laccase signal sequence was found to be seven-fold higher than for the construct encoding the α-factor secretion signal. Utilisation of the *P. pastoris pep4* mutant strain MD1168 was found to provide a two-fold higher level of activity compared with *P. pastoris* GS115 (Jönsson *et al.*, 1997).

Otterbein obtained a full-length cDNA coding for laccase (lac1) from *Pycnoporus cinnabarinus* I-937. The corresponding open reading frame is 1557 nucleotides long and encodes a protein of 518 amino acids. The cDNA encodes a precursor protein containing a 21 amino-acid signal sequence corresponding to a putative signal peptide. The deduced amino-acid sequence of the encoded protein was similar to that of other laccase proteins, with the residues involved in copper coordination sharing the greatest extent of similarity. The cDNA encoding for laccase was placed under the control of the *AOX1* promoter and expressed in the methylotropic yeast *Pichia pastoris* X33. The laccase leader peptide, as well as the *Saccharomyces cerevisiae* α-factor signal peptide, efficiently directed the secretion into the culture medium of laccase in an active form. Moreover, the laccase activity was directly detected in plates. The identity of the recombinant product was further confirmed by protein immunoblotting. The expected molecular mass of the mature protein is 81 kDa. However, the apparent molecular mass of the recombinant protein is 110 kDa, thus suggesting that the protein expressed in *P. pastoris* may be hyperglycosylated (Otterbein *et al.*, 2000).

In the research of Hong et al., the laccase gene lacD, cloned from a novel laccase-producing basidiomycete *Trametes* sp. 420, contained 2,052 base pairs (bp) interrupted by 8 introns. The lacD displayed a relatively high homology with laccase genes from other white rot fungi, whereas the homology between lacD and laccase genes from plants, insects, or bacteria was less than 25%. A 498-amino acid peptide encoded by the lacD cDNA was heterologously expressed in the *Pichia pastoris* strain GS115 under the control of the *AOX1* promoter, resulting in the highest yield of laccase (83 U/mL) as determined with ABTS (2,2'-azinobis [3-ethylbenzothia-zoline-6-sulfonic acid]) as the substrate. Additionally, the enzyme activity of recombinant laccase on decolorization of some industrial dyes was assessed (Hong *et al.*, 2002).

In another research of Hong et al., a laccase cDNA from *Trametes* sp. AH28-2 was expressed in *Pichia pastoris* GS115 under the control of the *AOX1* promoter, with the highest expression level of 4.0 mg/ L (1360 U/mg). The apparent K_m (24.6 mM) for ABTS (2,2'-azinobis [3-ethylbenzothia-zoline-6-sulfonic acid]) and the carbohydrate content of the recombinant laccase A (rLacA) are approximately identical to those of the native LacA (nLacA). However, the two enzymes differed in the pH optimum when both ABTS and guaiacol served as substrates. The optimum pH for enzyme stability is 5.5 for rLacA. Thermal stability was also investigated. The mutagenesis of rLacA utilizing low-energy nitrogen ion implantation resulted in the isolation of a yeast clone that produced 7.7 mg/ L (1085 U/mg) of laccase, 92.5% more than the nonirradiated control (4.0 mg/L). Compared with rLacA, the mutant LacA (mLacA) with five amino-acid residue changes in the coding sequence showed a slight change in its catalytic ability but superior thermal stability (Hong *et al.*, 2006).

Table 5. Overview of laccase activity with different Expression host under different promoter control

Expression host	Genetic source	Promoter	Laccase activity	Reference
Pichia pastoris GS115	*Trametes versicolor*	*GAP*	24U/mL	O'Callaghan *et al.* 2002
Pichia pastoris GS115	*Fome lignosus*	*AOX1*	9 U/mL	Liu *et al.* 2003
Pichia pastoris GS115	*Trametes versicolor*	*AOX1*	0.024 U/mL	Gelo-Pujic *et al.* 1999
Pichia pastoris GS115	*Trametes versicolor*	*AOX1*	92.7 U/mg	Soden *et al.*, 1999
Pichia pastoris SMD1168	*Trametes versicolor*	*AOX1*	5 U/mL	Jönsson *et al.* 1997
Pichia pastoris X33	*Pycnoporus cinnabarinus*	*AOX1*	25 U/mL	Otterbein *et al.* 2000
Pichia pastoris GS115	*Trametes* sp. 420	*AOX1*	83 U/mL	Hong *et al.* 2002
Pichia pastoris GS115	*Trametes* sp. AH28-2	*AOX1*	1085 U/mg	Hong *et al.* 2006
Pichia pastoris SMD1168	*Trametes versicolor*	*GAP*	2.8×10^{-3} U/mL	Bohlin *et al.* 2006

GAP: glyceraldehyde-3-phosphate dehydrogenase.
AOX I: alcohol oxidase I.

In the research of Bohlin et al, the laccase cDNAs *Iccl* and *Icc2* from *Trametes versicolor* were expressed in *Pichia pastoris* SMDl168 under control of their respective glyceraldehyde-3-phosphate dehydrogenase *(GAP)* promoters and with the native secretion signal directing catalytically active laccase to the medium.

P. pastoris batch cultures in shake-flasks gave higher volumetric activity (1.3 U/L) and a better activity to biomass ratio with glucose than with glycerol or maltose as carbon source. Preliminary experiments with fed-batch cultures of *P. pastoris* in bioreactors yielded higher activity (2.8 U/L) than the shake-flask experiments, although the levels remained moderate and useful primarily for screening purposes (Bohlin *et al.*, 2006). Overview of laccase activity with different expression host under different promoter control was shown in Table 5.

Food Enzyme

Lipases

Lipases [triacylglycerol-hydrolases (EC 3.1.1.3)] play an important role in several industrial applications. They catalyse the hydrolysis of triglycerides at the interface between the insoluble substrate and water. Besides their natural substrates, such as water-insoluble esters and triglycerides, lipases catalyze the enantio- and regioselective hydrolysis and synthesis of a broad range of natural and synthetic esters. Lipases from microorganisms have received a considerable interest as catalysts in many industrial applications, such as ester synthesis (Nakano *et al.*, 1991), transesterification (Kaieda *et al.*, 2004), additives in detergents and the elaboration of dietetic foods for use in the food industry.

Lipases occur widely in bacteria, yeasts and fungi. Fungi are broadly recognized as one of the best lipase sources and are used widely in the food industry. The methylotrophic yeast *Pichia pastoris* is an excellent host for the high level production of intracellular and extracellular proteins from different sources. Several lipases have successfully been expressed in *P. pastoris*: human pancreatic triglyceride lipase, human bile salt stimulated lipase, *Candida rugosa* lipase 1 (Lip 1), lipases A and B from *Geotrichum candidum* and the *Rhizopus oryzae* lipase (ROL).

Southern blot analysis showed that three lipase genes were integrated into the genome of *P. pastoris* GS115. Under the control of *AOX1* promoter, a high *Yarrowia lipolytica* lipase LIP2 (YlLIP2) activity of 42 900 U/mL (3.4 g total protein and 2.16 g lipase per liter) was obtained using the three copy integration clone in fed-batch fermentation using basal salt medium, which was 2.5-fold higher than that using a single copy clone (Yu *et al.*, 2004, Wang *et al.*, 2012).

To achieve fast, safe and stable expression of *Burkholderia cepacia* lipase in *Pichia pastoris*, overlap PCR was applied to modify the lipase gene and the optimized gene with *Pichia* codon usage and lower G+C content was cloned to obtain engineering strains. The optimized lipase activity was 184.3 U/mL and increased 4.6-fold. The GAP promoter was proved more appropriate than the *AOX1* promoter for the *B. cepacia* lipase expression (Jia *et al.*, 2010).

Different cultivation strategies have been compared for the production of *Rhizopus oryzae* lipase (ROL) from *Pichia pastoris*. It has been shown that ROL overexpression and secretion in *P. pastoris*, under the control of PFLD1, resulted in the highest maximum lipolytic activity of around 80 AU/mL and volumetric productivity of 6346 versus 5416 AU/(L·h) (Arnau *et al.*, 2010, Arnau *et al.*, 2011).

Pseudomonas lipases are important biocatalysts widely used in a variety of industrial fields. An extracellular lipase gene lipA with 1,854-bp open reading frame was cloned from *Pseudomonas fluorescens* 26-2. The lipA gene was integrated into *Pichia pastoris* GS115, and the methanol-inducible recombinants with Mut^S and Mut^+ phenotypes were acquired. The maximal activity of Mut^+ recombinants could reach 20.3 IU/mL after methanol-inducible expression for 72 h (Yang *et al.*, 2009).

The high-cell-density fermentation of *Candida rugosa* lipase in the constitutive *Pichia pastoris* expression system under P_{AOX} promoter was scaled up from 5 to 800 L in series by optimizing the fermentation conditions. A stable lipase activity of approximately 14,000 IU/mL was obtained (Zhao *et al.*, 2008, Dolors *et al.*, 2010).

Glucose Oxidase

Glucose oxidase (GOX; β-D-glucose: oxygen 1-oxidoreductase, EC 1.1.3.4), a glycoprotein, catalyzes the oxidation of β-D-glucose to D-glucono-δ-lactone and hydrogen peroxide. It is widely used in the fields of food engineering, biotechnology, and medicine like as a source of hydrogen peroxidase in food preservation, as a means for gluconic acid production, and tested as the basis for glucose sensors and glucose detection.

At present, *Aspergillus niger* and *Penicillum amagasakiense* are mostly utilized for industrial-scale fermentation of the enzyme. However, the production of GOD by the two species is difficult in the commercial process due to either low yield or concomitant production of other enzymes such as cellulase, catalase, and amylase. Thus heterologous expression systems such as *Escherichia coli* (Witt *et al.*, 1998) and *Pichia pastoris* have been investigated for GOX production to solve these problems.

A gene of GOX from *Aspergillus niger* Z-25 was cloned and sequenced. The entire open reading frame (ORF) consisted of 1,818 bp and encoded a putative peptide of 605 amino acids. The gene was fused to the pPICZαA plasmid and overexpressed in *Pichia pastoris* SMD1168. The recombinant GOX (rGOX) was secreted into the culture using MF-α factor signal peptide under the control of the *AOX1* promoter. The recombinant GOX (rGOX) was secreted into the culture using MF-α factor signal peptide under the control of the AOX1 promoter (Guo *et al.*, 2010).

The gene encoding the GOX from *Penicillium variabile* P16 was expressed in *Pichia pastoris* X 33 using the methanol inducible AOX1 promoter. The strain X33 c9, producing 0.33 U/mL of heterologous GOX after 11 days of fermentation, was selected from six Mut^+ strains. Recombinant GOX (ca. 50 U/mL) was produced in a 3-L fermenter. Moreover, that level of GOX was approximately four times the one reached by *P. variabile* P16 cultivated under optimized conditions (Crognale *et al.*, 2006).

A recombinant GOX from *P. amagasakiense* was overexpressed in *P. pastoris.* Coding sequence was introduced into pPICZα(a) plasmid, by using *Xho* I restriction site. Additional bases were added to complete the α-factor signal sequence and insert the coding DNA fragment with the correct reading frame.

DNA amplification was obtained after transformation of DH5α bacteria with pPICZα(a)-GOXpenag plasmid. The optimal production was obtained by adding 0.4% of methanol to the culture medium every day for 5 days. At the end of the induction, the GOX activity was 4 U/mL, which is lower than what was reported for overexpression of GOX from *A. niger* Z-25 in *P. pastoris* (Guo *et al.*, 2010). However, better specific activity (365 U mg^{-1}), which is correlated to a very limited amount of secreted protein in culture media, was observed (Courjean *et al.*, 2011).

Cyclodextrin Glycosyltransferase (CGTase)

Cyclodextrin glycosyltransferase (CGTase, 4-a-D-glucan: 1,4-a-glucanotransferase, EC 2.4.1.19) is a member of the α-amylase family with a low hydrolytic activity. It catalyzes four different reactions: cyclization, coupling, disproportionation and hydrolysis (Yenpetch *et al.*, 2011). CGTase is an important industrial extracellular enzyme which is used to produce CDs and oligosaccharides.

The cgt gene was isolated from *Paenibacillus macerans* by PCR amplification using *Eco*RI and *Not* I and was inserted into vectors of pPIC9K. The recombinant vectors pPCGT were transformed to *Pichia pastoris* KM71. Then different contents (0.5 mg/mL, 1 mg/mL, 2 mg/mL) of G418 on YPD/G418 plants were used to screen the correct transformant. After cultivation at 30°C for 120 h with shake flask by adding 0.5% methanol per 24 h, the biomass was collection and the enzyme activity was determined. The results showed that α-CGTase activity in the culture media of recombinant *P. pastoris* was 0.2 U/mL (Zhang *et al.*, 2009).

Feed Enzyme

Phytase

Phytase (myo-inositol hexakisphosphate phosphohydrolase, EC 3.1.3.8) catalyses the release of phosphate from phytate (myo-inositol hexakiphosphate), which is the principle type of phosphorus present in cereal grains, legumes and oilseeds (Pandey *et al.*, 2001). Therefore, phytase can be incorporated into commercial poultry, swine, and fish diets and has a wide range of applications in animal and human nutrition as it can reduce phosphorus excretion of monogastric animals by replacing inorganic phosphates in the animal diet, contributes significantly toward environmental protection and leads to improved availability of minerals, trace elements, amino acids and energy.

In cereals and legumes, phytate (myo-inositol hexaphosphate) is the major storage form of phosphate and accounts for 80% of the total phosphorus. Monogastric animals use phytate poorly or not at all, because they lack the digestive enzyme that hydrolyzes phytate (Jongbloed *et al.*, 1997). Thus the phytate decreases the nutritional value of feed because it can form complexes with essential minerals. On the other hand, the phytate phosphorus from animal waste pollutes the environment. To alleviate these problems, phytases (myo-inositol hexaphosphate phosphohydrolases, E.C.3.1.3.8) can be used in animal feed which release inorganic phosphorous from myoinositol. Therefore phytases with improved characteristics from various sources have been applied to animal feed (Kim *et al.*, 1998, Ullah *et al.*, 2003, Lei and Porres *et al.*, 2003). The addition of phytases to feed for monogastric animals increases nutritive value and decreases the need for inorganic phosphorus supplementation.

The *Ascomycetous* yeast *Pichia anomala* produces a cell-bound phytase with a proved beneficial effect in the poultry. The enzyme also has the requisite characteristics, such as thermostability, acid stability and broad substrate specificity, for use as an animal feed supplement. The high cost of phytases is the most cited limiting factor in its application in animal diets. Cane molasses, the by-product of the sugar refinery process, containing 45-50% sugars, is the most economical source of carbohydrate for various industrial fermentations. In this investigation, an attempt was made to optimize the cultural conditions for maximizing the production of phytase from *P. anomala* in an inexpensive cane molasses medium using statistical approaches. Further, a feasibility of large-scale production was attempted in a laboratory fermenter. This is the first report on use of statistical methods for improving yeast cell bound phytase yield in cane-molasses medium.

About 10 strains isolated from marine environments showed comparatively higher phytase activity. They include *Hanseniaspora uvarum* WZ1, *Y. lipolytica* W2B, *Candida* sp. N12C, *Issatchenkia orientalis* YF04C, *Candida* sp. MA6, *Y. lipolytica* YF08, *Candida* sp. NY4E, *Candida* sp. YF12C, *Candida* sp. MB2 and *Kodamaea ohmeri* BG3. They were isolated from the gut of the marine fish (*Scomberomorus niphonius*), the gut of sea cucumber (*Holothuria scabra*), seawater at Pacific Ocean, the gut of the marine fish (*Hexagrammes otakii*), seawater at Indian Ocean, the gut of the marine fish (*Synecogobius basts*), seawater from salterns, the gut of sea cucumber, seawater in South China Sea and the gut of the marine fish (H. otakii), respectively. This means that phytase producing yeasts are widely distributed in different marine environments. We found that *K. ohmeri* BG3, one of the yeasts, could produce more phytase than any other marine yeast strains tested. To our knowledge, phytase producing marine yeasts are still unexploited bioresources in marine environments. Phytase-producing marine yeasts may be more suitable as maricultural feed additives than the added phytase from terrestrial microorganisms.

The methylotrophic yeast, *Pichia pastoris*, is a powerful expression system for production of recombinant proteins. In recent years, more than 500 proteins have been cloned and expressed using this system. The advantages of this system include high expression potential, efficient secretion of extracellular protein, post-translational modifications such as glycosylation, and growth to high cell densities on a defined minimal basal salts medium. Nevertheless, a strong and tightly regulated alcohol oxidase 1 promoter (P_{AOX1}) is the major reason to facilitate *P. pastoris* to realize these advantages.

The *AOX1* promoter regulates the expression of alcohol oxidase, the first enzyme in the methanol metabolism pathway, at the transcription level by a combined repression/depression and methanol induction mechanism. That is, the *AOX1* promoter is strongly repressed when *Pichia* cells are grown on glucose or most other carbon sources, but is induced over 1000-fold when cells are shifted to a medium containing methanol as a sole carbon source. Therefore, *Pichia* fermentation has to be divided into two phases. Commonly, glycerol is used as the growth substrate in the first phase for biomass accumulation, whereas in the second phase only methanol is fed to induce the foreign protein expression.

In order to obtain phytases with a high activity or thermostability, phytase genes from *Escherichia coli*, *Bacillus* sp., *Aspergillus niger Emericella nidulans*, *Talaromyces thermophilus*, *Aspergillus terreus*, *Myceliophthora thermophila* were cloned and expressed. Among these phytase genes, the *E. coli* phytase gene (appA) has been reported to demonstrate the greatest specific activity compared to those from other microorganisms. The *appA* gene has been successfully expressed in *E. coli*, *Pichia pastoris* and *Streptomyces lividans*. For several years now, the methylotrophic yeast *P. pastoris* has been successfully developed for the heterologous expression of foreign proteins. The *Escherichia coli* phytase gene *appA* was highly expressed in the methylotrophic yeast *Pichia pastoris* under the control of the *AOX1* promoter. Replacement of culture medium with fresh medium in order to remove repressing glycerol and metabolic wastes prior to methanol induction significantly improved phytase expression. The phytase activity level was enhanced from 118 to 204 U/mL at the flask scale and 1880-4946 U/mL for high cell-density fermentation, respectively, by appropriately modifying the medium composition and fermentation strategy. Most of the protein in the culture supernatant was recombinant phytase, the enzyme characteristics of which were similar to native *E. coli* phytase.

Alkaline phytase, LlALP2, from lily pollen had been heterologously expressed in *P. pastoris* in a soluble active form, and this is the first report of the heterologous expression of a plant phytase in an active soluble form.

Watanabe purified a novel phytase from the wastewater treatment yeast *Hansenula fabianii* J640 (Hfphytase), cloned the 1456 bp open reading frame (ORF) encoding Hfphytase, and characterized Hfphytase. The molecular weight of Hfphytase after deglycosylation by PNGaseF was 49 kDa. The optimal pH and temperature for enzyme activity were 4.5 and 50°C, respectively. Hfphytase exhibits 40% identity with Debaryomyces castellii phytase, 37% identity with *Aspergillus niger* PhyB, and 34% identity with *Saccharomyces cerevisiae* Pho5p. Recombinant Hfphytase was transformed and expressed in *Pichia pastoris*. The yield was 23 g/L by jar fermenter cultivation. The marked phosphohydrolysis activity exhibited by Hfphytase on six substrates (pNP-P, sodium phytate, glucose-1 phosphate, glucose-6 phosphate, α-glycerophosphate and β-glycerophosphate) indicated that it is a non-specific acid phosphatase.

Replacing the culture medium immediately prior to the methanol induction phase significantly improves protein expression due to the removal of residual glycerol and metabolic waste both of which both repress induction. Chen and coworkers report an increase of 260% in recombinant phytase activity in high-density *P. pastoris* cultivations when the culture mediums replaced. In certain cases, data-driven models such as ANNs are more applicable than classic mechanical models based on mass balances. Data-driven models are capable of predicting process variables from global measurement variables such as the oxygen or carbon dioxide concentrations in the off-gas. Jin and coworkers developed an artificial neural network pattern recognition (ANNPR) model for the on line adaptive control of methanol feeding based on DO and pH measurements to describe phytase production by are recombinant *P. pastoris*. The model predicts the state of the process as either "substrate starved" or "substrate in excess" and a coupled controller then adjusts the feed rate accordingly. This model-based control lead to a three-fold increase in phytase production, compared to systems using traditional DO-stat or on line methanol electrode- based on–off control strategies. The same strategy was used for the production of recombinant porcine interfere on-α. The described models are only applicable top *AOX1*-regulated systems. Far fewer model shave been developed to describe pGAP- regulated ones. Tang and coworkers developed a simple model describing cell growth and recombinant phytase production in *P. pastoris* grown on glucose. Although based on data collected in continuous cultivations, the model provides good predictions of fed-batch behaviour under glucose-limited conditions.

An analysis of a projected pGAP-regulated *P. pastoris* fed-batch cultivation system expressing phytase was performed by Potvin' labo-ratory as part of an industrial report submitted to Zell Technologies Inc. (unpublished data). System performance a deconomics for cultivations on glucose and glycerol were compared for a process consisting of three 60-tonne fermenters. The phytase premix cost of manufacture for plants in the United States and China was also compared.

Mayer et al. did claim that a greater expression of phytase was achieved using *H. polymorpha* and Chen et al. reported that 1880-4946 U mL/L of phytase activity was obtained using *P. pastoris* system.

Some studies have been performed for the improvement of phytase thermostability as follows: phytase genes were reconstructed using site-directed mutagenesis; a thermostable phytase molecule was newly established by exploiting the consensus technique (Lehmann, M., EP patent 0897985 A2, 1999); phytase was modified through glycosylation; and thermostable strains producing phytases were isolated from various environments. In addition, protectants or stabilizers such as metals, polyols or other solutes have been applied to increase the thermostability of this enzyme. The gene *appA* encoding a pH-stable phytase from *Yersinia kristeensenii* was cloned and heterologously expressed in *Pichia pastoris*, and the recombinant phytase was subjected to detailed biochemical characterization. The *Y. kristeensenii phytase* is highly pH stable at pH 1.5-11.0 and thermostable, providing significant advantages for processing, transportation, storage and application.

Chen have successfully expressed the *appA* gene in *P. pastoris* and produced phytase at fermentor-scale. The level of phytase activity was tremendously enhanced in high cell-density fermentation as a consequence of our modifying the medium composition and the fermentation strategy. We also found that culture-medium replacement was crucial to achieving high levels of phytase production. This might be attributed to the complete removal of glycerol or metabolic wastes. Some earlier studies have demonstrated that the gradual addition of methanol prior to the glycerol depletion in the culture medium might have facilitated the de-repression of the *AOX1* promoter. Use of a methanol monitor/controller also significantly improved the enzyme production. FBSH appears to be an excellent medium for batch culture of *P. pastoris*. However, it does not appear to be suitable for protein induction. To the best of our knowledge, our results suggest the highest level of expression of phytase in *P. pastoris* that has been reported to date. Although in 1999, Mayer et al did claim a greater expression of phytase was achieved using Hansenula polymorpha featuring a high copy number of the phytase gene.

Most of the *P. pastoris*-secreted protein in the culture medium was recombinant phytase as evidenced by the results of the SDS-PAGE assay. According to *appA* gene-sequence analyses, there exist three predicted *N*-glycosylation sites. The molecular weight of recombinant phytase subsequent to deglycosylation by EndoHf appeared to be similar to that of the native form of phytase. Some minor bands did appear for phytase subsequent to the longer induction time, suggesting that some proteolytic enzymes may be produced by *P. pastoris* during the induction period. This observation is similar to chitinase expression by *P. pastoris*. In this study, we have demonstrated that the productivity of *E. coli* phytase in *P. pastoris* fermentation peaked at 4946 U/mL. This high yield would thus suggest that phytase production by *P. pastoris* was both economical and feasible.

Mannanase

Mannanase (endo-1,4-β-mannanase, EC 3.2.1.78) can catalyze the random hydrolyzation of the 1,4-mannosidic linkages within the main chains of mannan, galactomannan, glucomannan, and galactoglucomannan. Thus, mannanase is very useful in pulp bleaching, in the food, animal feed and detergent industries. Alkaline mannanase provides obvious advantages for the applications in pulp bleaching and the detergent industry, where high pH processes are common. Alkaliphilic *Bacillus* strains are the main producers of alkaline mannanases. However, the production of alkaline mannanases by alkaliphilic *Bacillus* strains is difficult in commercial process due to the low yield and the required special culture conditions. Heterologous expression could be a promising procedure for the efficient production of alkaline mannanases. To date, only the alkaline mannanase from alkaliphilic *Bacillus* sp. strain JAMB-750 was heterologously expressed in *Bacillus subtilis*. The methylotrophic yeast *Pichia pastoris* has been successfully used as a host system for high-level expression of heterologous proteins. The use of the strong methanol-induced *AOX1* promoter from this yeast has allowed efficient production of several enzymes of industrial interest. Recently, some constitutive promoters were developed for *P. pastoris*, which gave greater variability to the *P. pastoris*-based expression systems. The constitutive glyceraldehyde-3-phosphate dehydrogenase gene (GAP) promoter, sometimes, gave comparable expression levels to the *AOX1* promoter. The combined usage of *AOX1* promoter and GAP promoter in *P. pastoris* has been reported to express different proteins or the same protein in single *P. pastoris* cultivation. The blue mussel mannanase was expressed extracellularly using *P. pastoris* as the host, and an expression level of 900 mg/L protein was obtained after 10 days cultivation in fermentor. However, there are no reports on heterologous expression of alkaline mannanase in *P. pastoris*. Previously, a novel alkaline- mannanase gene *manA* was isolated from the strictly alkaliphilic *Bacillus* sp. N16-5. The properties of high thermal activity and stability in alkaline condition, combined with the character of insensitivity to some surfactants, would qualify *Bacillus* sp. N16-5-mannanase for application in the manufacture of kraft pulp and in the detergent industry. In this work, the alkaline mannanase of *Bacillus* sp. N16-5 was expressed extracellularly in *P. pastoris* by the combined usage of *GAP* and *AOX1* promoters. The main properties of the recombinant enzyme were investigated.

A moderately thermophilic fungus, *Chaetomium* sp. CQ31 was recently isolated from composting soil samples of Shandong province (China) in our lab. This species of fungus was shown to be a producer of xylanase and mannanase (Jiang *et al.*, 2010). Katroliahave cloned and sequenced a novel mannanase gene termed CsMan5A from *Chaetomium* sp. CQ31 and expressed it in *P. pastoris*. The enzyme expression levels are by far the highest obtained, thus making it highly cost-effective for commercial production. The enzyme exhibited high specific activity, good thermal and pH stability as well as resistance to many metal ions. Its efficiency in hydrolyzing various mannan polysaccharides makes it potentially useful in a wide variety of applications in the food and feed as well as paper and pulp industries.

The α-galactosidase gene (AgalB) was cloned from the acidophilic fungus *Bispora* sp. MEY-1 and expressed in *Pichia pastoris* by Wang. The deduced amino acid sequence showed highest identity (35%) to the α-galactosidase from *Penicillium simplicissimum*, belonging to the glycosyl hydrolase family 27. The purified recombinant α-galactosidase (r-AgalB) exhibited optimal activity at pH 3.5 and 55°C, was stable at pH 2.2-8.0, and showed higher hydrolytic activity towards galactomannan polysaccharides (guar gum and locust bean gum) than toward small galacto-oligosaccharides (melibiose, raffinose and stachyose). A synergistic (3-fold) increase in guar gum hydrolysis was observed when β-mannanase Man5A from *Bispora* sp. MEY-1 and r-AgalB were combined. Further, an increase in the reaction time from 5 h to 12 h or increase of the temperature from 37°C to 55°C enhanced guar gum degradation by the enzyme combination.

A. niger possesses a large number of genes encoding carbohydrate-active enzymes, which could be utilized in various biotechnological applications. *A. niger* CBS 513.88 is an induced mutant derived from a high glucoamylase yield strain, *A. niger* strain ATCC NRRL3122. Its genome has been sequenced by researchers of a Dutch company, DSM. The hypothetical mannanase (accession No. XM_001397260.1) from *A. niger* CBS 513.88 was predicted to be potential for industrial applications for its excellent properties. This report describes cDNA sequence synthesis, recombinant strain construction, successful expression of hypothetical endo-1,4-b-mannanase gene (accession No. XM_001397260.1) in *P. pastoris*, and the high cell-density fermentation of recombinant *P. pastoris* strain. The recombinant enzyme is thermo- and acidic-stable, cold-active and thus suitable for various industrial applications.

The gene *man5A* without ST-rich region coding sequence was also expressed in *P. pastoris* by Luo. The β-mannanase activity was still detected but decreased in some degree. In contrast, Huang et al. (2005) reported that removal of an *N*-terminal Ser/Thr-rich sequence from an acidophilic endo-β-glucanase from *Sulfolobus solfataricus* resulted in complete loss of enzyme activity (Huang *et al.*, 2005). Stalbrand et al. (1995) reported a Ser/Thr/ Pro-rich region at the C terminus of *T. reesei* β-mannanase with similarity to the carbohydrate-binding domains of fungal cellulases (Stalbrand *et al.*, 1995). However, the *N*-terminal Ser/Thr-rich sequence of *MAN5A* had no sequence similarity with the carbohydrate-binding domain of T.

reesei β-mannanase or with any cellulase. The function(s) of this Ser/Thr-rich sequence of *MAN5A* remains to be explored.

Enzymes optimally active under extreme conditions are of both biotechnological importance and scientific interest. The MAN5A enzyme examined here had optimal activity at pH 1.0-1.5, lower than any known mannanase. The optimum pH of most fungal mannanases ranges from pH2.4-6.0 (Dhawan *et al.*, 2007). MAN5A demonstrated excellent pH stability. This characteristic differs from other fungal β-mannanases, which were stable only at acidic pH (Stalbrand *et al.*, 1995, Setati *et al.*, 2001, Chen *et al.*, 2007). The molecular basis for the extraordinary stability and high activity of MAN5A at highly acidic pH are unknown. Some acidophilic enzymes, such as porcine pepsin (Sielecki *et al.*, 1990) and xylanase C (Fushinobu *et al.*, 1998), had an excess of negatively charged groups on the protein surface and low pI, which might account for the acidophilic nature. Due to the failure of MAN5A structure prediction, the molecular basis for the highly acidic ability of MAN5A cannot be explained right now. The enzymatic activity was stable in the presence of 1 mM Pb^{2+} and partly inhibited by 1 mM Hg^{2+}. This is the first study to report a β-mannanase with increased activity in the presence of Fe^{3+} and Ag^{+}. In contrast, metal ions, such as Ag^{+}, Hg^{2+}, Mn^{2+}, Pb^{2+}, and Fe^{3+}, have been shown to strongly inhibit other β-mannanases at 1 mM concentration (Chen *et al.*, 2007, Tamaru *et al.*, 1995, Zhu and Wu, 2007). Cu^{2+} has also been demonstrated to inhibit some mannanases (Tamaru *et al.*, 1995, Zakaria *et al.*, 1998). In this study, higher concentrations (5 mM and 10 mM) of Cu^{2+} partly inhibited MAN5A activity, but addition of 1 mM Cu^{2+} increased the β-mannanase activity of MAN5A, similar to that reported for the mannanase from *A. sulphureus* (Chen *et al.*, 2007). The observed resilience of MAN5A activity to metal ions might reflect the environment (a uranium mine) from which *Bispora* sp. MEY-1 was isolated. High specific activity and efficient hydrolysis are necessary for an enzyme to be applied in industries. The high specific activity (3,373 U/mg) and high level of expression in the fermentation supernatant (0.15 mg/mL) make MAN5A potentially more cost-effective than currently used mannanases. In addition, the enzyme activity during fermentation reached 500 U/mL, which is significantly higher than most of the mannanases reported to date (Chen *et al.*, 2007, Christgau *et al.*, 1994, Chen *et al.*, 2007). Furthermore, it may be possible to increase MAN5A expression by altering the nucleotide sequence to account for codon usage bias using a more favorable signal sequence or by increasing the gene copy number. The apparent molecular weight of r-MAN5A is much greater than that calculated one (46.8 kDa). Although mature MAN5A has a total of 82 Ser and The residues with *O*-glycosylation potential, Endo H treatment had little effect on MAN5A electrophoretic mobility. Thus, the protein may have other *O*-glycosylation sites and/or other posttranslational modifications (Trimble *et al.*, 2004). SDS-PAGE and activity assay indicated that purity of r-MAN5A changed little during the purification process. The good purity in the absence of purification might make the crude enzyme of r-MAN5A directly useful in production without purification, thus simplifying the processing procedure and reducing the production cost. Overall, MAN5A is optimally active under acidic conditions, has good thermal and pH stability, has high specific activity, and is highly resistant to pepsin and trypsin treatment and to most metal ions and several chemical reagents. All these properties suggest that this enzyme has great potential for use in animal feed and improvement of food quality.

In conclusion, Chen cloned the *A. sulphureus* β- mannanase gene and examined its expression in *P. pastoris*, and characterized the biochemical properties of the recombinant enzyme. The yield of the recombinant β-mannanase was higher than that for a previously identified. The purity of β-mannanase was 97%, which will facilitate the industrial application and decrease the product cost. In addition, the recombinant enzyme was highly specific for galactomannan, exhibited a broad pH range of 2.2–8.0 and was stable up to 40°C. These properties suggest that the recombinant enzyme may be potentially useful as a feed additive that could function well in the gastrointestinal tract conditions (pH 2–7). Further investigation on the recombinant β-mannanase is required to determine its three-dimensional structure to compare the structure of *A. sulphureus* β-mannanase and other β-mannanases of the glycoside hydrolase family 5. In addition, subsequent research will focus on how to increase the protein yield of the recombinant β-mannanase in fermentation. An alkaline β-mannanase from *Bacillus* sp. N16-5 was over-produced in *P. pastoris* using a series of genetic and process optimizations by Zhu. The removal of the native β-mannanase signal peptide and increasing the copy number of the mature mannanase gene remarkably improved the β-mannanase expression. While sorbitol co-feeding and temperature-lowering strategies can both increase the enzyme production level, the combined use of these two strategies achieved the most effective result the enzyme level reached 6336 U/mL.

Conclusion

With the growing interest in recombinant protein expression for various uses, yeast expression systems, such as the popular *Pichia pastoris*, are becoming increasingly important. The production of a wide range of recombinant proteins in *P. pastoris* makes it an attractive expression platform. *P. pastoris* can be grown cheaply and rapidly, and is amenable to high-cell-density fermentations (>400 g/L). Besides possessing com plex posttranslational modification pathways, it offers the advantage of being neither pyrogenic nor pathogenic and able to secrete more efficiently. Although P. pastoris has been successfully used in the production of many secreted and intracellular recombinant proteins, there is still room for improvement of this expression system.

References

Abdulaev, N. G., M. P. Popp, W. C. Smith and K. D. Ridge, 1997. Functional Expression of Bovine Opsin in the Methylotrophic Yeast *Pichia pastoris*. *Protein Expres. Purif.*, 10(1):61-69.

Arnau, C., C. Casas and F. Valero, 2011. The effect of glycerol mixed substrate on the heterologous production of a Rhizopus oryzae lipase in *Pichia pastoris* system. *Biochem. Eng. J.*, 57:30-37.

Arnau, C., R. Ramon, C. Casas and F. Valero, 2010. Optimization of the heterologous production of a *Rhizopus oryzae* lipase in *Pichia pastoris* system using mixed substrates on controlled fed-batch bioprocess. *Enzyme Microb. Tech.*, 46(6):494-500.

Arnau, C., R. Ramon, P. Ferrer and F. Valero, 2007. Sorbitol co-feeding an efficient strategy to reduce metabolic burden caused by the overexpression of a *Rhizopus oryzae* lipase in *Pichia pastoris*. *J. Biotechno.*, 131(2):S76-S76.

Barr, K., S. Hopkins and K. Sreekrishna, 1992. Protocol for efficient secretion of HSA developed from *Pichia pastoris*. *Pharm. Eng.*, 12(2):48-51.

Bohlin, C., L. J. Jönsson, R. Roth and W. H. Zyl, 2006. Heterologous expression of *Trametes versicolor* laccase in *Pichia pastoris* and *Aspergillus niger*. In*: 2006*: Springer; 195-214.

Bruhlmann, F., 1995. Purification and characterization of an extracellular pectate lyase from an *Amycolata* sp. *Appl. Environ. Microb.*, 61(10):3580.

Cereghino, G. P. L., J. L. Cereghino, C. Ilgen and J. M. Cregg, 2002. Production of recombinant proteins in fermenter cultures of the yeast *Pichia pastoris*. *Curr. Opin. Biotech.*, 13(4):329-332.

Chang, S. W., G. C. Lee and J. F. Shaw, 2006. Codon optimization of Candida rugosa lip1 gene for improving expression in *Pichia pastoris* and biochemical characterization of the purified recombinant LIP1 lipase. *J. Agr. Food Chem.*, 54(3):815-822.

Chantasingh, D., K. Pootanakit, V. Champreda, P. Kanokratana and L. Eurwilaichitr, 2006. Cloning, expression, and characterization of a xylanase 10 from *Aspergillus terreus* (BCC129) in *Pichia pastoris*. *Protein Expres. Purif.*, 46(1):143-149.

Chen, X., Y. Cao, Y. Ding, W. Lu and D. Li, 2007. Cloning, functional expression and characterization of *Aspergillus sulphureus* [beta]-mannanase in *Pichia pastoris. J. Biotechnol.*, 128(3):452-461.

Chen, X., Y. Qiao, H. Ding and M. Yue, 2007. Expression of β-mannanase gene from *Trichoderma reesei* RUTC-30 in *Pichia pastoris*. *J. Agr. Biotechnol.*, 15(1):142-143.

Cheng, Y. F., C. H. Yang and W. H. Liu, 2005. Cloning and expression of *Thermobifida* xylanase gene in the methylotrophic yeast *Pichia pastoris*. *Enzyme Microb. Tech.*, 37(5):541-546.

Christgau, S., S. Kauppinen, J. Vind, L. V. Kofod and H. Dalbøge, 1994. Expression cloning, purification and characterization of a beta-1, 4-mannanase from *Aspergillus aculeatus*. *Biochem. Mol. Biol. Int.*, 33(5):917.

Clare, J., F. Rayment, S. Ballantine, K. Sreekrishna and M. Romanos, 1991. High-level expression of tetanus toxin fragment C in *Pichia pastoris* strains containing multiple tandem integrations of the gene. *Nat. Biotechnol.*, 9(5):455-460.

Clare, J. J., M. A. Romanes., F. B. Rayment, J. E. Rowedder, M. A. Smith, M. M. Payne, K. Sreekrishna and C. A. Henwood, 1991. Production of mouse epidermal growth factor in yeast: high-level secretion using *Pichia pastoris* strains containing multiple gene copies. *Gene*, 105(2):205-212.

Collins, T., C. Gerday and G. Feller, 2005. Xylanases, xylanase families and extremophilic xylanases. *FEMS Microbiology Reviews*, 29(1):3-23.

Courjean, O. and N. Mano, 2011.Recombinant glucose oxidase from *Penicillium* amagasakiense for efficient bioelectrochemical applications in physiological conditions. *J. Biotechnol.*, 151(1):122-129.

Cregg, J., K. Barringer, A. Hessler and K. Madden, 1985. *Pichia pastoris* as a host system for transformations. *Mol. Cell. Biol.*, 5(12):3376.

Cregg, J., T. Vedvick and W. Raschke, 1993. Recent advances in the expression of foreign genes in *Pichia pastoris*. *Nat. Biotechnol.*, 11(8):905-910.

Crognale, S., V. Pulci, V. Brozzoli, M. Petruccioli and F. Federici, 2006. Expression of *Penicillium* variabile P16 glucose oxidase gene in *Pichia pastoris* and characterization of the recombinant enzyme. *Enzyme Microb. Tech.*, 39(6):1230-1235.

Daly, R. and M. T. W. Hearn, 2005. Expression of heterologous proteins in *Pichia pastoris*: a useful experimental tool in protein engineering and production. *J. Mol. Recognit.*, 18(2):119-138.

Damaso, M. C. T., M. S. Almeida, E. Kurtenbach, O. B. Martins, Jr. N. Pereira, C. M. M. C. Andrade and R. M. Albano, 2003. Optimized expression of a thermostable xylanase from *Thermomyces lanuginosus* in *Pichia pastoris*. *Appl. Environ. Microb.*, 69(10):6064-6072.

Deng, P., D. Li, Y. Cao, W. Lu and C. Wang, 2006. Cloning of a gene encoding an acidophilic endo-[beta]-1, 4-xylanase obtained from *Aspergillus niger* CGMCC1067 and constitutive expression in *Pichia pastoris*. *Enzyme Microb. Tech.*, 39(5):1096-1102.

Dhawan, S. and J. Kaur, 2007. Microbial mannanases: an overview of production and applications. *Crit. Rev. Biotechnol.*, 27(4):197-216.

Dolors Benaiges, M., M. Alarcon, P. Fucinos, P. Ferrer, M. Rua and F. Valero, 2010. Recombinant *Candida rugosa* Lipase 2 from *Pichia pastoris*: Immobilization and use as Biocatalyst in a Stereoselective Reaction. *Biotechnol. Progr.*, 26(5):1252-1258.

Dong, Z., Y. Yang, Z. Wang, S. Qin, Y. Jiang, L. Xing and B Zhao, 2010. Isolation, expression and comparison of a pectate lyase produced by *Fusarium oxysporum* f. sp. cubense race 1 and race 4. *Afr. J. Biotechnol.*, 9(53):8984-8990.

Fuchs, A., 1965. The trans-eliminative breakdown of Na-polygalacturonate by *Pseudomonas fluorescens*. *Anton. Van Leeuw.*, 31(1):323-340.

Fushinobu, S., K. Ito, M. Konno, T. Wakagi and H. Matsuzawa, 1998. Crystallographic and mutational analyses of an extremely acidophilic and acid-stable xylanase: biased distribution of acidic residues and importance of Asp37 for catalysis at low pH. *Protein Eng.*, 11(12):1121-1128.

Gellissen, G., 2000. Heterologous protein production in methylotrophic yeasts. *Appl. Microbiol. Biot.*, 54(6):741-750.

Gelo-Pujic, M., H. H. Kim, N. G. Butlin and G. T. R. Palmore, 1999. Electrochemical studies of a truncated laccase produced in *Pichia pastoris*. *Appl. Environ. Microb.*, 65(12):5515.

Gummadi, S. N. and D. S. Kumar, 2005.Microbial pectic transeliminases. *Biotechnol. Lett.*, 27(7):451-458.

Guo, J. P. and Y. Ma, 2008. High-level expression, purification and characterization of recombinant *Aspergillus oryzae* alkaline protease in *Pichia pastoris*. *Protein Expres. Purif.*, 58(2):301-308.

Guo, W., L. Gonzalez-Candelas and P. Kolattukudy, 1995. Cloning of a novel constitutively expressed pectate lyase gene pelB from *Fusarium solani* f. sp. pisi (Nectria haematococca, mating type VI) and characterization of the gene product expressed in *Pichia pastoris*. *J. Bacteriol.*, 177(24):7070.

Guo, Y., F. Lu, H. Zhao, Y. Tang and Z. Lu, 2010. Cloning and Heterologous Expression of Glucose Oxidase Gene from *Aspergillus niger* Z-25 in *Pichia pastoris*. *Appl. Biochem. Biotech.*, 162(2):498-509.

Hasan, F., A. A. Shah and A, Hameed, 2006. Industrial applications of microbial lipases. *Enzyme Microb. Tech.*, 39(2):235-251.

Heyland, J., J. Fu, L. M. Blank and A. Schmid, 2011. Carbon metabolism limits recombinant protein production in *Pichia pastoris*. *Biotechnol. Bioeng.*, 108(8):1942-1953.

Holmquist, M., D. C. Tessier and M. Cygler, 1997. High-level production of recombinant *Geotrichum candidum* lipases in yeast *Pichia pastoris*. *Protein Expres. Purif.*, 11(1):35-40.

Hong, F., N. Q. Meinander and L. J. Jönsson, 2002. Fermentation strategies for improved heterologous expression of laccase in *Pichia pastoris*. *Biotechnol. Bioeng.*, 79(4):438-449.

Hong, Y., Y. Xiao, H. Zhou, W. Fang, M. Zhang, J. Wang, L. Wu and Z. Yu, 2006. Expression of a laccase cDNA from *Trametes* sp. AH28-2 in *Pichia pastoris* and mutagenesis of transformants by nitrogen ion implantation. *FEMS Microbiol. Lett.*, 258(1):96-101.

Huang, Y., G. Krauss, S. Cottaz, H. Driguez and G. Lipps, 2005. A highly acid-stable and thermostable endo-β-glucanase from the thermoacidophilic archaeon *Sulfolobus solfataricus*. *Biochem. J.*, 385(Pt 2):581.

Inan, M. and M. M. Meagher, 2001. Non-repressing carbon sources for alcohol oxidase (AOX1) promoter of *Pichia pastoris*. *J. Biosci. Bioeng.*, 92(6):585-589.

Jeya, M., S. Thiagarajan, J. K. Lee and P. Gunasekaran, 2009. Cloning and expression of GH11 xylanase gene from *Aspergillus fumigatus* MKU1 in *Pichia pastoris*. *J. Biosci. Bioeng.*, 108(1):24-29.

Jia, B., W. Liu, J. Yang, C. Ye, L. Xu and Y. Yan, 2010. Burkholderia cepacia lipase gene modification and its constitutive and inducible expression in *Pichia pastoris*. *Acta Microbiol. Sinica*, 50(9):1194-1201.

Jiang, Z., Q. Cong, Q. Yan, N. Kumar and X. Du, 2010. Characterisation of a thermostable xylanase from *Chaetomium* sp. and its application in Chinese steamed bread. *Food Chem.*, 120(2):457-462.

Jönsson, L. J., M. Saloheimo and M. Penttilä, 1997. Laccase from the white-rot fungus *Trametes versicolor*: cDNA cloning of lcc1 and expression in *Pichia pastoris*. *Curr. Genet.*, 32(6):425-430.

Kaieda, M., M. Nagayoshi, S. Hama, A. Kondo and H. Fukuda, 2004. Enantioselective transesterification using immobilized *Aspergillus oryzae* overexpressing lipase. *Appl. Microbiol. Biot.*, 65(3):301-305.

Kalantzi, S., D. Mamma, P. Christakopoulos and D. Kekos, 2008. Effect of pectate lyase bioscouring on physical, chemical and low-stress mechanical properties of cotton fabrics. *Bioresource Technol.*, 99(17):8185-8192.

Kim, T. and X. G. Lei, 2005. Expression and characterization of a thermostable serine protease (TfpA) from *Thermomonospora fusca* YX in *Pichia pastoris*. *Appl. Microbiol. Biot.*, 68(3):355-359.

Kim, Y. O., J. K. Lee, H. K. Kim, J. H. Yu and T. K. Oh, 1998. Cloning of the thermostable phytase gene (phy) from *Bacillus* sp. DS11 and its overexpression in *Escherichia coli*. *FEMS Microbiol. Lett.*, 162(1):185-191.

Lee, G. C., L. C. Lee, V. Sava and J. F. Shaw, 2002. Multiple mutagenesis of non-universal serine codons of the *Candida rugosa* LIP2 gene and biochemical characterization of purified recombinant LIP2 lipase overexpressed in *Pichia pastoris*. *Biochem. J.*, 366:603-611.

Lei, X. G. and J. M. Porres, 2003. Phytase enzymology, applications, and biotechnology. *Biotechnol. Lett.*, 25(21):1787-1794.

Li, J., P. J. Shi, X. Y. Han, K. Meng, P. L. Yang, Y. R. Wang, H. Y. Luo, N. F. Wu, B. Yao and Y. L. Fan, 2007. Functional expression of the keratinolytic serine protease gene sfp2 from *Streptomyces fradiae* var. k11 in *Pichia pastoris*. *Protein Expres. Purif.*, 54(1):79-86.

Li, Z., F. Xiong, Q. Lin, M. d'Anjou, A. J. Daugulis, D. S. C. Yang and C. L. Hew, 2001. Low-temperature increases the yield of biologically active herring antifreeze protein in *Pichia pastoris*. *Protein Expres. Purif.*, 21(3):438-445.

Liu, M. Q., and G. F. Liu, 2008. Expression of recombinant *Bacillus licheniformis* xylanase A in *Pichia pastoris* and xylooligosaccharides released from xylans by it. *Protein Expres. Purif.*, 57(2):101-107.

Liu, M. Q., X. Y. Weng and J. Y. Sun, 2006. Expression of recombinant Aspergillus niger xylanase A in Pichia pastoris and its action on xylan. *Protein Expres. Purif.*, 48(2):292-299.

Liu, W., Y. Chao, S. Liu, H. Bao and S. Qian, 2003. Molecular cloning and characterization of a laccase gene from the basidiomycete *Fome lignosus* and expression in *Pichia pastoris*. *Appl. Microbiol. Biot.*, 63(2):174-181.

Liu, Z. M., Z. X. Lu, F. X. Lv, X. M. Bie and H. Z. Zhao, 2006. Heterologous expression and purification of protopectinase-N from *Bacillus subtilis* in *Pichia pastoris*. *Process Biochem.*, 41(4):975-979.

Macouzet, M., B. K. Simpson and B. H. Lee, 2005. Expression of a cold-adapted fish trypsin in *Pichia pastoris*. *FEMS Yeast Res.*, 5(9):851-857.

Matsumoto, T., Y. Sugiura, A. Kondo and H. Fukuda, 2002. Efficient production of protopectinases by *Bacillus subtilis* using medium based on soybean flour. *Biochem. Eng. J.*, 2000, 6(2):81-86.

Mayer, A. M. and R. C. Staples, 2002. Laccase: new functions for an old enzyme. *Phytochemistry*, 60(6):551-565.

Minning, S., C. Schmidt-Dannert and R. D. Schmid, 1998. Functional expression of *Rhizopus oryzae* lipase in *Pichia pastoris*: high-level production and some properties. *J. Biotechnol.*, 66(2-3):147-156.

Minning, S., A. Serrano, P. Ferrer, C. Sola, R. D. Schmid and F. Valero, 2001. Optimization of the high-level production of *Rhizopus oryzae* lipase in *Pichia pastoris*. *J. Biotechnol.*, 86(1):59-70.

Mitsuiki, S., H. Eguchi, Y. Hara, M. Sakai, Y. Moriyama, M. Gotoz and K. Furukawaz, 2002. Purification and Some Properties of Pectate Lyase from *Alkaliphilic Nocardiopsis* sp. T OA-1. *J. Appl. Glycosci.*, 49(4).

Nakano, H., S. Kitahata, Y. Tominaga, S. Takenishi, 1991. Esterification of Glycosides with Glycerol ant Trimethylolpropane Moieties by *Candida cylidracea* Lipase (Biological Chemistry). *Agr. Biol. Chem.*, 55(8):2083-2089.

Nasser, W., F. Chalet and J. Robert-Baudouy, 1990. Purification and characterization of extracellular pectate lyase from *Bacillus subtilis*. *Biochimie*, 72(9):689-695.

O'Callaghan, J., M. O'Brien, K. McClean and A. Dobson, 2002. Optimisation of the expression of a *Trametes versicolor* laccase gene in *Pichia pastoris*. *J. Ind. Microbiol. Biot.*, 29(2):55-59.

Otterbein, L., E. Record, S. Longhi, M. Asther and S. Moukha, 2000. Molecular cloning of the cDNA encoding laccase from *Pycnoporus cinnabarinus* I-937 and expression in *Pichia pastoris*. *Eur. J. Biochem.*, 267(6):1619-1625.

Pandey, A., G. Szakacs, C. R. Soccol, J. A. Rodriguez-Leon and V. T. Soccol, 2001. Production, purification and properties of microbial phytases. *Bioresource Technol.*, 77(3):203-214.

Pfeffer, J., S. Richter, J. Nieveler, C. E. Hansen, R. B. Rhlid, R. D. Schmid and M. Rusnak, 2006. High yield expression of Lipase A from *Candida antarctica* in the methylotrophic yeast *Pichia pastoris* and its purification and characterisation. *Appl. Microbiol. Biot.*, 72(5):931-938.

Quyen, D. T., C. Schmidt-Dannert, R. D. Schmid, 2003. High-level expression of a lipase from *Bacillus thermocatenulatus* BTL2 in *Pichia pastoris* and some properties of the recombinant lipase. *Protein Expres. Purif.*, 28(1):102-110.

Resina, D., M. Maurer, O. Cos, C. Arnau, M. Carnicer, H. Marx, B. Gasser, F. Valero, D. Mattanovich and P. Ferrer, 2009. Engineering of bottlenecks in *Rhizopus oryzae* lipase production in *Pichia pastoris* using the nitrogen source-regulated FLD1 promoter. *New Biotechnol.*, 25(6):396-403.

Romanos, M., 1995. Advances in the use of *Pichia pastoris* for high-level gene expression. *Curr. Opin. Biotech.*, 6(5):527-533.

Romanos, M. A., J. J. Clare, K. M. Beesley, F. B. Rayment, S. P. Ballantine, A. J. Makoff, G. Dougan, N. F. Fairweather and I. G. Charles, 1991. Recombinant Bordetella pertussis pertactin (P69) from the yeast *Pichia pastoris*: high-level production and immunological properties. *Vaccine*, 9(12):901-906.

Rotticci-Mulder, J. C., M. Gustavsson, M. Holmquist, K. Hult and M. Martinelle, 2001. Expression in *Pichia pastoris* of *Candida antarctica* lipase B and lipase B fused to a cellulose-binding domain. *Protein Expres. Purif.*, 21(3):386-392.

Ruanglek, V., R. Sriprang, N. Ratanaphan, P. Tirawongsaroj, D. Chantasigh, S. Tanapongpipat, K. Pootanakit and L. Eurwilaichitr, 2007. Cloning, expression, characterization, and high cell-density production of recombinant endo-1, 4-[beta]-xylanase from *Aspergillus niger* in *Pichia pastoris*. *Enzyme Microb. Tech.*, 41(1-2):19-25.

Scorer, C., J. Clare, W. McCombie, M. Romanos and K. Sreekrishna, 1994. Rapid Selection Using G418 of High Copy Number Transformants of *Pichia pastoris* for High¨Clevel Foreign Gene Expression. *Nat. Biotechnol.*, 12(2):181-184.

Setati, M. E., P. Ademark, W. H. Van Zyl, B. Hahn-Hägerdal and H Stålbrand, 2001. Expression of the *Aspergillus aculeatus* Endo-[beta]-1, 4-mannanase Encoding Gene (man1) in *Saccharomyces cerevisiae* and Characterization of the Recombinant Enzyme. *Protein Expres. Purif.*, 21(1):105-114.

Sielecki, A. R., A. A. Fedorov, A. Boodhoo, N. S. Andreeva and M. N. G. James, 1990. Molecular and crystal structures of monoclinic porcine pepsin refined at 1.8 Aoresolution. *J. Mol. Biol.*, 214(1):143-170.

Soden, D., J. O'callaghan and A. Dobson, 2002. Molecular cloning of a laccase isozyme gene from Pleurotus sajor-caju and expression in the heterologous Pichia pastoris host. *Microbiology*, 148(12):4003.

Sreekrishna, K., R. Brankamp, K. Kropp, D. Blankenship, J. Tsay, P. Smith, J. Wierschke, A. Subramaniam and L. Birkenberger, 1997. Strategies for optimal synthesis and secretion of heterologous proteins in the methylotrophic yeast *Pichia pastoris** 1. *Gene*, 190(1):55-62.

Sreekrishna, K., R. H. B. Potenz, J. A. Cruze, W. R. McCombie, K. A. Parker, L. Nelles, P. K. Mazzaferro, K. A. Holden, R. G. Harrison and P. J. Wood, 1988. High level expression of heterologous proteins in methylotrophic yeast *Pichia pastoris*. *J. Basic Microb.*, 28(4):265-278.

Stalbrand, H., A. Saloheimo, J. Vehmaanpera, B. Henrissat and M. Penttila, 1995. Cloning and expression in *Saccharomyces cerevisiae* of a *Trichoderma reesei* beta-mannanase gene containing a cellulose binding domain. *Appl. Environ. Microb.*, 61(3):1090.

Surribas, A., O. Cos, J. L. Montesinos and F. Valero, 2003. On-line monitoring of the methanol concentration in Pichia pastoris cultures producing an heterologous lipase by sequential injection analysis. *Biotechnol. Lett.*, 25(21):1795-1800.

Surribas, A., R. Ramon, J. L. Montesinos and F. Valero, 2007. Effect of methanol concentration on the production of *Rhizopus oryzae* lipase by a recombinant *Pichia pastoris* Mut(+) phenotype with a simple methanol model-based control. *J. Biotechnol.*, 131(2):S140-S140.

Tamaru, Y., T. Araki, H. Amagoi, H. Mori and T. Morishita, 1995. Purification and characterization of an extracellular beta-1, 4-mannanase from a marine bacterium, Vibrio sp. strain MA-138. *Appl. Environ. Microb.*, 61(12):4454.

Tan, Z., J. Li, M. Wu, C. Tang, H. Zhang and J. Wang, 2011. High-level heterologous expression of an alkaline lipase gene from *Penicillium cyclopium* PG37 in *Pichia pastoris*. *World J. Microb. Biot.*, 27(12):2767-2774.

Tanaka, H., T. Okuno, S. Moriyama, M. Muguruma and K. Ohta, 2004. Acidophilic xylanase from *Aureobasidium pullulans*: efficient expression and secretion in *Pichia pastoris* and mutational analysis. *J. Biosci. Bioeng.*, 98(5):338-343.

Tardy, F., W. Nasser, J. Robert-Baudouy and N. Hugouvieux-Cotte-Pattat, 1997. Comparative analysis of the five major Erwinia chrysanthemi pectate lyases: enzyme characteristics and potential inhibitors. *J. Bacteriol.*, 179(8):2503.

Trimble, R. B., C. Lubowski, C. R. Hauer, R. Stack, L. McNaughton, T. R. Gemmill and S. A. Kumar, 2004. Characterization of N-and O-linked glycosylation of recombinant human bile salt–stimulated lipase secreted by *Pichia pastoris*. *Glycobiology*, 14(3):265.

Ullah, A. H. J. and K Sethumadhavan, 2003. PhyA gene product of *Aspergillus ficuum* and *Peniophora lycii* produces dissimilar phytases. *Biochem. Bioph. Res. Co.*, 303(2):463-468.

Wang, X., Y. Sun, X. Shen, F. Ke, H. Zhao, Y. Liu, L. Xu and Y. Yan, 2012. Intracellular expression of Vitreoscilla hemoglobin improves production of *Yarrowia lipolytica* lipase LIP2 in a recombinant *Pichia pastoris*. *Enzyme Microb. Tech.*, 50(1):22-28.

Wang, Y., Z. Wang, G. C. Du, Z. Z. Hua, L. Liu, J. H. Li and J. Chen, 2009a. Enhancement of alkaline polygalacturonate lyase production in recombinant *Pichia pastoris* according to the ratio of methanol to cell concentration. *Bioresource Technol.*, 100(3):1343-1349.

Wang, Y., Z. Wang, Q. Xu, G. C Du, Z. Z. Hua, L. Liu, J.H. Li and J. Chen, 2009b. Lowering induction temperature for enhanced production of polygalacturonate lyase in recombinant *Pichia pastoris*. *Process Biochem.*, 44(9):949-954.

Wang, Z. H., Y. Wang, D. X. Zhang, J. H. Li, Z. Z. Hua, G. C. Du and J. Chen, 2010. Enhancement of cell viability and alkaline polygalacturonate lyase production by sorbitol co-feeding with methanol in *Pichia pastoris* fermentation. *Bioresource Technol.*, 101:1318-1323.

Wattad, C., D. Kobiler, A. Dinoor and D Prusky, 1997. Pectate lyase of*Colletotrichum gloeosporioidesattacking* avocado fruits: cDNA cloning and involvement in pathogenicity* 1. *Physiol. Mol. Plant P.*, 50(3):197-212.

White, C., N. Kempi and E. Komives, 1994. Expression of highly disulfide-bonded proteins in *Pichia pastoris*. *Structure (London, England: 1993)*, 2(11):1003.

White, C. E., M. J. Hunter, D. P. Meininger, L. R. White and E. A. Komives, 1995. Large-scale expression, purification and characterization of small fragments of thrombomodulin: the roles of the sixth domain and of methionine 388. *Protein Eng.*, 8(11):1177.

Witt, S., M. Singh and H. M. Kalisz, 1998. Structural and kinetic properties of nonglycosylated recombinant *Penicillium amagasakiense* glucose oxidase expressed in *Escherichia coli*. *Appl. Environ. Microb.*, 64(4):1405-1411.

Wittrup, M., M. Jahic and K. Hult, Enfors S.-O., 2007. Inducible versus constitutive expression of a lipase in *Pichia pastoris*: A comparative study using different fermentation techniques. *J. Biotechnol.*, 131(2):S149-S149.

Xu, L., X. Jiang, J. Yang, Y. Liu and Y. Yan, 2010. Cloning of a novel lipase gene, lipJ08, from *Candida rugosa* and expression in *Pichia pastoris* by codon optimization. *Biotechnol. Lett.*, 32(2):269-276.

Yang, J., B. Zhang and Y. Yan., 2009. Cloning and Expression of *Pseudomonas fluorescens* 26-2 Lipase Gene in *Pichia pastoris* and Characterizing for Transesterification. *Appl. Biochem. Biotech.*, 159(2):355-365.

Yao, J., 2010. Expression of pectate lyase from *Bacillus subtilis* in *Escherichia coli* and *Pichia pastoris*. PhD thesis.

Yenpetch, W., K. Packdibamrung, W. Zimmermann and P. Pongsawasdi, 2011. Biochemical properties and cyclodextrin production profiles of isoforms of cyclodextrin glycosyltransferase. *J. Incl. Phenom. Macro.*, 70(3-4):377-383.

Yu, M., S. Wen and T. Tan, 2010. Enhancing production of *Yarrowia lipolytica* lipase Lip2 in *Pichia pastoris*. *Eng. Life Sci.*, 10(5):458-464.

Yu, X. W., L. L. Wang and Y. Xu, 2009. *Rhizopus chinensis* lipase: Gene cloning, expression in *Pichia pastoris* and properties. *J. Mol. Catal. B-Enzym.*, 57(1-4):304-311.

Zakaria, M., S. Yamamoto and T. Yagi, 1998. Purification and characterization of an endo-1, 4-β-mannanase from *Bacillus subtilis* KU-1. *FEMS Microbiol. Lett.*, 158(1):25-31.

Zhang, G., L. Mao, Y. Zhao, Y. Xue and Y. Ma, 2010. Characterization of a thermostable xylanase from an alkaliphilic *Bacillus* sp. *Biotechnol. Lett.*, 32:1915-1920.

Zhang, G. M., Y. Hu, Y. H. Zhuang and X. E. Zhang, 2006. Molecular cloning and heterologous expression of an alkaline xylanase from *Bacillus pumilus* HBP8 in *Pichia pastoris*. *Biocatal. Biotransfor.*, 24(5):371-379.

Zhang, J., D. Wu, Z. Li, S. Chen, J. Chen and J. Wu, 2009. Expression of *Paenibacillus macerans* cyclodextrin glycosyltransferase in *Pichia pastoris* and *Bacillus subtilis*. *Chin. J. Biotechnol.*, 25(12):1948-1954.

Zhang, J. H. Y. Li, H. Liu, D. R. Liu and J. Chen, 2005. Isolation, phylogenetic analysis of a bacterium with high yield of alkaline pectate lyase and optimization of its culture conditions. *Chin. J. Appl. Environ. Biol.*, 11:354–358.

Zhao, W., J. Wang, R. Deng and X. Wang, 2008. Scale-up fermentation of recombinant *Candida rugosa* lipase expressed in *Pichia pastoris* using the GAP promoter. *J. Ind. Microbiol. Biot.*, 35(3):189-195.

Zhu, J. and M. Wu, 2007. Studies on the characterization of acidic β-mannanase from *Aspergillus niger*. *J. Food Sci. Biot.*, 26:21-25.

Zhuge, B., G. C. Du, W. Shen, J. Zhuge and J Chen, 2008. Expression of a *Bacillus subtilis* pectate lyase gene in *Pichia pastoris*. *Biochem. Eng. J.*, 40(1):92-98.

Chaen, H., T. Yamamoto, T. Nishimoto, T. Nakada, S. Fukuda, T. Sugimoto, M. Kurimoto, Y. Tujisaka, 1999. Purification and characterization of a novel phosphorylase, kojibiose phosphorylase, from *Thermoanaerobacter brockii. J. Appl. Glycosci.,* 46:423-429

In: Applications of Microbial Genes in Enzyme Technology ISBN: 978-1-62417-808-5
Editors: V.K.Gupta, M.G.Tuohy, G.D.Sharma et al.

Chapter 5

Biocatalysis: An Overview-Lipases, Amidases and Peptidases

Chandra S. Nayaka, Arakere C. Udayashankar, Raghavendra M. Puttaswamy[1,*], Nagaraju Shivaiah[2], Girish K. Subbaiah[3], Srinivas Chowdappa[4], Siddapura R. Niranjana and Harischandra S. Prakash

Department of Studies in Biotechnology, University of Mysore, Manasagangotri, Mysore, Karnataka, India
[1]Postgraduate Department of Microbiology, Maharani's Science College for Women, JLB Road, Mysore, Karnataka, India
[2]Department of Post graduate Studies and Research in Biochemistry, Tumkur University, Tumkur
[3]Department of Studies in Biochemistry, University of Mysore, Manasagangotri, Mysore, Karnataka, India
[4]Department of Studies in Microbiology and Biotechnology, Bangalore University, Jnana Bharathi Campus, Bangalore, Karnataka, India

Abstract

The demand for new and useful biocatalysts is steadily and rapidly increasing because microorganisms and enzymes to manufacture a large variety of chemical products which is referred to as white biotechnology is a new trend. Discovery of many novel enzymes by recombinant DNA technology which allows more efficient production, targeted or combinatorial alterations of individual enzymes, process development towards higher stability and volumetric productivity and synthesis routes in which one or all of the steps involves biocatalysis are increasingly precise and easy to use. Biocatalysis do not operate by different scientific principles from organic catalysts. In the present chapter

* Corresponding Author: Dr. M. Puttaswamy, Postgraduate Department of Microbiology, Maharani's Science College for Women, JLB Road, Mysore 570 005, Karnataka, India. E-mail: moonnayak@gmail.com.

we focus on synthesis, application and coding genes involved in the production of some industrially important biocatalysts.

Introduction

Biocatalysis – An Interdisciplinary Science

Biocatalysis is one of the main pillars of applied biotechnology, defined by the European Federation of Biotechnology as the *"integration of natural sciences and engineering sciences in order to achieve the application of organisms, cells, parts thereof and molecular analogs for products and services"*, and according to Europa-Bio, 2003, *"White Biotechnology is the application of Nature's toolset to industrial production"*. Both definitions have in common that biotechnology and thus biocatalysis are looked at as interdisciplinary sciences. Application of biotechnology requires knowledge in the areas shown in Figure 1.

It is a multidisciplinary subject requires knowledge of traditional subjects such as biology, chemistry, physics and mathematics new ones such as bioinformatics and material science. Even the key technology *nanoscience* which has promising applications in medicine and electronics is important in biotechnology. Nanotechnology would not exist without competent chemists knowing how to prepare nanoparticles for a certain application which are then analyzed for their properties (structure, magnetic behavior *etc.*) by physicists.

Millions of years of evolution have generated an unimaginable multiplicity of organisms. Biocatalysts regulate and control all metabolic reactions in microorganisms, plants and animals in a selective way and make the necessary high reaction rates possible. Reaction conditions are either mild or adapted to the special requirements of an organism. A few years ago, biocatalysis was restricted to those enzymes that might be captured from nature, but now scenario is changed as scientists now know how to apply mutagenesis and recombinant technologies to have a major impact on the activity, selectivity, and thus yield by biocatalysis.

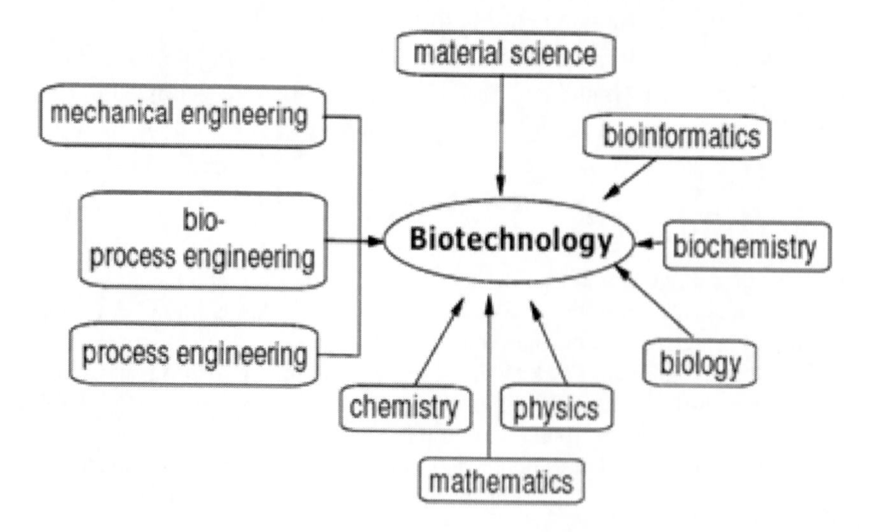

Figure 1. Scientific disciplines contributing to research and development in biotechnology; they are of relevance for biocatalysis.

The use of enzymes in organic synthesis is now widely accepted. As more and more synthetic research embraces the realization that enzymes are simply another source of catalysis that can be as robust as others, sometimes more so, then their use will continue to flourish.

The other reason for chemical producers seeking new and renewable feed stocks is the escalating raw material prices and concern towards environment and sustainable production processes. Simultaneously, scientists have made major strides in manipulating enzymes to the desired end.

The use of biocatalysis for industrial synthetic chemistry is on the verge of significant growth, because biocatalytic processes now carried out in organic solvents as well as aqueous environments, so that apolar organic compounds as well as water-soluble compounds can be modified selectively and efficiently with enzymes and biocatalytically active cells. As the use of biocatalysis for industrial chemical synthesis becomes easier, several chemical companies have begun to increase significantly the number and sophistication of the biocatalytic processes used in their synthesis operations.

Finally, the redesign of enzyme active sites and the alteration of activities should over the next few years become as common place as the modification of ligand structures in transition metal complex catalysts.

A primary goal of such work should be the tailoring of specificity, which is often a challenge neglected in favour of work aimed at enhancing activity. In this regard, subtle yet important strategic aspects need to be considered. The present chapter aims to give additional details about the biocatalysis and their applications, advantage and disadvantages of biocatalysts and important industrial application of amidases, peptidases and lipases as biocatalysts.

Definition

Biocatalysis can be defined as utilization of natural catalysts, such as protein enzymes, to carryout chemical transformations on organic compounds. Both enzymes that have been more or less isolated and enzymes still residing inside living cells are employed for biocatalysis.

History

Biocatalysis underpins some of the oldest chemical transformations known to humans. The oldest records of brewing are about 6000 years old and refer to the Sumerians. The employment of enzymes and whole cells has been important for many industries for centuries.

The most obvious usages have been in the food and beverage industries where the production of wine, beer, cheese etc., is dependent on the effects of the enzymes of microbial origin. More than one hundred years ago, biocatalysis was employed to do chemical transformations on non-natural man-made organic compounds, and for the last 30 years have seen a substantial increase in the application of biocatalysis to produce fine chemicals, especially for the pharmaceutical industry (wikipedia.org).

Table 1. Novel Microbial Enzymes (Ogawa and Sakayu, 1999)

Product	Enzyme	Origin
D-Amino acids (CF)	D-Hydantoinase D-Decarbamoylase	*Pseudomonas putida*, *Bacillus* sp. *Blastobacter* sp., *Agrobacterium* sp.
L-3,4-Dihydroxyphenylalanine	ß-Tyosinase	*Erwinia herbicola*
L-Serine (CF, H)	Serine hydroxy-methyltransferase	*Methylobacterium* sp.
Acrylamide (Ch)	Nitrile hydratase	*Rhodococcus rhodochrous*
Nicotinamide (H)	Nitrile hydratase	*Rhodococcus rhodochrous*
Acrylic acid (Ch)	Nitrilase	*Rhodococcus rhodochrous*
Nicotinic acid	Nitrilase	*Rhodococcus rhodochrous*
2S,3R-3-(4-Methoxyphenylglycidic acid) methyl ester	Lipase	*Serratia marcescens*
Carbacephem (H)	o-Phthalyl amidase	*Xanthobacter agilis*
Chiral epoxide	Alkene monooxygenase	*Nocardia corallina*
R-2-(4 Hydroxyphenoxy) propionic acid (Ch)	Hydroxylase	*Beauveria bassiana*
S-p-Chlorophenylethanol	Alcohol dehydrogenase	*Rhodococcus erythropolis*
Chiral 2,3-dichloro-1-propanol	Halyohydrin hydrogenhalidelyase	*Alcaligenes* sp., *Pseudomonas* sp.
S-1,2-Pentanediol	Alcohol dehydrogenase and reductase	*Candida parapsilosis*
D-Pantoic acid (H)	Lactonase	*Fusarium oxysporum*
Theobromine (CF) Adenosylmethionine (H)	Oxygenase Adenosylmethionine synthetase	*Pseudomonas putida* *Saccharomyces sake*
Adenosylhomocysteine (H)	Adenosylhomocysteine hydrolase	*Alcaligenes faecalis*
Adenine arabinoside	Nucleoside phosphorylase	*Enterobacter aerogenes*
Ribavirine (H)	Nucleoside phosphorylase	*Erwinia carotovora*
5-Methyluridine	Nucleoside phosphorylase	*Erwinia carotovora*
Arachidonic acid	Multistep conversion	*Mortierella alpina*
Eicosapentaenoic acid	Multistep conversion	*Mortierella alpina*

CF - commodity food; H - health related; Ch - chemical product or intermediate.

Advantages of Biocatalysis

Enzymes involved in biocatalysis are highly active at room temperature and gave access to new chiral building blocks such as amines, alcohols and hydroxy carboxylic acids, where no access was available before and now it is known as the most economical and ecologically feasible production route in industrial sector. Molecular biological tools are used to discover more stable enzymes and it is also employed to increase the stability of enzymes, because stability is directly related with more bulk products production. So, in the next five to 10 years, it is believed that more bulk chemical products will be synthesized by enzymatic processes.

Enzyme yielding microbes are being found in environments where they have adapted to unusual conditions or high concentrations of chemicals. Recently the technology has been available to design biocatalysts on the basis of selecting microorganisms from extreme environments such as archaebacteria and changing their catalytic profiles by genetic modification, if necessary. Archaebacteria are the highly neglected group of microorganisms in industrial application. But recently the mindset has been changed to exploit enzymes of these extreme environment loving bacteria for biocatalysis; one example is Taq polymerase isolated from *Thermus aquaticus* which is widely used in PCR technique. This shows that microbes, which can be grown inexpensively, have consortia of biocatalysts which need to be exploited in future. These microbes can be conveniently engineered to obtain different types of products including aromatics. When a particular biosynthetic route of these microbes are understood, it is easy to go back to these microbes, look for the genes and pathways of interest and then move them into an organism well suited for production process of our interest by genetic engineering technique.

Together with high-throughput screening methods, it is possible to adapt biocatalysts in a relatively short time to the conditions needed in chemical synthesis and this is especially important if reactions are not run under aqueous conditions, which is an enzyme's natural environment.

Biocatalysis is applied in production of fatty acid-derived esters and ceramides for personal care applications and its oligomers/silicones unit produces silicone acrylates as paint additives. Polyglycerine ester is chemically attainable by a multistep process using protecting groups, which is difficult and expensive. But now this being an active ingredient in deodorant applications can be synthesized by newest enzymatic processes which are more feasible with few steps involved in synthesis.

Biocatalysis also has many advantages because these enzymes display three major types of selectivities:

- *Chemoselectivity:* Since enzymes acts on a single type of functional group, biocatalytic reactions tend to be "cleaner" and laborious purification of product(s) from impurities emerging through side-reactions can largely be omitted (Peter and Voss, 2001).
- *Regioselectivity and Diastereoselectivity:* Due to their complex three-dimensional structure, enzymes may distinguish between functional groups which are chemically situated in different regions of the substrate molecule (Wolf and Thorleif, 2009).
- *Enantioselectivity:* Since almost all enzymes are made from L-amino acids, enzymes are chiral catalysts. As a consequence, any type of chirality present in the substrate molecule is "recognized" upon the formation of the enzyme-substrate complex. Thus a prochiral substrate transformed into an optically active product and both enantiomers of a racemic substrate may react at different rates (Secundo, 2009).

The above reasons and especially the latter one is one of the major reasons why synthetic chemists have become interested in biocatalysis. This interest in turn is mainly due to the need to synthesise enantiopure compounds as chiral building blocks for drugs and agrochemicals (wikipedia.org).

Another important advantage of biocatalysts is that they are environmentally acceptable, being completely degraded in the environment. Furthermore the enzymes act under mild conditions, which minimizes problems of undesired side-reactions such as decomposition, isomerization, racemization and rearrangement, which often plague traditional methodology (Straathof, et al., 2002).

Asymmetric Biocatalysis in Synthesis of Enentiopure Drugs

The use of biocatalysis to obtain enantiopure compounds can be divided into two different methods;

1. Kinetic resolution of a racemic mixture
2. Biocatalysed asymmetric synthesis

In kinetic resolution of a racemic mixture, the presence of a chiral object (the enzyme) converts one of the enantiomers into product at a greater reaction rate than the other enantiomer.

Disadvantages of Biocatalysis

1. Biocatalysts are often not sufficiently stable in the desired media
2. Very few biocatalysts exist for the desired reactions from available substrates to
3. targeted products, and
4. Development cycles are too long for new and improved biocatalysts because of
   - Poor operational stability
   - Unwanted reactions with impure preparations
   - Low volumetric productivity
   - High cost
   - Cells and enzymes are
     - Unstable at high temperatures
     - Unstable at extreme pH values
     - Unstable in aggressive solvents
     - Inhibited by some metal ions
     - Hydrolysed by peptidases
   - Some enzymes require expensive co-substrates
   - When inhaled or ingested enzymes are, as all foreign proteins, potential allergens

Lipases

Lipases, which are subclass of esterases are water-soluble enzyme that catalyzes the hydrolysis of ester bonds in water–insoluble lipid substrates. These enzymes are of choice for organic chemists, pharmacists, biophysicists, biochemical and process engineers, biotechnologists, microbiologists and biochemists. Lipases (triacylglycerol acylhydrolases) belong to the class of serine hydrolases and therefore do not require any cofactor. There are several lipase activities exist in nature, especially when the phospholipases and sphingomyelinases are considered.

Lipases differ from classic esterases in that their natural substrates are insoluble in water. Furthermore, esterases are just active in homogeneous aqueous phase, while lipases display maximal activity only at the water/oil interface. Lipases are the most often applied biocatalysts in biotechnology and organic chemistry, this is not only based on their high chemo-, regio- and stereoselectivity, but also on their interfacial activation because of which lipases represent a class of enzymes that is particularly suitable for the application in non-aqueous solvents including $scCO_2$ and in heterogeneous catalysis.

Lipases are readily available in large quantities since they are ubiquitous and can be isolated in high yields from microbial organisms such as fungi and bacteria. Finally, their use shows high commercial promise as many potential applications in the field of drugs, cosmetics and flavours exist.

Extensive research work has been carried out on plant, animal and microbial lipases, particularly bacterial and fungal lipases (Winkler and Gubernator, 1994). Although pancreatic lipases have been traditionally used for various purposes, it is well established that microbial lipases are preferred for commercial applications due to their multifold properties, easy extraction procedures and potential of unlimited supply.

Microbial Lipases

Bacterial Lipases

Compared to plant and fungal lipases, a relatively small number of bacterial lipases have been well studied and reviewed (Godtfredson, 1990). Generally, bacterial lipases are glycoproteins but some extracellular bacterial lipases are lipoproteins. The production of extracellular lipases from bacteria is often dependent on nitrogen and carbon sources, inorganic salts, presence of lipids, temperature and availability of oxygen. Majority of the bacterial lipases reported are constitutive and inhibited by some serine hydrolase inhibitors. Most bacterial lipases are non specific in substrate and a few are thermostable.

Different genera of bacteria including *Streptomyces* spp. produce lipase but the following genera have been well exploited for lipase production: *Achromobacter* spp., *Alcaligenes* spp., *Arthrobacter* spp., *Pseudomonas* spp. and *Chromobacterium* spp. (Godtfredson, 1990). *Staphylococcus* spp. and *Pseudomonas* spp. have been specifically investigated for commercial exploitation. Among the *Staphylococci, Staph. aureus* and *Staph. hyicus* are two important species described for lipase production. Lipases purified from these organisms have molecular weights ranging between 34 kDa on SDS-PAGE. They are usually stimulated by divalent ions such as Ca^{2+} and the chelator EDTA which acts as an inhibitor. The pH-optima of these enzymes vary between 7.5 and 9.0 and are lipoprotein in nature (Brune and Gotz, 1992).

Among *Pseudmonads*, three important species of *Pseudomonas* are *Ps. fragi*, *Ps. fluorescens* and *Ps. aeruginosa* have been exploited for production. The lipase from *Ps. fragi* was purified 68-fold by acidification of the culture supernatant, followed by ammonium sulphate precipitation and finally purified by sepharose CL-6B chromatography with 48% recovery. The purified lipase consisted of a single sub-unit with molecular weight 33kDa as determined by SDS-PAGE. The lipase was inhibited by Zn^{2+}, Fe^{2+}, Al^{3+}, whereas Ca^{2+} activated the hydrolysis of long-chain fatty acid esters (Nishio *et al.*, 1987).

Fungal Lipases

Many researchers have exploited fungi as valuable source of lipase due to its thermal and pH stability, substrate specificity and activity in organic solvents. Fungal lipases have benefits over bacterial ones due to the fact that present day technology favours the use of batch fermentation and low cost extraction methods. In this regard, a good number of fungi have been screened for lipase production (Kazlauskas and Bornscheuer, 1998). The chief producers of commercial lipase are *Aspergillus niger*, *A. carneus*, *Candida cylindracea*, *Humicola lanuginose*, *Mucor miehei*, *Rhizopus arrhizus*, *R. delemer*, *R. japonicus*, *R. niveus* and *R. oryzae*.

Species of the mould *Aspergillus* are well known lipase producers. Most of the experiments reported deal with the lipase from *Aspergillus niger* whose intracellular and extracellular lipases are 1,3-regio specific (Bradoo *et al.*, 1999). *Aspergillus oryzae* was found to be an efficient host for the heterologus expression of the lipases from *Rhizomucor miehei* and *Humicola lanuginose*. They have demonstrated that *Aspergillus terreus* produces a lipases that is thermostable (stable at 60^0C and 70^0 C for 15 minutes), pH stable (5.5 - 10.5), 1,3-regio-specific and capable of trans-esterification and esterification in organic solvents. This enzyme catalyses deacetylation of peracetates of polyphenolic ketonic compounds at both *ortho* and *para* positions and it also distinguishes between phenolic esters and the esters of aromatic acid and alcohol.

Structure

The active site, which is also referred as catalytic triad, is located in a lipophilic region of the lipase. In aqueous environments, the triad is buried in the interior of the enzyme and covered by a hydrophilic lid-like structural element in order to avoid direct contact between the hydrophobic region and water. Accordingly, the lipase is inactive or displays low activity in this state. Furthermore, there is a structure in which the active site is exposed permitting the substrates to gain access to the catalytic region. The conformational change is induced by an oil/water or lipid/water interface, which initiates the structural rearrangement such as the movement of the lid in order to reveal the hydrophobic part. In a few cases, there is evidence for both the closed and the open form from X-ray investigations on crystal structures. Diverse array of genetically distinct lipase enzymes are found in nature and represent several types of protein folds and catalytic mechanisms, most are built on an α/β hydrolase fold and employ a chymotrypsin-like hydrolysis mechanism involving a serine nucleophile, an acid residue (usually aspartic acid) and a histidine. The lipase genes from *Staph. hyicus* and *Staph. aureus* have been cloned, sequenced, and compared with other lipases. This revealed two conserved domains separated by 100 amino acids which are likely to form active site. Putative active site residues around His 269 and Ser 369 of the *Staph. hyicus* lipase are highly conserved in the *Staph. aureus* and several eukaryotic lipases (Saxena *et al.*, 2003).

Distribution of Lipases in Human Physiology

Lipases are involved in diverse biological processes ranging from routine metabolism of dietary triglycerides to cell signaling and inflammation. Thus, some lipase activities are confined to specific compartments within cells while others work in extracellular spaces, few examples are as follows

- Lysosomal lipase, the enzyme is confined within an organelle called the lysosome.
- Other lipase enzymes, such as pancreatic lipases are secreted into extracellular spaces where they serve to process dietary lipids into more simple forms that can be more easily absorbed and transported throughout the body.
- Fungi and bacteria may secrete lipases to facilitate nutrient absorption from the external medium (or in examples of pathogenic microbes, to promote invasion of a new host).
- Certain wasp and bee venoms contain phospholipases that enhance the "biological payload" of injury and inflammation delivered by a sting.
- As biological membranes are integral to living cells and are largely composed of phospholipids, lipases play important roles in cell biology.

Specificity of Lipases for Substrates

Specificity of lipases is controlled by the molecular properties of the enzyme, structure of the substrate and factors affecting binding of the enzyme to the substrate. Substrate specificity of lipases is often crucial to their application for analytical and industrial purposes. Specificity is shown both with respect to either fatty acyl or alcohol parts of their substrates.

Many microbes produce two or more extracellular lipases with different fatty acid specificities. It is reported that tributyrin is hydrolysed slowly by some microbial lipases and *M. miehei* lipase preferentially releases butyric acid from milk fat especially at low pH. *Geotrichum candidum* produces a lipase, which shows pronounced specificity for the hydrolysis of esters of a particular type of long-chain fatty acid. Lipases show both regio- and stereospecificity with respect to the alcohol moiety of their substrates. Lipases can be divided into two groups on the basis of the regiospecificity exhibited acylglycerol substrates.

Lipases in the first group catalyse the complete breakdown of triacylglycerol to glycerol and free fatty acids together with diacylglycerols and monoacylglycerol as intermediates in the reaction. These intermediates do not accumulate since they are hydrolysed more rapidly than the triacylglycerol. Examples of the first group of lipases include lipase from *Candida rugosa* (Formerly *Candida cylindracea*). The second group of lipases release fatty acids regiospecifically from the outer 1 and 3 positions of acylglycerols. These lipases hydrolyse triacylglycerol to give free fatty acids, 1,2-diacylglycerols and 2-monoacylglycerol. Many extracellular microbial lipases, such as those from *Aspergillus niger* and *Rhizopus arrhizus* shows 1,3-(regio)-specificity. Lipases excreted by *R. japonicus*, *Mucor miehei*, *Humicola lanuginosa*, *Chromobacterium viscosum*, and *Ps. fluorescens* are also 1,3-(regio)-specific. Partial stereospecificity in the hydrolysis of triacyl glycerols has been observed in *R. arrhizus*, *R. delemar*, *C. rugosa* and *Ps. aeruginosa*. Owing to this property, these enzymes can be used to isolate optically pure esters and alcohols (Saxena *et al.* 1999).

Application of Lipases

The industrial lipases are special classes of esterase enzymes that act on fats and oils, and hydrolyse them initially into the substituted glycerides and fatty acids and finally by total hydrolysis into glycerol and fatty acids. Lipases perform essential roles in the digestion, transport and processing of dietary lipids (e.g. triglycerides, fats, oils) in most- if not all- living organisms. Genes encoding lipases are even present in certain viruses. Lipases catalyse the hydrolysis of triglycerides into diglycerides, monoglycerides, glycerol and fatty acids, and under certain conditions the reverse reaction leads to esterification and formation of glycerides from glycerol and fatty acids. Most lipases act at a specific position on the glycerol backbone of a lipid substrate. In the example of human pancreatic lipase, which is the main enzyme responsible for breaking down fats in the human digestive system and it is involved in converting triglyceride substrates found in oils from food to monoglycerides and free fatty acids. Lipases are not involved in any anabolic processes. Since this enzyme acts at the oil–water interface, it can be used as a catalyst for the preparation of industrially important compounds. As lipases act on ester bonds, they have been used in fat splitting, interesterification (transesterification), development of different flavours in cheese, improving pallatability of beef fat for making dog food. A current application involves using lipases in water-deficient organic solvents for synthesizing different value-added esters from organic acids and alcohols. Most lipases display a wide substrate spectrum and have the ability to reversibly hydrolyse various esters. Apart from their hydrolytic activity, they generally catalyse acyl transfer reactions, where esters serve as acyl donors for the acylation of acyl acceptors such as alcohols, thiols and water (in the case of hydrolysis). Their pH optimum is generally between 5 and 9. The latter phenomenon is known as interfacial activation of lipases, which is based on at least two different conformational structures. Lipases have several applications in industry and important areas of the industrial application of microbial lipases are given in table 2.

Table 2. Industrial application of microbial lipases

Industry	Effect	Product
Bakery	Flavour improvement and shelf-life prolongation	Bakery products
Beverages	Improved aroma	Beverages
Chemical	Enantioselectivity	Chiral building blocks and chemicals
Cleaning	Synthesis Hydrolysis	Chemicals Removal of cleaning agents like surfactants
Cosmetics	Synthesis	Emulsifiers, moisturizing agents
Diary	Hydrolysis of milk fat Cheese ripening Modification of butter fat	Flavour agents Cheese Butter
Fats and oils	Trans-esterification Hydrolysis	Cocoa butter, margarine Fatty acids, glycerol, mono- and diglycerides
Food dressing	Quality improvement	Mayonnaise, dressings and whippings
Health Food	Trans esterification	Health food
Leather	Hydrolysis	Leather products
Meat and Fish	Flavour development and fat removal	Meat and fish products
Paper	Hydrolysis	Paper products
Pharmaceuticals	Trans-etherification Hydrolysis	Specialty lipids Digestive aids

Amidases

An amidase is an enzyme that catalyzes the chemical reaction as shown below

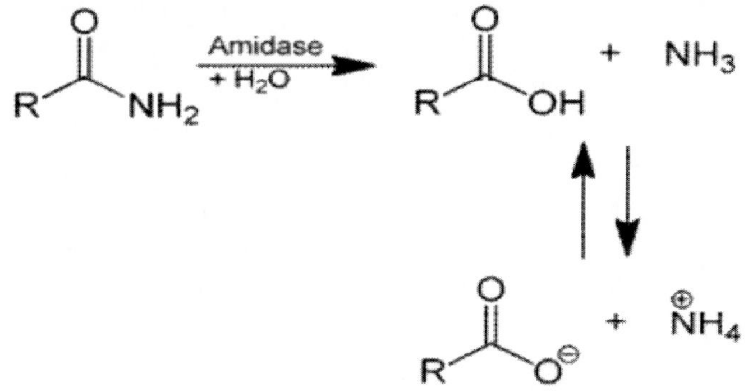

Monocarboxylic acid amide + $H_2O \rightleftharpoons$ Monocarboxylate + NH_3

Thus, monocarboxylic acid amide and water are the two substrates and monocarboxylate and ammonia are the two end products of the reaction.

This enzyme belongs to the family of hydrolases, those acting on carbon-nitrogen bonds other than peptide bonds, specifically in linear amides. The systematic name of this enzyme class is acylamide amidohydrolase and other names in common use include acylamidase, acylase, amidohydrolase, deaminase, fatty acylamidase, and N-acetylaminohydrolase.

Function

This enzyme participates in six metabolic pathways: Urea cycle and metabolism of amino groups, phenylalanine metabolism, tryptophan metabolism, cyanoamino acid metabolism, benzoate degradation via coagulation and styrene degradation.

Substrate Specificity

The substrate specificities of two fatty acyl amidases partially purified from the slime mold *Dictyostelium discoideum* have been studied. The amidase act on lipopolysaccharide derivatives, such as (4'- O-phosphoryl-N-beta-hydroxymyristyl-D-glucosaminyl)-beta-(1 leads to 6) - N-beta-hydroxymyristyl-D-glucosamine-1-phosphate (III) in a sequential manner. Amidase-I removes the beta-hydroxymyristyl residue present on the amino group adjacent to the 1-phosphate and the product formed is a substrate for amidase-II; the latter removes the remaining beta- hydroxymyristyl residue from the distal amino group. Compound III itself is resistant to amidase-II. Removal of the C-1 or C-4 phosphate groups does not influence recognition by the amidases or their sequential action. Both amidases are specific for long chain fatty amide linkages. Thus, a formyl group on the glucosamine amino group adjacent to the C-1 phosphate is not hydrolyzed by amidase-I; however, this substituent does not hinder the action of amidase-II on the distal fatty acyl amide. The presence of the beta-hydroxyl group in myristyl- amide residues is not required for hydrolysis. Further, while amidase-I requires disaccharide structures for its action, amidase-II acts on monosaccharides as well. Finally, the effects of a variety of substrate analogs and divalent ions on the activity of the enzymes are reported (Verret et al., 1982).

Previous studies on the substrate specificity of penicillin amidase (EC 3.5.1.11) from *Escherichia coli* have shown the enzyme to be capable of catalyzing the synthesis and hydrolysis of structurally diverse amides of the general form R-CO--NH-R'. The substrate specificity of the wild-type enzyme is largely determined by the characteristics of the acyl moiety, R. Substrates with hydrophobic acyl moieties are preferred to those with functional groups that depending on the reaction pH, can be polar (ionized). The means for the deliberate modification of the substrate specificity of penicillin amidase are required for the use of penicillin amidase in the semi-synthesis of 3-lactam antibiotics and other synthetic reactions (Forney 1989).

Amidases and Its Usages

Ammonia production is of great importance for the gastric pathogen *Helicobacter pylori* as a nitrogen source, a compound protecting against gastric acidity and as a cytotoxic molecule. In addition to urease, *H. pylori* possess two aliphatic amidases responsible for ammonia production: AmiE, a classical amidase and AmiF, a new type of formamidase. Both enzymes are part of a regulatory network consisting of nitrogen metabolism enzymes including urease and arginase.

Since amidases are found only in *Helicobacter* species able to colonize the stomach, their acquisition might be related to selective pressure in this particular gastric environment (Bury-Moné et al., 2003).

Enantioselectivity of Amidases

Stolz *et al*., (1998) have conducted the enantioselectivities of different enzymes. For their study they used different enrichment cultures with various nitriles as sole source of nitrogen, succinate or a mixture of sugars as carbon sources and soil samples as inocula. It was attempted to obtain a relationship between the selective nitrogen source and the enzyme systems which were synthesized by the isolates and also enzyme specificities and enantioselectivities. Various strains were obtained which harbored enantioselective nitrilases, nitrile-hydratases or amidases. The enantioselective amidase from the isolate *Rhodococcus erythropolis* MP50 and the enantioselective nitrile hydratase from *Agrobacterium tumefaciens* d3 were studied in greater detail. The purified amidase from *R. erythropolis* MP50 hydrolysed 2-phenylpropionamide, naproxen amide and ketoprofen amide with enantiomeric excesses (ee)>99% up to 49% conversion of the respective substrates. In the presence of hydroxylamine, the amidase also formed the corresponding hydroxamates enantioselectively. These chiral hydroxamates could be chemically converted by a Lossen rearrangement into chiral amines. The partially purified nitrile hydratase from *A. tumefaciens* d3 converted 2-phenylbutyronitrile and ketoprofen nitrile to the corresponding *S*-amides with ee values >90% at 30% conversion of the respective substrate.

Amidases in Preparation of Commercial Semi-Synthetic Antibiotics

For the preparation of a wide variety of commercial semi-synthetic antibiotics, the side-chain phenylacetic acid of penicillin G and the D-α-aminoadipic acid of cephalosporin C are first removed enzymatically to prepare the crucial intermediates 6-aminopenicillanic acid and 7-aminocephalosporanic acid. Both enzymatic processes replace classical chemical routes which were applied for many years to hydrolyse the amide bonds attaching the side chains. The phenylacetic acid is cleaved off the penicillin G with the enzyme penicillin G amidase (Ohno 1985).

Amidases in Peptidoglycan Synthesis

Most bacteria have multiple peptidoglycan hydrolases capable of cleaving covalent bonds in peptidoglycan sacculi or its fragments. Bacterial peptidoglycan hydrolases form a vast and highly diverse group of enzymes capable of cleaving bonds in polymeric peptidoglycan (sacculi) and/or its soluble fragments (Shockman and H¨oltje, 1994; Shockman *et al.*, 1996). They participate in bacterial cell wall growth and its regulation and also in different lysis phenomena.

It is often difficult to assign a distinct function to a peptidoglycan hydrolase for several reasons. First, many bacteria possess a high number of hydrolases and they appear to have redundant roles (Smith *et al.*, 2000). Second, a hydrolase may have more than one function. For example, *E. coli* has five N-acetylmuramyl-L-alanine amidases, six membrane-bound lytic transglycosylases and three peptidoglycan endopeptidases, all of which appear to contribute at variable extent to cleavage of the septum during cell division to allow separation of daughter cells (Heidrich *et al.*, 2002).

Genetic Regulation

Control of production of peptidoglycan hydrolases is important but in many cases is overridden by biochemical regulation as many of the enzymes are found to be associated with their substrate but controlled at the level of activity. Most of the enzymes involved in sporulation and germination are controlled at the transcriptional level by the sporulation-specific cascade of sigma factors that allows their production only in particular sporangial compartments and at particular times for their exact functions. During vegetative growth, the control of peptidoglycan hydrolase expression has been particularly illuminating in the determination of the role of some enzymes (Meisel *et al.*, 2003).

Coregulation with Flagellation and Motility

In *B. subtilis*, most autolysin activity is produced as the cells enter the stationary phase (Foster, 1992). The two major enzymes are LytC and LytD, an amidase and N-acetylglucosaminidase, respectively (Margot and Karamata, 1992, Margot *et al.*, 1994). Their production coincides with major morphological and physiological changes to the cells such as the short chains break up into single cell, they become motile, secrete large amounts of extracellular enzymes and develop natural competence. Many of these processes are coregulated by the alternative sigma factor SigD (Serizawa *et al.*, 2004). SigD controls expression of the 'flagellar, chemotaxis and motility regulon'.

Transcription of the lytABC operon proceeds from two promoters out of which one is controlled by sD, which accounts for 70–90% of the transcription during growth (Lazarevic *et al.*, 1992, Kuroda and Sekiguchi, 1993). Ninety-five percent of lytD transcription is controlled by sD (Margot *et al.*, 1994). The physiological rationale for the coregulation of the autolysins with motility lies in the phenotype of their respective mutants. The enzymes are required for dechaining as cells linked together are unable to chemotax effectively, the so-called pushmi-pullyu effect (Blackman *et al.*, 1998).

Elusive Essential Enzyme

For many years, it has been proposed that hydrolysis of existing bonds within peptidoglycan is necessary to allow wall expansion, cell growth and division (Shockman and H¨oltje, 1994). In number of Gram-positive species, a homologous essential sensor regulator has been characterized (originally called YycGF) (Fabret and Hoch, 1998; Martin *et al.*, 1999; Clausen *et al.*, 2003). Analysis of its regulon has revealed the control of a number of putative and proven peptidoglycan hydrolases (Howell *et al.*, 2003; Dubrac and Msadek, 2004). This alluded to their individual or combined essentiality for growth. In *Strep. pneumoniae* PcsB is essential and controlled by YycGF (VikSR) (Ng *et al.*, 2003). The hydrolytic bond specificity of PcsB is unknown but it contains a CHAP domain present in several hydrolases that may have amidase function (Kajimura *et al.*, 2005). Depletion of PcsB results in deregulated cell wall synthesis and bacteriostasis (Ng *et al.*, 2004). Whether the essentiality of PcsB is due directly to its hydrolytic properties and molecular basis for its role are currently unknown.

Programmed Cell Death

The LytSR sensor regulator of *Staph. aureus* has been proposed to respond to a decline in Proton Motive Force (PMF) across the cell membrane (Patton *et al.*, 2006). LytSR controls the expression of lrgAB, which encode a postulated antiholin system (Brunskill and Bayles, 1996). LrgAB may interact with their cognate holins (CidAB) and prevent cell lysis. Under conditions of stress such as the presence of penicillin, CidAB may collapse the PMF and allow access of autolysins to their substrate or deregulation of activity resulting in cellular lysis (Rice and Bayles, 2003).

Peptidoglycan Hydrolase Targeting

Secretion of peptidoglycan hydrolases occurs primarily by the well-established Sec dependent pathway but can also use the TAT system and in some cases there is no signal sequence (Smith and Foster, 1995, Bernhardt and de Boer, 2003). The interaction between the enzymes and the cell wall is crucial for their activity. Several conserved mechanisms have been found for a number of enzymes. Covalent binding of autolysins to their substrate, which may render the enzymes inactive until they are further processed, is rare but has been reported for the GSLE of *Bacillus megaterium* (Foster and Johnstone, 1988) and a sortase-linked enzyme from *Strep. mutans* (Catt and Gregory, 2005). Much more common is the use of conserved, often repeated, motifs or domains for ionic attachment to peptidoglycan or other cell wall components. Many enzymes have an overall basic charge at neutral pH, which may enhance their binding to negatively charged cell wall components.

In *E. coli*, five lytic transglycosylases are made as lipoproteins and they are targeted to the outer membrane. It has been postulated that this specific orientation in respect of the peptidoglycan opposite to the biosynthetic machinery would allow cell wall expansion and growth (Lommatzsch *et al.*, 1997).

Peptidoglycan Hydrolase Processing

Proteolytic processing of enzymes is common not only in their activation but also in their stability in response to a changing environment. The major autolysin of *Staph. aureus* called Atl is produced as a 138 kDa proenzyme that undergoes proteolytic processing to generate the two extracellular lytic enzymes found in the supernatant of S. aureus cultures identified as the 51 kDa endo-beta-N-acetylglucosaminidase and a 62 kDa N-acetylmuramyl-L-alanine amidase (Foster, 1995, Oshida *et al.*, 1995). Pro-Atl, amidase and glucosaminidase display peptidoglycan hydrolase activity in zymogram analysis. The signal peptide of 138 kDa pro-Atl is first cleaved, followed by further processing through intermediate forms of 115 and 85 kDa to result in the mature active 51 and 62 kDa cell surface-associated, and secreted, glucosaminidase and amidase (Komatsuzawa *et al.*, 1997). Proteases have also been postulated to maintain a balance between production and degradation of peptidoglycan hydrolases during growth of *B. subtilis* to maintain appropriate activity levels (Yamamoto *et al.*, 2003). Proteolytic cleavage of the lipoprotein precursor of a membrane bound lytic transglycosylase of *E. coli*, MltB, results in the formation of a soluble lytic transglycosylase (Slt35). It is not known whether this 'periplasmic solubilization' of MltB has a particular physiological role (Ehlert *et al.*, 1995).

Peptidases

Peptidases can either break specific peptide bonds (*limited proteolysis*) depending on the amino acid sequence of a protein, or break down a complete peptide to amino acids (*unlimited proteolysis*). This activity can be a destructive change, abolishing a protein's function or digesting it to its principal components; it can be an activation of a function, or it can be a signal in a signaling pathway.

Proteases, also known as proteinases or proteolytic enzymes, are a large group of enzymes. Proteases belong to the class of enzymes known as hydrolases, which catalyse the reaction of hydrolysis of various bonds with the participation of a water molecule.

Proteases are involved in digesting long protein chains into short fragments, splitting the peptide bonds that link amino acid residues. Some of them can detach the terminal amino acids from the protein chain (exopeptidases, such as aminopeptidases and carboxypeptidase A); the others attack internal peptide bonds of a protein (endopeptidases, such as trypsin, chymotrypsin, pepsin, papain and elastase).

Peptidases in Living Organisms

Enzymes that catalyze the hydrolysis of peptide bonds are generally referred to as proteases or peptidases. They are widely distributed in nature, where a variety of biological functions and processes depend on their activity. Regardless of the complexity of the organism, peptidases in general are essential at every stage in the life of every individual cell, since all protein molecules produced must be proteolytically processed and eventually degraded. Therefore, it is not surprising that throughout cellular life forms, genes encoding proteases occur at a relatively high frequency ranging from 1.15% (*Pirellula* spp.) to 6.06% (*Buchnera aphidicola*) of the total gene count with the average being about 3%.

Among bacterial species which are pathogenic for humans, the number of peptidases known and putatively functional ranges from 9-15 in small genomes, such as those of the *Mycoplasma* spp. (1.45-2.07% of the total gene count) to 98 (2.64%) and 121 (2.85%) in genomes such as *Ps. aeruginosa* and *E. coli* respectively. Fortunately, only a small fraction of the expressed peptidases in any pathogen impose a direct or indirect deleterious effect on their human host and may therefore be considered as a virulence factor. With respect to the number of protease genes, the record in the microbial world goes to *Bacillus cereus* where 179 potentially functional peptidase genes were observed out of 5,243 genes (3.99%). In comparison, only three times more functional protease genes (2.7% of the total gene count) have been identified in *Homo sapiens* i.e., 632 out of 23,531 genes (wikipedia.org).

Classification

Proteases are currently classified into six groups:

- Serine proteases
- Threonine proteases
- Cysteine (thiol) proteases
- Aspartic acid proteases
- Metalloproteases
- Glutamic acid proteases

The threonine and glutamic acid proteases were not described until 1995 and 2004 respectively. The mechanism used to cleave a peptide bond involves making an amino acid residue that has the cysteine and threonine (peptidases) or a water molecule (aspartic acid, metallo- and glutamic acid peptidases) nucleophilic so that it can attack the peptide carbonyl group. One way to make a nucleophile is by a catalytic triad, where a histidine residue is used to activate serine, cysteine, or threonine as a nucleophile. Attachment of a protease to a certain group depends on the structure of catalytic site and the amino acid (as one of the constituents) essential for its activity.

Distribution

Proteases occur naturally in all organisms. These enzymes are involved in a multitude of physiological reactions from simple digestion of food proteins to highly-regulated cascades such as the blood-clotting cascade, the complement system, apoptosis pathways, and the invertebrate prophenoloxidase-activating cascade.

Bacterium also secretes proteases to hydrolyse the peptide bonds in proteins and therefore break the proteins down into their constituent monomers. Proteases are also a type of exotoxin involved in destruction of extracellular structures and hence serves as a virulence factor in bacterial pathogenesis.

Functions/Uses

Proteases are used throughout an organism for various metabolic processes. The few are as follows

- Digestion of protein food: Acid proteases secreted into the stomach (such as pepsin) and serine proteases present in duodenum (trypsin and chymotrypsin) enable us to digest the protein in food
- Modulating blood clotting activity: Proteases present in blood serum (thrombin, plasmin, Hageman factor etc.,) play important role in blood-clotting as well as lysis of the clots and the correct action of the immune system
- Metabolic control: Elastase and cathepsin G proteases present in leukocytes play several different roles in metabolic control
- Regulation of physiological activity: Proteases determine the lifetime of other proteins playing important physiological role like hormones, antibodies, or other enzymes, this is one of the fastest "switching on" and "switching off" regulatory mechanisms in the physiology of an organism
- Modulating hormone activity; for example, angiotensin converting enzyme
- Punching holes in cell walls for such processes as fertilization
- By complex cooperative action the proteases may proceed as cascade reactions which result in rapid and efficient amplification of an organism's response to a physiological signal
- Involved in complement system, apoptosis pathways and the invertebrate prophenoloxidase-activating cascade
- Protease enzymes are also found used extensively in the bread industry as bread improver.

Various peptidases have been used in a novel method of encoding tentagel beads for use in the synthesis of peptide libraries. This so-called enzyme “shaving” method cleaves off peptide caps on a small proportion of surface (and therefore protein and enzyme accessible) sites. These sites can then have putative target sequences constructed on them before being screened against proteins. The remaining interior "unshaved" sequences, which do not interact with proteins can be used as a coding portion through Edman degradation for identification of the surface exposed sequences.

Peptidases in Organic Synthesis

Peptidases along with amidases have a wide application in organic synthesis as they can be used as biocatalysts. Davis and Boyer (2001) have listed the usage of these enzymes in organic synthesis and few are mentioned below.

The regioselective esterification of polyhydroxylated compounds such as sugars is a very useful enzyme-catalyzed technique. However, one of the problems is finding a solvent in which the sugar is soluble and yet in which the enzyme is still active. Very valuably, pyridine and DMF are solvents in which several peptidases are comfortable. This has allowed, for example, the selective subtilisin-BPN-catalyzed acetylation of *N*-acetylneuraminic acid (NeuAc) on its primary OH to give the natural product 9-*O*-Ac-(NeuAc).

Double resolutions in which racemic mixtures of both the acyl donor and acceptor are resolved are possible. The use of CLEC (Cross Linked Enzyme Crystals) - subtilisin and naphthylalanine as acyl donor and 1-naphthylethylamine as acceptor has been described as a nice example. Tertiary alcohols and their esters are rarely substrates for hydrolases, indeed they can often be used as solvents. However, the cysteine protease papain has been used to resolve the tertiary acetate.

Chymotrypsin has been used in the Dynamic Kinetic Resolution (DKR) of a phenylalanine iminoester in which 1,4-diazabicyclo[2.2.2]octane was used to epimerise the α-centre. Similarly, the use of electron-withdrawing trifluoroethyl thioesters allows DKR *via* base-catalyzed epimerization of the thioester α-chiral centre coupled with subtilisin Carlsberg-catalyzed transesterification to give the corresponding less acidic *n*-butyl ester.

Thermolysin featured as the key peptidase in the regioselective enzyme-catalyzed formation of an adipate tether between paclitaxel and *O*-6 of glucose. The thermolytic/proteolytic stability and the utility of thermolysin-CLEC has been described including its use in the ligation of aspartate, phenylalanine and alanine acyl donors in a variety of solvent systems.

In stunning examples of selectivity, subtilisins have also been used to catalyze the ligation of protein fragments to give lysozyme and a pure, non-natural glycoform of ribonuclease. They are also powerful ligating catalysts for a range of non-natural amino acids and glycopeptides.

As for most biocatalytic systems, overly stringent substrate specificity can limit synthetic utility of peptidases. A nice strategy for circumventing this problem is to utilize the concept of substrate mimicry. Thus, the incorporation of a 4-guanidinophenyl leaving group into the acyl donor reactant allows the use of trypsin, thrombin and clostripain, all peptidases with a P_1-specificity for positively charged side chains. Clostripain, a cysteine protease, proved most efficient in the synthesis of a number of polypeptides and advantageously this enzyme displays a wide P_1-specificity for ligation to a number of acyl acceptors. A phthalyl amidase has been isolated from *Xanthiobacter agillis* and used in selective deprotections.

Reproducibility of Peptidases in Organic Synthesis

The washing of CLEC-subtilisin with organic solvents has been studied in detail to ensure a reliable reproducible source of solid-supported enzyme. The washing method and solvent affects CLEC activity in acetonitrile and it has been suggested that this importance of hydration history and a hysteresis in activity is potentially due to "locking" of the enzyme structure in an active conformation. This work was extended to proteases supported on silica and then washed with *n*-propanol. In addition, the use of a solid acid and its conjugate base in organic solvents increases activity by a suggested buffering effect.

Similar effects have been observed in other systems and with dendritic buffers. The use of added salts controlled water activity to allow penicillin amidase-catalyzed peptide ligations of phenylacetyl acyl donors. Desolvation effects are proposed as critical in determining the difference in both level and sense of enantioselectivity in resolutions in organic solvents.

Application of Proteases/Peptidases in Food Industry

Certain proteases/peptidases have been used in food processing industries for centuries. Rennet (mainly chymosin), obtained from the fourth stomach (abomasum) of unweaned calves has been used traditionally in the production of cheese. Similarly, papain obtained from the leaves and unripe fruit of the pawpaw (*Carica papaya*) has been used to tenderise meats. These ancient discoveries have led to the development of various food applications for a wide range of available proteases from many sources including microbial origin. Proteases may be used at various pH values and they may be highly specific in their choice of cleavable peptide links or quite non-specific. Proteolysis generally increases the solubility of proteins at their isoelectric points.

The action of rennet in cheese making is an example of the hydrolysis of a specific peptide linkage, between phenylalanine and methionine residues ($-Phe_{105}-Met_{106}$) in the k-casein protein present in milk. The k-casein acts by stabilising the colloidal nature of the milk, its hydrophobic N-terminal region associating with the lipophilic regions of the otherwise insoluble a- and b-casein molecules, whilst its negatively charged C-terminal region associates with the water and prevents the casein micelles from growing too large. Hydrolysis of the labile peptide linkage between these two domains, resulting in the release of a hydrophilic glycosylated and phosphorylated oligopeptide (caseino macropeptide) and the hydrophobic para-k-casein, removes this protective effect, allowing coagulation of the milk to form curds, which are then compressed and turned into cheese. The coagulation process depends upon the presence of Ca^{2+} and is highly temperature dependent and hence can be controlled easily. Calf rennet, consisting of mainly chymosin with a small but variable proportion of pepsin, is a relatively expensive enzyme and various attempts have been made to find cheaper alternatives from microbial sources. These have ultimately proved to be successful and microbial rennets are used in about 70% of US cheese and 33% of cheese production world-wide.

The major problem that had to be overcome in the development of the microbial rennets was temperature liability. Chymosin is a relatively unstable enzyme and once it has done its major job, little activity remains. However, the enzyme from *Mucor miehei* retains activity during the maturation stages of cheese-making and produces bitter off-flavours. Treatment of the enzyme with oxidising agents (e.g. H_2O_2 and peracids), which convert methionine residues to their sulfoxides, reduces its thermostability by about 10°C and renders it more comparable with calf rennet. This is a rare example of enzyme technology being used to destabilise an enzyme. Attempts have been made to clone chymosin into *Escherichia coli* and *Saccharomyces cerevisiae* but, so far, the enzyme has been secreted in an active form only from the latter.

Many microorganisms are recently been screened for the production of rennet-like proteinases which can substitute the calf rennet. Microorganisms like *Rhizomucor pusillus*, *R. miehei*, *Endothia parasitica*, *Aspergillus oryzae* and *Irpex lactis* are used extensively for rennet production in cheese manufacture. Extensive research that has been carried out so far on rennet substitutes has been reviewed by several authors. Different strains of species of *Mucor* are often used for the production of microbial rennets. Whereas best yields of the milk-clotting protease from *Rhizomucor pusillus* are obtained from semisolid cultures containing 50% wheat bran, *R. miehei* and *Endothia parasitica* are well suited for submerged cultivation. Microbial rennets from various microorganisms (marketed under the trade names such as Rennilase, Fromase, Marzyme, Hanilase, etc.,) being marketed since the 1970s have proved satisfactory for the production of different kinds of cheese.

Site Directed Mutation for Generation of Enzymes

A combined site-directed mutagenesis and chemical modification strategy using the subtilisin from *Bacillus lentus* allows the generation of enzymes with better than wild-type kinetic activity which is matched by enhanced transesterification yields.

Conclusion

Biocatalysis has proven to be a useful supplementary technology for the chemical industry, allowing in some cases reactions which are not easily conducted by classical organic chemistry or in other cases allowing reactions which can replace several chemical steps. From different disciplines, biotechnology and biocatalysis are seen from very different angles and perspectives. Chemistry and chemists emphasize a molecularly-oriented perspective dominated by compounds and transformations, whereas chemical engineering and thus chemical engineers favor a process-oriented perspective of reactions and processes; lastly, biology and its practitioners contribute a systems-oriented perspective of description at the organism level as well as in their view of evolution. Different parts of each of the three disciplines are needed for the successful practice of biocatalysis: biochemistry and organic chemistry from chemistry; molecular biology, enzymology, and protein (bio) chemistry from biology; and catalysis, transport phenomena, and reaction engineering from chemical engineering are indispensable. Both biotechnology and biocatalysis are interdisciplinary areas; as most practitioners tend to hail from one of the three major contributing disciplines, hardly anybody has an equally strong command of all the sub-disciplines of biocatalysis. Substantially increased emphasis on biocatalyst development is an important goal for chemistry-related industries. This needs to be supported by a broad and concerted effort by those who understand the opportunities and challenges that the creation of a new generation of environmentally friendly, profitable and diverse biocatalysts will bring. All groups concerned consumers, industrialists, environmentalists and scientists, will benefit in a very significant way.

References

Bernhardt, T.G. and P.A. de Boer, 2003. The *Escherichia coli* amidase AmiC is a periplasmic septal ring component exported via the twin-arginine transport pathway. *Mol. Microbiol.* 48: 1171–1182.

Blackman, S.A., T.J. Smith. and S.J. Foster, 1998. The role of autolysins during vegetative growth of *Bacillus subtilis* 168. *Microbiology*. 144: 73–82.

Bradoo, S., R.K. Saxena. and R. Gupta, 1999. High yields of ascorbyl palmitate by thermostable lipase mediated esterification. *J. Am.Oil. Chem. Sco.* 76:1291-1295.

Brune, A.K. and F. Gotz, 1992. Degradation of lipids by bacterial lipases. In: Winkelmann (Ed) *Microbial degradation of natural products.* VCH, Weinheim. pp.243-263.

Brunskill, E.W. and K.W. Bayles, 1996. Identification of LytSR regulated genes from *Staphylococcus aureus*. *J. Bacteriol.* 178: 5810–5812.

Bury-Moné S., S. Stéphane., C.D.J. M. Thiberge., D. Dailidiene., D.E. Berg., A. Labigne. and H. Reuse, 2003. Presence of Active Aliphatic Amidases in *Helicobacter* species able to colonize the stomach. *Infect. Immun.* (71) 10 5613-5622

Catt, D.M. and R.L. Gregory, 2005. *Streptococcus mutans* murein hydrolase. *J. Bacteriol.* 187: 7863–7865.

Clausen, V.A., W. Bae, J. Throup, M.K. Burnham, M. Rosenberg. and N.G. Wallis, 2003. Biochemical characterization of the first essential two-component signal transduction system from *Staphylococcus aureus* and *Streptococcus pneumoniae*. *J. Mol. Microbiol. Biotechnol.* 5: 252–260.

Davis, B.G. and V. Boyer, 2001. Biocatalysis and enzymes in organic synthesis. *Nat. Prod. Rep.* 18: 618-640.

Dubrac, S. and T. Msadek, 2004. Identification of genes controlled by the essential YycG/YycF two-component system of *Staphylococcus aureus*. *J. Bacteriol.* 186: 1175-1181.

Ehlert, K., J.V. Holtje. and M.F. Templin, 1995. Cloning and expression of a murein hydrolase lipoprotein from *Escherichia coli*. *Mol. Microbiol.* 16: 761–768.

Fabret, C. and J.A. Hoch, 1998. A two-component signal transduction system essential for growth of *Bacillus subtilis*: implications for anti-infective therapy. *J. Bacteriol* 180: 6375-6383.

Forney, L.J., D.C. Wong and D.M. Ferber, 1989. Selection of Amidases with Novel Substrate Specificities from Penicillin Amidase of *Escherichia coli*. *Applied and Environmental Microbiology*. 55: 2550-2555.

Foster, S.J, 1992. Analysis of the autolysins of *Bacillus subtilis* 168 during vegetative growth and differentiation by using renaturing polyacrylamide gel electrophoresis. *J. Bacteriol.* 174: 464-470.

Foster, S.J, 1995. Molecular characterization and functional analysis of the major autolysin of *Staphylococcus aureus* 8325/4. *J. Bacteriol.* 177: 5723-5725.

Foster, S.J. and K. Johnstone 1988. Germination-specific cortex-lytic enzyme is activated during triggering of *Bacillus megaterium* KM spore germination. *Mol. Microbiol.* 2: 727-733.

Godtfredson, S.E. 1990. Microbial Lipases. In: Fogarty W.M. and E.T. Kelly (Ed), Microbial enzymes and biotechnology. Elsevier *Applied Sciences,* Amsterdam. pp. 255-273.

Heidrich, C., A. Ursinus, J. Berger, H. Schwarz. and J.V. Holtje, 2002. Effects of multiple deletions of murein hydrolases on viability, septum cleavage, and sensitivity to large toxic molecules in *Escherichia coli*. *J. Bacteriol.* 184: 6093-6099.

Howell, A., S. Dubrac, K.K. Andersen, D. Noone, J. Fert, T. Msadek. and K. Devine, 2003. Genes controlled by the essential YycG/YycF two-component system of *Bacillus subtilis* revealed through a novel hybrid regulator approach. *Mol. Microbiol.* 49: 1639-1655.

Kajimura, J., T. Fujiwara, S. Yamada, Y. Suzawa, T. Nishida, Y. Oyamada, I. Hayashi, J. Yamagishi, H. Komatsuzawa, M. Sugai, 2005. Identification and molecular characterization of an N-acetylmuramyl-L-alanine amidase Sle1 involved in cell separation of *Staphylococcus aureus*. *Mol. Microbiol.* 58: 1087-1101.

Kazlauskas, R.J. and U.T. Bornscheuer, 1998. Biotransformation with lipases. In: Rehm HJ. Reed G eds. *Biotechnology.* Vol.8a. New York, USA: VCH Publishers.pp 137-192.

Komatsuzawa, H., M. Sugai, S. Nakashima, S. Yamada, A. Matsumoto, T. Oshida. and H. Suginaka, 1997. Subcellular localization of the major autolysin, ATL and its processed proteins in *Staphylococcus aureus*. *Microbiol. Immunol.* 41: 469-479.

Kuroda, A. and J. Sekiguchi, 1993. High-level transcription of the major *Bacillus subtilis* autolysin operon depends on expression of the sigma D gene and is affected by a sin (flaD) mutation. *J. Bacteriol.* 175: 795-801.

Lazarevic, V., P. Margot, B. Soldo. and D. Karamata, 1992. Sequencing and analysis of the *Bacillus subtilis* lytRABC divergon: a regulatory unit encompassing the structural genes of the N-acetylmuramoyl-L-alanine amidase and its modifier. *J. Gen. Microbiol.* 138(9): 1949-1961.

Lommatzsch, J., M.F. Templin, A.R. Kraft, W. Vollmer. and J.V. Holtje, 1997. Outer membrane localization of murein hydrolases: MltA, a third lipoprotein lytic transglycosylase in *Escherichia coli*. *J. Bacteriol.* 179: 5465–5470.

Margot, P. and D. Karamata, 1992. Identification of the structural genes for N-acetylmuramoyl-L-alanine amidase and its modifier in *Bacillus subtilis* 168: inactivation of these genes by insertional mutagenesis has no effect on growth or cell separation. *Mol. Gen. Genet.* 232: 359–366.

Margot, P., C. Mauel. and D. Karamata, 1994. The gene of the N-acetylglucosaminidase, a *Bacillus subtilis* 168 cell wall hydrolase not involved in vegetative cell autolysis. *Mol. Microbiol.* 12: 535–545.

Margot, P., C. Mauel. and D. Karamata, 1994. The gene of the N-acetylglucosaminidase, a *Bacillus subtilis* 168 cell wall hydrolase not involved in vegetative cell autolysis. *Mol. Microbiol.* 12: 535–545.

Martin, P.K., T. Li, D. Sun, D.P. Biek. and M.B. Schmid, 1999. Role in cell permeability of an essential two-component system in *Staphylococcus aureus*. *J. Bacteriol.* 181: 3666–3673.

Meisel U., J.V. H¨oltje and W. Vollmer, 2003. Overproduction of inactive variants of the murein synthase PBP1B causes lysis in *Escherichia coli*. *J. Bacteriol.* 185: 5342–5348.

Ng, W.L., G.T. Robertson, K.M. Kazmierczak, J. Zhao, R. Gilmour. and M.E. Winkler, 2003. Constitutive expression of PcsB suppresses the requirement for the essential VicR (YycF) response regulator in *Streptococcus pneumoniae* R6. *Mol. Microbiol.* 50: 1647–1663.

Ng, W.L., K.M. Kazmierczak. and M.E. Winkler, 2004. Defective cell wall synthesis in *Streptococcus pneumoniae* R6 depleted for the essential PcsB putative murein hydrolase or the VicR (YycF) response regulator. *Mol. Microbiol.* 53: 1161–1175.

Nishio, T., T. Chikano. and M. Kamimura, 1987. Purification and some properties of lipase produced by *Pseudomonas fragi* 22.39B. *Agric. Biol. Chem.* 51: 181-187.

Ogawa, J. and Sakayu S, 1999. Microbial enzymes: new industrial applications from traditional screening methods. *Trends in Biotechnology.* 17(1):13-20.

Ohno, M., M. Otsuka, M. Yagisawa, S. Kondo, H. Öppinger, H. Hoffmann, D. Sukatsch, L. Hepner and C. Male, 1985. *Antibiotics,* in *Ullmann's Encyclopedia of Industrial Chemistry*, ed. W. Gerhartz, VCH Verlagsgesellschaft, Weinheim,

Oshida, T., M. Sugai, H. Komatsuzawa, Y.M. Hong, H. Suginaka. and A. Tomasz, 1995. A *Staphylococcus aureus* autolysin that has an N-acetylmuramoyl-L-alanine amidase domain and an endobeta-N-acetylglucosaminidase domain: cloning, sequence analysis, and characterization. *Proc. Natl. Acad. Sci.* USA. 92: 285–289.

Patton, T.G., S.J. Yang. and K.W. Bayles, 2006. The role of proton motive force in expression of the *Staphylococcus aureus* cid and lrg operons. *Mol. Microbiol.* 59: 1395–1404.

Peter, R.J. and E. Voss, 2001. *Enzyme-catalyzed processes in pharmaceutical industry Applied Catalysis A: General* 221: 145–158.

Rice, K.C. and K.W. Bayles, 2003. Death's toolbox: examining the molecular components of bacterial programmed cell death. *Mol. Microbiol.* 50: 729–738.

Saxena, R.K., A. Sheoran, B. Giri and W.S. Davidson, 2003. Purification strategies for microbial lipases. *J. Microbiol. Methods.* 52: 1-18.

Saxena, R.K., P.K. Ghosh, R. Gupta, W.S. Davidson, S. Bradoo and R. Gulati, 1999. Microbial lipases: Potential biocatalysts for the future industry. *Curr. Sci.* 77: 101-115.

Secundo, F. 2009. Importance of Enzyme Formulation for the Activity and Enantioselectivity of Lipases in Organic Solvents, in *Modern Biocatalysis: Stereoselective and Environmentally Friendly Reactions* (Eds) W.D. Fessner and T. Anthonsen), Wiley-VCH Verlag GmbH and Co. KGaA, Weinheim, Germany.

Serizawa, M., H. Yamamoto, H. Yamaguchi, Y. Fujita, K. Kobayashi, N. Ogasawara and J. Sekiguchi, 2004. Systematic analysis of SigD regulated genes in *Bacillus subtilis* by DNA microarray and Northern blotting analyses. *Gene.* 329: 125–136.

Shockman, G.D. and J.V. Holtje, 1994. Microbial peptidoglycan (murein) hydrolases. *Bacterial Cell Wall* (Ghuysen J-M and Hakenbeck R, eds), Elsevier, Amsterdam. pp. 131–166.

Shockman, G.D., M.L. Daneo, R. Kariyama. and O. Massidda, 1996. Bacterial walls, peptidoglycan hydrolases, autolysins, and autolysis. *Microb. Drug Resist.* 2: 95–98.

Smith, T.J. and S.J. Foster, 1995. Characterization of the involvement of two compensatory autolysins in mother cell lysis during sporulation of *Bacillus subtilis* 168. *J. Bacteriol.* 177: 3855–3862.

Smith, T.J., S.A. Blackman. and S.J. Foster, 2000. Autolysins of *Bacillus subtilis*: multiple enzymes with multiple functions. *Microbiology*. 146: 249–262.

Stolz, A., S. Trott, M. Binder, R. Bauer, B. Hirrlinger, N. Layh, and H.J. Knackmuss, 1998. Enantioselective nitrile hydratases and amidasess from different bacterial isolates. *J. Molec. Cat.* B: Enzymatic. 5: 137-141.

Straathof, A. J. J., S. Panke. and A. Schmid, 2002. The production of fine chemicals by biotransformation. *Current opinion in Biotechnology*. 13:548-556.

Verrett, C. R., M.R. Rosnerg. and H.G. Khorana, 1982. Fatty acyl amidases from *Dictyostelium discoideum* that act on lipopolysaccharide and derivatives. II. Aspects of substrate specificity. *J. Biol. Chem.* 257: 10228-10234.

Winkler, F.K. and K. Gubernator, 1994. Structure and mechanism of human pancreatic lipase. In: Wooley P. and S.B. Petersen (Ed), *Lipases, their structure, biochemistry and application.* Cambridge University Press, Great Britain. pp. 139-157.

Wolf, D.F. and A. Thorleif, 2009. *Modern Biocatalysis: Stereo selective and environmentally friendly reactions.* (Eds) W.D. Fessner and T. Anthonsen), Wiley-VCH Verlag GmbH and Co. KGaA, Weinheim, Germany.

Yamamoto, H., S. Kurosawa. and J. Sekiguchi, 2003. Localization of the vegetative cell wall hydrolases LytC, LytE, and LytF on the *Bacillus subtilis* cell surface and stability of these enzymes to cell wall-bound or extracellular proteases. *J. Bacteriol.* 185: 6666–6677.

In: Applications of Microbial Genes in Enzyme Technology ISBN: 978-1-62417-808-5
Editors: V.K.Gupta, M.G.Tuohy, G.D.Sharma et al.

Chapter 6

Microbial Glycosyltransferases; Recent Insight and Application

Joo-Ho Lee, Tae-Jin Oh and Jae Kyung Sohng*
Institute of Biomolecule Reconstruction (IBR),
Department of Pharmaceutical Engineering, SunMoon University, Kalsan-ri,
Tangjeong-myeon, Asansi, Chungnam, Republic of Korea

Abstract

Glycosyltransferases are synthetic control tools for the structure-diversification of many natural products which contains the bioactivity as the secondary metabolites containing antibiotics and anti-tumors etc. This review presents the introduction of the function and specificity of some biosynthetic-related microbial glycosyltransferases and their *in vivo/in vitro* protein engineering. In addition, the generation of novel compounds using glycosyltransferase targeting toolbox on flavonoid aglycones can help to understand their useful application for combinatorial biosynthetic approaches.

Introduction

Importance of Carbohydrate in Nature

Nature produces a number of products which have clinical biological activities, and these natural products also continue to serve for the development of novel therapeutics (Butler and Buss, 2006; Gullo *et al.,* 2006). Many relevant natural products are attached with carbohydrates by known enzyme, glycosyltransferases (GTs), and their structural diversity is further increased by decorating at different positions. The important role of sugars as energy

* Corresponding author: Jae Kyung Sohng. E-mail: sohng@sunmoon.ac.kr. Institute of Biomolecule Reconstruction (IBR), Department of Pharmaceutical Engineering, SunMoon University, Kalsan-ri, Tangjeong-myeon, Asansi, Chungnam, 336-708, Republic of Korea.

resources and key structural backbones has been well-known, and they also contribute to a variety of biological processes, including active transport, stabilization of protein folding and enzyme activity/inhibition (Bolen, 2001; Pilobello and Mahal, 2007). In contrast to many plant natural compounds contain sugars (D-glucose, D-galactose, L-fucose, L-rhamnose and D-xylose), microorganisms which are producers of a variety of natural products (vancomycin, pikromycin, oleandomycin, dihydrochalcomycin etc.) include mostly deoxygenated sugars (Figure 1). These deoxysugar components have enjoyed increasingly widespread appreciation as essential biological molecules exhibiting functions as a cellular adhesive, in the immune response, fertilization, as well as in the molecular recognition and affinity of its cellular target (Poulsen *et al.,* 2000).

Classification of Microbial GTs

Most GT essential in the biosynthesis of glycosylated natural products catalyze the transfer of sugar moieties from activated donor molecules to specific acceptor molecules for the structural diversity of glycosides produced. About 94 GT families are being reported at the CAZY database (http://www.cazy.org/GlycosylTransferases.html) on the basis of amino acid sequence similarity. In addition, GTs can be classified into two groups (retaining and inverting) according to the stereochemical mechanisms of the substrates and reaction products (Sinnott, 1990). Inverting GT most likely follow a single displacement mechanism where the acceptor performs a nucleophilic attack at carbon C-1 of the sugar donor. On the other hand, retaining GT does not appear to operate via a two-step mechanism involving the formation of a glycosylic-enzyme intermediate.

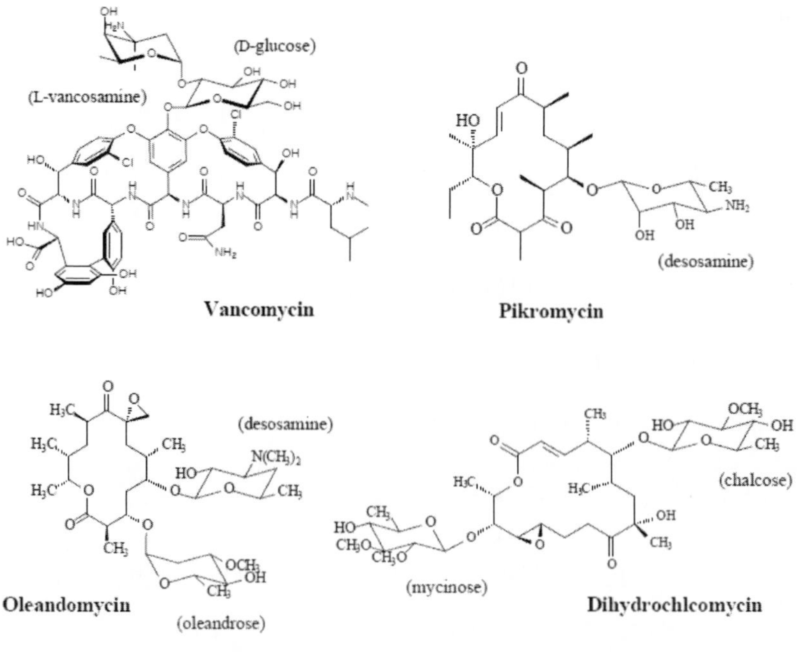

Figure 1. The chemical structures of glycosylated natural products containing vancomycin, pikromycin, oleandomycin and dihydrochalcomycin.

Instead, an internal return SNi-like mechanism has been proposed, in which leaving group departure and nucleophilic attack occur in a concerted but asynchronous manner on the same face of the glycoside (Lairson et al.,2008).

In spite of the variation in substrate specificity, GTs can be fallen mainly into two classes, the GT-A and GT-B families, on the basis of structural fold (Campbell *et al.,* 1997; Coutinho *et al.,* 2003). The GT-A superfamily is characterized by a single domain with an Rossman-like β/α/β fold exemplified by the structures of the retaining GTs, and the NDP-sugar-binding region of GT-A enzymes contains a signature DXD (Asp-XAsp) motif for binding essential a divalent metals (Breton *et al.,* 1998; Wiggins and Munro, 1998; Persson *et al.,* 2001). In contrast, GT-B superfamily members have two domains resembling Rossman folds with interdomain cleft, and they aremetal-ion-independent and lack universally conserved amino acid residues (Thibodeaux *et al.,* 2008). Most all natural product GTs are inverting members of the GT-B superfamily, and these GT-B superfamily members have two domains separated by a flexible linker region, which forms a deep cleft between the two domains (N-terminal domain, aglycone binding site; C-terminal domain, sugar binding site) (Hu and Walker, 2002).

Recent Insight of Microbial GT

GTs Involved in the Biosynthesis

More than 3,000 genes encoding GT are being reported from representatives of prokaryotic and eukaryotic organisms which catalyze the glycosylation of small molecules containing C-, N-, O- and S-glycosidic linkages. Most genes encoding GT are being reported from the gene clusters of secondary metabolites-producing Actinomycetes, and many of them have been characterized biochemically. It was recently discovered that the macrolide GT DesVII required an auxiliary protein, DesVIII, for their activities (Hong *et al.,* 2005; Hong *et al.,* 2007), as is the case of AknS/AknT (Lu *et al.,* 2005), TylM2/TylM3 (Melancon *et al.,* 2004). These systems have been shown to be especially "flexible" in accepting different deoxysugars, which leads to further structural variations, and it can be applied to the design of strategies for novel hybrid compound (Hong *et al.,* 2004; Lee *et al.,* 2006). However, due to a lack of knowledge about the exact biological relationship of GTs between structure and function, the use of GTs as biotechnological tools is still a challenge.

GT Engineering (*In Vitro/In Vivo*)

In order to explore the synthetic potential of GTs *in vitro*, the availability of purified GTs (from *Escherichia coli*) in active soluble form as well as the aglycone scaffolds (obtained from partial degradation of the parent compounds or chemical synthesis) and nucleotide activated sugars (obtained from complete enzymatic synthesis or real organic synthesis) are required. Recently, Eguchi's group has demonstrated that VinC catalyses the thymidinediphosphate-dependent deglycosylation, and this result may revolutionize *in vitro* glycodiversification of natural products because it gives access to the activated sugars in a single enzyme-catalyzed step (Luzhetskyy and Bechthold, 2008). In addition, Thorson and co-workers have shown that it is possible to activate a variety of sugars (natural or synthetic), and they also have been able to generate a library of 50 different glycoforms of vancomycin derivatives (Zhang *et al.,* 2006).

A large pool of well-known natural product GT has been characterized by several approaches containing gene inactivation and gene expression experiments that are shown in figure 2 (Oh *et al.,* 2007). These manipulations led to novel derivatives produced by mutated microorganisms. GT gene inactivation and overexpression of a GT gene in its own producer strain are an important step to elucidate the function of a GT, and it may also lead to the formation of novel glycosylated derivatives. The resulting GT gene mutant organisms may be used as cell factories containing all necessary building blocks for the production of modified natural products. The expression of heterologous GT resulted in the accumulation of several novel glycosylated derivatives, which are of particular interest from the pharmaceutical viewpoint (Luzhetskyy *et al.,* 2005). In addition, modification of the host sugar pathways by gene inactivation and expression may also lead to the generation of novel glycosylated compounds. Sugar biosynthetic pathway can be modified in producer strain, thus providing the host with the capability to synthesize new sugars. For example, Yoon's group showed generation of novel hybrid macrolide antibiotics containing olivose and quinovose (Hong *et al.,* 2004).

GT Protein Engineering

Although some GTs are promiscuous for altering the glycosylation patterns, the substrate specificity remains a limiting factor in natural product diversification and therefore, protein engineering is a powerful tool to modify substrate specificity. The first successful result on the GT engineering was obtained from urdamycin biosynthetic GTs (UrdGT1b and UrdGT1c) which show different specificities for both nucleotide sugar and acceptor substrates (Hoffmeister *et al.,* 2001).

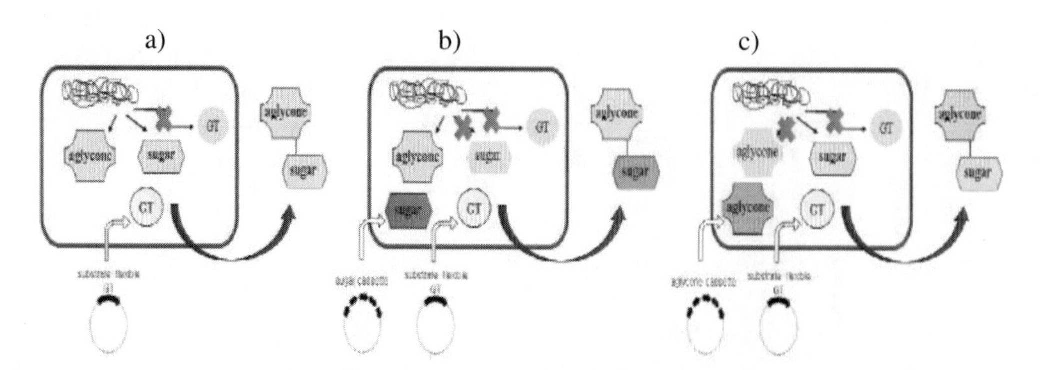

Figure 2. A concept for the generation of novel glycosylated natural products by genetically engineered several approaches. A, Formation of derivative in a GT-deficient mutant by overexpression of the substrate-flexible GT; B, Formation of derivative in a sugar-deficient and GT-deficient mutant by overexpression of the heterologous sugar cassette genes and substrate-flexible GT; C, Formation of derivative in a aglycone-deficient and GT-deficient mutant by overexpression of the heterologous aglycone cassette genes and substrate-flexible GT.

Thus, in order to overcome the narrow substrate specificity of GTs, a domain swapping strategy for the *in vitro* evolution was proposed, considering the structures of GTs involved in natural product biosynthesis. Interestingly, the GT-B superfamily of the enzymes has very distinctive acceptor-recognition (N-terminus) and donor-recognition (C-terminus) domains, connected by a linker loop region (Mulichak *et al.,* 2001; Mulichak *et al.,* 2003; Coutinho *et al.,* 2003; Hu *et al.,* 2003). The point mutation study was begun by determining the crystal structure of phenolic GT (UGT72B1) with effort to estimate 44 mutation sites (Brazier-Hicks *et al.,* 2007). Validamycin GT (ValG) contains an unusual DTG motif in place of the DXD motif proposed for metal ion binding and/or NDP-sugar binding. The DTG motif of ValG to DCD altered its preferences for metal ion binding, but did not seem to affect its substrate specificity (Xu *et al.,* 2008). A recent study on the oleandomycin GT (OleD) showed that the point mutation study (A242V/S132F/P67T) permitted to expand its acceptor specificity as well as its sugar donor specificity. This result displayed the improvement in proficiency and substrate promiscuity (Williams *et al.,* 2007; Williams *et al.,* 2008a). The mutated OleD glucosylate a diverse range including anthraquinones, β-lactams, indolocarbozoles, polyenes, cardenolides, steroids, enediynes, and macrolides (Williams *et al.,* 2007; Williams *et al.,* 2008a; Williams *et al.,* 2008b). Domain swapping is one of strategy for biological systems that have distinct substrate binding and catalytic/regulatory regions. An early domain swapping study identified that the N-domain of rat UDP-glucuronyltransferases is responsible for acceptor binding (Mackenzie et al.,1990). A few GT domain swapping examples have been reported, including moving the C-domains between UDP-glucosyltransferases (Cartwright *et al.,* 2008) and chimeras of urdamycin GTs (Hoffmeister *et al.,* 2001, 2002). A recent study on the vancomycin GT chimeras (GtfB) which generate hybrid glycopeptides have demonstrated that domain swapping can result in a predictable switchof substrate specificity, illustrating that N- and C-terminal domains predominantly dictate acceptor and donor specificity, respectively (Truman *et al.,* 2008). The generality of GT domain swapping is known by the groups of Bowles (Brazier-Hicks *et al.,* 2007; Cartwright *et al.,* 2008), Kim (Park *et al.,* 2009a), and Bechthold (Krauth *et al.,* 2009), who have reported interesting examples of functional chimeric GTs (plant flavanoid, bacterial aminoglycoside-glycopeptide, and bacterial angucycline GTs, respectively).

Application for the Generation of Novel Compounds

GTs for Oligosaccharide Synthesis

It is well known that oligosaccharides are enormous potential as therapeutic agents. However, the development of oligosaccharides of clinical utility is far from being realized due to the only very limited quantities of oligosaccharides can be obtained by chemical method and their complex structure of oligosaccharides which makes classical chemical synthesis difficult (Perugino *et al.,* 2004). Recently enzymatic synthesis using GTs could circumvent the drawbacks of the chemical methods, because GTs involved in the biosynthesis of oligosaccharides have a regio- and stereo-specific activities which can show almost no side products.

Table 1. Some microbial GTs

GTs	Source	Reference
Fucosyltransferase (FucT)		
α1,2-FucT	*Helicobacter pylori*	Wang *et al.*, 1999
α1,3-FucT	*Helicobacter pylori*	Ge *et al.*, 1997
α1,3/4-FucT	*Helicobacter pylori*	Rasko *et al.*, 2000
α1,4-FucT	*Helicobacter pylori*	Rabbani *et al.*, 2005
Galactosyltransferase (GalT)		
α1,3-GalT	*Salmonella enterica*	Heinrichs *et al.*, 1998
α1,3/β1,4-GalT	*Neisseria meningitidis*	Jennings *et al.*, 1998
α1,4-GalT	*Neisseria gonorrhoeae*	Gotschlich, 1994
α1,4-GalT	*Neisseria meningitidis*	Jennings *et al.*, 1995
α1,6-GalT	*Streptococcus thermophilis*	Stingele *et al.*, 1996
β1,2-GalT	*Haemophilus influenzae*	Deadman *et al.*, 2006
β1,3-GalT	*Campylobacter jejuni*	Gilbert *et al.*, 2000
β1,3-GalT	*Streptococcus agalactiae*	Watanabe *et al.*, 2002
β1,4-GalT	*Helicobacter pylori*	Logan *et al.*, 2000 Endo *et al.*, 2000
β1,4-GalT	*Streptococcus agalactiae*	Yamamoto *et al.*, 2000
β1,4-GalT	*Streptococcus pneumoniae*	Kolkman *et al.*, 1997
Sialyltransferase (SiaT)		
α2,3-SiaT	*Campylobacter jejuni*	Gilbert *et al.*, 2000
α2,3-SiaT	*Haemophilus influenzae*	Hood *et al.*, 2001
α2,3-SiaT	*Haemophilus ducreyi*	Bozue *et al.*, 1999
α2,3-SiaT	*Neisseria gonorrhoeae*	Gilbert *et al.*, 1996
α2,3-SiaT	*Neisseria meningitidis*	Gilbert *et al.*, 1996
α2,3-SiaT	*Streptococcus agalactiae*	Chaffin *et al.*, 1996
α2,3/6-SiaT	*Pasteurella multocida*	Yu *et al.*, 2005
α2,3/8-SiaT	*Campylobacter jejuni*	Gilbert *et al.*, 2002
α2,6-SiaT	*Photobacterium damsela*	Yamamoto *et al.*, 1998
α2,8/9-SiaT	*Escherichia coli*	Shen *et al.*, 1999

A large number of GTs have been shown to be useful for oligosaccharide synthesis and therefore recent progress in genetic engineering and recombinant protein production methods has now made several GTs available. Examples of some microbial, by far most bacterial, GTs whose activities were characterized are shown in Table 1. The wide variety of GTs already cloned from several microbial origins, and the many more anticipated to be identified in bacterial genomes promise to be valuable for novel oligosaccharide synthesis.

GT Targeting Toolbox on Secondary Metabolites

Vancomycin belongs to the glycopeptide class of antibiotics, which are effective in the treatment of life-threatening methicillin-resistant Gram-positive bacterial infections, and more importantly, it is useful in the treatment of clinically resistant *Staphylococcus aureus*. Recent enzymatic and chemoenzymatic alterations have revealed that vancomycin's disaccharide attachment may be one alteration route for new bioactive compounds (Chen *et al.,* 2000; Losey *et al.,* 2002). Walsh group and coworkers showed regio-specific enzymatic reconstitution of the antibiotic chloroeremomycin from the heptapeptide aglycone by three GTs, GtfA, GtfB and GtfC (Lu *et al.,* 2004), and a systematic utility of chemoenzymatic approaches to diversify complex natural product architectures by using glycopeptides GTs, GtfD and GtfE, which are the most versatile enzyme for the synthesis of vancomycin analogs(Fu *et al.,* 2005;Oberthur *et al.,* 2005).

In addition, recently Sohng's group showed an enzymatic approach to generate novel vancomycin derivatives using two GTs (□1,4-GalT and □2,3-SiaT) from other origins as shown in figure 3 and they demonstrated the incorporation of galactose and Sia onto the D-glucose glycone of both vancomycin and pseudo-vancomycin (Oh *et al.,* 2011).

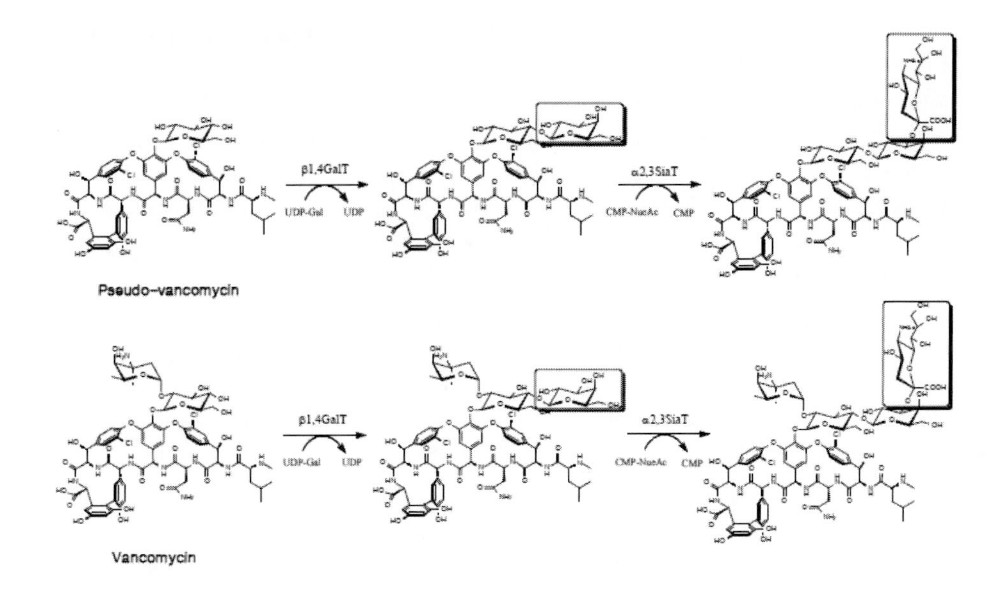

Figure 3. Overall enzymatic incorporations scheme of galactose and sialic acid into (pseudo) vancomycin to give hybrid new compounds.

In addition, the MIC test results showed that the antibiotic activities of galactose-containing derivatives against the MRSA and VSEF are the same or better than those of galactose/Sia-containing derivatives.

It was well-known that one of these antibiotics, the pikromycin biosynthetic system in *S. venezuelae*ATCC15439, produced two distinct groups of macrolactones, including the 12-membered ring 10-deoxymethynolide and the 14-membered ring narbonolide obtained fromsingle multifunctional polyketide synthase (pikA) (Xue *et al.,* 1998). The set of genes required for the biosynthesis of a TDP-D-desosamineis clustered downstream of pikA. In addition,the pikromycinGTDesVII/DesVIII system,which replaces the native partner with a heterologousactivator protein, affects the efficiency of glycosylation (Hong *et al.,* 2004; Hong *et al.,* 2006; Lee *et al.,* 2006). These unique features of *S. venezuelae* in generating structural variability can be applied tocombinatorial biosynthesis of novel hybrid macrolides. Recent Sohng and co-workers showed that the formation of 4-amino-4,6-dideoxy-L-glycosylatedmacrolide derivatives using *S. venezuelae*mutants (YJ003 and YJ003-OTBP3) (Jaishy *et al.,* 2006; Pageni *et al.,* 2008). These results reveal the usefulness of these deoxysugargenes for the biosynthesis of hybrid macrolide compounds.

GTs for Combination of Microbial Glycones and Flavonoid Aglycones

Flavonoids comprise a large group of low molecular weight polyphenolic secondary plant metabolites. It is important natural pharmaceutical compounds found showing antioxidant, antibacterial and anti-viral activities as well as anti-allergic effects, and possess anti-inflammatory, anti-angiogenic, analgesic, hepatoprotective, cytostatic, apoptotic estrogenic or anti-estrogenic properties. Biosynthesis of glycosylated natural compound results in the formation of an overwhelming number of natural glycosides with numerous applications like solubility, stabilization and detoxification.

The talosins are the first isoflavonol glycosides with a 6-deoxy-talose sugar component (Figure 4) and they may be useful as antifungal agents with low toxicity. This example is rare case that the falvonoids have a microbial deoxysugar. The talosins A and B were isolated from *Kitasatosporakifunensis* MJM341 in soybean meal, but were not produced in GSS. Also the talosin biosynthetic gene cluster was not isolated from *Kitasatosporakifunensis.* Accordingly, it is suggested that strain *Kitasatosporakifunensis*combined its own 6-deoxy-talose to the genistein of the soybean meal by GT (Yoon *et al.,* 2006).

The engineered *E. coli* BL21(DE3, *Δpgi*) cells generated by deleting the glucose-phosphate isomerase (*pgi*) and heterologously expressing TDP-deoxysugars and GT genes from various microbial sources were used as whole cell biotransformation reaction by feeding exogeneously. To generate glycosylated flavonoids, the engineered *E. coli* cells were fed with quercetin, keampferol and fisetin, the flavonol (or 3-hydroxyflavone) exogenously.

The products were analyzed to be 3-O-rhamnosyl-flavonoids, 3-O-deoxyallose flavonoids, 7-O-glucuronyl flavonoids and 3-O-aminodeoxysugar flavonoids. Since the glycosylated flavonoids have shown enormous pharmaceutical properties, the recombinant host generated can be utilize to discover unusual glycosylated flavonoids as functional materials and drugs (Simkhada *et al.,* 2010a).

A different approach has been used to produce glycosylated flavonoids from the *E. coli* by enhancing the pool of different activated sugars. For example, UDP-glucose dehydrogenase (CalS8) and UDP-glucuronic acid decarboxylase (CalS9) from *Micromonosporaechinospora* spp. *calichensis*expressed together with an integrated copy of *E. coli* K12 UDP-glucose pyrophosphorylase (GalU) in back ground strain *E. coli* BL21(DE3) with the glucose phosphate isomerase (*pgi*)-deleted mutant for the excess availability of UDP-xylose along with 7-O-glycosyltransferase (ArGt-4) from *Arabidopsis thaliana.* This newly engineered strain was also fed with naringenin to produce naringenin 7-O-xyloside (Simkhada *et al.,* 2009).

Similarly, the pools of TDP-L-rhamnose and TDP-D-allose sugars was developed separately by expressing respective sugar biosynthetic pathway related genes from different bacterial sources in the same *pgi*-deleted *E. coli* BL21(DE3) along with *Arabidopsis thaliana*GT (ArGt-3).

When these recombinants were fed with quercetin and kaempferol; 3-O-rhamosyl quercetin, 3-O-rhamnosyl kaempferol, and only 3-O-allosyl quercetin were produced from respective sugar producing strains (Simkhada *et al.,* 2010b).

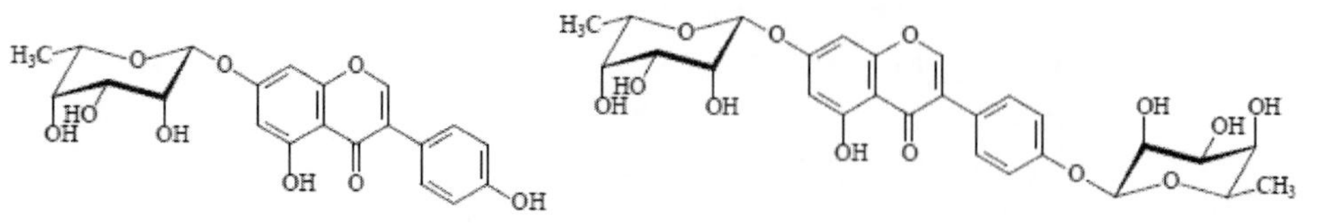

Talson A

Talson B

Figure 4. Structure of talosins.

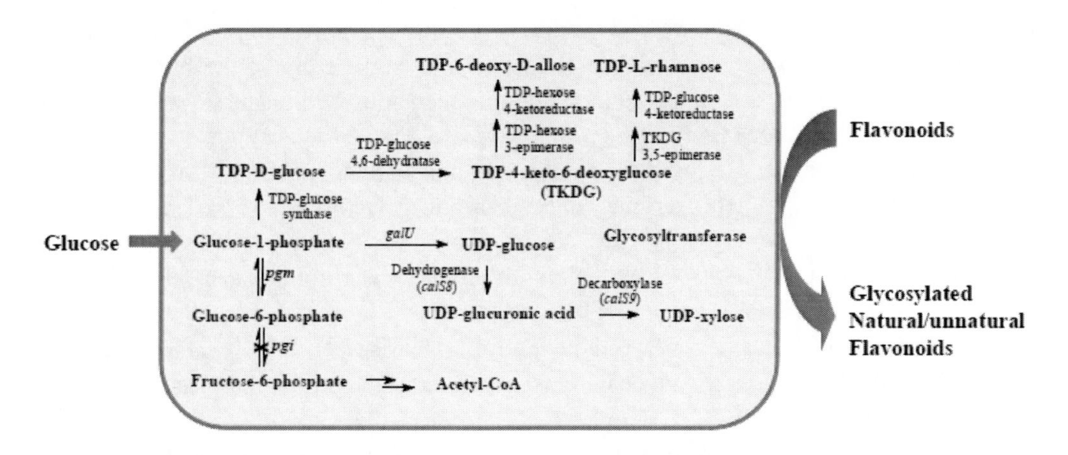

Figure 5. General production scheme of flavonoid glycosides by engineering sugar pathway in *E. coli.*

In another similar recent report, *E. coli* BL21(DE3) carrying three genes, *ugd* (UDP-glucose dehydrogenase), *arnA* (UDP-L-Ara4N formyltransferase/ UDP-GlcA C-4”-decarboxylase) and *arnB* (UDP-L-Ara4O C-4” transaminase) along with GT AtUGT78D3 from *Arabidopsis thaliana* produced quercetin-3-O-Ara4FN, when quercetin was fed (Kim *et al.,* 2010). This approach of producing flavonoid glycosides might be helpful to generate medically important novel/unnatural flavonoids from *E. coli.* The general scheme of such approach is shown in figure 5.

Conclusion

Recently, the efficient GT toolbox opened the possibility of generating novel glycosylated compounds using *in vivo* and *in vitro* GT engineering techniques which can attach unnatural deoxysugars to the diverse aglycones. Thus, the rational design of the genes that encode the enzymes in the deoxysugar biosynthetic pathways shows great potential for use in the redesign of natural products to create new activities.

References

Aguirrezabalaga, I., C. Olano, N. Allende, L. Rodriguez, A. F. Brana, C. Mendez and J. A. Salas, 2000. Identification and expressionof genes involved in biosynthesis of L-oleandrose and its intermediate L-olivose in the oleandomycin producer *Streptomyces antibioticus*. *Antimicrob. Agents Chemother.* 44: 1266-1275.

Bolen, D. W. 2001. Protein stabilization by naturally occurring osmolytes. *Meth. Mol. Biol.* 168: 17-36.

Bozue, J. A., M. V. Tullius, J. Wang, B. W. Gibson and R. S. Jr. Munson, 1999. *Haemophilus ducreyi* produces a novel sialyltransferase. Identification of the sialyltransferase gene and construction of mutants deficient in the productionof the sialic acid-containing gycoform of the lipooligosaccharide. *J. Biol. Chem.* 274: 4106-4114.

Brazier-Hicks, M., W. A. Offen, M. C. Gershater, T. J. Revett, E. K. Lim, D. J. Bowles, G. J. Davies and R. Edwards, 2007. Characterization and engineering of the bifunctional N- and O-glucosyltransferase involved in xenobiotic metabolism in plants. *Proc. Natl. Acad. Sci. US* 104: 20238-20243.

Breton, C., E. Bettler, D. H. Joziasse, R. A. Geremia and A. Imberty, 1998. Sequence-function relationships of prokaryotic and eukaryotic galactosyltransferases. *J. Biochem.* 123: 1000-1009.

Butler, M. S. and A. D. Buss, 2006. Natural products-The future scaffolds for novel antibiotics? *Biochem. Pharmacol.* 71: 919-929.

Campbell, J. A., G. J. Davies, V. Bulone and B. Henrissat, 1997. A classification of nucleotide-diphospho-sugar glycosyltransferases based on amino acid sequence similarities. *Biochem. J.* 326: 929-939.

Cartwright, A. M., E. K. Lim, C. Kleanthous and D. J. Bowles, 2008. A kinetic analysis of regiospecificglucosylation by two glycosyltransferases of *Arabidopsis thaliana*: domain swapping to introduce new activities. *J. Biol. Chem.* 283: 15724-15731.

Chaffin, D. O., K. McKinnon and C. E. Rubens, 1996. CpsK of *Sterptococcus agalactiae* exhibits alpha2,3-sialyltransferase activity in *Haemophilus ducreyi*. *Mol. Microbiol.* 45: 109-122.

Chen, H., M. G. Thomas, B. K. Hubbard, H. C. Losey, C. T. Walsh and M. D. Burkart, 2000. Deoxysugar in glycopeptides antibiotics: enzymatic synthesis of TDP-L-epivancosamine in chloroeremomycin biosynthesis. *Proc. Natl. Acad. Sci. US* 97: 11942-11947.

Coutinho, P. M., E. Deleury, G. J. Davies and B. Henrissat, 2003. An evolving hierarchical family classification for glycosyltransferases. *J. Mol. Biol.* 328: 307-317.

Deadman, M. E., S. L. Lundstrom, E. K. H. Schweda, E. R. Moxon and D. W. Hood, 2006. Specific amino acids of the glycosyltransferases LpsA direct the addition of glucose or galactose to the terminal inner core heptose of *Haemophilus influenza*e lipopolysaccharide via alternative linkages. *J. Biol. Chem.* 281: 29455-29467.

Endo, T., S. Koizumi, K. Tabata and A. Ozaki, 2000. Cloning and expression of beta 1,4-galactosyltransferase gene from *Helicobacter pylori*. *Glycobiology* 10: 809-813.

Fu, X., C. Albermann, C. Zhang and J. S. Thorson, 2005. Diversifying vancomycin via chemoenzymatic strategies. *Org. Lett.* 7: 1513-1515.

Ge, Z., N. W. C. Chan, M. M. Palcic and D. E. Taylor, 1997. Cloning and heterologous expression of an α1,3-fucosyltransferase gene from the gastric pathogen *Helicobacter pylori*. *J. Biol. Chem.* 272: 21357-21363.

Gilbert, M., D. C. Watson, A. M. Cunningham, M. P. Jennings, N. M. Young and W. W. Wakarchuk, 1996. Cloning of the lipooligosaccharide α-2,3-sialyltransferase from the bacterial pathogens *Neisseria meningitides* and *Neisseria gonorrhoeae*. *J. Biol. Chem.* 271: 28271-28276.

Gilbert, M., J. R. Brisson, M. F. Karwaski, J. Michniewicz, A. M. Cunninghan, Y. Wu, M. Young and W. W. Wakarchuk, 2000. Biosynthesis of ganglioside mimics in *Campylobacter jejuni* OH4384. Identification of the glycosyltrnasferase genes, enzymatic synthesis of model compounds, and characterization of nanomole amount by 600 mHz ^{1}H and ^{13}C NMR analysis. *J. Biol. Chem.* 275: 3896-3906.

Gilbert, M., M. F. Kawarski, S. Bernatchez, N. M. Young, E. Taboada and J. Michniewicz, 2002. The genetic bases for the variation in the lipo-oligosaccharide of the mucosal pathogen, *Campylobacter jejuni*. *J. Biol. Chem.* 277: 327-337.

Gotschlich, E. C. 1994. Genetic locus for the biosynthesis of the variable portion of *Neisseria gonorrhoeae* lipooligosaccharide. *J. Exp. Med.* 180: 2181-2190.

Gullo, V. P., J. McAlpine, K. S. Lam, D. Baker and F. Petersen, 2006. Drug discovery from natural products. *J. Ind. Microbiol. Biotechnol.* 33: 523-531.

Heinrichs, D. E., M. A. Monteiro, M. B. Perry and C. Whifield, 1998. The assembly system for the lipopolysaccharide R2 core-type of *Escherichia coli* is hybrid of those found in *Escherichia coli* K-12 and *Salmonella enteric. J. Biol. Chem.* 273: 8849-8859.

Hoffmeister, D., B. Wilkinson, G. Foster, P. J. Sidebottom, K. Ichinose and A. Bechthold, 2002. Engineered urdamycinglycosyltransferases are broadened and altered in substrate specificity. *Chem. Biol.* 9: 287-295.

Hoffmeister, D., K. Ichinose and A. Bechthold, 2001. Two sequence elements of glycosyltransferases involved in urdamycin biosynthesis are responsible for substrate specificity and enzymatic activity. *Chem. Biol.* 8: 557-567.

Hong, J. S., S. H. Park, C. Y. Choi, J. K. Sohng and Y. J. Yoon, 2004. New olivosyl derivatives of methymycin/pikromycin from an engineered strain of *Streptomyces venezuelae. FEMS Microbiol. Lett.* 238: 391-399.

Hong, J. S., S. J. Park, N. Parajuli, S. R. Park, H. S. Koh, W. S. Jung, C. Y. Choi and Y. J. Yoon, 2007. Functional analysis of *desVIII* homologues involved in glycosylation of macrolide antibiotics by interspecies complementation. *Gene* 386: 123-130.

Hong, J. S., W. S. Jung, S. K. Lee, W. S. Koh, H. S. Park, S. J. Park, Y. S. Kim and Y. J. Yoon, 2005. The role of a second protein (DesVIII) in glycosylation for the biosynthesis of hybrid macrolide antibiotics in *Streptomyces venezuelae. J. Microbiol. Biotechnol.* 15: 640-645.

Hood, D. W., A. D. Cox, M. Gilbert, K. Makepeace, S. Walsh, M. E. Deadman, A. Cody, A. Martin, M. Mansson, E. K. H. Schweda, J.-R. Brisson, J. C. Richards, E. R. Moxon and W. W. Wakarchuk, 2001. Identification of a lipopolysaccharide α-2,3-sialyltransferase from *Haemophilus influenza. Mol. Microbiol.* 39: 341-350.

Hu, Y., L. Chen, S. Ha, B. Gross, B. Falcone, D. Walker, M. Mokhtarzadeh and S. Walker, 2003. Crystal structure of the MurG:UDP-GlcNAc complex reveals common structural principles of a superfamily of glycosyltransferase. *Proc. Natl. Acad. Sci. US* 100: 845-849.

Hu, Y. and S. Walker, 2002. Remarkable structural similarities between diverse glycosyltransferases. *Chem. Biol.* 9: 1287-1296.

Jaishy, B. P., S. K. Lim, I. D. Yoo, J. C. Yoo, J. K. Sohng and D. H. Nam, 2006. Cloning and characterization of a gene cluster for the production of polyketide macrolide dihydrochalcomycin in *Streptomyces* sp. KCTC0041BP. *J. Microbiol. Biotechnol.* 16: 764-770.

Jennings, M. P., D. W. Hood, I. R. A. Peak, M. Virji and E. R. Moxon, 1995. Molecular analysis of a locus for the biosynthesis and phase-variable expression of the lacto-*N*-neotetraose terminal lipopolysaccharide structure in *Neisseria meningitides. Mol. Microbiol.* 18: 729-740.

Jennings, M. P., M. Virji, D. Evans, V. Foster, Y. N. Srikhanta and L. Steeghs, 1998. Identification of a novel gene involved in pilin glycosylation in *Neisseria meningitides. Mol. Microbiol.* 29: 975-984.

Kang, Y. B., Y. H. Yang, K. W. Lee, S. G. Lee, J. K. Sohng, H. C. Lee, K. Liou and B. G. Kim, 2006. Preparative synthesis of dTDP-L-rhamnose through combined enzymatic pathways. *Biotechnol. Bioeng.* 93: 21-27.

Kim, B. G., N. R. Jung, E. J. Joe, H. G. Hur, Y. Lim, Y. Chong and J. H. Ahn, 2010. Bacterial synthesis of a flavonoid deoxyaminosugar conjugate in *Escherichia coli* expressing a glycosyltransferase of *Arabidopsis thaliana. ChemBioChem 11: 2389-2392.*

Kolkman, M. B. A., W. W. Wakarchuk, P. J. M. Nuijten and B. A. M. van der Zeijst, 1997. Capsular polysaccharide synthesis in Streptococcus pneumonia serotype 14: molecular analysis of the complete cps locus and identification of genes encoding glycosyltransferases required for the biosynthesis of the tetrasaccharide subunit. *Mol. Microbiol.* 26: 197-208.

Krauth, C., M. Fedoryshyn, C. Schleberger, A. Luzhetskyy and A. Bechthold, 2009. Engineering a function into a glycosyltransferase. *Chem. Biol.* 16: 28-35.

Lairson, L. L., B. Henrissat, G. J. Davies and S. G. Withers, 2008. Glycosyltransferases: structures, functions, and mechanisms. *Annu. Rev. Biochem.* 77: 521-555.

Lee, S. K., J. W. Park, J. W. Kim, W. S. Jung, S. R. Park, C. Y. Choi, E. S. Kim, B. S. Kim, J. S. Ahn, D. H. Sherman and Y. J. Yoon, 2006. Neopikromycin and novapikromycin from the pikromycin biosynthetic pathway of *Streptomyces venezuelae*. *J. Nat. Prod.* 69: 847-849.

Logan, S. M., J. W. Conlan, M. A. Monteiro, W. W. Wakarchuk and E. Altman, 2000. Functional genomics of *Helicobacter pylori*: identification of a beta-1,4 galactosyltransferase and generation of mutants with altered lipopolysaccharide. *Mol. Microbiol.* 35: 1156-1167.

Losey, H. C., J. Jiang, J. B. Biggins, M. Oberthur, X. Y. Ye, S. D. Dong, D. Kahne, J. S. Thorson and C. T. Walsh, 2002. Incorporation of glucose analogs by GtfE and GtfD from the vancomycin biosynthetic pathway to generate variant glycopeptides. *Chem. Biol.* 9: 1305-1314.

Lu, W., C. Leimkuhler, G. J. JrGatto, R. G. Kruger, M. Oberthur, D. Kahne and C. T. Walsh, 2005. AknT is an activating protein for the glycosyltransferaseAknS in L-aminodeoxysugar transfer to the aglycone of aclacinomycin A. *Chem. Biol.* 12: 527-534.

Lu, W., M. Oberthur, C. Leimkuhler, J. Tao, D. Kahne and C. T. Walsh, 2004. Characterization of a regiospecificepivancosaminyltransferaseGtfA and enzymatic reconstitution of the antibiotic chloroeremomycin. *Proc. Natl. Acad. Sci. US* 101: 4390-4395.

Luzhetskyy, A. and A. Bechthold, 2008. Features and applications of bacterial glycosyltransferases: current state and prospects. *Appl. Microbiol. Biotechnol.* 80: 945-952.

Luzhetskyy, A., T. Taguchi, M. Fedoryshyn, C. Durr, S. E. Wohlert, V. Novikov and A. Bechthold, 2005. LanGT2 catalyzes the first glycosylation step during landomycinA biosynthesis. *ChemBioChem.* 6: 1406-1410.

Mackenzie, P. I. 1990. Expression of chimeric cDNAs in cell culture defines a region of UDP glucuronosyltransferase involved in substrate selection. *J. Biol. Chem.* 265, 3432-3435.

Melancon, C. E. III, H. Takahashi and H. W. Liou, 2004. Characterization of TylM3/TylM2 and MydC/MycB pairs required for efficient glycosyltransfer in macrolide antibiotic biosynthesis. *J. Am. Chem. Soc.* 126: 16726-16727.

Mulichak, A. M., H. C. Losey, C. T. Walsh and R. M. Garavito, 2001. Structure of the UDP-glucosyltransferaseGtfB that modifies the heptapeptideaglycone in the biosynthesis of vancomycin group antibiotics. *Structure* 9: 547-557.

Mulichak, A. M., H. C. Losey, W. Lu, Z. Wawrzak, C. T. Walsh and R. M. Garavito, 2003. Structure of the TDP-epi-vancosaminyltransferaseGtfA from the chloroeremomycin biosynthetic pathway. *Proc. Natl. Acad. Sci. US* 100: 9238-9243.

Oberthur, M., C. Leimkuhler, R. G. Kruger, W. Lu, C. T. Walsh and D. Kahne, 2005. A systematic investigation of the synthetic utility of glycopeptidesglycosyltransferases. *J. Am. Chem. Soc.* 127: 10747-10752.

Oh, J., S. G. Lee, B. G. Kim, J. K. Sohng, K. Liou and H. C. Lee, 2003. One-pot enzymatic productionof dTDP-4-keto-6-deoxy-D-glucose from dTMP and glucose-1-phosphate. *Biotechnol. Bioeng.* 84: 452-458.

Oh, T. J., D. H. Kim, S. Y. Kang, T. Yamaguchi and J. K. Sohng, 2011. Enzymatic synthesis of vancomycin derivatives using galactosyltransferase and sialyltransferase. *J. Antibiot.* 64: 103-109.

Oh, T. J., S. J. Mo, Y. J. Yoon and J. K. Sohng, 2007. Discovery and molecular engineering of sugar-containing natural product biosynthetic pathways in Actinomycetes. *J. Microbiol. Biotechnol.* 17: 1909-1921.

Pageni, B. B., T. J. Oh, K. Liou, Y. J. Yoon and J. K. Sohng, 2008. Genetically engineered biosynthesis of macrolide derivatives including 4-amino-4,6-dideoxy-L-glucose from *Streptomyces venezuelae* YJ003-OTBP3. *J. Microbiol. Biotechnol.* 18: 88-94.

Park, S. H., H. Y. Park, J. K. Sohng, H. C. Lee, K. Liou, Y. J. Yoon and B. G. Kim, 2009. Expanding substrate specificity of GT-B fold glycosyltransferase via domain swapping and high-throughput screening. *Biotechnol. Bioeng.* 102: 988-994.

Persson, K., H. D. Ly, M. Dieckelmann, W. W. Wakarchuk, S. G. Withers and N.C. Strynadka, 2001. Crystal structure of the retaining galactosyltransferase LgtC from *Neisseria meningitides* in complex with donor and acceptor sugar analogs. *Nat. Struct. Biol.* 8: 166-175.

Perugino, G., A. Trincone, M. Rossi and M. Moracci, 2004. Oligosaccharide synthesis by glycosynthases. *Trend Biotechnol.* 22: 31-37.

Pilobello, K. T. and L. K. Mahal, 2007. Deciphering the glycocode: the complexity and analytical challenge of glycomics. *Curr. Opin. Chem. Biol.* 11: 300-305.

Poulsen, S. M., C. Kofoed and B. Vester, 2000. Inhibition of the ribosomal peptidyltransferase reaction by the mycarose moiety of the antibiotics carbomycin, spiramycin and tylosin. *J. Mol. Biol.* 304: 471-481.

Rabbani, S., V. Miksa, B. Wipf and B. Ernst, 2005. Molecular cloning and functional expression of a novel *Helicobacter pylori* α-1,4 fucosyltraansferase. *Glycobiology* 15: 1076-1083.

Rasko, D. A., G. Wang, M. M. Palcic and D. E. Taylor, 2000. Cloning and characterization of the α(1,3/4)fucosyltransferase of *Helicobacter pylori*. *J. Biol. Chem.* 275: 4988-4994.

Shen, G. J., A. K. Datta, M. Izumi, K. M. Koeller and C. H. Wong, 1999. Expression of α2,8/2,9-polysialyltransferase from *Escherichia coli* K92. *J. Biol. Chem.* 274: 35139-35146.

Simkhada, D., E. Kim, H. C. Lee and J. K. Sohng, 2009, Metabolic engineering of *Escherichia coli* for the biological synthesis of 7-O-xylosyl naringenin. *Mol. Cells.* 28: 397-401.

Simkhada, D., H. C. Lee and J. K. Sohng, 2010b, Genetic engineering approach for the production of rhamnosyl and allosyl flavonoids from *Escherichia coli*. *Biotechnol. Bioeng.* 107: 154-162.

Simhada, D., N. P. Kurumbang, H. C. Lee and J. K. Sohng, 2010a, Exploration of glycosylated flavonoids from metabolically engineered *E. coli*. *Biotech. Bioprocess Eng.* 15: 754-760.

Sinnott, M. L. 1990. Catalytic mechanisms of enzymatic glycosyl transfer. *Chem. Rev.* 90: 1171-1202.

Sohng, J. K., H. J. Kim, D. H. Nam, D. O. Lim, J. M. Hang, H. J. Lee and J. C. Yoo, 2004. Cloning, expression, and biological function of a dTDP-deoxyglucoseepimerase (*gerF*) gene from *Streptomyces* sp. GERI-155. *Biotechnol. Lett.* 26: 185-191.

Sohng, J. K., T. J. Oh and C. G. Kim, 1998. Method for cloning biosynthetic genes of secondary metabolites including deoxysugar from Actinomycetes. *J. Biochem. Mol. Biol.* 31: 475-483.

Sohng, J. K., T. J. Oh, J. H. Cha, J. J. Hahn, J. W. Kim, J. W. Suh and H. C. Lee, 2001. Cloning and identification of a gene cluster in *Streptomyces spectabilis*-spectinomycin producer. *J. Biochem. Mol. Biol. Biophys.* 5: 209-218.

Sohng, J. K., T. J. Oh, J. J. Lee and C. G. Kim, 1997. Identification of a gene cluster of biosynthetic genes of rubradirin substructures in *S. achromogenes* var. *rubradiris* NRRL3061. *Mol. Cells* 7: 674-681.

Stingele, F., J. R. Neeser and B. Mollet, 1996. Identification and characterization of the *eps* (exopolysaccharide) gene cluster from *Streptococcus thermophilus* Sfi6. *J. Bacteriol.* 178: 1680-1690.

Thibodeaux, C. J., C. E. III Melancon and H. W. Liu, 2008. Natural-product sugar biosynthesis and enzymatic glycodiversification. *Angew. Chem. Int. Ed. Engl.* 47: 9814-9859.

Thuy, T. T., K. Liou, T. J. Oh, D. H. Kim, D. H. Nam, J. C. Yoo and J. K. Sohng, 2007. Biosynthesis of dTDP-6-deoxy-beta-D-allose, biochemical characterization of dTDP-4-keto-6-deoxyglucose reductase (*gerK1*) from *Streptomyces* sp. KCTC0041BP. *Glycobiology* 17: 119-126.

Truman, A. W., M. V. Dias, S. Wu, T. L. Blundell, F. Huang and J. B. Spencer, 2009. Chimeric glycosyltransferases for the generation of hybrid *Chem. Biol.* 16: 676-685.

Wang, G., D. A. Rasko, R. Sherburne and D. E. Taylor, 1999. Molecular genetic basis for the variable expression of Lewis Y antigen in *Helicobacter pylori*: analysis of the α(1,2)fucosyltransferase gene. *Mol. Microbiol.* 31: 1265-1274.

Watanabe, M., K. Miyake, K. Yanae, Y. Kataoka, S. Koizymi, T. Endo, A. Ozaki and S. Iijima, 2002. Molecular characterization of a novel beta 1,3-galactosyltransferase for capsular polysaccharide synthesis by *Streptococcus agalactiae* type Ib. *J. Biochem.* 131: 183-191.

Wiggins, C. A. and S. Munro, 1998. Activity of the yeast MNN1 alpha-1,3-mannosyltransferase requires a motif conserved in many other families of glycosyltransferases. *Proc. Natl. Acad. Sci. US* 95: 7945-7950.

Williams, G. J., C. Zhang and J. S. Thorson, 2007. Expanding the promiscuity of a natural-product glycosyltransferase by directed evolution *Nat. Chem. Biol.* 3: 657-662.

Williams, G. J. and J. S. Thorson, 2008a. A high-throughput fluorescence-based glycosyltransferase screen and its application in directed evolution. *Nat. Protoc.* 3: 357-362.

Williams, G. J., R. D. Goff, C. Zhang and J. S. Thorson, 2008b. Optimizing glycosyltransferase specificity via "hot spot" saturation *Chem. Biol.* 15: 393-401.

Xu, H., K. Minagawa, L. Bai, Z. Deng and T. Mahmud, 2008. Catalytic analysis of the validamycin glycosyltransferase (ValG) and enzymatic production of 4"-epi-validamycin A. *J. Nat. Prod.* 71: 1233-1236.

Xue, Y., L. Zhao, H. W. Liu and D. H. Sherman, 1998. A gene cluster for macrolide antibiotic biosynthesis in *Streptomyces venezuelae*: Architecture of metabolic diversity. *Proc. Natl. Acad. Sci. US* 95: 12111-12116.

Yamamoto, S., K. Miyzke, Y. Koike, M. Watanabe, Y. Machida, M. Ohta and S. Iijima, 2000. Molecular characterization of type-specific capsular polysaccharide biosynthesis genes of *Streptococcus agalactiae* type Ia. *J. Bacteriol.* 181: 5176-5184.

Yamamoto, T., M. Nakashizuka and I. Terada, 1998. Cloning and expressionof a marine bacterial β-galactoside α2,6-sialyltransferase from *Photobacterium damsel* JT0160. *J. Biochem.* 123: 94-100.

Yoon, T. M., J. W. Kim, J. G. Kim, W. G. Kim and J. W. Suh, 2006. TalosinsA and B: new isoflavonol glycosides with potent antifungal activity from *Kitasatosporakifunensis* MJM341. I. Taxonomy, fermentation, isolation, and biological activities. *J. Antibiot.* 59: 633-639.

Yu, H., H. Chokhawala, R. Karpel, H. Yu, B. Wu and J. Zhang, 2005. A multifunctional *Pasteurella multocida* sialyltransferase: a powerful tool for the synthesis of sialoside libraries. *J. Am. Chem. Soc.* 127: 17618-17619.

Zhang, C., C. Albermann, X. Fu and J. S. Thorson, 2006. The in vitro characterization of the iterative avermectinglycosyltransferase AveBI reveals reaction reversibility and sugar nucleotide flexibility. *J. Am. Chem. Soc.* 128: 16420-16421.

In: Applications of Microbial Genes in Enzyme Technology ISBN: 978-1-62417-808-5
Editors: V.K.Gupta, M.G.Tuohy, G.D.Sharma et al.

Chapter 7

Microbial Synthesis of Polygalacturonases and Its Industrial Applications

Arakere C. Udayashankar,[1] Chandra S. Nayaka*,[1] Nirmala Devi,[1] Nagaraju Shivaiah,[3] Chowdappa Srinivas,[2†] Siddapura R. Niranjana[1] and Harischandra S. Prakash[1#]*

[1]Department of Studies in Biotechnology, University of Mysore, Manasagangotri, Mysore, Karnataka, India

[2]Department of Studies in Microbiology and Biotechnology, Bangalore University, Jnana Bharathi Campus, Bangalore, Karnataka, India

[3]Department of Post graduate Studies and Research in Biochemistry, Tumkur University, Tumkur, Karnataka, India

Abstract

Enzymes are precious biocatalysts with increasing applications in biotechnology. Microorganisms are wealthy resources of enzymes. Pectinases are a cluster of enzymes that contribute to the degradation of pectin, a ubiquitous complex acidic polysaccharide present in the primary cell wall and middle lamella of higher plant tissues. Polygalacturonases produced by various microorganisms are involved in the degradation of pectic substances. Pectinases can be applied in diverse industrial sectors wherever the degradation of pectin is favourable for a particular process. Microbial production of

* Authors contribute equally.

† Corresponding author: Chowdappa Srinivas. Department of Studies in Microbiology and Biotechnology, Bangalore University, Jnana Bharathi Campus, Bangalore- 560 056, Karnataka, India. Ph: +91-080-22961461; Fax: + 91-080-23219295 E-mail: moonnayak@gmail.com.

Arakere C. Udayashankar, Chandra S. Nayaka, Nirmala Devi, Siddapura R. Niranjana, Harischandra S. Prakash: Department of Studies in Biotechnology, University of Mysore, Manasagangotri, Mysore - 570 006, Karnataka, India. Nagaraju Shivaiah: Department of Post graduate Studies and Research in Biochemistry, Tumkur University, Tumkur-572102.

pectinolytic enzymes is mainly from filamentous fungi, yeasts and bacteria. Microbial pectinases are widely used in industries. Pectinolytic enzymes are of significant importance in the current biotechnological era and have been described as one of the future enzymes of the commercial sector, especially the juice and food industry. This chapter focuses on microbial polygalacturonase source, structural aspects, microbial polygalacturonase genes and industrial applications of polygalacturonase.

Introduction

Enzymes are versatile catalysts with an increasing number of biotechnological applications (Demarche *et al.*, 2011). Since their discovery, enzymes have been extensively used in several industrial processes. The enzyme world market grew at a double-digit rate in the last seven years and was about $5.1 billion in 2009 (Sanchez and Demain, 2010). The biotechnological application of enzymes demonstrate striking features such as improved stability, high activity, specific biocatalysis and reduction of undesirable byproducts. The biodegradable property of enzymes eliminates chemical toxicity, thus being more environment-friendly and also a viable alternative in economic terms (Hoondal *et al.*, 2002; Lara-Marquez *et al.*, 2011).

Pectic substances are prominent structural constituents of primary cell walls and middle lamella in non-woody plant tissues. Pectinases are a group of enzymes that contribute to the degradation of pectin by various mechanisms. In nature, pectinases are important for plants as they help in cell wall extension and fruit ripening. They have a significant role in maintaining ecological balance by causing decomposition and recycling of plant materials. Pectinases are complex group of enzymes that degrade various pectic substances present in plant tissues (Jacob, 2009). Fungal enzymes involved in plant polysaccharide degradation are assigned to at least 35 glycoside hydrolase families, three carbohydrate esterase families and six polysaccharide lyase families (Coutinho *et al.*, 2009; Battaglia *et al.*, 2011).

Protopectinases, polygalacturonases, lyases and pectin esterases are among the extensively studied pectinases or pectinolytic enzymes. Polygalacturonases (PGases) are the pectinolytic enzymes that catalyze the hydrolytic cleavage of the polygalacturonic acid chain with the introduction of water across the oxygen bridge. They are the most studied among the family of pectinolytic enzymes (Jayani *et al.,* 2005). Endopolygalacturonase and exopolygalacturonase are of industrial interest as they act on pectin, hydrolyzing its internal and external glycosidic bonds, producing shorter pectin molecular structures, declining the viscosity and improving the yield of juices (Souza *et al.*, 2003).

Microbial pectinases are widely used in industries. Pectinolytic enzymes are of significant importance in the current biotechnological era and have been described as one of the future enzymes of the commercial sector, especially the juice and food industry (Kashyap *et al.*, 2001) paper and pulp industry (Viikari *et al.*, 2001), scouring of cotton, degumming of plant fibers, waste water treatment, tea and coffee fermentations, poultry feed additives, alcoholic beverages (Jayani *et al.,* 2005), wood preservation (Gummadi and Panda, 2003) maceration, liquefaction and extraction of vegetable tissues (Bohdziewiez and Bodzek, 1994).

It has been estimated that microbial pectinases account for 25% of the global food enzymes sales (Jayani *et al.,* 2005). Novozymes (Denmark), Novartis (Switzerland), Roche

(Germany) and Biocon (India) are some important commercial producers of pectinases (Gummadi and Panda, 2003).

Microbial production of pectinolytic enzymes is mainly from filamentous fungi, yeasts and filamentous and non-filamentous bacteria. Pectinolytic enzymes are produced by two different techniques *viz*, submerged fermentation (SmF) and solid-state fermentation (SSF). Agricultural and agro-industrial residues are used as substrates for SSF enzyme production. As these residues are renewable and in an abundant supply, they represent a potential low cost raw material for microbial enzyme production (Jacob, 2009).

Significant uniqueness displayed by filamentous fungi such as their capacity for fermentation, the production of large quantities of extracellular enzymes (e.g. several grams per liter in strains of *Aspergillus* spp.), easier cultivation on cheap raw materials, and the economical production in large bioreactors makes them first choice and excellent models for industrial applications (de-Vries and Visser 2001; Aro *et al.*, 2005). *Trichoderma reesei* and a number of strains of *Aspergillus* spp. and *Penicillium* spp. are filamentous fungi most frequently employed for the production of polymer-degrading enzymes (Aro *et al.*, 2005; Cardoso *et al.*, 2007). *Aspergillus niger* is the most generally employed fungal species for commercial pectinolytic enzyme production (Naidu and Panda, 1998) because this strain posses GRAS (Generally Regarded As Safe) status (Pariza and Foster, 1983). *Aspergillus niger* produces diverse pectinases including polymethylgalacturonase, polygalacturonase and pectinesterase (Gummadi and Panda, 2003).

Pectin

The structural constituents of a young plant cell wall are cellulose, hemicellulose and pectic substances. Pectic substances such as pectin, protopectin and pectic acids, present in cell wall and middle lamella, provide firmness and organization to plant tissues (Gummadi and Panda, 2003). The cellulose microfibrils provide strength to the cell wall, while hemicelluloses and pectic substances act as the cementing substance for the cellulose network (Jacob, 2009). Pectin, probably the most complex macromolecule in nature is composed of as many as 17 different monosaccharides (Vincken *et al.*, 2003).

In plant cell wall, three major pectic polysaccharides are known, all containing galacturonic acid to a greater or lesser extent. Homogalacturonan is a linear polymer consisting of 1,4-linked α-D-galacturonic acid residues that may be methylesterified and acetylated (Ridley *et al.*, 2001). Xylogalacturonan is a branched galacturonan consisting of 1,3-β-D-xylose side chains (Schols and Voragen, 1996; Visser and Voragen, 1996). The galacturonic acid residues of xylogalacturonan can be methyl-esterified as in homogalacturonan (Schols *et al.*, 1995; Visser and Voragen, 1996). Rhamnogalacturonan I consists of the repeating disaccharide unit [$\rightarrow$4)-α-D-galacturonic acid-(1$\rightarrow$2)-α-L-rhamnnose-(1$\rightarrow$] to which a variety of different glycan chains (principally arabinan and galactan) are attached to the rhamnose residues (Figure 1).

The rhamnogalacturonan II has a backbone of homogalacturonan, with complex side chains of arabinose, galactose, rhamnose and more unusual monosaccharides such as apiose, aceric acid, deoxylyxo-heptulopyranosylaric acid and ketodeoxymanno-octulopyranosylonic acid attached to the galacturonic acid residues (Ridley *et al.*, 2001; Willats *et al.*, 2001).

Previously it was established that rhamnogalacturonan and homogalacturonan domains comprise the 'backbone' of pectic polymers.

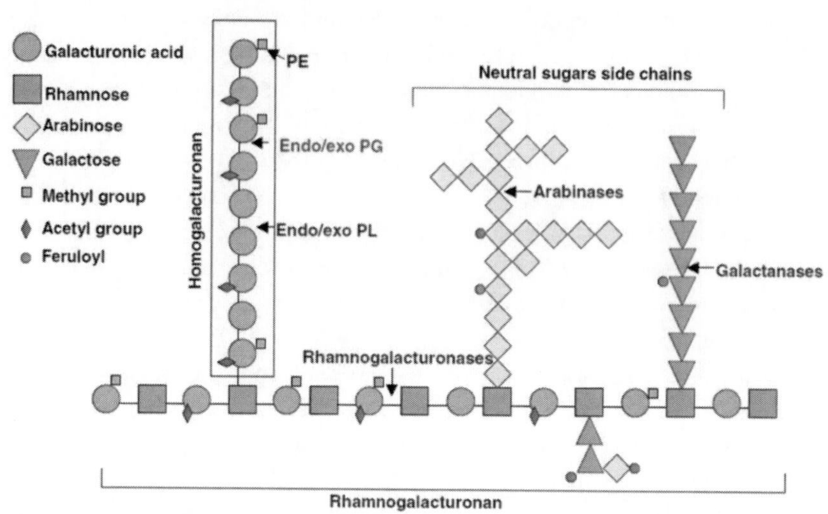

Source: Niture, 2008.

Figure 1. Diagrammatic representation of different components of pectin molecule and associated different neutral sugars side-chains. The cleavage sites of pectin degrading enzymes are also represented (Vincken et al. 2003). PG, polygalacturonase; PL, pectate lyase; PE, pectinesterase.

However, lately, a substitute structure has been lately proposed in which homogalacturonan is a long side chain of rhamnogalacturonan I (Vincken *et al.*, 2003) (Figure 1).

Pectic substances are extensively dispersed in fruits and vegetables (10-30% in turnips, peels of orange and in pulps of tomato, pineapple and lemon), therefore they form significant natural substrates for pectinases. In common pectinases are classified into de esterification and depolymerizing enzymes based on the degradation mechanism. The structure of pectin present in fruits and vegetables depends on enzymatic and chemical modifications occurring during these processes. One of the most characteristic changes during the ripening of fleshy fruits is softening. The change is attributed to enzymatic degradation and solubilization of pectic substances (Jacob, 2009).

Pectinases

Pectin being a highly complex and heterogeneous polymer, requires the combined action of different enzymes for its degradation. The enzymes that hydrolyse pectic substances are known as pectic enzymes, pectinases, or pectinolytic enzymes (Alkorta *et al.*, 1998). Pectinolytic enzymes are naturally produced by many organisms like bacteria, actinomycetes, fungi, yeasts, insects, nematodes, protozoan and plants (Pedrolli *et al.*, 2009). Microbes are prolific producers of pectinases. In general, fungal enzymes are acidic in nature, while bacterial strains produce alkaline enzymes (Pandey *et al.,* 1999). In common, homogalacturonan regions of pectin are known as 'sooth-regions' and rhamnogalacturonan regions as 'hairy/branched region'. These two diverse regions of pectin can be cleaved by some specific enzymes, which are classified into two key classes such as esterases and depolymerases. Pectin methylesterase (EC 3.1.1.11) can remove methoxyl group from pectin or partially esterified homogalacturonan. The hairy regions of pectin can be cleaved by rhamnogalacturonases (EC 3.2.1.40), endo-xylogalacturonan hydrolases, arabinases, and galactanases. Partially esterified homogalacturonan or polygalacturonic acid can be cleaved by two distinct depolymerases such as hydrolase and lyase. The esterified homogalacturonan can be cleaved by pectin lyase (EC 4.2.2.10), whereas partially esterified homogalacturonan is the best substrate for pectate lyase (PL). Endo-PL (EC 4.2.2.2) causes random cleavage in polygalacturonic acid by a trans-elimination process, while exo-PL (EC 4.2.2.9) causes sequential cleavage in polygalacturonic acid by a trans-elimination process and produces unsaturated galacturonic acid (Niture, 2008). Further, homogalacturonan or polygalacturonic acid can be hydrolysed by two more enzymes such as endo-PG (EC 3.2.1.15) which hydrolyses polygalacturonic acid in a random fashion and liberates saturated oligogalacturonides and galacturonic acid. Exo-PG (EC 3.2.1.67) catalyses the hydrolytic release of one saturated galacturonic acid residue from non-reducing end of homogalacturonan, whereas another exo-poly-α-galacturonosidase (EC 3.2.1.82), mostly produced by bacterial species, liberates digalacturonic acid residues form the non-reducing end of galacturonan (Niture, 2008). Different pectic substances and their mode of reaction are illustrated in Figure 2 (Gummadi and Panda, 2003).

Microbial Polygalacturonases

Initial research on pectinases began with understanding the structure of pectic substances and the mechanism by which pectolytic enzymes degrade pectic substances.

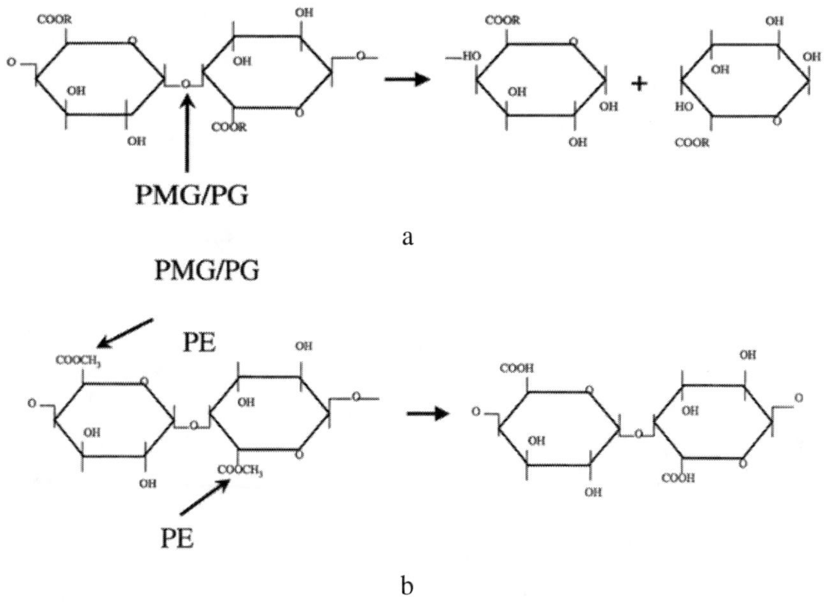

PMG/PG

a

PMG/PG

PE

PE

b

Figure 2. (Continued).

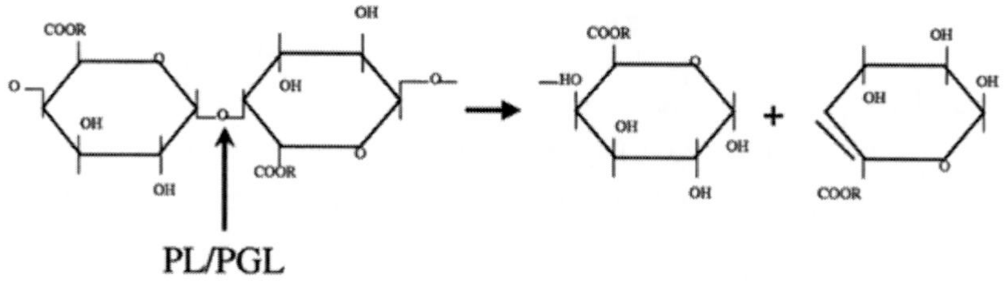

PL/PGL

c

Source: Gummadi and Panda, 2003.

Figure 2. Different types of pectinases and their mode of action on pectic substances (a) R. H for PG and CH3 for PMG (b) PE and (c) R. H for PGL and CH3 for PL. The arrow indicates the place where the pectinases reacts with pectic substances. PMG: polymethylgalacturonase, PG: polygalacturonase (EC 3.2.1 15). PE: pectinesterase (EC 3.1.1 11), PL: pectinlyase (4.2.2 10). Apart from these other pectinases, viz., protopectinase (degrading protopectin), Oligogalacturonases (degrading D-galactosiduronates) exists. The pectinases are further subclassified based on the nature of reaction. Endopectinases cleaves the substrate in random fashion while exopectinases cleaves in end-wise fashion.

Shortly the microbial production of pectinases became prominent for many decades. Various microorganisms, *viz*., bacteria, yeast and fungi produce pectinases, inducible and they can be produced from different carbon sources (Nair and Panda, 1997; Friedrich *et al*., 1994). Polygalacturonases production has been reported from bacteria such as *Ralstonia solanacearum* (Huang and Allen, 1997), *Bacillus* spp. (Koboyashi *et al*., 2001), *Agrobacterium tumefaciens* (Rodrigues-Palenzuela *et al*., 1991), *Bacillus sphaericus* (Jayani *et al*., 2010), *Erwinia carotovora* (Palomaki and Saarilahti 1997), *E. chrysanthemi* (Shevchik *et al*., 1999) and actinomycete, *Streptomyces lydicus* (Nicemol *et al*., 2006).

Polygalacturonase producing fungi have been isolated from different sources/ diverse habitats including soil, decomposed plant parts, infected host tissue of plants and from mangrove/estuarine environments. In laboratory conditions and in submerged culture, the production of PGs generally depends on medium compositions such as pectin source, nitrogen source, initial pH of the medium, temperature and agitation. Since fungi prefer to grow on semi-solid medium, semi-solid fermentation is the best system in which the moisture content, crude agricultural source and pH are the main factors (Niture, 2008).

Polygalacturonases production has been extensively reported from filamentous fungi belonging to several genera such as, *Aspergillus niger* (Kester and Visser 1990), *A. flavus* (Whitehead *et al*., 1995), *A. ustus* (Rao *et al*., 1996), *A. awamori* (Blandino *et al*., 2002), *Aureobasidium pullulans* (Sakai and Takaoka, 1984), *Rhizopus stolonifer* (Manachini *et al*., 1987), *Rhizopus oryzae* (Xiao *et al*., 2008), *Alternaria mali* (Nozaki *et al*., 1997), *A. citri* (Isshiki *et al*., 2001), *Botrytis cinerea* (Cabanne and Doneche, 2002), *Peacilomyces clavisporus* (Souza *et al*., 2003), *Colletorichum lindemuthianum* (Herert *et al*., 2004), *Claviceps purpurae* (Tenberg *et al*., 1996) *Fusarium oxysporum* (Maceira *et al*., 1997), *F. oxysporum* f. sp. *melonis* (Martinez *et al*., 1991), *Fusarium moniliforme* (Lorenzo *et al*., 1987), *Penicillium griseoroseum* (Ribon *et al*., 2002), *P. frequentans* (Barense *et al*., 2001), *Neurospora crassa* (Lourdes *et al*., 1991), *Phytophthora parasitica* (Wu *et al*., 2008), *Rhizoctonia solani* (Marcus *et al*., 1986), *Thermomyces lanuginosus* (Kumar and Palanivelu, 1999), *Burkholderia cepacia* (Massa *et al*., 2007), *Burkholderia glumae* (Degrass *et al*., 2008), *Trichoderma viride* (Arotupin and Emmanuel, 2011), yeast species including

Saccharomyces fragilis (Luh and Phaff, 1954), *Kluyveromyces marxianus* (Barnby *et al.*, 1990), *Cryptococcus albidus* (Federici, 1985) and *Saccharomyces cerevisiae* (Blanco *et al.*, 1994).

Polygalacturonases production is induced by galacturonic acid and its polymer (pectin and polygalacturonic acid), galactose and structural associates (mucic acid, tartonic acid and dulcitol) (Maldonado and Saad, 1998; Malvessi and da-Silveira, 2004; Teixeira *et al.*, 2000). The maximum production of PG activity (500 U/mL) was reported in *Aspergillus japonicas*, grown of pectin and glucose containing liquid medium (Teixeira *et al.*, 2000). PGases have also been cloned and genetically studied in a large number of microbial species.

Polygalacturonase Structure

The X-ray analysis reveals that all of these pectinolytic enzymes have a very characteristic fold called a parallel β-helix (Cho *et al.*, 2001). Proteins with known crystal structures include pectate lyases from *Erwinia chrysanthemi* (Lietzke *et al.*, 1994) and *Bacillus subtilis* (Pickersgill *et al.*, 1994), pectin lyases B and C from *Aspergillus niger* (Mayans *et al.*, 1997; Vitali *et al.*, 1998), rhamnogalacturonase from *A. aculeatus* (RGA) (Petersen *et al.*, 1997), polygalacturonase from *E. carotovora* ssp. *carotovora* (PGC) (Pickergill *et al.*, 1998), polygalacturonase II from *A. niger* (PGN) (van-Santen *et al.*, 1999) and pectin methylesterase from *E. chrysanthemi* (Jenkins *et al.*, 2001). The first crystal structure of PG II from *Aspergillus niger* was solved by van-Santen *et al.*, (1999) representing enzyme folded into a right handed parallel *β*-helix with 10 complete turns (Figure 3a). The number of amino acids per turn varied from 22 to 39, averaging to 29 residues per turn. The crystal structure of endo-PG I from *Aspergillus niger*, very similar (60% sequence identity) to *Aspergillus niger* PG II (van-Santen *et al.*, 1999) was revealed by van-Pouderoyen *et al.*, (2003) comprising 10 complete turns and folds into right handed parallel *β*-helical structure. The crystal structure of *Aspergillus aculeatus* was solved by Cho *et al.*, (2001) which was quite similar to that of *Aspergillus niger* endo-PG II, with some dissimilarities. *Aspergillus aculeatus* PG A folds into a large right handed parallel *β*-helix with overall dimensions of 65 Å x 34 Å × 36 Å with 10 complete turns and the number of residues per turn varied from 22 to 29, excluding the residues in the loop regions (Figure 3b) similar to PG II of *Aspergillus niger*. Among the notable differences between PG A and PGII structures is a long T1 loop that forms the 9th complete turn and contains a catalytic tyrosine residue.

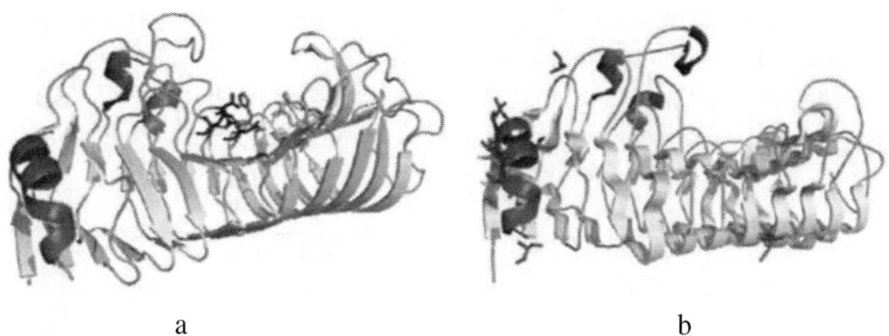

Figure 3. (Continued).

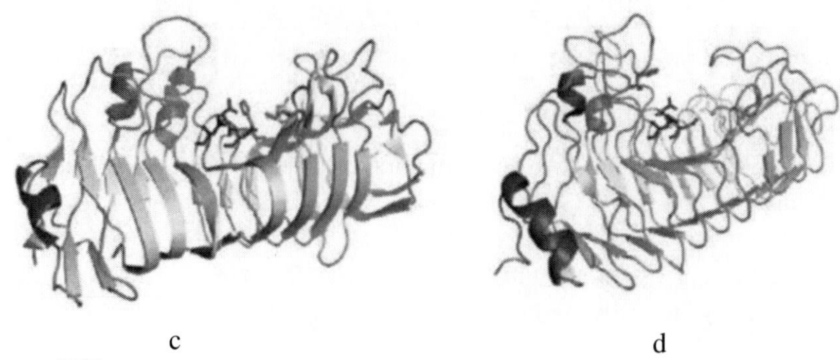

Source: Nature, 2008.

Figure 3. Schematic representation of crystal structures of some fungal PGs. The structures are viewed from the C-terminal side. (a) The endo-PG II from *Aspergillus niger* (PDB code: 1CZF). The active site cleft is formed by the loop regions T1 (left side) and T3 (right side). The active site residues present in the cleft are shown in different colors: Asp180, Asp201 and Asp202 are in blue, His223 in red, Arg256 in orange, and Lys258 in purple (adapted from van-Santen *et al.,* 1999). (b) The PGA from *Aspergillus aculeatus* (PDB code: 1IB4). The N-glycosylated Asn219 residue is shown in purple color at the C terminus region (right side) whereas, Thr5, Thr8 and several serine residues present in the N-terminus are shown in red color which are glycosylated by O-linked mannose residues (left side) (adapted from Cho *et al.*, 2001). (c) The endo-PG I from *Stereum purpureum* (PDB code: 1KSC). A large active site cleft is formed by the parallel β-sheet, PB1, and the loops of both sides of PB1. The three aspartate residues, Asp153, Asp173 and Asp174, from the active site are shown in blue color, His195 in red, Arg226 in yellow and Lys228 in purple (adapted from Shimizu *et al.*, 2002). (d) The endo-PG from *Fusarium moniliforme* (PDB code: 1HG8). Important active site residues are highlighted as follows: Asp191, Asp213 and Asp212 in blue, His188 in red, Arg267 in yellow and Lys269 in turquoise (adapted from Federici *et al.*, 2001).

The T1 loop of PG A comprises 15 residues from Gln^{268} whereas in PG II, 17 residues are present from the equivalent Gln^{289}. The second major difference between PG A and PG II is the glycosylation pattern, because PG II is a recombinant protein. PG A has one N-glycosylation site and is highly O-glycosylated at the N-terminal site (Figure 3b), whereas PG II has only one N-glycosylation site at Asn^{240}.

Employing molecular modelling approach Shimizu *et al.*, (2002) determined the structure of endo-PG I produced by *Stereum purpureum* with complex oligogalacturonide, also has a righthanded β-helical structure (Figure 3c). Structural comparison of *Stereum purpureum* endo-PG I with *Aspergillus niger* endo-PG II revealed that most of the secondary structural elements are in the same positions (Figure 3a, c).

The two structures differ only in their C-terminal regions, the *Aspergillus niger* endo-PG II is fixed by a disulfide bridge, while that of endo-PG I is fixed by an extra β-sheet structure, PB2c composed of two β-strands, 36 and 38.

The crystal structure of endo-PG produced by phytopathogenic fungus *Fusarium moniliforme* was solved by Federici *et al.*, (2001). Similar to other PG structures, it has a right-handed parallel β-helix, resulting in the tandem repetition of 10 coils, each formed by three or four β-strands (Figure 3d). The length of the β-strands is generally short (3 to 5 residues); more variable is the length of the turns (T) between β-strands. The 3-D structure deduced by crystallographic analysis of *Fusarium phyllophilum* polygalacturonase (FpPG) reveals characteristic pectic enzyme structure, a right-handed parallel beta helix, formed by

10 coils with tandem repetition of 3-4 beta strands for coil, and the active site located in a deep cleft on one side of the enzyme (Federici *et al.*, 2001, Herron *et al.*, 2000).

Most recently, Abbott and Boraston (2007) have determined the crystal structure of native exo-PG (YeGH28) and digalacturonic acid complex with exo-PG from Gram-negative enteric pathogen *Yerisinia enterocolitica*. The protein possessed 570 amino acids and adopts a conventional right-handed parallel β-helix topology, containing ten complete turns that comprise four discernable β-sheets, and fibronectin-type III domain grafted to its N-terminal. The protein shows significant sequence and structural similarities with other GH28 members. Eight conserved important catalytic residues which are present in other fungal endo-PGs are stringently conserved in this protein also. The fibronectin-type III domain is very common in bacterial carbohydrate-active proteins and it may be involved in a variety of molecular recognition processes, such ascell adhesion, cell surface hormone and cytokine receptor.

Microbial Polygalacturonase Genes and Strain Improvement

Polygalacturonase is classified into glycosyl-hydrolases family 28. Based on their mode of action, polygalacturonases are classified into two groups: (i) Endopolygalacturonases (E.C.3.2.1.15) break the polymer chain in a random pattern liberating saturated oligogalacturonides and galacturonic acid, (ii) Exopolygalacturonases (EC 3.2.1.67), cleave the penultimate polymer bonds releasing one saturated galacturonic acid residue from non-reducing end of homogalacturonan. Another exoPG called exo-poly-α-galacturonosidase (EC 3.2.1.82), produced by bacterial species, liberates digalacturonic acid residues form the non-reducing end of galacturonan.

Several fungal endopolygalacturonases have been cloned and characterized, including those from *Aspergillus niger*, *Aspergillus tubigensis*, *Cochliobolus carbonum*, *Fusarium moniliforme*, *Sclerotinia sclerotiorum* and *Aspergillus flavus* (Bussink *et al.*, 1991a; Bussink *et al.*, 1992; Bussink *et al.*, 1991; Caprari *et al.*, 1993; Walton and Cervone, 1990; Whitehead *et al.*, 1995). Most of the commercial pectinases produced by *Aspergillus* spp., contain several kinds of pectinase activity; some examples are polygalacturonase, pectin methyl esterase and pectin lyase. Of these, polygalacturonase is the most important because it depolymerizes the principal chains of pectin, and is the preferred pectinase for baby foods. Therefore, recombinant fungal strains that produce a large amount of PG without other pectinolytic activities are desirable (Lang and Dornenburg, 2000).

Aspergillus niger, the industrial fungus has revealed to harbor a complete family of *endo*polygalacturonase-encoding genes (Bussink *et al.*, 1992), most of which have now been cloned, sequenced and individually overexpressed (Bussink *et al.*, 1990; 1991; 1992; Parenicova *et al.*, 1998). The filamentous fungus *Aspergillus flavus* produces a diverse range of polymer hydrolyzing enzymes, such as pectinases (Cotty *et al.*, 1990) and proteinases (Mellon and Cotty, 1995) to assist in the degradation of complex substrates. The capability of *A. flavus* isolates to extend between locules of developing cotton bolls is strongly associated with the production of a specific endopolygalacturonases (Cleveland and Cotty, 1991).

Moreover, this specific pectinases (P2c) is not catabolite repressed in culture by low molecular weight saccharides present in developing cotton bolls (Brown *et al.*, 1992). Further evidence for the importance of P2c in *A. flavus* invasiveness of cotton bolls is provided by the transformation of *A. flavus* strains lacking P2c with *pecA*, the gene which encodes this pectinase. Such transformants acquire an increased ability to cause intercarpellary membrane damage and invade adjacent locules. In addition, removal of *pecA* activity through targeted disruption significantly reduces boll invasiveness (Shieh *et al.*, 1997).

The genome of *Aspergillus niger* contains seven endopolygalacturonases, each of them exhibiting diverse kinetic properties, substrate methylation sensitivity and mode of action (Martens-Uzunova and Schaap 2009; Benen *et al.*, 2000; Bussink *et al.*, 1991; Parenicova *et al.*, 1998; 2000) and four potential exopolygalacturonases: PgaX, PgxA, PgxB, and PgxC (Martens-Uzunova *et al.*, 2006). Two PG genes, *pgaA* and *pgaB*, have been cloned from *Aspergillus oryzae* and their gene products were characterized (Kitamoto *et al.*, 1998). The *TEF1* gene, encoding translation-elongation factor 1a, was cloned from the same strain and used for expression of polygalacturonase genes. A recombinant *Aspergillus oryzae* strain, PGB3 was generated by constructing the PG gene (*pgaB*) overexpression vector pGBmR, and used the vector to transform the *A. oryzae* strain, RIB40. When cultured in potato pulp solid medium, PGB3 grew more rapidly and produced 4.5 times more PG than RIB40. Suzuki *et al.*, (2010) observed maximum production (173 U/g) of PG after 2 days of culture of PGB3 in potato pulp solid medium.

Two polygalacturonase genes *pecA* and *pecB* have been cloned from *Aspergillus flavus* and their gene products were characterized by Whitehead *et al.*, (1995). Based on virulence, two strains of *A. flavus* can be isolated from naturally infected cotton bolls. Highly virulent strains degrade the intercarpellary membrane that divides a cotton boll and are able to spread throughout the boll.

Moderately virulent strains cannot degrade this membrane, and thus their growth is restricted to individual locules. The only consistent difference detected between these two strain types is their pectinase production. The *pecA* gene was reported to contain 1,228 bp encoding a protein of 363 amino acids with a predicted molecular mass of 37.6 kDa, interrupted by two introns of 58 and 81 bp in length.

Accumulation of *pecA* mRNA in both pectin- or glucose-grown mycelia in the highly virulent strain matched the activity profile of a pectinase previously identified as P2c. Transformants of a moderately virulent strain containing a functional copy of the *pecA* gene produced P2c *in vitro*, confirming that *pecA* encodes P2c. The coding region of *pecB* was reported to be 1,217 bp in length interrupted by two introns of 65 and 54 bp in length. The predicted protein of 366 amino acids had an estimated molecular mass of 38 kDa. The two genes, *pecA* and *pecB* share a high degree of sequence identity with polygalacturonase genes from *Aspergillus parasiticus* and *Aspergillus oryzae* (Whitehead *et al.*, 1995). *A. niger* strains are employed as the main industrial producer of pectinases for use in the food industry. Considerable effort has been placed on increasing the production of pectinases in culture.

If the mechanism by which *pecA* produces pectinase in the presence of glucose is determined, it may be possible to genetically alter native *A. niger* pectinase genes or introduce the *A. flavus pecA* gene and increase the productivity of pectinase manufacturers (Whitehead *et al.*, 1995).

Wubben *et al.*, (1999) employed molecular genetic approach to study the process of pectin degradation by *Botrytis cinerea*, a gray mold fungus infecting over 200 different plant species. Six different endoPG genes were isolated from *B. cinerea* SAS56 by Wubben *et al.*, (1999) (Figure 4).

The sequence identity at the amino acid level within the endoPG family of *B. cinerea* varied between 34 and 73%. The expression of the *Bcpg* gene family was analyzed when the fungus was grown on two different carbon sources: glucose and polygalacturonic acid. Clear differences in gene expression levels could be observed between members of the *Bcpg* gene family.

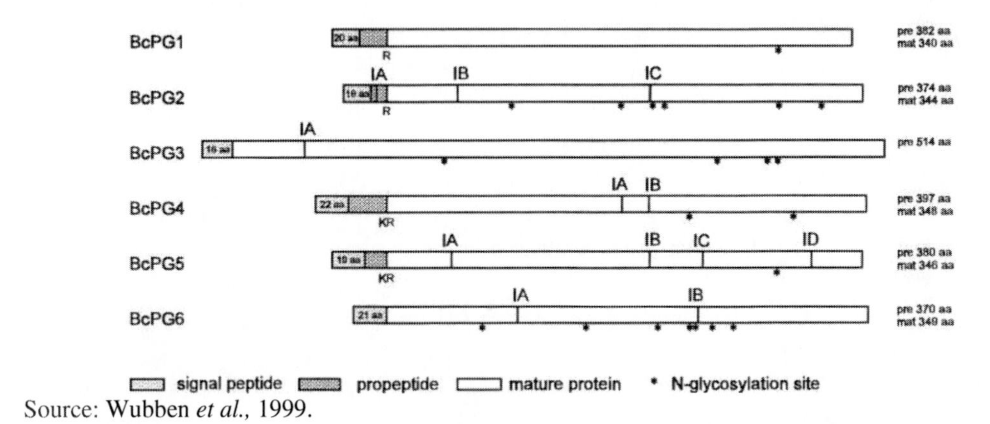

Source: Wubben *et al.,* 1999.

Figure 4. Genomic organization of the endopolygalacturonase gene family of *B. cinerea*. Indicated are the positions of the introns in the original DNA sequence (IA, IB, IC, or ID), the presence of a putative monobasic (R) or dibasic (KR) cleavage sites, and the presence of *N*-glycosylation signals (*). Also depicted in the figure are the derived lengths of unprocessed proteins (pre) and mature processed proteins (mat). The lengths of predicted signal peptides for each of the proteins are indicated in the respective boxes.

Expression of *Bcpg*1, -2, and -6 gene family members was observed on both carbon sources, while *Bcpg*3 and -5 gene family members were predominantly expressed on either glucose or polygalacturonic acid. They envisaged that a coordinated regulation of gene expression occurs during infection of plants. EndoPGs from constitutively expressed genes might release pectin degradation products which can induce the expression of other endoPG-encoding genes. An endopolygalacturonases gene *Bcpg*1 is required for full virulence in *B. cinerea*. Elimination of this gene resulted in a mutant with reduced virulence on different hosts (ten-Have *et al.*, 1998).

The endoPG-encoding genes of *B. cinerea* are differentially expressed in liquid culture when grown in liquid culture on different carbon sources. Wubben *et al*., (2000) were able to distinguish four different patterns of expression: firstly, a basic level of gene expression for the two basic endoPGs (*Bcpgl* and *Bcpg2*) was observed on all carbon sources tested; secondly, galacturonic acid was observed to induce the expression of *Bcpg4* and *Bcpg6*; thirdly, a low pH of the culture medium resulted in induced expression of the *Bcpg3* gene, almost irrespective of the carbon source present; and finally, induced expression of the *Bcpg4* gene was repressed by the presence of a more favourable carbon source. Expression of the *Bcpg5* gene was inducible; however the inducing factors were not identified.

The pattern of *B. cinerea Bcpg* gene expression in four hosts indicated that gray mold fungus is equipped with flexible enzymatic pectate degradation machinery. The expression pattern of endopolygalacturonases encoding genes (*Bcpgl-6*) of *Botrytis cinerea* studied on four hosts: tomato, broad bean, apple and courgette (Zucchini) were differentially expressed, depending on the stage of infection and the host. *Bcpgl* was expressed in all tissues tested with differences in transcript levels. Among four plant tissues tested, *Bcpg2* expression was detected early in three plant tissues. *Bcpg3* and *Bcpg5* were expressed in apple fruit tissue, probably as a result of different regulatory mechanisms (ten-Have *et al.*, 2001).

Using the *pgaII* gene of *Aspergillus niger* as a probe, two putative polygalacturonase genes (*pg1* and *pg2*) were isolated from strain T5 of *Claviceps purpurea*, probably code for mature proteins of 343 and 344 amino acids, respectively and share significant homology with endo-PGs of other filamentous fungi. The potential substrate of the putative products of pg1 and pg2 for the first time was shown to be a component of host cell walls in rye ovaries (Tenberge *et al.*, 1996).

Polygalacturonase from yeasts could possibly be good substitutes for pectinases from fungal origin reported in some cases to contain undesirable enzymes (Luh and Phaff, 1954; Whitaker 1984). Blanco *et al.*, (1997) reported several genes to be involved in PG production and reported the presence of an open reading frame in the chromosome X of *Saccharomyces cerevisiae* exhibiting high homology with polygalacturonase genes of *A. niger*.

An endo-polygalacturonase-encoding gene (*PGU1*) from *Saccharomyces cerevisiae* IM1-8b has been cloned, sequenced and over-expressed in several *S. cerevisiae* strains (Blanco *et al.*, 1998). The predicted protein comprised of 361 amino acids, with a signal peptide between residues 1 and 18 and two potential glycosylation points in residues 318 and 330. The putative active site was a conserved histidine in position 222. The polygalacturonase showed 54% homology with fungal species and only 24% homology with their plant and bacterial counterparts. The amino acid sequence of yeast polygalacturonase encoded by *PGU1* gene was compared with other PGs from different origins. An alignment among yeast, fungal, plant and bacterial PGs showed PGs in yeast and filamentous fungi were similar in all domains. Bacterial and plant PGs were identical only within the C-terminal region. The similarity between *S. cerevisiae* PG and fungal PGs in Domain 1 was 13% and the similarity between Domain 2 was found to be 64%. The Domains 3 and 4 were common to all sequences compared and contained a highly conserved region. The similarity among PGs from all origins was 25% in Domain 3 and 50% in Domain 4. Evolutionary conservation of these domains reveals that they must be essential for the structure and formation of the active site of PGs and may indicate the existence of a common ancestral gene for prokaryotic and eukaryotic PGs (Blanco *et al.*, 1998). The gene was present in a single gene copy per haploid genome and was detected in all strains, regardless of their phenotype. The expression of *PGU1* gene in several strains of *S. cerevisiae* revealed that the polygalacturonase activity increased (up to 200 times) and can be regarded as a significant first stage for over-production PGs for industrial purposes in *S. cerevisiae*.

Polygalacturonase genes of *Aspergillus niger*, *A. oryzae*, *A. tubigenesis*, *Sclerotinia sclerotiorum* and *Fusarium moniliforme* contain similar putative TATA boxes, CAAT sequences and pyrimidine-rich regions upstream from the transcription start site and similar polyadenylation and transcription termination sites downstream from the coding region (Bussink *et al.*, 1992; Caprari *et al.*, 1993; Frassinet-Tachet *et al.*, 1995; Kitamoto *et al.*, 1993; Reymond *et al.*, 1994). However in *A. flavus*, no recognizable TATAA or CAAT motif was observed in the 5' region of *pecA*. Nevertheless, sequences of TATACA and CAAAT are at -57 and -108, respectively, for *pecB* (Whitehead *et al.*, 1995). Both these genes obeyed the translation start rule of having a purine, normally an ‘A’, at the -3 position, to direct efficient ribosomal binding.

Even though *Penicillium* spp. can also be considered an important fungal model, no compilation of gene organization data from these organisms has been performed until now that could reveal important sequences for gene expression as already reported for *Neurospora* and *Aspergillus* (Ribon *et al.*, 2002). They have been studying the pectinolytic system of *Penicillium griseoroseum* as a model system for gene organization and regulation in filamentous fungi to obtain overproducing strains that can be used in the textile industry to degum natural fibers. Two genes encoding endoPGs, *pgg1* and *pgg2*, have been cloned and are differentially expressed in response to the growth medium (Ribon *et al.,* 1999; Ribon *et al.,* 2002). All endoPG genes described until now for filamentous fungi have a homologous domain of approximately 400 bp assumed to contain residues that are relevant for PG activity. The two endopolygalacturonase-coding genes of *pgg1* and *pgg2* exist as single copies in the *P. griseoroseum* genome as confirmed by Southern blot analysis (Ribon *et al.*, 2002). Single copies have been demonstrated for other PG genes including the *clpg1* and *clpg2* genes of *Colletotrichum lindemuthianum*, *pg1* and *pg2* of *P. olsonii*, and *bcpg1* of *Botrytis cinerea* (Centis *et al.,* 1996; Centis *et al.,* 1997; ten-Have *et al.,* 1998; Wagner *et al.,* 2000). As opposed to *Penicillium*, gene families consisting of at least five PG members have been detected in *Aspergillus niger*, *B. cinerea*, and *Sclerotinia sclerotiorum* (Fraissinet-Tachet *et al.,* 1995; Parenicová *et al.,* 1998; Wubben *et al.,* 1999). Wagner *et al.,* (2000) characterized two PG genes in *P. olsonii* that showed significant homology to endoPG of other filamentous fungi and suggested the presence of at least one more gene in the fungus genome.

Seven PG genes from *P. griseoroseum*, *P. expansum*, *P. digitatum*, *P. janthinellum*, and *P. olsonii* compared for general features such as number, length, splice sites, and position of introns, consensus sequences flanking the translation initiation codon, and codon usage revealed that all polypeptides started invariantly with AUG. The highest identity (42%) was found between the second introns of *P. griseoroseum* and *P. digitatum*. The average length of the introns was 61 bp and the largest one (88 bp) was observed in the PG gene from *P. janthinellum*. The *pepg1* gene from *P. expansum* and the *pg2* from *P. olsonii* showed an additional intron conserved at the same position, while the only intron detected in the *pg1* gene of *P. olsonii* was placed with the second intron of the other genes (Ribon *et al*., 2002a). Genes encoding PG and their corresponding enzymes are well studied in *Aspergillus* spp., traditionally used as the model genus in filamentous fungi. Nonetheless, *Penicillium* is an option that can be used to study aspects of gene organization and regulation due to the presence of multigenic families, genes differentially expressed and transposon-like elements, as well as its importance and potential application of the proteins and secondary metabolites in the food and pharmaceutical industry (Ribon *et al*., 2002a).

Among many *Fusarium* spp. polygalacturonase is encoded by a single gene in many *Fusarium* species for this reason, the *pg* gene has been proposed as a molecular marker for taxonomic studies of *Fusarium* spp. (Posada *et al.*, 2000) [*F. episphaeria* and *F. solani* (Posada *et al.*, 2000), *F. oxysporum* f. sp. *lycopersici*, *F. oxysporum* f. sp. *radicis-lycopersici* (Patiño *et al.*, 1997), *F. verticillioides* (Sella *et al.*, 2004). The N-terminus and several internal tryptic peptides of *endo*polygalacturonase purified from *Fusarium moniliforme* were sequenced. The amino acid sequences of the N-terminus and of one of the tryptic peptides were used to design redundant oligonucleotides. A DNA fragment of 288 bp, encoding part of the polygalacturonase gene, was amplified by the polymerase chain reaction (PCR) using the oligonucleotides as primers and, as a template, cDNA synthesized from poly$(A)^+$ RNA extracted from mycelium grown on pectin as a sole carbon source. The PCR-generated fragment was utilized as a probe to screen a genomic and a cDNA library of *F. moniliforme*. Genomic and cDNA copies of the *endo*polygalacturonase gene were isolated and sequenced. A cloned 1272 bp cDNA consisted of a single open reading frame encoding 359 amino acids (including the entire 349 aa mature protein and part of the N-terminal signal peptide), the 3' transcribed untranslated region (173 nt), and the poly(A) tail. The nucleotide sequence of the genomic *endo*polygalacturonase gene was interrupted by four short introns (50–54 bp) and revealed the presence of a 24 amino-acid signal peptide. By RNAse protection experiments, multiple sites of initiation for the transcription of the *endo*polygalacturonase gene were demonstrated, from 33 to 45 nt downstream from the putative TATA box (Caprari *et al.*, 1993). Details of polygalacturonase encoding genes studied in saprophytic and phytopathogenic fungi are presented in table 1.

Table 1. Polygalacturonases encoding genes studied in saprophytic and phytopathogenic fungi

Fungi	PG gene	Mode of action	Reference
Aspergillus flavus	*pecA, pecB*	Endo	Whitehead *et al.*, 1995
Aspergillus parasiticus	*pecA*	Endo	Cary *et al.*, 1995
Aspergillus niger	*pgaA, pgaB, pgaC, pgaD, pgaE, pgaI, pgaII*	Endo	Parenicova *et al.*, 2000; Parenicova *et al.*, 2000a; Parenicova *et al.*, 1998; Bussink *et al.*, 1992; Kester and Visser, 1990
Aspergillus niger	*pgxA, pgxB, pgxC, pgaX*	Exo	Martens-Uzunova *et al.*, 2006
Aspergillus tubigensis	*pgaII*	Endo	Kester *et al.*, 1996
Alternaria citri	*Acpg1*	Endo	Isshiki *et al.*, 2001
Alternaria alternate	*Aapg1*	Endo	Isshiki *et al.*, 2001
Botrytis cinerea	*Bcpg1-6*	Exo/Endo	ten-Have *et al.*, 2001
Claviceps purpurae	*cpg1, cpg2*	Endo	Tenberge *et al.*, 1996
Colletotrichum lindemuthianum	*CLPG1, CLPG2*	Endo	Centis *et al.*, 1997
Cochliobolus carbonoum	*pgn1/pgx1*	Endo/Exo	Scott Craig *et al.*, 1998
Cryphonectria parasitca	*enpg1*	Endo	Gao *et al.*, 1996.
F. oxysporum f. sp. *lycopersici*	*pg1, pg5/pgx4*	Endo/Exo	Garcia *et al.*, 2000; Pietro and Roncero, 1998
Penicillium griseoroseum	*Pgg1 and pgg2*	Endo	Ribon *et al.*, 2002
Fungi	*PG gene*	Mode of action	Reference
Penicillium olsonii	*pg1, pg2*		Wagner *et al.*, 2000
Penicillium expansum	*pepg1*		Ribon *et al.*, 2002
Phytophthora infestans	*pipg1*	Endo	Torto *et al.*, 2002
Phytophthora parasitica	*pppg1 pppg2-10*	Endo	Yan and Liou, 2005; Wu *et al.*, 2008
Sclerotinia sclerotiorum	*sspg1, sspg3, sspg5, sspg6, ssxpg1, ssxpg2*	Endo/Exo	Li *et al.*, 2004

Industrial Applications of Polygalacturonases

Fruit and Vegetable Processing

Fruit juice production process involves washing, sorting and crushing followed by pressing and maceration (Kashyap *et al.*, 2001). The crushing of fruits leads to a high viscosity juice which stays linked to the fruit pulp in a gelatinous structure. This is due to the rich content of pectin in fruits which passes into juice making it cloudy (Pedrolli *et al.*, 2009).

In fruit juice processing, Pectinolytic enzymes have been used to reduce the viscosity by degrading the pectin gel structure, fruit juice clarification, improve the yield and concentration, and stability (Wu *et al.*,, 2007; Alkorta *et al.*, 1998).

They also increase the volume of the juice and soften the peels aiding their easy removal (Kashyap *et al.*, 2001). Mash treatment with pectinolytic enzymes improves the juice flow, leading to a shorter press-time, without the need for pressing aids (Pilnik and Voragen, 1993). Enzymatic maceration improves colour, flavour and nutritional properties of the juice. There is 90% and above increase in yield compared to conventional mechanical juicing (Rombouts and Pilnik, 1980).

In apple juice preparation pectic enzymes facilitate pressing and juice extraction and help in the separation of a flocculent precipitate by sedimentation, filtration or centrifugation. Pectinases remove suspended matter in apple, pear, grape and strawberry juices to give sparkling clear juices which are free of haze (Kashyap *et al.*, 2001). Pectinases added to macerated grapes before the addition of wine yeast improve the chromaticity and stability of red wines as compared to the untreated wines (Revilla and Ganzalez, 2003).

Unicellular Products

Products formed by the maceration of organized tissues into a suspension of intact cells are called unicellular products. The enzymes used for the preparation of unicellular products are called as macerases.

Maceration involves the separation of whole cells using pectinases along with other cell wall degrading enzymes for selective hydrolysis and limited degradation of polysaccharides to maintain the integrity of the cells (Kashyap *et al.*, 2001). Enzymatic maceration keeps the cells intact, preserving the vitamins, colour and aroma, the cell contents are protected from oxygen and prevents starch leaking out of the cells avoiding the quality defect of gluiness of the reconstituted product (Kashyap *et al.*, 2001; Lang and Dornenburg 2000). Unicellular products are useful ingredients in baby food, in dairy products such as puddings and yogurt and used as base material for pulpy juices and nectars and in the preparation of carrot and dried instant potato mash (Bock *et al.*, 1984).

Oil Extraction

The traditional method of oil extraction from plants involves the use of hazardous solvents like hexane which are carcinogenic. However, in the aqueous process, plant cell wall degrading enzymes including pectinase can be efficiently used to extract vegetable, coconut germ, sunflower seed, rape seed, palm, and kernel oils. Depolymerizing enzymes degrade the cell wall components promoting oil liberation from the seeds and other sources used for oil extraction. Citrus fruits are rich in pectic substances. Extraction of citrus oils such as lemon oil with pectinolytic enzymes destroys the emulsifying properties of pectin, which interfere with the collection of oils from citrus peel extracts (Scott, 1978).

In citrus peel oils, pectinases improve the process time, yield of oil from the emulsion, and the quality of the final product. Hydrolysis of the pectin-protein complexes, releases the oil more easily into the aqueous phase (Kashyap *et al.,* 2001). Addition of enzymes during the grinding of olives, aided in easier release of oil and its separation (West, 1996). Kashyap *et al.,* (2001) reported a higher yield and increased content of polyphenols and vitamin E when enzyme preparations containing pectinases were used for the extraction of olive oil.

Coffee and Tea Fermentation

Pectionolytic enzymes are used in the manufacture of tea and coffee powders. Addition of pectinolytic microorganisms or their enzymes reduces the fermentation time in tea and coffee manufacture (Amorim and Amorim, 1977; Carr, 1985). During tea-leaf fermentation, addition of enzyme preparations containing pectinases resulted in a 5% increase in the tea quality index (Angayarkanni *et al.,* 2002). Pectinolytic enzyme preparations used during coffee fermentation help in removing the pectin rich mucilaginous coat from the coffee beans. Moreover, they also accelerate the fermentation process by reducing the fermentation time (Amorim and Amorim, 1977; Carr, 1985, Godfrey, 1985).

PGs in Bioscouring and Fiber Processing

In textile processing, the applied sizing agent and the non-cellulosic portions have to be removed from cotton before dying the fabric. Bioscouring involves the use of specific enzymes for the removal of sizing agents and non-cellulosic materials. Pectinolytic enzymes used in addition with amylases, cellulases, hemicellulases and lipases make the fabric surface more hydrophilic (Li and Hardin, 1998). Enzymatic treatment also proves to be a more eco-friendly process resulting in a decreased discharge of hazardous chemicals from textile processing industries. Pectinolytic enzymes play a major role in the processing of jute, sunn hemp, flax, ramie and coconut fibers since 40% of the dry weight of plant cambium cells is comprised of pectin (Bajpai, 1999). Plant fibers are used in textiles, making of ropes, bags, nets. Fibers for such applications require a thorough processing since the bast fiber bundles are located inside the cuticle where they are glued to pectin in the middle lamella and to a woody core of short lignified fibers (Hamilton, 1986; van-Sumere, 1992).

Traditional method of fiber processing called 'dew-retting' involves the exposure of straws in open fields for microbial degradation. The disadvantage of this method is the influence of weather and damage by cellulolytic fungi (Henriksson *et al.,* 1997; Akin *et al.,* 1998). Species of *Aspergillus*, *Penicillium*, *Cladosporium*, and *Rhodotorula* have been isolated from dew-retted plants (Fogarty and Ward, 1972). Enzymatic degumming has several advantages over the traditional dewretting and the hazardous chemical treatments used for the degumming of fibres. 'Degumming', the removal of non-cellulosic gummy portion from the cellulosic part of plant fibers is essential before industrial utilization of fibers (Said *et al.*, 1991).

Kapoor *et al.*, (2001) reported the efficiency of alkaline and thermostable polygalacturonase from *Bacillus* sp. for the degumming of ramie and sunn hemp bast fibers. The use of PG along with mild chemical treatment resulted in a complete removal of non-cellulosic gummy material from the surface of the fibers (Kapoor *et al.*, 2001). *R. oryzae* isolated from dew-retted flax was found to contain extracellular PG activity which was capable of producing good quality flax fibers (Henriksson *et al.*, 1997; 1999; Akin *et al.*, 2002).

Paper and Pulp Industry

Acidic polysaccharides like Pectins get solubilized during the alkaline peroxide bleaching of pulps and increase the cationic demand in the filtrate (Viikari *et al.*, 2001). Hexamers and higher oligomers of galacturonic acid have higher ability to complex cationic polymers (cationic demand) compared to monomers and dimers (Pedrolli *et al.*, 2009). This problem can be overcome by the use of pectinolytic enzymes which depolymerize the polymers of galacturonic acids thus reducing the cationic demand (Reid and Ricard, 2000). Beg *et al.*, (2001) reported efficient biobleaching of eucalyptus kraft pulp with a combination of alkaline pectinase and xylanase from *Streptomyces* sp.

Waste Water Treatment

Wastewater from fruit and vegetable processing industries are rich in pectinaceous material. Enzymatic pretreatment of such waters offer advantages over the traditional physical and chemical procedures. Treatment of pectic wastewaters with pectinases is a environmental friendly and cost effective method. The activity of alkalophilic pectinolytic microbes and their alkaline pectinases in pectic wastewater facilitates removal of pectinaceous material and makes it suitable for decomposition by activated sludge treatment (Horikoshi 1990; Tanabe *et al.*, 1987; 1988).

PGs in Animal and Poultry Feed

Enzymes incorporated in feed are usually multi enzyme cocktails of pectinase, amylase, glucanase, xylanase, and protease. PGs and other enzymes in feed increase the feed digestibility and improved nutrient absorption (Hoondal *et al.*, 2000).

Feed enzymes like pectinases improve the feed utilization by removing the anti-nutritional effects of some non-degradable polysaccharides either by hydrolysis or by liberating nutrients blocked by these fibers, and reduce the amount of faeces (Murad and Azzaz, 2011). Multi-enzyme preparations containing pectinases efficiently improved the digestibility of vegetable protein mixture consisting of sorghum, soy and canola resulting in efficient feed conversion and weight gain in broilers (Petersen, 2001). PGs in animal and poultry feed allow the utilization of a wider range of cheap raw materials as feed ingredients as well as their efficient utilization.

PGs in Prebiotics

Prebiotic oligosaccharides are a new class of food ingredients that are consumed by humans and fed to animals. Oligosaccharides produced by the enzymatic degradation of Pectin are called oligogalacturonides (OGAs). They are emerging as bio-active food ingredients (Lang and Dornenburg, 2000). Gibson *et al.,* 2004 described 'prebiotics' as those which are resistant to gastric activity, hydrolysis by digestive enzymes and gastrointestinal absorption. Prebiotics selectively stimulate the growth and multiplication of beneficial 'prebiotics' bacteria in the intestine. Production of OGAs by chemical or biochemical processes is difficult. Recent advances in oligomer engineering involve the synthesis of OGAs by micro-biotechnology procedures involving the degradation of pectic polysaccharides using region- and stereospecific enzymes such as PGs (Barreteau *et al.,* 2006). Immobilized *Aspergillus pulverulentus* endoPG was used for to produce OGAs (Iwasaki *et al.,*, 1998). Grapefruit pectin, used as a food stabiliser, has health benefits (Cerda, 1987) and cotton boll pectin in infant food resulted in better nutrition and physical development of infants (Salomov *et al.,* 1994). Bioactive pectic polysaccharides, from the roots of *Bupleurum falcatum* have potent anti-ulcer activity (Yamada *et al.,* 1991). PGs and other polysaccharide degrading enzymes have been exploited to develop bioactive oligosaccharides with bifidogenic application (Playne and Crittenden, 1996).

Conclusion

Enzymes are precious biocatalysts with innumerable industrial applications. Microbes are relentless source of industrially important enzymes. Enzymes that degrade pectin are relevant in numerous biotechnological applications worldwide. The efforts to improve their production and to implement their use in several industrial processes are escalating as they are more efficient and environment-friendly. Many polygalacturonase encoding genes from microbes have been cloned, sequenced and individually overexpressed. These genes have not only helped to scale-up enzyme production efficiently to industrial levels but also products will be produced with better features. Once stabilized, costs and production time is anticipated to come down drastically with more efficient usage of raw materials.

References

Abbott, D. W. and A. B. Boraston, 2007. The structural basis for exopolygalacturonase activity in a family 28 glycoside hydrolase. *J. Mol. Biol.* 368:1215-1222.

Akin, D. E., D. Slomczynski, L. L. Rigsby and K. L. Eriksson, 2002. Retting flax with endopolygalacturonase from *Rhizopus oryzae*. *Text. Res. J.* 72:27–34.

Akin, D. E., G. Henriksson, W. H. Morrison and K. E. L. Eriksson, 1998. Enzymatic retting of flax. In: Eriksson, K. E. L., Cavaco-Paulo, A. (Eds.), Enzyme Applications in Fiber Processing, ACS Symposium Series 687. American Chemical Society, Washington DC.

Alkorta, I., C. Garbisu, M. J. Llama and J. L. Serra, 1998. Industrial applications of pectic enzymes: a review. *Process Biochem.* 33:21-28.

Amorim, H. V. and V. L. Amorim, 1977. Coffee enzymes and coffee quality. In: Ori, R., Angelo, A. (Eds.) Enzymes in food and beverage processing, Vol. 47. ACS Symposium Series, Washington, pp 27–56.

Angayarkanni, J., M. Palaniswamy, S. Murugesan and K. Swaminathan, 2002. Improvement of tea leaves fermentation with *Aspergillus* spp. pectinase. *J. Biosci. Bioeng.* 94: 299-303.

Aro, N., T. Pakula and M. Penttila, 2005. Transcriptional regulation of plant cell wall degradation by filamentous fungi. *FEMS Microbiol. Rev.* 29:719-739.

Arotupin, D. J. and O. F. Emmanuel, 2011. Effect of carbon and nitrogen sources on polygalacturonase production by *Trichoderma viride* (BITRS-1001) isolated from tar sand in Ondo State, Nigeria. *Malaysian J. Microbiol.* 7:153-158

Bajpai, P. 1999. Application of enzymes in the pulp and paper industry. *Biotechnol. Prog.* 15:147-157

Barense, R. I., M. A. D. S. C. Chellegatti, M. J. V. Fonseca and S. Said, 2001. Partial purification and characterization of exopolygalacturonase II and III of *Penicillium frequentans. Braz. J. Microbiol.* 32:327-330.

Barnby, F. M., F. F. Morpeth and D. L. Pyle, 1990. Endopolygalacturonase production from *Kluyveromyces marxianus.* I. Resolution, purification and partial characterization of the enzyme. *Enzyme Microb. Technol.* 12:891-897.

Barreteau, H., C. Delattre and P. Michaud, 2006. Production of Oligosaccharides as Promising New Food Additive Generation. *Food Technol. Biotechnol.* 44:323-333.

Battaglia, E., I. Benoit J. van-den-Brink, A. Wiebenga, P. M. Coutinho, B. Henrissat and R. P. de-Vries, 2011. Carbohydrate-active enzymes from the zygomycete fungus *Rhizopus oryzae*: a highly specialized approach to carbohydrate degradation depicted at genome level. *BMC Genomics* 12:38.

Beg, Q. K., M. Kapoor, R. P. Tiwari and G. S. Hoondal, 2001. Bleach-boosting of eucalyptus kraft pulp using combination of xylanase and pectinase from *Streptomyces* sp. QG-11-3. *Res. Bull. Punjab Univ. Sci.* 51:71-78

Benen, J. A., H. C. Kester, L. Parenicova and J. Visser, 2000. Characterization of *Aspergillus niger* pectate lyase A. *Biochemistry* 39:15563-15569.

Blanco, P., C. Sieiro, A. Diaz and T. G. Villa, 1994. Production and partial characterization of an endopolygalacturonase from *Saccharomyces cerevisiae. Can. J. Microbiol.* 40: 974-977.

Blanco, P., C. Sieiro, N. M. Reboredo and T. G. Villa, 1997. Genetic determination of polygalacturonase production in wild-type and laboratory strains of *Saccharomyces cerevisiae. Arch. Microbiol.* 167:284-288.

Blanco, P., C. Sieiro, N. M. Reboredo and T. G. Villa, 1998. Cloning, molecular characterization, and expression of an endo-polygalacturonase-encoding gene from *Saccharomyces cerevisiae* IM1-8b. *FEMS Microbiol. Lett.* 164:249-255.

Blandino, A., T. Iqbalsyah, S. S. Pandiella, D. Cantero and C. Webb, 2002. Polygalacturonase production by *Aspergillus awamori* on wheat in solid-state fermentation. *Appl. Microbiol. Biotechnol.* 58:164-169.

Bock, W., M. Kraose, H. Kenniger, M. Andeerson and I. Molar, 1984. Verfahren zur enzymatischem verussingung von gemuse und speisekartoffeln. *DDR Patent* 216617.

Bohdziewiez, J. and M. Bodzek, 1994. Ultra-filtration preparation of pectinolytic enzymes from citric acid fermentation broth. *Proc. Biochem.* 29:99-107.

Brown, R. L., T. E. Cleveland P. J. Cotty and J. E. Mellon, 1992. Spread of *Aspergillus flavus* in cotton bolls, decay of intercarpellary membranes, and production of fungal pectinases. *Phytopathol.* 82:462-467.

Bussink, H. J. D., F. P. Buxton and J. Visser, 1991. Expression and sequence comparison of the *Aspergillus niger* and *Aspergillus tubigensis* genes encoding polygalacturonase II. *Curr. Genet.* 19:467-474.

Bussink, H. J. D., F. P. Buxton, B. A. Fraaye, L. H. de-Graaf and J. Visser, 1992. The polygalacturonases of *Aspergillus niger* are encoded by a family of diverged genes. *Eur. J. Biochem.* 208:83-90.

Bussink, H. J. D., H. C. M. Kester and J. Visser, 1990. Molecular cloning, nucleotide sequence and expression of the gene encoding prepropolygalacturonase II of *Aspergillus niger*. *FEBS Lett.* 273:127-130.

Bussink, H. J. D., K. B. Brouwer, L. H. de-Graaf, H. C. M. Kester and J. Visser, 1991a. Identification and characterization of a second polygalacturonase gene of *Aspergillus niger*. *Curr. Genet.* 20:301-307.

Cabanne, C. and B. Doneche, 2002. Purification and characterization of two isozymes of polygalacturonase from *Botrytis cinerea*. Effect of calcium ions on polygalacturonase activity. *Microbiol. Res.* 157:183-189.

Caprari, C., A. Richter, C. Bergmann, S. L. Cicero, G. Salvi, F. Cervone, and G. de-Lorenzo, 1993. Cloning and characterization of a gene encoding the endopolygalacturonase of *Fusarium moniliforme*. *Mycol. Res.* 97:497-505.

Cardoso, P. G., J. B. Ribeiro, J. A. Teixeira, M. V. Queiroz and E. F. Araujo, 2007. Overexpression of the plg1 gene encoding pectin lyase in *Penicillium griseoroseum*. *J. Ind. Microbiol. Biotechnol.* 35:159-166

Carr, J. G. 1985. Tea, coffee and cocoa. In: Wood, B. J. B. (Ed) *Microbiology of fermented food*, Vol. 2. Elsevier, London, pp 133-154.

Cary, J. W., R. Brown, T. E. Cleveland, M. Whitehead and R. A. Dean, 1995. Cloning and characterization of a novel polygalacturonase-encoding gene from *Aspergillus parasiticus*. *Gene* 153:129-133.

Centis, S., B. Dumas, J. Fournier, M. Marolda and M. T. Esquerré-Tugayé, 1996. Isolation and sequence analysis of *Cplg1*, a gene coding for an endopolygalacturonase of the phytopathogenic fungus *Colletotrichum lindemuthianum*. *Gene* 170:125-129.

Centis, S., I. Guillas, N. Séjalon, M. T. Esquerré-Tugayé and B. Dumas, 1997. Endopolygalacturonase genes from *Colletotrichum lindemuthianum*: cloning of *Clpg2* and comparison of its expression to that of *Clpg1* during saprophytic and parasitic growth of the fungus. *Mol. Plant Microbe Interact.* 10:769-775.

Cerda, J. J., 1987. The role of grapefruit pectin in health and disease. *Trans. Am. Clin. Climatol. Assoc.* 99: 203-213.

Cho, S. W., S. Lee and W. Shin, 2001. The X-ray structure of *Aspergillus aculeatus* polygalacturonase and a modeled structure of the polygalacturonase-octagalacturonate complex. *J. Mol. Biol.* 311:863-878.

Cleveland, T. E. and P. J. Cotty, 1991. Invasiveness of *Aspergillus flavus* isolates in wounded cotton bolls is associated with production of a specific fungal polygalacturonase. *Phytopathol.* 81:155-158.

Cotty, P. J., T. E. Cleveland, R. L. Brown and J. E. Mellon, 1990. Variation in polygalacturonase production among *Aspergillus flavus* isolates. *Appl. Environ. Microbiol.* 56:3885-3887.

Coutinho, P. M., M. R. Andersen, K. Kolenova, P. A. van-Kuyk, I. Benoit, B. S. Gruben, B. Trejo-Aguilar, H. Visser, P. van-Solingen, T. Pakula, B. Seiboth, E. Battaglia, G. Aguilar-Osorio, J. F. de-Jong, R. A. Ohm, M. Aguilar, B. Henrissat, J. Nielsen, H. Stalbrand and R. P. de-Vries, 2009. Post-genomic insights into the plant polysaccharide degradation potential of *Aspergillus nidulans* and comparison to *Aspergillus niger* and *Aspergillus oryzae*. *Fungal Genet. Biol.* 46:S161-S169

Degrassi, G., G. Devescovi, J. Kim, I. Hwang and V. Venturi. 2008. Identification, characterization and regulation of two secreted polygalacturonases of the emerging rice pathogen *Burkholderia glumae*. *FEMS Microbiol. Ecol.* 65:251-262.

Demarche, P., C. Junghanns, R. R. Nair and S. N. Agathos, 2011. Harnessing the power of enzymes for environmental stewardship. *Biotech. Adv.* doi:10.1016/j.biotechadv. 2011.05.013

De-Vries, R. P. and J. Visser, 2001. *Aspergillus* enzymes involved in degradation of plant cell wall polysaccharides. *Microbiol. Mol. Biol. Rev.* 65:497-522.

Federici, F, 1985. Production, purification and partial characterization of an endopolyagalacturonase from *Cryptococcus albidus* var. *albidus*. *Antonie Van Leeuwenhoek* 51: 139-150.

Federici, L., C. Caprari, B. Mattei, C. Savino, A. D. Matteo, G. D. Lorenzo, F. Cervone and D. Tsernoglou, 2001. Structural requirements of endopolygalacturonase for the interaction with PGIP. *Proc. Nat. Aca. Sci.* 98:13425-13430.

Fogarty, M. W. and O. P. Ward, 1972. Pectic substances and pectolytic enzymes. *Proc. Biochem.* 7, 17-31.

Fraissinet-Tachet, L., P. Reymond-Cotton and M. Févre, 1995. Characterization of a multigene family encoding an endopolygalacturonases in *Sclerotinia sclerotiorum*. *Curr. Genet.* 29:96-99.

Friedrich, J., A. Cimeramn and W. Steiner, 1994. Concomitant synthesis of *Aspergillus niger* pectolytic enzymes and citric acid on sucrose. *Enzyme Microbiol. Biotechnol.* 16:703-707.

Gao, S., G. H. Choi, L. Shain and D. L. Nuss, 1996. Cloning and targeted disruption of enpgl, encoding the major in vitro extracellular endopolygalacturonase of the chestnut blight fungus, *Cryphonectria parasitica*. *App. Environ. Microbiol.* 62: 1984-1990.

Garcia-Maceira, F. I., A. D. Pietro and M. I. G. Roncero, 2000. Cloning and disruption of *pgx4* encoding an inplanta expressed endo-polygalacturonase from *Fusarium oxysporum*. *Mol. Plant Microbe Interac.* 13:359-365.

Gibson, G. R., H. M. Probert, J. van-Loo, R. A. Rastall and M. B. Roberfroid, 2004. Dietary modulation of the human colonic microbiota: Updating the concept of prebiotics, *Nutr. Res. Rev.* 17: 259-275.

Godfrey, A. 1985. Production of industrial enzymes and some applications in fermented foods. In: Woods, B. J. B. (Ed.), Microbiology of Fermented Foods, Vol. 1. Elsevier Applied Science, London, pp. 345-373.

Gummadi, S. N and T. Panda, 2003. Purification and biochemical properties of microbial pectinases- a review. *Process Biochem.* 38:987-996.

Hamilton, I. T. 1986. *Linnen. Textiles* 15: 30-34.

Henriksson, G., D. E. Akin, D. Slomczynski and K. L. Eriksson, 1999. Production of highly efficient enzymes for flax retting by *Rhizomucor pusillus*. *J. Biotechnol.* 68:115-123.

Henriksson, G., D. E. Akin, R. T. Hanlin, C. Rodriguez, D. D. Archibald and L.L. Rigsby, 1997. Identification and retting efficiencies of fungi isolated from dew-retted flax in the United States and Europe. *Appl. Environ. Microbiol.* 63:3950-3956

Herert, C., R. O'Connell, E. Gaulin, V. Salesses, M. T. Esquerre-Tugaye and B. Dumas, 2004. Production of a cell wall-associated endo-polygalacturonase by *Colletotrichum lindemuthianum* and pectin degradation during bean infection. *Fungal Genet. Biol.* 41:140-147.

Herron, S. R., J. A. Benen, R. D. Scavetta, J. Visser and F. Jurnak, 2000. Structure and function of pectic enzymes: virulence factors of plant pathogens. *Proc. Nat. Aca. Sci.* 97:8762-8769.

Hoondal, G., R. P. Tiwari, R. Tewari, N. Dahiya and Q. Beg, 2002. Microbial alkaline pectinases and their industrial applications: a review. *Appl. Microbiol. Biotechnol.* 59:409-418.

Hoondal, G. S., R. P. Tiwari, R. Tiwari, N. Dahiya and Q. K. Beg, 2000. Microbial alkaline pectinases and their applications: a review. *Appl. Microbiol. Biotechnol.* 59:409-418.

Horikoshi, K. 1990. Enzymes from alkalophiles. In: Fogarty, W. M., Kelly, C. T. (Ed.) Microbial enzymes and biotechnology, 2nd Edn. Elsevier, Ireland, pp 275–295

Huang, Q. and C. Allen, 1997. An exo-poly-a-D-galacturonosidase, *Peh B*, is required for wild type virulence of *Ralstonia solanacearum*. *J. Bacteriol.* 179:7369-7378.

Isshiki, A., K. Akimitsu, M. Yamamoto and H. Yamamoto, 2001. Endopolygalacturonase is essential for citrus black rot caused by *Alternaria citri* but not brown spot caused by *Alternaria alternata*. *Mol. Plant Microbe Interac.*14:749-757.

Iwasaki, K. I., M. Inoue and Y. Matsubara, 1998. Continuous hydrolysis of pectate by immobilized endo-polygalacturonase in a continuously stirred tank reactor. *Biosci. Biotech. Biochem.* 62: 262-267.

Jacob, N., 2009. Pectinolytic enzymes. In: Nigam, P. S. and A. Pandey, (Eds.), *Biotechnology for Agro-Industrial Residues Utilisation.* Springer Science+Business Media B.V. pp 383-396.

Jayani, R. S., S. Saxena and R. Gupta, 2005. Microbial pectinolytic enzymes: A review. *Process Biochem.* 40:2931-2944.

Jayani, R. S., S. K. Shukla and R. Gupta, 2010. Screening of bacterial strains for polygalacturonase activity: Its production by *Bacillus sphaericus* (MTCC 7542). *Enzyme Res.*1-5.

Jenkins, J., O. Mayans, D. Smith, K. Worboys and R. W. Pickersgill, 2001. Three-dimensional structure of *Erwinia chrysanthemi* pectin methylesterase reveals a novel esterase active site. *J. Mol. Biol.* 305:951-960.

Kapoor, M., Q. K. Beg, B. Bhushan, K. Singh, K. S. Dadhich and G. S. Hoondal, 2001. Application of an alkaline and thermostable polygalacturonase from *Bacillus* sp. MG-cp-2 in degumming of ramie (*Boehmeria nivea*) and sunn hemp (*Crotalaria juncea*) bast fibers. *Process Biochem.* 36:803-807

Kashyap, D. R., P. K. Vohra, S. Chopra and R. Tewari, 2001. Applications of pectinases in commercial sector: a review. *Biores. Technol.* 77:215-227.

Kester, H. C. and J. Visser, 1990. Purification and characterization of polygalacturonases produced by the hyphal fungus *Aspergillus niger*. *Biotechnol. Appl. Biochem.* 12: 150-160.

Kester, H. C., M. A. K. Someren, Y. Muller and J. Visser, 1996. Primary structure and characterization of an exopolygalacturonase from *Aspergillus tubingensis*. *Eur. J. Biochem.* 240: 738-746.

Kitamoto, N., J. Matsui, Y. Kawai, A. Kato, S. Yoshino, K. Ohmiya and N. Tsukagoshi, 1998. Utilization of the TEF1-a gene (*TEF1*) promoter for expression of PG genes, *pgaA* and *pgaB*, in *Aspergillus oryzae*. *Appl. Microbiol. Biotechnol.* 50:85-92.

Kitamoto, N., T. Kimura, Y. Kito, K. Ohmiya and N. Tsukagoshi. 1993. Structural features of a polygalacturonase gene cloned from *Aspergillus oryzae* KBN616. *FEMS Microbiol. Lett.* 111:37–42.

Koboyashi, T., N. Higaki, N. Yajima, A. Suzumatsu, H. Haghihara, S. Kawai and S. Ito, 2001. Purification and properties of a galacturonic acid releasing exopolygalacturonase from a strain of *Bacillus*. *Biosci. Biotechnol. Biochem.* 65:842-847.

Kumar, S. S. and P. Palanivelu, 1999. Purification and characterization of an exoplolygalacturonase from the thermophilic fungus, *Thermomyces lanuginosus*. *World J. Microbiol. Biotechnol.* 15:643-646.

Lang, C. and H. Dornenburg, 2000. Perspectives in the biological function and the technological application of polygalacturonases. *Appl. Microbiol. Biotechnol.* 53:366-375.

Lara-Marquez, A., M. G. Zavala-Paramo, E. Lopez-Romero and H. C. Camacho, 2011. Biotechnological potential of pectinolytic complexes of fungi. *Biotechnol. Lett.* 33:859-868.

Li, R., R. Rimmer, L. Buchwaldt, A. G. Sharpe, G. Seguin-Swartz and D. D. Hegedus, 2004. Interaction of *Sclerotinia sclerotiorum* with *Brassica napus*: Cloning and characterization of endo- and exo-polygalacturonase expressed during saprophytic and parasitic modes. *Fungal Genetics and Biol.* 41:754-765.

Li, Y. and I. R. Hardin, 1998. Enzymatic scouring of cotton-surfactants, agitation, and selection of enzymes. *Textile Chemist. Colorist.* 30:23-29.

Lietzke, S. E., M. D. Yoder, N. T. Keen and F. Jurnak, 1994. The three-dimensional structure of pectate lyase E, a plant virulence factor from *Erwinia chrysanthemi*. *Plant Physiol.* 106:849-862.

Lorenzo, G. D., G. Salvi, L. Degra, R. D'Ovidio and F. Cervone. 1987. Induction of extracellular polygalacturonase and its mRNA in the phytopathogenic fungus *Fusarium moniliforme*. *Microbiology* 133:3365-3373.

Lourdes, M., T. M. Polizeli, J. A. Jorge and H. F. Terenzi, 1991. Pectinase production by *Neurospora crassa*: Purification and biochemical characterization of extracellular polygalacturonase activity. *J. Gen. Microbiol.* 137: 1815–1823.

Luh, B. S. and H. J. Phaff, 1954. Properties of yeast polygalacturonase. *Arch. Biochem. Biophys.* 48:23-37.

Maceira, F. I. G., A. D. Pietro and M. I. G. Roncero, 1997. Purification and characterization of a novel exopolygalacturonase from *Fusarium oxysporum* f. sp. *lycopersici*. *FEMS Microbiol. Lett.* 154:37-43.

Maldonado, M. C. and A. M. S. de-Saad, 1998. Production of pectinesterase and polygalacturonase by *Aspergillus niger* in submerged and solid state systems. *J. Ind. Microbiol. Biotechnol.* 20:34-38.

Malvessi, E. and M. M. da-Silveira, 2004. Influence of medium composition and pH on the production of polygalacturonases by *Aspergillus oryzae*. *Braz. Arch. Biol. Technol.* 47:693-702.

Manachini, M., C. Fortina and C. Parini, 1987. Purification and properties of an endopolygalacturonase produced by *Rhizopus stolonifer*. *Biotechnol. Lett.* 9:219-224.

Marcus, L., I. Barash, B. Sneh, Y. Koltin and A. Finkler, 1986. Purification and characterization of pectolytic enzymes produced by virulent and hypovirulent isolates of *Rhizoctonia solani* Kuhn. *Physiol. Mol. Plant Pathol.* 29:325-336.

Martens-Uzunova, E. S. and P. J. Schaap, 2009. Assessment of the pectin degrading enzyme network of *Aspergillus niger* by functional genomics. *Fungal Genet. Biol.* 46:S170-S179.

Martens-Uzunova, E. S., J. S. Zandleven, J. A. Benen, H. Awad, H. J. Kools, G. Beldman, A. G. Voragen, J. A. van-den-Berg and P. J. Schaap, 2006. A new group of exo-acting family 28 glycoside hydrolases of *Aspergillus niger* that are involved in pectin degradation. *Biochem. J.* 400:43

Martinez, M. J., M. T. Alconada, F. Gillen, C. Vasquez and F. Reyes, 1991. Pectic activities from *Fusarium oxysporum* f. sp. *melonis*: Purification and characterization of an exopolygalacturonase. *FEMS Microbiol. Lett.* 81:145-150.

Massa, C., G. Degrassi, G. Devescovi, V. Venturi and D. Lamba. 2007. Isolation, heterologous expression and characterization of an endo-polygalacturonase produced by the phytopathogen *Burkholderia cepacia*. *Protein Expr. Purif.* 54:300-308.

Mayans, O., M. Scott, I. Connerton, T. Graveses, J. Benen, J. and J. Visser, 1997. Two crystal structures of pectin lyases A from *Aspergillus* reveal a pH driven conformational change and striking divergence in the substrate-binding clefts of pectin and pectate lyase. *Structure* 5: 677-689.

Mellon, J. E., P. J. Cotty, 1995. Expression of elastinolytic activity among isolates in *Aspergillus* section *Flavi*. *Mycopathol.* 131:115-120.

Murad, H. A. and H. H. Azzaz, 2011. Microbial pectinases and ruminant nutrition. *Res. J. Microbiol.* 6: 246-269.

Naidu, G. S. N. and T. Panda, 1998. Production of pectolytic enzymes-a review. *Bioprocess Engg.* 19:355-361.

Nair, S. R. and T. Panda, 1997. Statistical optimization of medium components for improved synthesis of pectinase by *Aspergillus niger*. *Bioproc. Engg.* 16:169-173.

Nicemol, J. and P. Parukuttyamma, 2006. Influence of Mode of Fermentation on Production of Polygalacturonase by a Novel Strain of *Streptomyces lydicus*. *Food Technol. Biotechnol.* 44: 263-267.

Niture, S. K, 2008. Comparative biochemical and structural characterizations of fungal polygalacturonases. *Biologia* 63:1-19.

Nozaki, K., K. Miyairi, S. Hizumi, Y. Fukui and T. Okuno, 1997. Novel exopolygalacturonases produced by *Alternaria mali*. *Biosci. Biotechnol. Biochem.* 61:75-80.

Palomaki, T. and H. T. Saarilahti, 1997. Isolation and characterization of new C-terminal substitution mutation affecting secretion of polygalacturonases in *Erwinia carotovora* ssp. *carotovora*. *FEBS Lett.* 400:122-126.

Pandey, A., P. Selvakumar, C. R. Soccol and P. Nigam, 1999. Solid-state fermentation for the production of industrial enzymes. *Curr. Sci.* 77:146-162.

Parenicova, L., H. C. Kester, J. A. Benen, J. Visser, 2000a. Characterization of a novel endopolygalacturonase from *Aspergillus niger* with unique kinetic properties. *FEBS Lett.* 467:333-336.

Parenicova, L., J. A. Benen, H. C. Kester and J. Visser, 2000. *pgaA* and *pgaB* encode two constitutively expressed endopolygalacturonases of *Aspergillus niger. Biochem. J.* 345:637-644

Parenicová, L., J. A. E. Benen, H. C. M. Kester and J. Visser, 1998. *pgaE* encodes a fourth member of the endopolygalacturonase gene family from *Aspergillus niger. Eur. J. Biochem.* 251:72-80.

Pariza, M. W. and E. M. Foster, 1983. Determining the safety of enzyme used in food processing. *J. Food Prot.* 46:453-68.

Patino, B., M. L. Posada, M. T. González-Jaén and C. Vázquez, 1997. The course of pectin degradation by polygalacturonases from *Fusarium oxysporum* f.sp. *radicis lycopersici. Microbios* 91: 47-54.

Pedrolli, D. B., A. C. Monteiro, E. Gomes and E. C. Carmona, 2009. Pectin and Pectinases: Production, Characterization and Industrial Application of Microbial Pectinolytic Enzymes. *Open Biotechnol. J.* 3:9-18.

Petersen, S. 2001. Enzymes to upgrade plant nutrients. *Feed Mix.* 9:12-15.

Petersen, T. N., S. Kauppinen, and S. Larsen, 1997. The crystal structure of rhamnogalacturonase A from *Aspergillus aculeatus*: a right-handed parallel β-helix. *Structure*, 5: 533-544.

Pickergill, R., D. Smith, K. Worboys, and J. Jenkins, 1998. Crystal structure of polygalacturonase from *Erwinia carotovora* ssp. *carotovora. J. Biol. Chem.* 273, 24660-24664.

Pickersgill, R., J. Jenkins, G. Harris, W. Nasser and J. Robert-Baudouy, 1994. The structure of *Bacillus subtilis* pectate lyase in complex with calcium. *Nature Struct. Biol.* 1: 717-723.

Pietro, A. D. and M. I. G. Roncero, 1998. Cloning, characterization and role in pathogenicity of pg1 encoding the major extracellular endopolygalacturonase of the vascular wilt pathogen *Fusarium oxysporum. Mol. Plant Microbe Interac.* 11: 91-98.

Pilnik, W. and A. G. J. Voragen, 1993. Pectic enzymes in fruit and vegetable juice manufature. In: Nagodawithama, T.; Reed, G. (Ed.) *Enzymes in Food Processing*, Academic Press, New York, pp 363-399.

Playne M. J. and R. Crittenden, 1996. Commercially available oligosaccharides. *Bulletin of IDF* 313:10-22.

Posada, M. L., Patiño, B., De la Heras, A., Mirete, S., Vazquez, C., Gonzalez-Jaen, M. T., 2000. Comparative analysis of an endopolygalacturonase coding gene in isolates of seven *Fusarium* species. *Mycological Research* 104: 1342-1347.

Rao, M. N., A. A. Kembhavi and A. Pant, 1996. Implication of tryptophan and histidine in the active site of endo-polygalacturonase from *Aspergillus ustus*: Elucidation of the reaction mechanism. *Biochim. Biophys. Acta* 1296: 167-173.

Reid, I. and M. Ricard, 2000. Pectinase in papermaking: solving retention problems in mechanical pulps bleached with hydrogen peroxide. *Enzyme Microb. Technol.* 26:115-123.

Revilla, I. and G. M. L. Jose, 2003. Addition of pectolytic enzymes: an enological practice which improves the chromaticity and stability of red wines. *Int. J. Food Sci. Technol.* 38:29-36.

Reymond, P., G. Deleage, C. Rascle and M. Fevre, 1994. Cloning and sequence analysis of a polygalacturonase-encoding gene from the phytopathogenic fungus *Sclerotinia sclerotiorum. Gene* 146:233-237.

Ribon, A. O. B., J. L. C. Coelho, E. G. de-Barros and E. F. de-Araújo, 1999. Cloning and characterization of a gene encoding the endopolygalacturonases of *Penicillium griseoroseum. Biotechnol. Lett.* 21:365-399.

Ribon, A. O. B., M. V. Queiroz and E. F. de-Araújo, 2002a. Structural organization of polygalacturonase-encoding genes from *Penicillium griseoroseum. Genetics and Mol. Biol.* 25:489-493.

Ribon, A. O. B., M. V. Queiroz, J. L. C. Coelho and E. F. de-Araújo, 2002. Differential expression of polygalacturonase-encoding genes from *Penicillium griseoroseum* in different carbon sources. *J. Ind. Microbiol. Biotechnol.* 29:145-148.

Ridley, B. L., M. A. O'Neill and D. Mohnen, 2001. Pectins: Structure, biosynthesis, and oligogalacturonide-related signaling. *Phytochem.* 57:929-967.

Rodrigues-Palenzuela, P., T. J. Burr and A. Collmer, 1991. Polygalacturonase is a virulence factor in *Agrobacterium tumifaciens* biovar 3. *J. Bacteriol.* 173:6547-6552.

Rombouts, F. M. and W. Pilnik, 1980. Pectic enzymes. In: Rose, A. H., Ed. *Microbial Enzymes and Bioconversions.* Academic Press, London, 5: 227-272.

Said, S., M. J. V. Fonseca and V. Siessere, 1991. Pectinase production by *Penicillium frequentans. World J. Microbiol. Biotechnol.* 7: 607-608.

Sakai, T. and A. Takaoka, 1984. Purification, crystallization and some properties of endo-polygalacturonase from *Aureobasidium pullulans. Agric. Biol. Chem.* 49:449-458.

Salomov, I. T., A. R. Ashurov, K. H. M. Oblakulav, U. I. Salomov and B. M. Dzhalilov, 1994. Effect of pectin additives from cotton on the physical development, nutrition and erythrocytes in infants. *Vopr. Pitan.* 6: 16-18.

Sanchez, S. and A. L. Demain, 2010. Enzymes and bioconversions of industrial, pharmaceutical, and biotechnological significance. *Org. Process Res. Dev.* 15:224-230.

Schols, H. A. and A. G. H. Voragen, 1996. Complex pectins: structure elucidation using enzymes, pp. 3-19. In: Visser, J. and A. G. J. Voragen (Ed.) Progress in Biotechnology, vol 14: Pectins and Pectinases, Elsevier Science, Amsterdam.

Schols, H. A., E. J. Bakx, D. Schipper and A. G. J. Voragen, 1995. A xylogalacturonan subunit present in the modified hairy regions of apple pectin. *Carbohydr. Res.* 279:265-279.

Scott, D. 1978. Enzymes, industrial. In: Grayson, M., Ekorth, D. (Ed.) *Kirk-othmer encyclopedia of chemical technology*. Wiley, New York, pp 173-224.

Scott-Craig, J. S., Y. Cheng, F. Cervone, G. D. Lorenzo, J. W. Pitkin and J. D. Walton, 1998. Targeted mutants of *Cochliobolus carbonum* lacking two major extracellular polygalacturonases. *App. Environ. Microbiol.* 64:1497-1503.

Sella, L., C. Castiglioni, S. Roberti, R. D'Ovidio and F. Favaron, 2004. An endo-polygalacturonase of *Fusarium moniliforme* escaping inhibition by plant polygalacturonase-inhibiting proteins (PGIPs) provides new insights into the PG-PGIP interaction. *FEMS Microbiol. Lett.* 240:117-124.

Shevchik, V. E., H. C. M. Kester, J. A. E. Benen, J. Visser, J. Robert-Baudouy and N. Hugouvieux-Cotte-Pattat, 1999. Characterization of the exopolygalacturonate lyase *PelX* of *Erwinia chrysanthemi* 3937. *J. Bacteriol.* 181:1652-1663

Shieh, M. T., R. L. Brown, M. P. Whitehead, J. W. Cary, P. J. Cotty, T. E. Cleveland and R. A. Dean, 1997. Molecular genetic evidence for the involvement of a specific polygalacturonase, P2c, in the invasion and spread of *Aspergillus flavus* in cotton bolls. *Appl. Environ. Microbiol.* 63:3548-3552.

Shimizu, T., T. Nakatsu, K. Miyairi, T. Okuno and H. Kato, 2002. Active-site architecture of endopolygalacturonase I from *Stereum purpureum* revealed by crystal structures in native and ligand-bound forms at atomic resolution. *Biochem.* 41:6651-6659.

Souza, J. V. B., T. M. Silva, M. L. S. Maia and M. F. S. Teixeira, 2003. Screening of fungal strains for pectinolytic activity: endopolygalacturonase production by *Peacilomyces clavisporus* 2A.UMIDA.1. *Process Biochem.* 4:455-458.

Suzuki, S., M. Fukuoka, S. Tada, M. Matsushita-Morita, R. Hattori, N. Kitamoto and K. Kusumoto, 2010. Production of polygalacturonase by recombinant *Aspergillus oryzae* in solid-state fermentation using potato pulp. *Food Sci. Technol. Res.* 16:517-521.

Tanabe, H., Y. Kobayashi and T. Akamatsu. 1988. Pretreatment of pectic waste water with pectate lyase from an alkalophilic *Bacillus* sp. *Agric. Biol. Chem.* 52:1853-1856

Tanabe, H., Y. Yoshihara, K. Tamura, Y. Kobayashi and T. Akamatsu, 1987. Pretreatment of pectic wastewater from orange canning process by an alkalophilic *Bacillus* sp. *J. Ferment. Technol.* 65: 243-246

Teixeira, M. F. S., J. L. L. Filho and N. Durán, 2000. Carbon sources effect on pectinase production from *Aspergillus japonicus* 586. *Braz. J. Microbiol.* 31:286-290.

Tenberge, K. B., V. Homann, B. Oeser and P. Tudzynski, 1996. Structure and expression of two polygalacturonase genes of *Claviceps purpurea* oriented in tandem and cytological evidence for pectinolytic enzyme activity during infection of rye. *Phytopathol.* 86:1084-1097.

Ten-Have A, W. Mulder, J. Visser and J. A. L. van-Kan, 1998. The endo-polygalacturonase gene *Bcpg1* is required for full virulence of *Botrytis cinerea. Mol. Plant-Microbe Interact.* 11:1009-1016.

Ten-Have, A., W. O. Breuil, J. P. Wubben, J. Visser and J. A. L. van-Kan, 2001. *Botrytis cinerea* endopolygalacturonases genes are differentially expressed in various plant tissues. *Fungal Genetics and Biology* 33:97-105.

Torto, T. A., L. Rauser and S. Kamoun, 2002. The *pipg1* gene of the oomycete *Phytophthora infestans* encodes a fungal-like endopolygalacturonase. *Curr. Genet.* 40:385-90.

Van-Pouderoyen, G., H. J. Snijder, J. A. Benen and B. W. Dijkstra, 2003. Structural insights into the processivity of endopolygalacturonases I from *Aspergillus niger. FEBS Lett.* 554:462-466.

Van-Santen, Y., J. A. E. Benen, K. H. Schroter, K. H. Kalk, S. Armand, J. Visser and B. Dijkstra, 1999. 1.68–Å crystal structure of endopolygalacturonase II from *Aspergillus niger* and identification of active site residues by site-directed mutagenesis. *J. Biol. Chem.* 274:30474-30480.

Van-Sumere, C. F. 1992. Retting of flax with special reference to enzymatic retting. In: Sharma, H. S. S., Van Sumere, C. F. (Ed.), *The Biology and Processing of Flax.* M Publications, Belfast, Northern Ireland, pp. 157-198.

Viikari, L., M. Tenkanen and A. Suurnakki, 2001. Biotechnology in the pulp and paper industry. In: Rehm, H. J. (Ed.) *Biotechnology*, 2nd Edn, vol 10. VCH-Wiley, pp 523-546.

Vincken, J. P., H. A. Schols, R. J. Oomen, M. C. McCann, P. Ulvskov, A. G. Voragen and R. G. Visser, 2003. If homogalacturonan were a side chain of rhamnogalacturonan I. Implications for cell wall architecture. *Plant Physiol.* 132:1781-1789.

Visser, J. and A. G. J. Voragen, 1996. Pectins and Pectinases. *Progress in Biotechnology*, Vol. 14, Elsevier, Amsterdam.

Vitali, J., B. Schick, H. C. M. Kester, J. Visser and F. Jurnak, 1998. The three-dimensional structure of *Aspergillus niger* pectin lyase B at 1.7-Å resolution. *Plant Physiol.* 116: 69-80.

Wagner, F., H. Kusserow and W. Schäfer, 2000. Cloning and targeted disruption of two polygalacturonase genes in *Penicillium olsonii. FEMS Microbiol. Lett.* 186:293-299.

Walton, J. D. and F. Cervone. 1990. Endopolygalacturonase from the maize pathogen *Cochliobolus carbonum. Physiol. Mol. Plant Pathol.* 36:351-359.

West, S. 1996. Olive and other edible oils. In: Godfrey, T., West, S. (Ed.), *Industrial Enzymology*, 2nd Edn. Stockholm Press, New York, pp. 293-300.

Whitaker, J. R., 1984. Pectic substances, pectic enzymes and haze formation in fruit juices. *Enzyme Microbe. Technol.* 6:341-349.

Whitehead, M. P., M. T. Shieh, T. E. Cleveland, J. W. Cary and R. A. Dean, 1995. Isolation and characterization of polygalacturonase genes (*pecA* and *pecB*) from *Aspergillius flavus* I. *Appl. Environ. Microbiol.* 61:3316-3322.

Willats, W. G., L. McCartney, W. Mackie and J. P. Knox, 2001. Pectin: cell biology and prospects for functional analysis. *Plant Mol. Biol.* 47:9-27

Wu, C. H., H. Z. Yan, L. F. Liu and R. F. Liou, 2008. Functional characterization of a gene family encoding polygalacturonases in *Phytophthora parasitica. Mol. Plant-Microbe Interact.* 21:480-489.

Wu, M. C., C. M. Jiang, P. H. Huang, M. Y. Wu and Y. T. Wang, 2007. Separation and utilization of pectin lyase from commercial pectic enzyme via highly methoxylated cross-linked alcohol-insoluble solid chromatography for wine methanol reduction. *J. Agric. Food Chem.* 55:1557-1562.

Wubben, J. P., A. ten-Have, J. A. L. van-Kan and J. Visser, 2000. Regulation of endopolygalacturonase gene expression in *Botrytis cinerea* by galacturonic acid, ambient pH and carbon catabolite repression. *Curr. Genet.* 37:152-157.

Wubben, J. P., W. Mulder, A. ten-Have, J. A. L. van-Kan and J. Visser, 1999. Cloning and partial characterization of endopolygalacturonases genes from *Botrytis cinerea. Appl. Environ. Microbiol.* 65:1569-1602.

Xiao, Z., S. Wang, H. Bergeron, J. Zhang and P. C. K. Lau, 2008. A flax-retting endopolygalacturonase-encoding gene from *Rhizopus oryzae. Antonie van Leeuwenhoek.* 94:563-571.

Yamada, H., M. Hirano and H. Kiyohara, 1991. Partial structure of an anti-ulcer pectic polysaccharide from the roots of *Bupleurum falcatum* L. *Carbohydr. Res.* 219: 173-192.

Yan, H. Z. and R. F. Liou, 2005. Cloning and analysis of *pppg1*, an inducible endopolygalacturonase gene from the oomycete plant pathogen *Phytophthora parasitica. Fungal Genet. Biol.* 42:339-350.

In: Applications of Microbial Genes in Enzyme Technology ISBN: 978-1-62417-808-5
Editors: V.K.Gupta, M.G.Tuohy, G.D.Sharma et al. © 2013 Nova Science Publishers, Inc.

Chapter 8

Dehydrogenase, Phosphatase and Lipase

Mohammad Miransari*

College of Biological Sciences, Tarbiat
Modares University, Tehran, Iran

Abstract

There are numerous microbial enzymes, with a wide range of applications in the industry, agriculture and environment, including catalyzing different biochemical processes, enhancing soil nutrient solubility and removing pollutants from soil. It is accordingly important to utilize methods, which may result in the enhanced efficiency of microbes to produce enzymes. For example, modifying microbial genes may be a suitable method to increase the microbial ability to produce enzymes. In this chapter the enzymes dehydrogenase, as an enzyme for microbial respiration, phosphatase, turning insoluble phosphate products into soluble products, and lipase with the ability to catalyze lipophytic products are reviewed. Such kind of analysis may result in the more applicable use of enzymes for different usages.

Introduction

Enzymes are naturally or synthetically produced. All organisms have the ability to produce a wide range of enzymes. There are about 4000 enzymes among which 200 can be used commercially. Enzymes are biochemical products with the ability to act on their specific substrate increasing the rate of biochemical reactions. It is because under normal temperature and pH conditions the cells would not be able to perform cellular reactions (Singh et al. 2007; Palmer *et al.,* 2001). While acting on their substrate, the properties of enzymes do not change and hence the enzymes properties remain unchanged (Soetan *et al.,* 2010).

* Corresponding author: Mohammad Miransari. Mehrabad Rudehen, Imam Ali Blvd., Kucheyeh Mahtab, # 55, postal number: 3978147395, Tel.: (98)9133014844, E-mail: Miransari1 @gmail.com.

In addition, the enzymatic activities of soil microbes are suitable to determine soil biological conditions. The activity of oxidases (proxidases, dehydrgenases and catalases) and hydrolases (ureases, phosphatases, proteinases and invertases) can be used as biological indicators to determine soil quality. Most organisms are able to produce these enzymes (Taylor *et al.,* 2002; Gerhardt *et al.,* 2009).

Like other organisms, microbes are also able to produce different enzymes for catabolyzing different biochemical pathways, dissolving insoluble products, bioremediating pollutants, etc. Turning waste products into useable material is among the biochemical pathways performed by different microbes (Neklyudov *et al.,* 2008; Li *et al.,* 2009; Pandey *et al.,* 2009). Such kind of activities by microbes results in the recycling of energy sources and hence with environmental and economical advantages. Amongst the beneficial effects of plant growth promoting rhizobacteria (PGPR) on plant growth are the production of different enzymes such as phosphatase, dehydrogenase and nitrogenase (Abbas Zadeh *et al.,* 2010; Zabihi *et al.,* 2010).

Dehydrogenase

Dehydrogenase is an enzyme produced by different biochemical pathways dehydrogenating different compounds. For example, using deoxygenase enzyme prokaryotic microorganisms utilize oxygen from the oxygen molecule into aromatic compounds resulting in the production of *cis*-dihydrodiols, dehydrogenated by *cis*-dihydrodiol dehydrogenases (Kanaly and Harayama, 2000; Fernández-Luqueño *et al.,* 2011).

Numerous endocellular enzymes, with the ability to transfer electrons and protons from the substrate to the acceptor are able to carry dehydrogenases during the oxidation processes of organic compounds. Accordingly, the mineralizing activity of dehydrogenases can be used as a suitable indicator of soil quality (Neto *et al.,* 2007). Such kind of dehydrogenase activity is applicable to different soil types (Merlin *et al.,* 1995) such as soils contaminated with metals (ellis *et al.,* 2001) and hydrocarbons (Neto *et al.,* 2007), wastewaters (Tam, 1998) and sediments (Mosher *et al.,* 2003). Furthermore, the activity of dehydrogenase can be the indicator of microbial respiration and biomass production.

The high sensitivity of dehydrogenase to pollutants makes it as one of the most suitable biological indicators in polluted soils (Ellis *et al.,* 2001; Irha *et al.,* 2003, Malkomes, 2006). For example the presence of pollutants in the soil can alter the activity of enzymes such as dehydrogenase and hence in a polluted soil it is possible to estimate the level of pollution by measuring dehydrogenase activity. Moreover, dehydrogenase is also necessary for carbon cycling (Neto *et al.,* 2007).

Phosphatase

Phosphatases are a group of enzymes, which are able to catalyze phosphate esters and anhydrides, which include phytases, phosphomonoesterases, phosphoprotein phosphatases, phosphodieserases, alkaline and acid phosphatase, etc. (Adesemoye and Kloepper, 2009). Phosphatases can solubilize insoluble P products into soluble ones. For example, soil bacteria including *Bacillus*, *Pseudomonas* and *Actinomycetes*, as well as soil fungi such as

Aspergillus, *Penicillium* spp. and mycorrhizal fungi are able to produce the enzyme, which significantly increases P solubility and its uptake by plant (Khan *et al.,* 2007).

Phosphate solubilizing bacteria, which are about 10% of soil microorganisms and include a wide range of soil microbes such as *Bacilus*, *Pseodomonas* and *Burkholderia* are able to solubilize inorganic phosphate by producing inorganic (sulfuric and carbonic) and organic (oxalic, citric, butyric, malonic, lactic, etc.) acids as well as phosphatase enzyme (Whitelaw, 1997; Sundara, 2001).

Soil microbes are an important part of the ecosystem recycling the nutrients of different organic products including P. It is hence of significant importance to evaluate the role of different soil microorganisms in P cycling and the methods by which the efficiency of P availability can increase. Such a case is also important due to the common P deficiency in different parts of the world including the tropical and alkaline soils, especially because the price of P fertilization is increasing and just a part of soil total P is available to plant. The sources of rock P in the world are finite and hence it is necessary to develop methods, which may result in plant or microbes with higher P efficiency uptake and utilization (Sanchez, 2010; Miransari, 2011a, b; Richardson and Simpson, 2011; Zabihi *et al.,* 2011).

It was first in 1948 when Gerretsen (1948) indicated that soil bacteria are able to enhance the availability of soil P to plant being followed by an extensive set of research work regarding the increased availability of P using soil microbes (Richardson, 2001; Khan *et al.,* 2007; Richardson *et al.,* 2009; Abbas Zadeh *et al.,* 2010; Zabihi *et al.,* 2011). Plant absorbs P from the soil solution in form of orthophosphate through a set of high-affinity transporters localized on the root epidermis and expressed under P deficient conditions and during interaction with mycorrhizal fungi (Richardson and Simpson, 2011). Using the following mechanisms soil microbes are able to increase plant ability to absorb higher amounts of P: 1) increased plant growth, especially root growth by establishing symbiotic association with plant roots, resulted by for example enhanced production of plant hormones and different enzymes by soil microbes including mycorrhizal fungi and soil PGPR, 2) through alteration of chemical and biochemical reactions, which may affect the exchange of orthophosphate between soil colloids and soil solution, and 3) by inducing different metabolisms, which may increase the solubility of soil organic and inorganic P (Figure 1) (Richardson and Simpson, 2011; Miransari, 2011a,b). Such metabolisms include production of siderophore, phosphatase and cellulolytic enzymes as well as the efflux of organic anion and proton.

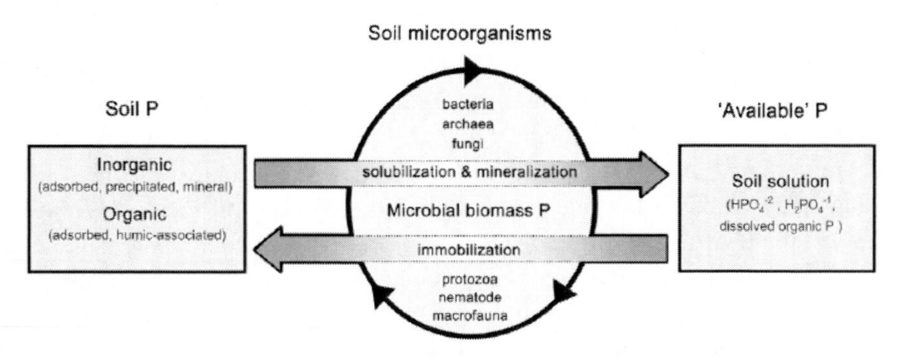

Source: Richardson and Simpson, 2011 (www.plantphysiol.org, "Copyright American Society of Plant Biologists.")

Figure 1. Chemical and biochemical processes affecting soil P dynamic.

For the organic P sources to be available to the plant the phosphatase enzymes, which are of plant or microbe origins are necessary. P deficiency is among the most important parameters, which can induce the metabolic activity of plant or microbe to produce phosphatase (Chen *et al.,* 2002). Soil microorganisms are able to produce phosphatases, which can solubilize different P organic sources such as the dominant form of organic P, phytate (inositol phosphate) in different soils (Lim *et al.,* 2007). Plant rhizosphere can also have a profound effect on the activity of soil microbes including the production of different enzymes such as phosphatases, which is due to the production of different exudates by plant roots with high rate of carbon products.

It is important to modify plant in a way so that they can behave more efficiently. For example, to absorb higher amounts of nutrients under nutrient deficient conditions.

Adjusting root exudates may be a useful way to enhance plant ability for the uptake of nutrients. The C products, which are produced by plant roots also contain different enzymes, which can directly influence nutrient uptake by increasing their solubility or indirectly by increasing microbial activity. For example, by genetically modifying plants to produce extracellular fungal phytase (from *Aspergillus niger*) plants were able to acquire P from phytate, which is also controlled by the microbial activities in the rhizosphere (Rhichardson *et al.,* 2005; George *et al.,* 2005a,b). Researchers have been able to isolate the bacteria, which are able to mineralize phytate in the plant rhizosphere. Such kind of bacteria can be used as inoculum, especially under nutrient deficient conditions (Rhichardson and Simpson, 2011).

The P regulatory protein PhoB, which is regulated by PhoR (a membrane sensor protein) is able to regulate P uptake by plant. PhoB phosphorylation results in the activation of *pho* gene. Accordingly, the *phoB* gene is able to regulate plant response to the environmental stress of P. For example, the study of *phoB* gene in *Bradyrhizobium japonicum* indicated that rather than affecting N fixation by the two symbionts, the gene can regulate soybean response under phosphate limited conditions (Minder *et al.,* 1998).

Lipase

The activity of lipases (Triacylglycerol acylhydrolases E.C.3.1.1.3) result in the hydrolysis of triacylglycerols to glycerols and free fatty acids at the lipid-water interface. With respect to their biochemical nature, lipases have a wide range of applications, for example in the pharmaceuticals and biotechnological field such as the production of polymers, biosurfactants, bioremediation, agrochemicals, perfumes, etc. Using the DNA recombinant technique it is likely to improve the applicability of lipases (Dharmsthiti and Kuhasuntisuk, 1998; Li *et al.,* 2007; Singh *et al.,* 2007; Sharma *et al.,* 2011).

There are different microorganisms, which are able to produce enzymes including bacteria, fungi and actinomycetes. Such kind of microorganisms can be isolated from the soil or from spoiled food. Although bacterial lipases are made of glycoproteins, there are some extracellular bacterial lipases, (for example, Staphylococcal lipase), which are naturally lipoproteins (Sharma *et al.,* 2011). Usually lipases are nonspecific regarding their substrate. Some of the bacteria with the ability to produce lipases are *Arthrobacter* sp., *Achromobacter* sp., *Alcaligenes* sp., *Staphylolococcus* sp., *Pseudomonas* sp., and *Chromobacterium* sp. There have also been lipases isolated from different environmental conditions such as antarctic ocean (Feller *et al.,* 1990), highly saline environments (Ghanem *et al.,* 2000), hot springs (Lee *et al.,* 1999) and composts (Rathi *et al.,* 2000). Bacterial lipases differ in their properties. For example, the pH of bacterial lipases is neutral or alkaline, with the exception of a strain of *Pseudomonas fluorescence*, which produces acidic lipase with a pH of 4.8. Bacterial pH's are stable in a wide range of pH's ranging from 4.8 to 11 (Khyami-Horani, 1996; Gupta *et al.,* 2004). Calcium is able to stimulate the activity of lipase, however the enzyme activity is inhibited by EDTA. The optimum range of temperature for the enzyme activity is 30-60 °C.

Details related to the thermal stability of species such as *Pseudomonas*, *Bacillus*, *Staphylococcus*, and *Chromobacterium* are previously investigated. Addition of stabilizing products such as ethylene glycol, glycerol and sorbitol increased the thermostability of lipase produced by *Bacillus* sp. Accordingly, the enzyme remained active even 150 min after incubation at 70 °C (Nawani and Kaur, 2000). The fungal lipases have the pH range of 4-8 (Sharma *et al.,* 2011). However, the fungi such as Trichosporonasteroides are able to grow both under acidic and alkaline conditions. The optimum temperature for the activity of fungi is in the range of 25-30 °C. However, some thermophilic fungi are able to act at the temperature range of 45-75 °C (Dharmsthiti and Ammaranond, 1997). Enzyme production is a function of C and N availability. It is also likely to genetically modify the production of extracellular enzymes by different microbes. Accordingly, it is possible to modify enzyme behavior, such as the optimal pH range of activity, enzyme specificity, thermal stability, etc. so that the enzyme can be used more efficiently. Researchers were able to purify two thermostable extra-cellular lipases including lipase I and II from Trichosporontermentans. Lipase I indicated a 30-min stability at 40 °C at pH 5.5 and for lipase II and under the same conditions, the thermostability temperature of the enzyme was up to 50 °C. The lipase enzyme produced by *Aspergillus niger* indicated optimal activity at the pH range of 4.5-5.5 at 25 °C. A 24-hr activity was resulted by the enzyme in the pH range of 3-10.5 at 30 °C. Metal ions such as Zn, Fe and Hg significantly inhibited the enzyme activity (Sharma *et al.,* 2011).

Conclusion

With respect to the importance of enzymes including dehydrogenase, phosphatase and lipase, in different fields such as industry, agriculture and environment some of their important properties were reviewed in this chapter. They are of both natural and synthetic origin and can handle a wide range of biochemical reactions. Properties such as optimum pH, temperature, specificity, reacting substrate, etc. determine enzyme activity under different conditions. Considering such kind of properties makes it likely to genetically modify the enzyme to act more efficiently. Hence, further research is necessary to find out more about enzyme properties and activities under different conditions, because there are a couple of hundred of enzymes, which are used commercially for different usages.

References

Abbas-Zadeh, P., Saleh-Rastin. N., Asadi-Rahmani, H., Khavazi, K., Soltani, A., Shoary-Nejati, A. R., and M. Miransari. 2010. Plant growth promoting activities of fluorescent pseudomonads, isolated from the Iranian soils. *Acta Physiol. Plantarum.* 32:281-288.

Adesemoye, A. and J. Kloepper. 2009. Plant–microbes interactions in enhanced fertilizer-use efficiency. *Appl. Microbiol. Biotechnol.* 85:1–12.

Chen, C. R., Condron, L. M., Davis, M. R., and R. R. Sherlock.2002. Phosphorus dynamics in the rhizosphere of perennial ryegrass (*Lolium perenne* L.) and radiata pine (*Pinus radiata* D. Don.). *Soil Biol. Biochem.* 34:487–499.

Dharmsthiti, S. and Ammaranond. 1997. Purification and characterization of lipase from a raw-milk yeast (*Trichosporon asteroids*). *Biotechnol. Appl. Biochem.* 26:111-116.

Dharmsthiti, S. and B. Kuhasuntisuk. 1998. Lipase from pseudomonas aeruginosa LP602: Biochemical properties and application for wastewater treatment. *J. Ind. Microbiol. Biotechnol.* 21:75-80.

Ellis, R. J., Neish, B., Trett, M. W., Best, J. G., Weightman, A. J., Morgan, P. and J. C. Fry. 2001. Comparison of microbial and meiofaunal community analyses for determining impact of heavy metal contamination. *J. Microbiol. Methods.* 45:171–185.

Feller, G., Thiry, M., Arpigny, J. L., Mergeay, M. and C. Gerday. 1990. Lipase from psychrotrophic Antarctic bacteria. *FEMS Microbiol. Lett.* 66:239-244.

Fernández-Luqueño, F., Valenzuela-Encinas, C., Marsch, R., Martínez-Suárez, C., Vázquez-Núñez, E. and L. Dendooven. 2011. Microbial communities to mitigate contamination of PAHs in soil-possibilities and challenges: a review. *Environ. Sci. Poll. Res.* 18:12–30.

George, T. S., Richardson, A. E., Smith, J. B., Hadobas, P. A. and R. J. Simpson. 2005a. Limitations to the potential of transgenic *Trifolium subterraneum* L. plants that exude phytase when grown in soils with a range of organic P content. *Plant Soil.* 278:263–274.

George, T. S., Simpson, R. J., Hadobas, P. A. and A. E. Richardson. 2005b. Expression of a fungal phytase gene in *Nicotiana tabacum* improves phosphorus nutrition of plants grown in amended soils. *Plant Biotechnol. J.* 3:129–140.

Gerhardt, K., Dong H. X., Glick, B. and B. Greenberg. 2009. Phytoremediation and rhizoremediation of organic soil contaminants: Potential and challenges. *Plant Sci.* 176: 20–30.

Gerretsen, F. C. 1948. The influence of microorganisms on the phosphate intake by the plant. *Plant Soil.* 1:51–81.

Ghanem, E. H., Al-Sayeed, H. A. and K. M. Saleh. 2000. An alkalophilic thermostable lipase produced by new isolate of *Bacillus alcalophilus*. *World J. Microbiol. Biotechnol.* 16:459-464.

Gupta, R., Gupta, N. and P. Rathi. 2004. Bacterial lipases: An overview of production, purification and biochemical properties. *Appl. Microbiol. Biotechnol.* 64:763-781.

Irha, N., Slet, J. and V. Petersell. 2003. Effect of heavy metals and PAH on soil assessed via dehydrogenase assay. *Environ. Internat.* 28:779–782

Kanaly, R. A. and S. Harayama. 2000. Biodegradation of high-molecularweight polycyclic aromatic hydrocarbons by bacteria. *J. Bacteriol.* 182:2059–2067.

Khan, M. S., Zaidi, A. and P. A. Wani. 2007. Role of phosphate-solubilizing microorganisms in sustainable agriculture—a review. *Agron. Sust. Develop.* 27: 29–43.

Khyami-Horani H. 1996. Thermotolerant strain of *Bacillus licheniformis* producing lipase. *World J. Microbiol. Biotechnol.* 12:399-401.

Lee, D. W., Koh, Y. S., Kim, B. C., Choi, H. J., et al. 1999. Isolation and characterization of thermophilic lipase from *Bacillus thermoleovorans* ID-1. *FEMS Microbiol. Lett.* 179:393-400.

Li, H., Y. Zhang, Kravchenko I., Xu H., and C. G. Zhang. 2007. Dynamic changes in microbial activity and community structure during biodegradation of petroleum compounds: A laboratory experiment. *J. Environ. Sci.* 19:1003-1013.

Li, Y. T., Rouland, C., Benedetti, M., Li, F., Pando, A., Lavelle, P., and J. Dai. 2009. Microbial biomass, enzyme and mineralization activity in relation to soil organic C, N and P turnover influenced by acid metal stress. *Soil Biol. Biochem.* 41:969–977.

Lim, B. L., Yeung, P., Cheng, C., and J. E. Hill. 2007. Distribution and diversity of phytate-mineralizing bacteria. *ISME J.* 1:321–330.

Malkomes, H.-P. 2006. Microbiological-ecotoxicological soil investigations of two herbicidal fatty acid preparations used with high dosages in weed control. UWSF – Z Umweltchem Ökotox 18:13–20.

Merlin, G., Lissolo, T., Morel, V., Rossel, D., and J. Tarradellas. 1995. Precautions for routine use of INT-Reductase activity for measuring biological activities in soil and sediments. *Environ. Toxicol. Water Qual.* 10:185–192.

Minder, A. C., Narberhaus, F., Hans-Martin, F., and H. Hennecke. 1998. The Bradyrhizobium japonicum phoB gene is required for phosphate limited growth but not for symbiotic nitrogen fixation. *FEMS Microbiol. Lett.* 161:47–52.

Miransari, M. 2011a. Interactions between arbuscular mycorrhizal fungi and soil bacteria. Review article, *Appl. Microbiol. Biotechnol.* 89:917-930.

Miransari, M. 2011b. Soil microbes and plant fertilization. Review article. *Appl. Microbiol. Biotechnol.* 92:875-885.

Mosher, J. J., Levison, B. S. and C. G. Johnston. 2003. A simplified dehydrogenase enzyme assay in contaminated sediment using 2-(piodophenyl)-3(p-nitrophenyl)-5-phenyl tetrazolium chloride. *J. Microbiol. Methods.* 53:411–415.

Nawani, N. and J. Kaur. 2000. Purification, characterization and thermostablity of lipase from a thermophilic Bacillus sp. J33. *Molecul. Cell Biochem.* 206:91-96.

Neklyudov, A. D., Fedotov, G. N. and A. N. Ivankin. 2008. Intensification of composting processes by aerobic microorganisms: A Review. *Appl. Biochem. Microbiol.* 44:6-18.

Neto, M., Ohannessian, A., Delolme C., and J-P. Bedell. 2007. Towards an optimized protocol for measuring global dehydrogenase activity in storm-water sediments. *J. Soil Sediment* 7:101–110.

Palmer T. 2001. *Enzymes: Biochemistry, Biotechnology and Clinical Chemistry*. First Edition, Horwood Publishing Ltd., Chichester, West Sussex, England, 3: 345, 349-350.

Pandey, A. K., Gaind, S., Ali, A. and L. Nain. 2009. Effect of bioaugmentation and nitrogen supplementation on composting of paddy straw. *Biodegradation*. 20:293–306.

Rathi, P. S., Bradoo, S., Saxena, R. K. and R. Gupta. 2000. A hyper thermostable, alkaline lipase from *Pseudomonas* sp. with the property of thermal activation. *Biotechnol. Lett.* 22:495-498.

Richardson, A. E. 2001. Prospects for using soil microorganisms to improve the acquisition of phosphorus by plants. *Aust. J. Plant Physiol.* 28:897–906.

Richardson, A. E., George, T. S., Hens, M. and R. J. Simpson. 2005. Utilization of soil organic phosphorus by higher plants. In: B. L. Turner, E. Frossard, D. S. Baldwin, eds, Organic Phosphorus in the Environment. CABI, Wallingford, UK, pp 165–184.

Richardson, A. E., Barea, J. M., McNeill, A. M., and C. Prigent-Combaret. 2009. Acquisition of phosphorus and nitrogen in the rhizosphere and plant growth promotion by microorganisms. *Plant Soil.* 321:305–339.

Richardson, A. E. and R. J. Simpson. 2011. Soil microorganisms mediating phosphorus availability. *Plant Physiol.* 156:989–996.

Sanchez, P. A. 2010. Tripling crop yields in tropical Africa. *Nature Geosci.* 3:299–300.

Sharma, D., Sharma, B. and A. K. Shukla. 2011. Biotechnological approaches of microbial lipase: a review. *Biotechnol.* 10:23-40.

Singh, A., Van Hamme, J. and O. P. Ward. 2007. Surfactants in microbiology and biotechnology: Part 2. Application aspects. *Biotechnol. Adv.* 25:99-121.

Soetan, K. O., Aiyelaagbe, O. O. and C. O. Olaiya. 2010. A review of the biochemical, biotechnological and other applications of enzymes. *Afric. J. Biotechnol.* 9:382-393.

Sundara, B., Natarayan, V. and K. Hari. 2001. Influence of phosphorus solubilising bacteria on soil available P-status and sugarcane development on a tropical vertisol. *Proc. Internat. Soc. Sugarcane Technol.* 24:47-51.

Tam, N. F. Y. 1998. Effects of wastewater discharge on microbial populations and enzyme activities in mangrove soils. *Environ. Poll.* 102:233–242.

Taylor, J. P., Wilson, B., Mills, M. S. and R. G. Burns. 2002. Comparison of microbial numbers and enzymatic activities in surface soils and subsoils using various techniques. *Soil Biol. Biochem.* 34:387–401.

Whitelaw, M. A., Harden, T. Y. and G. L. Bender. 1997. Plant growth promotion of wheat inoculated with *Penicillium radicum* sp. Nov. *Aust. J. Soil Res.* 38:291-300.

Zabihi, H. R., Savaghebi, G. R., Khavazi, K., Ganjali, A., and M. Miransari. 2011. *Pseudomonas* bacteria and phosphorous fertilization, affecting wheat (*Triticum aestivum* L.) yield and P uptake under greenhouse and field conditions. *Acta Physiol. Plant.* 33:145-152.

In: Applications of Microbial Genes in Enzyme Technology ISBN: 978-1-62417-808-5
Editors: V.K.Gupta, M.G.Tuohy, G.D.Sharma et al.

Chapter 9

Biotechnological Attributes of Phytases: An Overview

Ravish Rana,[1] Kushagr Punyani,[1]
Vijai Kumar Gupta[2*] and Smriti Gaur[†1]
[1]Department of Biotechnology,
Jaypee Institute of Information Technology
(Deemed University), Noida, India
[2]Molecular Glycobiotechnology Group,
Department of Biochemistry,
School of Natural Sciences,
National University of Ireland Galway,
Galway City, Ireland

Abstract

Phytase belongs to a class of enzymes called *meso*-inositol hexaphosphate phosphohydrolases that yields lower inositol phosphate esters and inorganic phosphates from phytate. Phytase finds use in an assortment of utilities. However the natural sources are neither sufficient, nor provide the task-suited phytases, and hence there is a need to develop microbial strains (or other sources) that can generate the enzyme in higher amounts, and altered as per requisite.

This chapter encompasses the natural sources and classification of phytase, chemical and biochemical features of the enzyme, modus operandi of catalysis, commercial production of phytase through genetic engineering, and the scope of use of the enzyme.

[*] Email:vijai.gupta@nuigalway.ie.
[†] Corresponding author: Smriti Gaur. Department of Biotechnology, Jaypee Institute of Information Technology (Deemed University), A-10, Sec. 62, Noida, 201307,India. E-mail: taru10@gmail.com.

Introduction

Phytase is a commercial animal feed additive serving as a phosphate supplement that enhances the uptake of native phytate by releasing the inorganic phosphate from phytic acid. The properties of the enzyme vary in accord to the source organism. Thermostability and pH tolerance are the key desired traits of phytase, besides catalytic action and enzyme kinetics. Phytase avails the undigestible phytate in seeds and grains, through the release of digestible phosphorus, calcium and other mineral nutrients.

For commercial production, phytase is produced through genetic manipulation of wild strains of phytase producing microbes for efficient yields of enzyme and desired enzymatic properties. Alternatively plant derived phytases are produced. Other than its use as a feed additive, phytase finds a utility niche in bakery industry and soy production.

Phytase and Its Classification

Phytases are *meso*-inositol hexaphosphate phosphohydrolases catalyzing the stepwise reaction of phosphate splitting of phytate to produce lower inositol phosphate esters and inorganic phosphate (Lei and Porres, 2003). Phytases belong to a class of enzymes called Phosphoric-monoester hydrolases (http://www.genome.jp/dbget-bin).

Kyoto Encyclopedia of Genes and Genomes and ExplorEnz classify phytases into three categories namely, 3-Phytase, 4-Phytase and 5-Phytase. (http://www.genome.jp/dbget-bin, http:// www.enzyme-database.org).

1. 3-Phytases

These hydrolases act on myo-inositol hexakisphosphate to produce 1D-myo-inositol 1,2,4,5,6-pentakisphosphate and orthophosphate; and are also known as myo-inositol-hexakisphosphate 3-phosphohydrolase (http://www. genome.jp).

2. 4-Phytases

Also known as myo-inositol-hexakisphosphate 4-phosphohydrolase, these enzymes utilize myo-inositol hexakisphosphate to yield 1D-myo-inositol 1,2,3,5,6-pentakisphosphate and orthophosphate(http://www.genome.jp).

3. 5-Phytases

5-Phytase or myo-inositol-hexakisphosphate 5-phosphohydrolase use myo-inositol hexakisphosphate to produce 1L-myo-inositol 1,2,3,4,6-pentakisphosphate and orthophosphate (http://www.genome.jp).

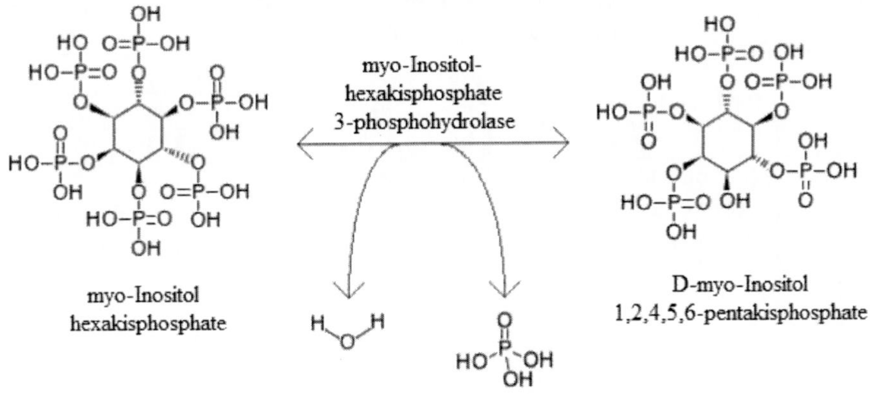

Figure 1. Activity of Phytase-3 Enzyme (http://www.genome.jp/dbget bin/www_bget?rn:R03371).

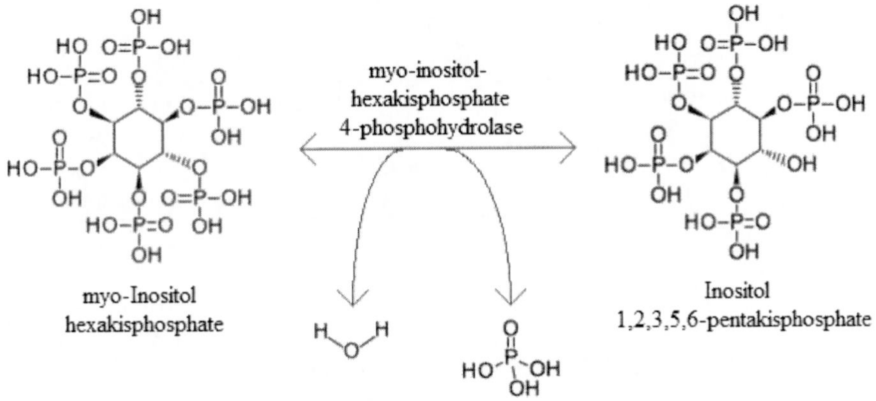

Figure 2. Activity of Phytase-4 Enzyme (http://www.genome.jp/dbget-bin/www_bget?rn:R03372).

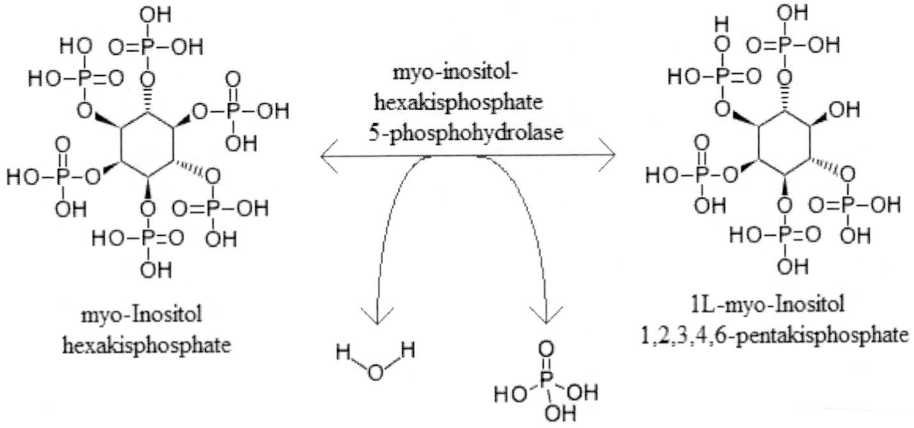

Figure 3. Activity of Phytase-5 Enzyme (http://www.genome.jp/dbget-bin/www_bget?rn:R07583).

Table 1. Chemical properties of Phytase (http://www.genome.jp/dbget-bin, http://www.enzyme-database.org)

Enzyme	Phytase-3	Phytase-4	Phytase-5
EC No.	EC 3.1.3.8	EC 3.1.3.26	EC 3.1.3.72
Systematic Name	myo-inositol-hexakisphosphate 3-phosphohydrolase	myo-inositol-hexakisphosphate 4-phosphohydrolase	myo-inositol-hexakisphosphate5-phosphohydrolase
Synonyms	3-phytase; 1-phytase; Phytase; phytate 1-phosphatase; phytate 6-phosphatase	4-phytase; 6-phytase*; phytase; phytate 6-phosphatase; myo-inositol-hexakisphosphate 6-phosphohydrolase*	---
Substrate	myo-inositol hexakisphosphate; H2O	myo-inositol hexakisphosphate; H2O	myo-inositol hexakisphosphate; H2O
Product	1D-myo-inositol 1,2,4,5,6-pentakisphosphate; phosphate	1D-myo-inositol 1,2,3,5,6-pentakisphosphate; Phosphate	1L-myo-inositol 1,2,3,4,6-pentakisphosphate; phosphate

*name based on 1L-numbering system and not 1D-numbering.

Based on their catalytic pH optimum, phytases have been distinguished as acid, neutral and alkaline; while according to the geometry of the active site of the phytase and the mechanism of catalysis, phytases are classified into Histidine Acid Phosphatase, β-Propeller Phytase and Purple Acid Phosphatase (Mullaney and Ullah, 2003).

1 Histidine Acid Phosphatases: Histidine Acid Phosphatases (HAP) are the ones that are most exclusively studied and maximum utilized, and are also known to occur in animals, plants and microorganisms (Wodzinski and Ullah, 1996). All HAPs share a 7 residue common motif of RHGXRXP in their active sites at the N-terminal end and a HD motif at the C-terminal end in their DNA sequences (Ullah *et al.*, 1991). The histidine residue is responsible for hydrolysis of phosphate monoesters. The active site of the HAP is positively charged and is located at the interface of its two subunits-the larger α/β-domain and the smaller α-domain (Kostrewa *et al.*, 1997; Jia *et al.*, 1998; Lim *et al.*, 2000).

2 β -Propeller Phytase: β-Propeller Phytase (BPP) has a propeller like structure, with 6 blades primarily consisting of β sheets along and a negatively charged narrow active site, which unlike HAPs, harbours calcium binding sites but no RHGXRXP or HD motifs (Ha *et al.*, 2000). BAP bears an affinity site that binds to the substrate; a cleavage site which is responsible for hydrolysis; and two phosphate-binding sites (Shin *et al.*, 2001).

3 Purple Acid Phosphatases: Purple Acid Phosphatases are metalloenzymes (Strater *et al.*, 1995; Guddat *et al.*, 1999). It has been found by the characterization of soybean

phytase that it has a PAP sequence motif. Phytase extracted from the germinating *Glycine max* has the active site motif of a PAP (Hegeman and Grabau, 2011). Binuclear metallic center is a characteristic of PAPs native to animals and is composed of two irons, whereas plant PAPs bear an iron ion linked to zinc or manganese ion (Olczak *et al.*, 2003).

Catalytic Mechanism of Phytase

The catalytic mechanism of action of HAPs for phosphomonoester hydrolysis has been studied by site-directed mutagenesis and crystallographic studies (Ostanin *et al.*, 1992; Ostanin and Van Etten, 1993; Lim *et al.*, 2000). The catalytic histidine of the RHGXRXP motif participates nucleophilically to produce a covalent phosphohistidine intermediate, while the aspartic acid residue borne by the HD motif donates proton to the oxygen of the phosphomonoester bond (Ostanin *et al.*, 1992; Lindqvist *et al.*, 1994; Porvari *et al.*, 1994; Oh *et al.*, 2004).

Mechanisms of alkaline phytase catalysis have been established via site-directed mutagenesis studies, crystallographic analysis and kinetic analysis (Oh *et al.*, 2001; Shin *et al.*, 2001). A water molecule in the active site associated to a divalent calcium ion attacks the phosphomonoester linkage of the calcium-phytate complex (Oh *et al.*, 2001; Shin *et al.*, 2001; Oh *et al.*, 2004).

Biochemical Properties of Phytase

The kinetics and specificities of an enzyme are the pivot of utility of an enzyme in any process, industry or otherwise. The enzyme must be stable and active during the processing as well as catalysis. Due to the same reasons, the temperature and pH requirements of the enzyme, substrate specificities, resistance to inhibitory molecules are crucial parameters. In this section, we review the biochemical features of representative phytases from different sources, including fungal, yeast, bacterial and plant origin.

Aspergillus niger, is used as the most important producer of phytase, and has been used to purify and characterize the enzyme for molecular weight, pH and temperature optima and kinetic activity. The molecular weight was determined as 39 kDa. Two pH optima at pH 2.62 and pH 5.05 were found for the enzyme, with temperature optima at 55 and 58 ºC. Study of kinetics for hydrolysis of sodium phytate indicated a K_m of 0.929 µM and V_{max} of 52.36 nkat/cm^3. Pb and Ag were found to activate the enzyme, Ba^{2+} and Ca^{2+} stimulated activity, while Hg, Cu, Zn, Fe, Al were inhibitory (Sariyska *et al.*, 2005).

The thermostable and pH-tolerant phytase of *Pichia anomala* (molecular weight 64 kDa) has also been characterized and found to have temperature and pH optima of 60°C and pH 4.0, respectively. With broad substrate specificity, the enzyme shows a K_m of 0.20 mM and V_{max} was 6.34 lmol/mg protein/min. The enzyme is not metal-dependent and unaffected by Sodium azide, DTT, β-mercaptoethanol, EDTA, toluene, glycerol, PMSF, iodo-acetate and N-bromosuccinimide. However, 2,3-butanedione inhibits its activity. Phytase activity is stable in presence of inorganic phosphate upto 10 mM, and with a long shelf life of 6 months (at

4°C), yeast phytase appears to be suitable as an animal feed additive (Vohra and Satyanarayana, 2002).

Bacillus species also produce thermostable phytases. Phytase isolated from *Bacillus* sp. DS11 has been found to specifically hydrolyze phytate in rice floor efficiently. It has a molecular weight of 44 kDa, temperature optima of 70°C and pH optima of 7.0. Being thermotolerant, in presence of calcium chloride, it retains a considerable activity after a 10 min heat treatment at 90°C, though it is calcium dependent for thermal stability, activity remains considerably stable in a pH range of 4.0–8.0. A K_m of 0.55mM is shown for phytate hydrolysis, which is inhibited by EDTA, Cd^{2+} and Mn^{2+} (Kim *et al.*, 1998). Soybean phytase finds much use in animal and bird feed supplements. Phytase from germinating cotyledons was purified found to contain two bands of 59 and 60 KDa on SDS-PAGE. The enzyme possesses characteristic plant pH and temperature optima of 4.5–4.8 and 55 °C, respectively, and a high affinity for phytic acid. The enzyme was found to be inhibited by phosphate, vanadate, and fluoride (Gibson and Ullah, 1988).

Biotechnological Production of Phytase- the Role of Genetic Engineering

The potential of phytase as an active catalyst in myriad industrial applications immediately called for development of processes for effective and large scale production of the enzyme. Seeking the adequate quality of the enzyme with the tailor made functionality for specific field application, the answer lay in genetic engineering. Genes responsible for phytase production could be manipulated and cloned in new hosts for efficient production. In this section, we discuss some phytase sources and production techniques that have been researched upon. Phytases from *Aspergillus* species currently dominate the market of animal feed. In 2003, Xiong *et al.* (2004) cloned the cDNA encoding a phytase from *A. niger* 113 into *Pichia pastoris*. The post-purification yield so obtained was 4.2 g phytase per litre of culture, with an activity of 9.5 U/mg.

Microbial Phytase

The primary aim of genetic engineering in enzyme production is to obtain pure yields with improved efficacy and specificity (Chang *et al.*, 2008). Tian *et al.* (2011) created site directed mutants, Q53R and K91D, of phyIls gene from *A. niger* 113 and cloned them into *Escherichia coli*. The mutants were created based on sequence analysis and comparison, aiming to improve the phytase activity. The mutants showed enhanced specific activity, affinity for sodium phytate and catalytic efficiency of phytase.

Enzymes with wider pH and temperature tolerance ranges find use in myriad industrial applications. pH specificity is crucial in phytase supplemented animal feed in accord with the native pH of the gut. Temperature mediated inactivation of phytase during processing of the feed additives calls for higher temperature tolerance of the enzyme. Several research groups have genetically engineered microbial phytases to yield enzymes with varied pH and temperature optima. *Bacillus* species are the key source of β-propeller phytases- the thermotolerant enzymes showing optimal activity in a temperature range of 55 to 70°C and neutral pH range and exhibiting divalent calcium dependent catalysis (Olazaran *et al.*, 2010). Phytase from a particular CF92 strain of *B. subtilis* exhibits an optimal activity at 60°C, is highly tolerant to temperature (40% activity after 30 min heat incubation at 80°C), and has a pH optimum at 7.0, with fair stability in 4.0 to 8.0 pH (Hong *et al.*, 2011).

Rao *et al.* (2008) cloned the *Bacillus* phytase gene in *Escherichia coli* which was modified for broader optimal pH range by introducing a specific amino acid sequence of the acid phosphatases from fungi; followed by manifestation of the enzyme by inclusion body separation and in vitro refolding of enzyme. The harvested phytase exhibited broader pH and temperature tolerance and in silico studies confirmed the β-propeller structure. In another study (Olazaran *et al.*, 2010), *Bacillus* phytase gene was cloned in *Pichia pastoris*, post modification for N-Glycosylation. The recombinant enzyme showed an optimal pH range of 2.5 to 9, high thermal tolerance (85% activity after 10 min heat treatment at 80°C) and was resistant to shrimp digestive enzymes and porcine trypsin.

Plant Derived Phytase

Another methodology adopted for phytase production, based on in situ remediation, is expression of microbial phytase genes in plants. Monogastric animals cannot digest phytate and the phytate released in the streams through the excreta to cause eutrophication in the water bodies. Phytase is also required for better uptake of phosphorous and metal ions bound as phytate by the organism. The plants expressing the phytase are generally the components of feed of monogastric animals. Based on a construct driven by embryo-specific globulin-1 promoter, Chen *et al.* (2008) over-expressed *A. niger phyA2* gene in maize seeds with the objective of developing maize to do away with the requirement of addition of external phosphorus in monogastric animal feed. Phytase activity incremented 50-fold in the transgenic variety, accompanied by stable expression and normal germination. Grain seeds like soy and corn find utility in avian feed. Phytase inclusion in these feeds aids in efficient absorption of phosphate. Bilyeu *et al.* (2008) created a *Glycine max* line expressing the *appA* gene of *E. coli*, encoding for periplasmic phytase, in order to increase its bioavailabilty to monogastrics, as well as to convert phytates of admixed meals to utilizable phosphorus. To check and compare the efficacy of plant derived phytases, Nyannor and Adeola. (2008) did a study in which they checked and compared the efficacy of *Escherichia Coli*-Derived Phytase Gene expressed in corn and *E. coli*-derived microbial phytase expressed in *Pichia pastoris*. The results indicated that corn derived phytase effectively improves the growth of phosphorous deficient broiler chicks.

Applications of Phytase in Animal Feed

Phytase has been popularly used as an animal feed phosphate supplement, in monogastric animals, to increase the bioutilization capacity of the native phytate and hence enhancing the nutritive value of the feed by releasing the inorganic phosphate from phytic acid (myo-inositol hexakisphosphate) and its derivatives.

Monogastric animals do not possess the ability to generate endogenous phytase and hence phytase is needed to be supplied externally. Phytase (myo-inositol hexakisphosphate phosphohydrolases) catalyzes the release of orthophosphate from myo-inositol hexakisphosphate (Ins P6) and plays an important role in breaking down the indigestible phytic acid (phytate) part that exists in grains and oil seeds, and thus releases digestible phosphorus, calcium and other mineral nutrients (Li *et al.*, 2010).

The feed of pigs contains phytate in a major quantity. The phosphorus present in phytate is of little value to the pig, because of the inability of pigs to secrete adequate amount of phytase enzyme. To cope up with the less quantity of phosphorous in the main feed, pork producers have added phosphorus-rich ingredients to the diet to ensure that the pig's requirement for this mineral is met. The undigested phosphorus passes through the pig and enriches manure with phosphorus. If manure is applied to crop land at excessive rates, phosphorus will accumulate in the soil.

Also, non renewable nature of phosphates could have lead to a crisis in Phosphorous supply (Montminy *et al.*, 2010).

To address the above issues, feeding strategies have been developed to limit phosphorous overfeeding and Phosphorous excretion by pigs. The introduction of exogenous phytases has been recognized as a reliable means to increase the availability of phytate phosphorous to pigs and, thus, decrease the need for supplemental inorganic phosphorous.

In 1990, addition of phytase from microbial origin resulted in increased availability of phosphorus, which commercially reduced the amount of phosphorus that was additionally added to the diet. The technique of addition of phytase has since then been commercially used and and now is a common ingredient in a pig's diet (Augspurger *et al.*, 2007).

Addition of microbial phytases to diets is said to increase digestibility of plant phosphorous but experiments found out the efficiency to be a maximum of 60–65%. The major obstacle was the shortage of time for phytate degradation inside the stomach of pigs. This was due to the traditional following of feeding of dry feed. This has lead to the use of liquid feeding which improves the digestibility of plant phosphorous, aiming at pre-digestion of phytate in liquid feeding (Blaabjerg and Poulsen, 2010).

Applications of Phytase in Poultry Feed

Dietary phytate has an important application in intensively farmed livestock where it is known to influence performance and nutrient utilization. Ingestion of phytate is shown to have a considerable effective on digestive physiology, modifying secretion and absorption dynamics (Liu *et al.*, 2008).

Cereal grains, by-products of plant food processing, fat-rich seeds and legume seeds are the main components of diets for poultry. Feed has a direct relation with the cost of producing a kilogram of chicken, a kilogram of turkey or a dozen eggs with feed accounting to around 70% of the cost. Hence feed cost is minimized while taking into consideration the optimum production and performance goals. The most expensive part of poultry feed includes energy, protein, and phosphorus, - energy and protein are required to deposit lean tissue, and phosphorus is required to support the skeletal and egg structures. Hence proper utilization of phosphorous is important for maintaining production outputs as well as to decrease costs (Augspurger *et al.*, 2011).

Most of the phosphorous available to the poultry birds is present in complexes with phytic acid. The utilization of this phosphorus depends on the enzyme phytase present in the digestive tract of laying hens or other birds. Production of phytase by the poultry birds as well by microorganisms in the GI tract is in very small quantities. Some grains of selected cereals (barley, wheat, triticale, rye) are reported to contain phytase whose activity is partly sufficient to hydrolyse phytin but not efficient enough to meet optimum production standards. Seed plants, including maize, have also shown minimal activity levels of phytase hence stressing on the requirement of external phytase. Inefficient utilization of phosphorous also leads to increase of phosphorous levels in the farmland leading to hazardous environmental consequences (Kozłowsk and Jeroch, 2011).

Phytase enzymes are provided externally in the poultry feed which increases the utilization of phosphorous from phytate to the bird, thus meeting the minimum requirement of phosphorous and reducing the phosphorous levels in farmlands which decreases the environmental costs of poultry production.

Phytate is also reported to bind other nutrients in addition to phosphorous, which are subsequently released on the addition of phytase and allows their absorption by the bird. The release of energy and protein by phytase from phytate further allows reduction of extra ingredients in the feed and hence leading to overall decrease in the cost associated with the feed (Silversides and Hruby, 2009; McGrath *et al.*, 2010).

Applications of Phytase in Human Nutrition

Phytic acid (PA) is considered an antinutritional factor in the diet of humans because of the inability to utilize phytate. The inability leads to low bioavailability of the minerals bound in the phytate. The bound minerals include zinc, iron, calcium, magnesium, manganese and copper. The decrease in availability of these essential minerals can lead to deficiencies in human populations where staples like wheat, rice and maize are the major or the only source of nutrition. The chelating effect of the phosphate groups is the main cause behind binding of PA to mineral cations, especially to Cu^{2+} and Zn^{2+} which tend to have a high affinity for inositol phosphates. Phytate is also reported to form a strong complex with some proteins to resist their proteolysis and also reduces the blood glucose response (Bohn *et al.*, 2008).

Although consumption of phytate majorly has negative effects on human health, some benefits have also been reported. Phytate has been reported to prevent kidney stone formation, and to protect against atherosclerosis and coronary heart disease as well as against a variety of cancers. The levels of phytate and its dephosphorylation products in urine, plasma and other biological fluids are seen to be fluctuating with ingestion or deprivation of phytate in the human diet.

Therefore, the reduction in phytate intake in developed compared to developing countries might be a factor responsible for the increase in diseases typical for Western societies such as diabetes mellitus, renal lithiasis, cancer, atherosclerosis and coronary heart diseases (Greiner R. and U. Konietzny. 2006).

Improving of the nutritional value of phytate involves dephosphorylation of phytate which leads to opening up of inositol rings leading to removal of phosphate groups which results in decreasing the mineral binding strength of phytate. This has resulted in increased bioavailability of essential dietary minerals.

The major efforts to reduce phytate quantity in food include food processing and preparation techniques, along with the addition of exogenous enzymes. Hydrolysis of phytate during food processing (and then preparation, for example by germination, soaking, cooking and fermentation) is a result of the phytate-degrading activity of phytase, which is naturally present in plants and microorganisms.

Thus, phytases have an important application in human nutrition both for degradation of phytate during food processing and in the gastrointestinal tract (Kumar *et al.*, 2010).

Other Commercial Applications of Phytase

In Home fortification: Due to a lack of resources and vitamin-rich foods, many developing nations are plagued with micronutrient deficiencies that lead to anaemia, diarrhoea, and/or blindness-related diseases. In-home fortification involves adding of a powdered mix of multiple micronutrients in single-dose sachets to home-cooked meals on a daily basis. It is reported that in-home fortification of complementary foods with micronutrient powders containing low amounts of iron may be potentially safer than powders containing high amounts of iron.

However, low iron doses have little nutritional effect, unless iron absorption is high. Phytase is used to increase the bioavailability of iron. Experiments showed that addition of phytase when iron was present as either NaFeEDTA or FeSO4, with or without ascorbic acid, significantly increased iron absorption. The combined addition of phytase, ascorbic acid, and NaFeEDTA resulted in absorption of 7.4%, compared with absorption of 1.5% from FeSO4 without enhancers in the same meal (Troesch *et al.*, 2009).

Bakery technology: Bread is a staple food in the world and is an important source of both iron and the inhibiting phytate. It is considered that whole wheat bread with low phytic acid level and increased mineral bioavailability would be beneficial and attractive in improving mineral status and consequently in supporting preventive nutrition. Phytase is reported to be a distinct supplement in improving the bread making technology. The supplementation of commercial fungal phytase from *Aspergillus niger* in the dough ingredients containing fiber formulation leads to an acceleration of the proofing, an improvement of the bread shape, a slight increase of the specific volume, and also confers softness to the crumb. These improvements in bread quality were suggested to be associated with an indirect impact of phytase on α-amylase activity.

From the nutritional point of view, a further hydrolysis of the phytates which considered as anti-nutritional compounds is reached by adding exogenous phytase, therefore an enhancement in the mineral adsorption can be obtained with the consumption of phytase supplemented bread (Afinah *et al.*, 2010).

Soybean and Soybean By-products: Soyabean is a rich source of protein for humans and food for animals besides being a rich source of vegetable oil. Soybean meal is rich in the amino acids lysine, tryptophan, threonine, isoleucine, and valine which are deficient in cereal grains such as corn and sorghum most utilized in poultry and swine diets. Soybeans and soybean meal are also a source of isoflavones which are known to improve growth, promote tissue growth in pigs, and prevent diseases. However, soybean meal possesses anti-nutritional properties which must be overcome to increase its nutritional value. These include antitrypsin inhibitors, oligosaccharides, such as rafinose and stachyose, which are poorly utilized by most food animals. Phytic acid and antigenic factors found in certain soybean proteins cause inflammatory response in the gastrointestinal tract of monogastric animals.

The use of microbial phytase enzymes in soy-based diets of swine and poultry increases phosphorus bioavailability and minimizes excess phosphorus excretion. It was also reported that phytase activity in the direct-fed microbial and that supplementation of the corn-soy based diets with the probiotics (lactobacilli) to a 0.25% available phosphorus diet improved phosphorus retention and layer performance (Nahashon and Kilonzo-Nthenge, 2011; Konietzny and Greiner, 2004).

Conclusion

The enzymatic properties of phytase are responsible for its ability to hydrolyse phytate in the digestive tract. Two main types of phytases have been used; acid phytases with a pH optimum around pH 5.0 and alkaline phytases with a pH optimum around pH 8.0. The effectiveness of phytase supplementation depends on different factors one of them being substrate specificity.

Experiments have suggested that for animal nutrition purposes, phytases with broad substrate specificity are more suitable than phytases with narrow substrate specificity. The major difference between the two being that phytases with broad substrate specificity are easily able to degrade phytate to *myo*-inositol monophosphate with no major accumulation of intermediates, whereas phytases with narrow substrate specificity resulted in *myo*-inositol tris- and bisphosphate accumulation during phytate degradation coupled with a progressive rate of phosphate release.

Alkaline phytases from *Bacillus subtilis* and *Bacillus amyloliquefaciens* and the acid phytases from *Escherichia coli, Raoultella terrigena*, *Aspergillus niger* and *Aspergillus terreus* are considered to be highly specific for phytate. Researches have to be done on to combine high specific phytase activity with broad substrate specificity to reduce costs and increase activity of phytases.

References

Afinah, S., A. M. Yazid, M. H. Anis Shobirin and M. Shuhaimi. 2010. Phytase: application in food industry, *Int. Food Res. J.* 17: 13-21.

Augspurger, N. R., D. M. Webel and D. H. Baker. 2007. An Escherichia coli phytase expressed in yeast effectively replaces inorganic phosphorus for finishing pigs and laying hens. *J. Anim. Sci.* 85:1192-1198.

Augspurger, N. R., S. D. Frankenbach and F. Goldflus. Phytase and Phosphorus: An overview of the US Poultry Industry. 2011 Dec. 25. http://en.engormix.com/MA-poultry-industry/genetic/articles/phytase-phosphorus-in-poultry-nutrition-t1611/103-p0.htm.

Bilyeu, K. D., P. Zeng, P. Coello, Z. J. Zhang, H. B. Krishnan, A. Bailey, P. R. Beuselinck and J. C. Polacco. 2008. Quantitative Conversion of Phytate to Inorganic Phosphorus in Soybean Seeds Expressing a Bacterial Phytase. *Plant Physiol.* 146: 468–477.

Blaabjerg, K. and H. D. Poulsen. 2010. Microbial phytase and liquid feeding increase phytate degradation in the gastrointestinal tract of growing pigs. *Livest. Sci.* 134: 88–90.

Bohn, L., A. S. Meyer and S. K. Rasmussen. 2008. Phytate: impact on environment and human nutrition. A challenge for molecular breeding. *J. Zhejiang Univ. Sci. B.* 9: 165-191.

Chang, M. H., C. C. Young, S. Y. Chien, A. B. Arun. 2008. Expression of recombinant *Pichia pastoris* X33 phytase for dephosphorylation of rice bran fermented liquid. *Ann. Microbiol.* 58: 233-238.

Chen, R., G. Xue, P. Chen, B. Yao, W. Yang, Q. Ma, Y. Fan, Z. Zhao, M. C. Tarczynski and J. Shi. 2008. Transgenic maize plants expressing a fungal phytase gene. *Transgenic Res.* 17: 633–643.

Gibson, D. M. and A. J. H. Ullah. 1988. Purification and characterization of phytase from cotyledons of germinating soybean seeds. *Arch Biochem. and Biophysics.* 260: 503-513.

Greiner, R. and U. Konietzny. 2006. Phytase for Food Application. *Food Technol. Biotechnol.* 44: 125–140.

Guddat, L. W., A. S. McAlpine, D. Hume, S. Hamilton, J. de Jersey and J. L. Martin. 1999. Crystal structure of mammalian purple acid phosphatise. *Structure.* 7: 757-767.

Ha, N. C., B. C. Oh, S. Shin, H. J. Kim, T. K. Oh, Y. O. Kim, K. Y. Choi and B. H. Oh. 2000. Crystal structures of a novel, thermostable phytase in partially and fully calcium-loaded states. *Nat. Struct. Biol.* 7: 147-53..

Hegeman, C. E. and E. A. Grabau. 2011. A Novel phytase with sequence similarity to purple acid phosphatases is expressed in Cotyledons of Germinating Soybean Seedlings. *Plant Physiol.* 126: 1598-1608.

Hong, S. W., I. H. Chu and K. S. Chung. 2011. Purification and Biochemical Characterization of Thermostable Phytase from Newly Isolated *Bacillus subtilis* CF92. *J. Korean Soc. Appl. Biol. Chem.* 54: 89-94.

Jia, Z., S. Golovan, Q. Ye and Forsberg C. W. 1998. Purification, crystallization and preliminary X-ray analysis of the Escherichia coli phytase. *Acta. Crystallogr. D. Biol. Crystallogr.* 54: 647-649.

Kim, Y. O., H. K. Kim, K. S. Bae, J. H. Yu and T. K. Oh. 1998. Purification and properties of a thermostable phytase from *Bacillus* sp. DS11. *Enz. and Microbiol. Technol.* 22: 2-7.

Konietzny, U. and R. Greiner 2004. Bacterial Phytase: Potential Application, *In Vivo* Function and Regulation of Its Synthesis. *Brazilian J. Microbiol.* 35: 11-18.

Kostrewa, D., F. Gruninger-Leitch, A. D'Arcy, C. Broger, D. Mitchell and A. P. G. M. van Loon. 1997. Crystal structure of phytase from *Aspergillus ficuum* at 2.5 Å resolution. *Nat. Struct. Biol.* 4: 185-190.

Kozłowsk, K. and H. Jeroch. 2011. Efficacy of different levels of *Escherichia coli* phytase in hens fed maize-soyabean meal based diets with a decreased non-phytate phosphorus content. *J. Anim. Feed. Sci.* 20: 224–235.

Kumar, V., A. K. Sinha, H. P. S. Makkar and K. Becker. 2010. Dietary roles of phytate and phytase in human nutrition: A review. *Food Chem.* 120: 945–959.

Lei, X. G. and J. M. Porres. 2003. Phytase enzymology, applications, and biotechnology. *Biotechnology Letters*. 25: 1787–1794.

Li, R., J. Zhao, C. Sun, W. Lu, C. Guo and K. Xiao. 2010. Biochemical properties, molecular characterizations, functions, and application perspectives of phytases. *Front. Agric. China*. 4: 195–209.

Lim, D., S. Golovan, C. W. Forsberg and Z. Jia. 2000. Crystal structures of Escherichia coli phytase and its complex with phytate. *Nat. Struct. Biol.* 7: 108–113.

Lindqvist, Y., G. Schneider and P. Vihko. 1994 Crystal structures of rat acid phosphatase complexed with the transition-state analogs vanadate and molybdate. Implications for the reaction mechanism. *Eur. J. Biochem.* 221: 139–142.

Liu, N., Y. J. Ru, A. J. Cowieson, F. D. Li and X. C. Cheng. 2008. Effects of Phytate and Phytase on the Performance and Immune Function of Broilers Fed Nutritionally Marginal Diets. *Poult. Sci.* 87:1105–1111.

McGrath, J. M., J. T. Sims, R. O. Maguire, W. W. Saylor and R. Angel. 2010. Modifying Broiler Diets with Phytase and Vitamin D Metabolite (25-OH D3): Impact on Phosphorus in Litter, Amended Soils, and Runoff. *J. Environ. Qual.* 39: 324–332.

Montminy, M. P. L., A. Narcy, M. Magnin, D. Sauvant, J. F. Bernier, C. Pomar and C. Jondreville. 2010. Effect of reduced dietary calcium concentration and phytase supplementation on calcium and phosphorus utilization in weanling pigs with modified mineral status. *J. Anim. Sci.* 88:1706-1717.

Mullaney, E. J. and A. H. Ullah. 2003. The term phytase comprises several different classes of enzymes. *Biochem. Biophys. Res. Commun*. 5:179-84..

Nahashon, S. N. and A. K. Kilonzo-Nthenge 2011. Advances in Soybean and Soybean ByProducts in Monogastric Nutrition and Health. *Soybean and Nutr.* 127-156.

Nyannor, E. K. D. and O. Adeola. 2008. Corn Expressing an *Escherichia Coli*-Derived Phytase Gene: Comparative Evaluation Study in Broiler Chicks. *Poult. Sci.* 87: 2015–2022..

Oh, B. C., B. S. Chang, K. H. Park, N. C. Ha, H. K. Kim, B. H. Oh and T. K. Oh. 2001. Calcium-dependent catalytic activity of a novel phytase from *Bacillus amyloliquefaciens* DS11. *Biochemistry*. 40: 9669–9676..

Oh, B. C., W. C. Choi, S. Park, Y. O. Kim and T. K. Oh. 2004. Biochemical properties and substrate specificities of alkaline and histidine acid phytases. *Appl. Microbiol. Biotechnol.* 63: 362–372.

Olazaran, M. G., L. R. Blanco, J. G. C Trevino, J. A. G. Lopez and J. M. V. Salvado. 2010. Expression of a *Bacillus* Phytase C Gene in *Pichia pastoris* and Properties of the Recombinant Enzyme. *Appl. Environ. Microbiol.* 76: 5601–5608.

Olczak, M., B. Morawiecka and W. Watorek. 2003. Plant purple acid phosphatases genes, structures and biological function. *Acta. Biochimica. Polonca*. 50: 1245-1256..

Ostanin, K., E. H. Harms, P. E. Stevis, R. Kuciel, M. M. Zhou and R. L.Van Etten. 1992. Overexpression, site-directed mutagenesis, and mechanism of Escherichia coli acid phosphatase. *J. Biol. Chem.* 267: 22830–22836.

Ostanin, K. and R. L. Van Etten. 1993. Asp304 of Escherichia coli acid phosphatase is involved in leaving group protonation. *J. Biol. Chem.* 268: 20778–20784.

Porvari, K. S., A. M. Herrala, R. M. Kurkela, P. A Taavitsainen, Y. Lindqvist, G. Schneider and P. T. Vihko. 1994. Site-directed mutagenesis of prostatic acid phosphatase. Catalytically important aspartic acid 258, substrate specificity, and oligomerization. *J. Biol. Chem.* 269: 22642–22646.

Rao, D. E. C. S., K. V. Rao and V. D. Reddy. 2008. Cloning and expression of *Bacillus* phytase gene (phy) in *Escherichia coli* and recovery of active enzyme from the inclusion bodies. *J. Appl. Microbiol.* 105: 1128-1137.

Sariyska, M. V., S. A. Gargova, L. A. Koleva and A. I. Angelov. 2005. A*spergillus niger* phytase: purification and characterization; *Biotechnol. and Biotechnol.* 19: 98-105..

Shin, S., N. C. Ha, B. C. Oh, T. K. Oh and B. H. Oh. 2001. Enzyme Mechanism and Catalytic Property of β Propeller Phytase. *Structure.* 9: 851-858.

Silversides, F. G. and M. Hruby. 2009. Feed formulation using phytase in laying hen diets. *J. Appl. Poult. Res.* 18: 15–22.

Strater, N., T. Klabunde, P. Tucker, H. Witzel and B. Krebs. 1995. Crystal structure of a purple acid phosphatase containing a dinuclear Fe(III)-Zn(II) active site. *Science.* 9: 1489-1492.

Tian, Y. S., R. H. Peng, J. Xu, W. Zhao, F. Gao, X. Y. Fu, A. S. Xiong and Q. H. Yao 2011. Semi-rational site-directed mutagenesis of phyI1s from *Aspergillus niger* 113 at two residue to improve its phytase activity. *Mol. Biol. Rep.* 38: 977–982.

Troesch, B., I. Egli, C. Zeder, R. F. Hurrell, S. De Pee and M. B. Zimmermann. 2009. Optimization of a phytase-containing micronutrient powder with low amounts of highly bioavailable iron for in-home fortification of complementary foods. *Am. J. Clin. Nutr.* 89: 539–44..

Ullah, A. H. J., B. J. Cummins and Jr. H. C. Dischinger. 1991. Cyclohexanedione modification of arginine at the active site of phytase. *Biochem. Biophys. Res Commun.* 178: 45-53.

Vohra, A. and T. Satyanarayana. 2002. Purification and characterization of a thermostable and acid-stable phytase from *Pichia anomala. World J. Microbiol and Biotechnol.* 18: 687–691..

Wodzinski, R. J. and A. H. J. Ullah. 1996. Phytase. *Adv. Appl. Microbiol.* 42: 263-302.

Xiong, A. S., Q. H. Yao, R. H. Peng, X. Li, H. Q. Fan, M. J. Guo and S. L. Zhang. 2004. Isolation, Characterization, and Molecular Cloning of the cDNA Encoding a Novel Phytase from *Aspergillus niger* 113 and High Expression in *Pichia pastoris. J. Biochem. Mol. Biol.* 37: 282-291.

2011 December 22 *http://www.genome.jp/dbget-in/www_bfind_sub?mode=bfindandmax_hit=1000anddbkey=enzymeandkeywords=phytase.*

2011 December 22 *http://www.enzyme-database.org/query.php?name=phytaseandsearch=search_someandcn=onandon=onandsn=onanddisplay=show_someandsc=onandso=onandss=onandorder=ec_numandnr=all.*

2011 December 22 *http://www.genome.jp/dbget-bin/www_bget?ec:3.1.3.8.*

2011 December 22 *http://www.genome.jp/dbget-bin/www_bget?rn:R03371.*

2011 December 22 *http://www.genome.jp/dbget-bin/www_bget?ec:3.1.3.26.*

2011 December 22 *http://www.genome.jp/dbget-bin/www_bget?rn:R03372.*

2011 December 22 *http://www.genome.jp/dbget-bin/www_bget?ec:3.1.3.72.*

2011December 22 *http://www.genome.jp/dbget-bin/www_bget?rn:R07583.*

In: Applications of Microbial Genes in Enzyme Technology ISBN: 978-1-62417-808-5
Editors: V.K.Gupta, M.G.Tuohy, G.D.Sharma et al.

Chapter 10

Production and Technological Applications of Enzymes from Microbial Sources

Vishal Prasad, Vivek Kumar Singh, Mukesh Meena, Arti Tiwari, Andleeb Zehra and R. S. Upadhyay*
Department of Botany, Banaras Hindu University,
Varanasi, India

Abstract

Enzymes are bio-catalyst, which are produced by every living cell and which enhances the rate of chemical reactions. Enzymes are very specific in their action, highly efficient and environment friendly. Enzymes produced by plants, animals and microorganisms are exploited at industrial level for commercial use. Amongst these enzyme sources, microorganisms are preferred over plants and animals for enzyme production at the industrial level. The present chapter is aimed at providing very brief information on some aspects of microbial enzymes related to their applications in various industries, their production process and the possible tools of modern biology for the betterment of enzymes to enhance their activity and make them more beneficial for the respective industries in which they are employed.

Introduction

Enzymes are natural protein molecules that act as highly efficient catalysts in biochemical reactions, that is, they help a chemical reaction take place quickly and efficiently. Enzymes not only work efficiently and rapidly, they are also biodegradable. Enzymes are highly efficient in increasing the reaction rate of biochemical processes that otherwise

* Corresponding author: R. S. Upadhyay. Department of Botany, Banaras Hindu University, Varanasi 221 005, India. E-mail: upadhyay_bhu@yahoo.co.uk.

proceed very slowly, or in some cases, not at all. Enzymes provide several advantages over chemicals, which includes their specificity, their high efficiency and their compatibility with the environment. They are produced from renewable resources and are in turn degraded by microorganisms occurring in nature.

Presently more than 3000 different enzymes are known and classified. The enzymes are classified into six major categories (table 1) based on the nature of the chemical reaction they catalyse. For century's humans have been using enzymes. The history of use of enzymes dates back to 1833 when Payen and Persoz isolated diastase, an amylase complex from germinating barley and demonstrated its property to convert starch into sugars with maltose being one of the primary product (Underkofler *et al.,* 1957).

Berzelius in 1835 coined the term catalysis for conversion of starch by using malt extract. The term enzyme was used for the first time by Kuhne in 1878 for the factors present in yeast which were responsible for carrying out the process of fermentation. Cell-free extracts from yeast were reported to break down glucose into ethanol and carbon dioxide by Buchner brothers in 1897 (Underkofler *et al.,* 1957; Cowan, 1996; Kirk *et al.,* 2002; van Beilen and Li, 2002). Traditional foods and beverages like bread, yogurt, cheese, beer, vinegar, wine, and other fermented drinks were produced with the help of enzymes as early as 6000 B.C. in various parts of the world. Enzymes have a wide variety of role and they are used in diverse fields. Industries where enzymes are widely used include detergent, baking, beverage, dairy, feed and paper and pulp applications. All of these industries are traditional users of enzymes. Only a limited number of all the known enzymes are commercially available at industrial scale. Presently more than fifty commercial industrial enzymes are available and their number is increasing steadily (Coughlan, 1985; Ryu and Mandels, 1980; Gilbert and Hazelwood, 1993; Bhat and Bhat, 1997; Alkorta *et al.,* 1998; Kumar and Takagi, 1999).

Today, nearly all commercially prepared foods contain at least one ingredient that has been made with enzymes. Some of the typical applications include enzyme use in the production of sweeteners, chocolate syrups, bakery products, alcoholic beverages, precooked cereals, infant foods, fish meal, dairy products including cheese, egg products, fruit juice, soft drinks, vegetable oil, candy and spices extracts as well as for dough conditioning, chill proofing of beer, flavor development and meat tenderizing (Janseens *et al.,* 1992; Hagedorn and Kaphmmer, 1994; Tyrell, 1995; Cowan, 1996; Kirk *et al.,* 2002; van Beilen and Li, 2002). Enzymes also play a significant role in non-food applications. Industrial enzymes are used in laundry and dishwashing detergents, stonewashing jeans, pulp and paper manufacture, leather dehairing and tanning, desizing of textiles, deinking of paper and degreasing of hides (Cowan, 1996; Kirk *et al.,* 2002).

Table 1. List of different classes of enzymes

S. No.	Type of Enzyme	Function
1.	Oxidoreductases	Carries out oxidation or reduction of their substrates
2.	Transferases	Carries out group transfer
3.	Hydrolases	Carries out bond breakage with the addition of water
4.	Lyases	Carries out removal of groups from their substrates
5.	Isomerases	Carries out intramolecular rearrangements
6.	Ligases	Carries out the joining of two molecules

A very wide range of sources which include microorganisms, plants and animal are used for enzyme production at the industrial scale. Of the hundred or so enzymes being used industrially, more than half are from fungi while over a third are from bacteria and the remaining is divided between animals and plants.

Microorganisms are preferred over plants and animals as sources of enzymes because: (i) Microorganisms are cheap source of enzyme production, (ii) Microorganisms are easy to handle, (iii) Enzyme production from microbial sources can be easily controlled and accordingly scaled, (iv) Microorganisms occupy less production space, (v) The downstream processing is relatively easier, (vi) Large and constant supply of raw material with uniform chemical composition, and (vii) Very less amount of other interfering and potentially harmful materials are present in comparison to plants and animals.

Microorganisms as Enzyme Source

Enzymes are the product of several million years of biological evolution. All living cells produce enzymes as biocatalysts in the form of protein to bring about specific biochemical reactions. They are very significant biomolecules and possess a unique specificity in their action. Enzymes occur in every living cell, including all microorganisms. Although enzymes are produced within living cells, they function to their full capacity even outside the cell under *in vitro* conditions and their unique ability to perform very specific chemical transformations under *in vitro* conditions makes them extremely useful in industrial processes (Bhat, 2000; Kashyap *et al.,* 2001; Hoondal *et al.,* 2002).

A large number of enzymes with a diverse nature of activity are produced by a single strain of microorganism. There is a noticeable variation in the relative amounts of the various individual enzymes produced by microorganisms, and they vary markedly between species and even between strains of the same species and depend upon the conditions in which they are produced (Pukart *et al.,* 1999; Thippeswamy *et al.,* 2006; Adeyanju *et al.,* 2007; Saxena *et al.,* 2007; Ahmed and Hanan, 2011).

Hence, it is customary to select strains for the commercial production of specific enzymes which have the capacity for producing highest amounts of the particular enzymes desired (Rao *et al.,* 1998; Pandey *et al.,* 2000; van der Maarel *et al.,* 2002). Some of the enzymes produced at a commercial scale for industrial applications using microbial sources are listed in table 2.

At the industrial scale, the great majority of microbial enzymes come from a very limited number of genera, of which *Aspergillus* sp. and *Bacillus* sp. predominate. Most of the strains used have either been employed for many years or have been derived from such strains by mutation and selection. Some of the commercial companies producing microbial enzymes at industrial scale for a variety of potential applications in diverse fields are listed in table 3.

Applications of Microbial Enzymes

As mentioned earlier enzymes have applications in wide variety of industries. Some of the major industries with microbial enzymes employed are very briefly discussed here.

Table 2. Some industrially important enzymes and their microbial sources

Enzyme	Microbial Source
Amylase	*Aspergillus* sp. *Bacillus* sp.
Aminoacylase	*Aspergillus* sp.
Asparaginase	*Escherichia coli*
Catalase	*Aspergillus* sp.
Cellulase	*Aspergillus* sp., *Trichoderma* sp.
Dextranase	*Penicillium* sp.
Galactose oxidase	*Aspergillus* sp.
Glucoamylase	*Aspergillus* sp., *Rhizopus* sp.
Glucose isomerase	*Bacillus* sp., *Streptomyces* sp.
Glucose oxidase	*Aspergillus* sp., *Penicillium* sp.
Invertase	*Saccharomyces* sp.
Melibiase	*Mortierella* sp.
Naringinase	*Aspergillus* sp.
Lactase	*Aspergillus* sp., *Kluyveromyces* sp.
Lipase	*Aspergillus* sp., *Rhizopus* sp., *Candida* sp.
Pectinase	*Aspergillus* sp., *Coniosthyrium* sp.
Pectin lyase	*Aspergillus* sp.
Penicillin amidase	*Bacillus* sp.
Protease	*Aspergillus* sp., *Bacillus* sp., *Streptomyces* sp.
Pullulanase	*Klebsiella* sp.
Raffinase	*Mortierella* sp., *Saccharomyces* sp.
Rennin	*Mucor* sp.

Table 3. List of Companies producing Microbial enzymes at Industrial scale

Company	Country Located
Ab Enzymes	Germany
Bachauna Technology	India
BASF	Germany
Biocon India	India
Biozyme Laboratories	UK
ChemGen Corp.	US
Danisco	Denmark
DSM	The Netherlands
Finnzymes	Finland
Genzyme	US
Gist Brocades	The Netherlands
Nova Chemauxi	India
Novozymes	Denmark
Prodigene	US
Rhone-Poulenc	France
Sinobios	China
Specialty Enzymes and Biotechnologies	US
Roche Molecular Biochemicals	US
Worthigton Biochemical Corporation	US

Enzymes Employed in Food and Feed Industry

Food and feed industry had been a very big market for application of microbial enzymes (Dwendy, 1973; Rombouts, 1978; Rexen, 1981; Voragen, 1992; Bhoopathy, 1994; Baker and Wicker, 1996; Fox, 1998; Longo and Sanroman, 2006). The enzyme glucoamylase is used for complete breakdown of starch to glucose. Another enzyme glucose isomerase is used in immobilized form for the industrial production of high fructose syrup (Bhosale *et al.,* 1996; Milichova and Rosenberg, 2006; Sivaramakrishnan *et al.,* 2006; Das *et al.,* 2011). The use of enzymes provides many advantages, including higher quality products, energy efficiency, and a safer working environment. Processing equipment also lasts longer since the milder conditions reduce corrosion. An enzyme, invertase, converts the sucrose to two simple sugars, glucose and fructose and thus prevents the formation of sugar crystals that otherwise would severely shorten the shelf life of the products having sucrose, like candies and chocolates (Dwendy, 1973; Bhoopathy, 1994; Baker and Wicker, 1996; Bhosale *et al.,* 1996; Milichova and Rosenberg, 2006). A thermostable α-amylase is added at early stages of the multistep evaporation of the cane juice (Najafpour and Shan, 2003; Aiyer, 2005; Asghar *et al.,* 2006). This facilitates the crystallization process by completely hydrolyzing the starch. Another enzyme dextranase is also used in sugar processing to degrade the accumulated dextran which is also a polysaccharide and is produced by bacterial growth (Najafpour and Shan, 2003).

In baking processes as soon as the dough for bread is made, the added yeast in it starts to work on the fermentable sugars, transforming them into alcohol and carbon dioxide, which makes the dough rise. Amylases hydrolyse starch present in wheat flour and produce small dextrins for the yeast to act upon. Amylase also modifies starch during baking to give a significant antistaling effect. Amylase maximizes the fermentation process to obtain an even crumb structure and a high loaf volume (Leon *et al.,* 2002; Aiyer, 2005; Sivaramakrishnan *et al.,* 2006; Das *et al.,* 2011). Glucose oxidase cross-links gluten to make weak doughs stronger, drier and more elastic (Gujral and Rosell, 2004; Rasiah *et al.,* 2005). Lipase modifies the natural lipids in flour to strengthen the dough (Saxena *et al.,* 1999; Houde *et al.,* 2004; Aravindan *et al.,* 2007). Lipoxygenase bleaches and strengthens dough. Asparaginase reduces the amount of acrylamide formed during baking (Plomp *et al.,* 2011). Over the years, bromate has been used to bake bread of high quality. The enzyme glucose oxidase has been used to replace the unique effect of bromate (Gujral and Rosell, 2004).

During cheese preparation proteases are used to accelerate cheese ripening, to modifying the functional properties of cheese and to modifying milk proteins and reduce its allergenic properties (Muir, 1996; Fox, 1998). The varieties of cheeses enjoyed today are due in part to the action of enzymes called lipases. The lipases contribute to the distinctive flavor development during the ripening stage of production. Lipases act on the butterfat in cheese to produce flavors that are characteristic of different types of cheese. Specific lipases are responsible for the different flavors in cheeses.

Proteases are also used for production of infant milk formulas from cow's milk. The proteases are used to convert the milk proteins into peptides and free amino acids (Garcia-Carreno, 1991; Kumar and Takagi, 1999; Rani *et al.,* 2010). The protease treatment of cow's milk reduces the likeliness of developing allergies in the infants. Lactase, an enzyme that occurs naturally in the intestinal tract of children and many adults, is either absent or not present in sufficient quantity in lactose intolerant adults. Lactase converts the milk sugar found in dairy products, such as milk, ice cream, yogurt, and cheese, to two readily digestible sugars, glucose and galactose. Without adequate lactase, the lactose in the food ferments in the intestine, producing undesirable side effects. People who could not consume dairy products can now enjoy these nutritious foods due to the activity of commercially available digestive enzyme, lactase. Many dairy products present today are labeled *lactose-free* as the result of pretreatment of the milk or final product with the enzyme lactase (Gekas and Lopez-Levia, 1985; Holsinger and Kilgerman, 1991). Additionally, lactase is available at retail outlets for use in treating lactose containing dairy products at home.

Pectolytic enzymes are widely used in fruit juices production. They help in obtaining clear and stable juices with good yields, and high-quality concentrates (Demir *et al.,* 2001; Soares *et al.,* 2001; Corredig and Wicker, 2002; Mantovani *et al.,* 2005; Ribero *et al.,* 2010). While pectinases naturally occur in most fruits used to make juice, the manufacturer often adds more to produce clear juice in a reasonable amount of time (Alexander and Sulebele, 1980; Ribero *et al.,* 2010). In the process of pet food production proteases are used that hydrolyze meat or meat by-products that liquefy the raw material and create a good flavor when mixed with pet foods. Enzymes are a successful tool that allows feed producers to extend the range of raw materials used in animal feed, and also to improve the efficiency of existing formulations (Cheason, 1993; Walsh *et al.,* 1993). Enzymes are added to the feed either directly or as a premix together with vitamins, minerals, and other feed additives. A wide range of enzymes like proteases, amylases and cellulases are now available for addition in animal feed to degrade substances such as phytate, glucan, starch, protein, pectin-like polysaccharides, cellulose, hemicelluloses, xylan, raffinose, and stachyose (Graham *et al.,* 1988; Bedford, 1995). Animal feed grains contain phosphorus in bound phytate form which is not available to animals and is excreted out as such. As phosphorus is required by the animals for bone growth and other biochemical processes an enzyme phytase is added to the animal feed which releases the bound phosphorus and makes it available to the animals compensating for the phosphorus (Graham *et al.,* 1988; Walsh *et al.,* 1993; Bedford, 1995). Enzyme addition reduces viscosity, which increases absorption of nutrients, liberates nutrients either by hydrolysis of non-degradable fibers or by liberating nutrients blocked by these fibers, and hence reduces the amount of faeces.

Enzymes Employed in Wine and Beer Industry

Microbial glucanases and related enzymes play important roles in fermentation processes to produce alcoholic beverages including beers and wines (Galante *et al.,* 1993; van Rensburg and Pretorius, 2000).These enzymes are employed to improve both quality and yields of the fermented products (Servili *et al.,* 1992; Bamforth, 2008).

During wine production, enzymes such as pectinases, glucanases, and hemicellulases help in improving colour extraction, skin maceration, clarification, filtration, and stability of the product (Hammond 1988; Galante *et al.,* 1993; van Rensburg and Pretorius, 2000). In the process of beer production by using enzymes like amylases and glucanases to transform the complex carbohydrates to simpler sugars, the desired alcohol content can be achieved with a smaller amount of added grain. This results in a beer with fewer carbohydrate calories and ultimately, a lower calorie beer (Bamforth, 2008).

Enzymes Employed in the Detergent Industry

Detergent industries are amongst the primary consumers of enzymes, in terms of both volume and value. Application of enzymes increases ability of the detergents to remove tough stains and makes the detergents more environment friendly and safe. Enzymes now comprise as one of the major ingredients of modern compact detergents (Kumar *et al.,* 1998; Olsen and Falholt, 1998; Basketter *et al.,* 2008). The main advantage of enzyme application in detergents is due to much milder conditions than with enzyme free detergents. Each of the major classes of detergent enzymes which include proteases, lipases, amylases, mannanases, and cellulases, provide specific benefits in detergent industry.

Historically, proteases were the first to be used extensively in laundering. Present day detergents also incorporate lipases, amylases and mannanases along with proteases for increasing the effectiveness of detergents, especially for household laundering at lower temperatures and, in industrial cleaning operations, at lower pH (Andree *et al.,* 1980; Gormsen *et al.,* 1991; Hemchander and Puvanakrishnan, 2000; Hasan *et al.,* 2006). The obvious advantages of enzymes make them universally acceptable for meeting consumer demands. Due to their catalytic nature, they are ingredients requiring only a small space in the formulation of the overall product. Surfactants lower the surface tension at interfaces and enhance the repulsive force between the original stain, enzymatically degraded stain and fabric.

One of the main reasons behind the development of new enzymes or the modification of existing ones for detergents is to make enzymes more tolerant to other ingredients, like builders, surfactants, and bleaching chemicals, and also to the alkaline conditions present in wash solutions (Thom *et al.,* 1990; Mitideri *et al.,* 2006; Ahmed *et al.*, 2007; Kumar *et al.,* 2009).

The range of use of commercial detergent products is relatively large, and they are used in such varied applications like laundering, dishwashing, and in industrial and institutional cleaning (Olsen and Falholt, 1998). Bacterial proteinases are still the most important detergent enzymes. Lipases decompose fats into more water-soluble compounds. Amylases are used in detergents to remove starch based stains. Essentially all of the enzymes found in detergents are hydrolytic in nature and catalyse the hydrolysis of chemical bonds present within a polymeric substrate randomly in the interior of the polymer (Olsen and Falholt, 1998; Kumar and Takagi, 1999; Aiyer, 2005; Hasan *et al.,* 2010; Rani *et al.,* 2010; Das *et al.,* 2011). Amylase also aid in lowering down of wash temperatures.

Proteases catalyse the hydrolysis of amide bonds within proteinaceous substrates that are present in stains generated by various sources. Hydrolysis breaks down the proteinaceous substrates into smaller fragments (i.e., amino acids or oligopeptides), thereby increasing the ease with which the dirt and stain can be solubilized in the wash liquid by surfactants (Kumar and Takagi, 1999; Rani *et al.,* 2010).

Amylases catalyse the hydrolysis of glucosidic linkages in gelatinized starch polymers found in stains produced by a variety of food articles. Starch is also known to attract for many types of particulate matter hence removal of starch from surfaces provides a whiteness benefit (Aiyer, 2005; Das *et al.,* 2011).

Lipases break down triglycerides present in greasy and fatty stains into their component glycerol and fatty acid units, thereby increasing their water solubility. Removal of these stains with lipases generates a whitening look on the fabric and also improves the odor (Jaeger and Reetz, 1998; Saxena *et al.,* 1999; Houde *et al.,* 2004; Aravindan *et al.,* 2007; Hasan *et al.,* 2010). Cellulases hydrolyse the cellulose in cotton and polycotton fabrics to provide cleaning and fabric-care benefits. Presence of cellulases in detergents provides benefits like antipilling, softness, whiteness, and also enhances color clarification (Sukumaran *et al.,* 2005; Kuhad *et al.,* 2011; Karmakar and Ray, 2011).

Another enzyme mannanases is also widely used in detergents to remove polysaccharides like starch and guar gum from dirt and stains (Dhawan and Kaur, 2007).

Enzymes Employed in Personal Care Industry

Enzymes have very potential applications in the personal care industry. Toothpastes and mouthwashes incorporate glucoamylase and glucose oxidase. This system of enzymes produces hydrogen peroxide, which helps killing bacteria and has a positive effect in preventing plaque formation (Bankar *et al.,* 2009). Products containing proteases are used to clean dentures with high efficiency (Canay *et al.,* 1991). Enzyme applications are also established in the field of contact lens cleaning. Contact lenses are cleaned using solutions containing proteases or lipases or both. After disinfection, the residual hydrogen peroxide is decomposed using a catalase (Bhatia, 1990).

Lipases are used in cosmetics and perfumeries because it shows activities in surfactants and in aroma production. Monoacyl glycerols and diacylglycerols are produced by esterification of glycerols and are used as a surfactant in cosmetics and perfume industries (Gandhi, 1997; Metzger and Bornscheuer, 2006).

Enzymes Employed in Textile Industry

Enzymes have found wide application in the textile industry for improving production methods and fabric finishing. Amylases are used in textile industry for desizing process. Desizing involves the removal of starch from the fabric which serves as the strengthening agent to prevent breaking of the warp thread during the weaving process.

For this purpose a removable protective layer is applied to the threads. The materials that are used for this size layer are quite different. Starch is a very efficient and economical sizing agent, because it is cheap, easily available in most regions of the world, and it can be removed quite easily. Good desizing of starch sized textiles is achieved by the application of α-amylases, which selectively remove the size and do not attack the fibers. It also randomly cleaves the starch into dextrins that are water soluble and can be removed by washing (Aiyer, 2005: Kumar, 2007; Das *et al.,* 2011).

Cellulases are the most successful enzymes used in textile wet processing, especially for finishing of cellulose-based textiles (Hebeish and Ibrahim, 2007; Kumar, 2007). Cellulases have been successfully used for the biostoning of jeans and biopolishing of cotton and other cellulosic fabrics (Pederson *et al.,* 1992; Tyndall, 1996; Kumar *et al.,* 2008; Vigneswaran *et al.,* 2011). Traditionally, to get the look and feel of stonewashed jeans, pumice stones were used.

However, with the introduction of cellulase enzymes in the textile industry they have become the tool for biostoning of fabrics. Cellulases are used to achieve the stonewashed look replacing the abrasive action of pumice stones on fabrics to achieve the same. The advantages in the replacement of pumice stones by a cellulase-based treatment include less damage of fibers and increased productivity of the machines (Sukumaran *et al.,* 2005; Kuhad *et al.,* 2011). Cellulases are also used to prevent pilling and improve the smoothness and color brightness of cotton fabrics (Bhat, 2000).

Catalases are used for degrading residual hydrogen peroxide after the bleaching of cotton. Hydrogen peroxide has to be removed before dyeing. With the use of catalase, the reducing agent can be eliminated or the amount of rinse water for removing hydrogen peroxide can be reduced, resulting in less polluted wastewater and simultaneously lower water consumption (Amorim *et al.,* 2002; Zhang *et al.,* 2010).

Proteases are used for wool treatment and the degumming of raw silk (Kumar, 2007; Gaffar, 2009; Rajasekhar *et al.,* 2011). Threads of raw silk are degummed to remove sericin, a proteinaceous substance that covers the silk fiber. Traditionally, degumming was performed in an alkaline solution containing soap. This was a harsh treatment and lead to the damage of the fiber itself. However, with the use of selected proteolytic enzymes the sericin is effectively removed without attacking the fiber (Kumar and Takagi, 1999; Rani *et al.,* 2010).

Enzymes Employed in Paper Industry

Enzymes applied in the pulp and paper processes typically reduce production costs by saving chemicals and energy along with water. The enzyme solutions also provide more environmental friendly solutions for use in paper and pulp industry in comparison to the traditional processes employing chemical solutions alone (Noe *et al.,* 1986; Freiermth *et al.,* 1994; Bajpai, 1999; Demuner *et al.,* 2011). Enzymes like amylases, xylanases, lipases, esterases and cellulases form an integral part of the chemical solutions used in the paper mills.

Hemicellulase enzymes such as xylanase enhance the bleaching efficacy during paper making allowing a reduction in the consumption of toxic chlorine oxidants which used to chemically bleach the pulp. The enzymatic treatment opens up the pulp matrix allowing better penetration of the bleaching chemicals and better extraction or washout of lignin and the associated dark brown compounds. Use of xylanases helps to achieve the desired level of brightness of the finished pulp using less chlorine or chlorine dioxide (Buchert *et al.,* 1992; Ahlawat *et al.,* 2007).

Pulp treatment with lipase significantly reduces the level of pitch deposition on the paper machine and also reduces the number of defects on the paper web. This increases the overall machine speed and turn over (Gutierrez *et al.,* 2009). Lipase treatment leads to a significant improvement in the tensile strength of pulp fibers.

The recycling of waste paper is also achieved very efficiently with the use of enzymes. The cellulosic fibers can readily be separated by repulping and cleaning, and made into new paper by the use of cellulases. The majority of the fillers and binders used in the original paper can be easily extracted during reprocessing (Buchert *et al.,* 1994; Pere *et al.,* 1995).

The residual printing inks and adhesives are the most difficult of the components to remove. The most widely used enzyme classes for deinking are cellulases, amylases, and lipases. Amylase can effectively degrade starch size and release ink particles from the fiber surface.

Different from amylases, cellulases function as surface-cleaning agents during deinking. They defibrillate the microfibrils attached to the ink and increase deinking efficiency (Prasad *et al.,* 1992). Lipases used for deinking of vegetable oil-based newsprint exhibits remarkable ink removal and brightness improvement (Prasad *et al.,* 1993). The use of enzymes helps in reducing the quantity of chemicals used and reduces the amount of wash water.

Amylases are used in the pulp and paper industry for the modification of starch sizes. Sizing of paper is performed to protect the paper against mechanical damage during processing. It also improves the quality of the finished paper. The size enhances the stiffness and strength in paper. It also improves the erasibilty and is a good coating for the paper (Aiyer, 2005; Das *et al.*, 2011).

Enzymes Employed in Leather Industry

Enzymes have always been a part of leather-making. Proteases are used for selective hydrolysis of non-collagenous constituents of the skin and for removal of nonfibrillar proteins such as albumins and globulins (Taylor *et al.,* 1987; Thanikaivelan *et al.,* 2004; Kamini *et al.,* 1999; Choudhary *et al.,* 2004). Hides and skins have hair attached to them that must be removed for their use as leather. With enzyme-assisted dehairing, it is possible to reduce the chemical requirements and obtain a cleaner product and a higher area yield with fewer chemicals in the wastewater. Proteins and fats are present between the collagen fibers of the hides and are enzymatically removed before tanning the hides (Peper and Wyatt, 1989; Rize *et al.,* 2003; Jatavathu *et al.,* 2011).

Proteases active under alkaline conditions are used to clean the stock and facilitate the water uptake of the hide. The enzyme increases water uptake by breaking down soluble proteins inside the matrix, thus facilitating the removal of salt and hyaluronic acid (Dayanandan *et al.,* 2003). Lipases provide synergy in leather processing along with proteases (Jaeger and Reetz, 1998; Saxena *et al.,* 1999; Houde *et al.,* 2004).

Elastin is a retractile protein situated especially in the grain layer of hides and skins and prevents the relaxation of the grain layer. Elastase enzymes are applied to degrade this elastin. Degradation of elastin results in increased area and improved softness, without impairing strength (Chen *et al.,* 2007).

Enzymes Employed in Fuel Industry

Agricultural crops such as corn, sugar cane, and sugar beet or agricultural byproducts such as whey from cheese making and potato processing can be used for production of fuel ethanol which in turn can be used as a replacement for petroleum fuels (Wyman, 1999; Serrat *et al.*, 2011). Ethanol can also be utilized in petroleum fuels as a replacement for the toxic oxygenates Methyl t-Butyl Ether. Biodiesel is considered to be a sustainable energy substitute for petroleum based diesel derived from renewable sources, such as oils, animal fats and recycled or waste oils (Hamelinck and Faaiji, 2006; Shimada *et al.,* 2002).

Biodiesel production using enzymatic reaction catalysed by lipase is a clean and promising technology due to its non-toxic and environment friendly nature. Also, the process produces highly pure product which is easily seperable from glycerol produced as byproduct (Fukuda *et al.,* 2001; Iso *et al.,* 2001; Shimada *et al.,* 2002; Noureddini *et al.,* 2005; Ranganathan *et al.,* 2008; Winayanuwattikun *et al.,* 2011). Enzymes such as α-amylase, glucoamylase, invertase and lactase hydrolyze starch, sucrose and lactose into fermentable sugars (Aiyer, 2005; Das *et al.,* 2011). The sugars are then fermented with yeast to produce ethanol (Sedlak and Ho, 2004).

Cellulases are also widely used in bioethanol production. Enzymatic saccharification of lignocellulosic materials such as sugarcane bagasse, corncob, rice straw, switch grass, saw dust, and forest residues by cellulases for biofuel production is also practiced (Bhatt, 2000; Sukumaran *et al.,* Kuhad *et al.,* 2011).

Enzymes Employed in Biocatalysis Industry

Biocatalysis is the general term for the process of transformation of non-natural compounds by enzymes for synthesis of organic compounds. The accelerated reaction rates, together with the unique stereo-, regio-, and chemoselectivity, and mild reaction conditions offered by enzymes, makes them highly attractive as catalysts for organic synthesis (Koeller and Wong, 2001; Schmid *et al.,* 2001). Enzymes work across a broad pH and temperature range, as well as in organic solvents.

Many enzymes have been found to catalyse a variety of reactions that can be dramatically different from the reaction and substrate with which the enzyme is associated in nature (Yamada and Shimizu, 1988; Shimizu *et al.,* 1997). Lipases are among the most versatile and flexible biocatalysts for organic synthesis as they are highly compatible with several organic solvents, and therefore the most frequently used enzyme in the field of organic synthesis family. Lipases are used for enantiomeric separation of alcohols and separate racemic amine mixtures and also used in transesterification. Aromatic and aliphatic polymers are also produced by using lipases (Jaeger and Reetz, 1998; Saxena *et al.,* 1999; Houde *et al.,* 2004; Metzger and Bornscheuer, 2006).

A proteolytic enzyme thermolysin is used for production of aspartame an intensive non-calorie sweetener under non-aqueous conditions (Nagayasu *et al.,* 1994). Genetically modified strains of *Penicillium* are used for penicillin production. An immobilized enzyme acylase converts penicillin to 6-aminopenicillanic acid, which serves as a backbone for many semisynthetic penicillins (Chandel *et al.,* 2008).

Enzymes Employed in Medical/Analytical Industry

Some of the medical applications of enzymes include use of asparginase and glutaminase to hydrolyse L-aspargine and L-glutamine to aspartic and glutamic acid respectively during treatment of leukemia (Imada *et al.,* 1973; Asselin *et al.,* 1991; Turowski *et al.,* 1994; Dibenedetto *et al.,* 1995; Kelo *et al.,* 2009). Urokinase and streptokinase are used for dissolving the blood clot during heart attack by dissolving plasminogen to plasmin (WuDunn,

1997, Banerjee *et al.,* 2004). Hyaluronidase is used to hydrolyse hyaluronate during heart attack (Stern *et al.,* 2007; El-Safory *et al.,* 2010). Collagenase is used for hydrolysing collagen during skin cancer (Suphatharaprateep *et al.,* 2011). Uricase are used for oxidising uric acid in gout (Geweely *et al.,* 2011).

Enzymes are also widely used in the analytical methodology. An important development in analytical chemistry is biosensors. The most widely used application is a glucose biosensor involving glucose oxidase catalysed reaction (Kunzelmann and Bottcher, 1997; Wua *et al.,* 2009).

Several commercial instruments are available which apply this principle for measurement of molecules like glucose, lactose, sucrose, ethanol, methanol, cholesterol and some amino acids. The quantitative determination of triacylglycerol is of great importance in clinical diagnosis and in food industry. The lipid sensing device as a biosensor are rather cheaper and less time consuming as compared to the chemical methods for the determination of triacylglycerols. Lipases are used to generate glycerol from triacylglycerol in the analytical sample and to quantify the released glycerol by enzymatic or chemical methods (Setzu *et al.,* 2007; Herrera-Lopez, 2012).

Production of Microbial Enzymes

Enzymes occur in every living cell, hence in all microorganisms. Each single strain of a microorganism produces a large number of enzymes, hydrolyzing, oxidizing or reducing, and metabolic in nature. But the absolute and relative amounts of the various individual enzymes produced vary markedly between species and even between strains of the same species. Hence, it is customary to select strains for the commercial production of specific enzymes which have the capacity for producing highest amounts of the particular enzymes desired. Commercial enzymes are produced from strains of fungi, bacteria, and yeasts.

When suitable nutrient medium and the right conditions of temperature, pH and oxygen are provided, it is easy to grow microbes on a laboratory scale in petri dishes, test tubes and flasks.

However, producing enzymes from microbes on an industrial scale causes serious problems because fairly large number of organisms have to be grown for commercial use.

The purpose is solved by growing microorganisms in very large vessels called fermenters. The large stainless steel cavity is filled with a sterile nutrient solution, which is then inoculated with a pure culture of the carefully selected fungus or bacterium (Pandey, 1991; Antier, 1993; Acuna-Arguelles *et al.,* 1995; Kapoor and Kuhad, 2002; Sandhya *et al.,* 2005; Dominguez *et al.,* 2001).

Paddles rotate the mixture so that the suspension is mixed well. As the nutrients are used up, more can be added. Probes monitor the mixture and changes in pH, oxygen concentration and temperature are all computer controlled. A water jacket surrounding the fermenter contains fast flowing cold water to cool the fermenter since fermentation is a heat generating process. Most of the air, including carbon dioxide and other gases produced by cell metabolism, leave the fermenter by an exhaust pipe.

At industrial level the two main types of fermentation processes employed for microbial enzyme production are as follows:

Solid State Fermentation

Solid-state fermentation involves the cultivation of microorganisms on a solid substrate, such as grains, rice and wheat bran. Solid-state fermentation provides several benefits which include high volumetric productivity, relatively high concentration of product, less effluent generated and simple fermentation equipment (Hesseltine, 1977; Chen, 1992; Losane *et al.*, 1992; Durand *et al.*, 1993; Pandey *et al.*, 1999; Pandey *et al.*, 2000).

There are many substrates that can be utilized for the production of enzymes by solid-state fermentation. These include wheat bran, rice bran, sugar beet pulp and flours of wheat and corn. The selection of substrate depends on many factors, which is mainly related to the cost and the availability of the substrate.

Other factors include particle size and the level of moisture. Smaller substrate particles have a larger surface area for the proliferation of the microorganisms, but if too small the efficiency of respiration will be impeded and poor growth and hence poor production of enzymes will result. Larger particles provide more efficient aeration and respiration, but there is a reduction in the surface area. Solid-state fermentation requires moisture to be present on the substrate, for the microorganisms to produce enzymes.

Hence, the water content of the substrate must also be optimized, as a higher or lower presence of water may adversely affect the microbial activity. Water also has implications for the physicochemical properties of the solid substrate. Enzymes of industrial importance have been produced by Solid-state fermentation. Some examples are proteases, pectinases, glucoamylases and cellulases (Riviera-Munoz *et al.*, 1991; Babu and Satyanarayana, 1995; Berovic and Ostroversnik, 1997; Krishna, 1999; Castilho *et al.*, 2000; Medrios *et al.*, 2001; Martins *et al.*, 2002; Dominguez *et al.*, 2003; Germano *et al.*, 2003; Kashyap *et al.*, 2003; Holer *et al.*, 2004; Kuhad *et al.*, 2004).

Submerged Fermentation

Submerged fermentation is the cultivation of microorganisms in liquid nutrient broth. Industrial enzymes are also produced using this process. This involves growing carefully selected micro organisms in closed vessels containing a rich broth of nutrients (the fermentation medium) and a high concentration of oxygen. As the microorganisms break down the nutrients, they release the desired enzymes into solution.

Most industrial enzymes are secreted by microorganisms into the fermentation medium in order to break down the carbon and nitrogen sources (Fredurek and Ilczuk, 1983; Sunnotel and Nigan, 2002; Sharma and Satyanarayana, 2005). Fed-batch and continuous fermentation processes are common practice. In the fed-batch process, sterilised nutrients are added to the fermenter during the growth of the biomass. In the continuous process, sterilised liquid nutrients are fed into the fermenter at the same flow rate as the fermentation broth leaving the system. This enables in achieving a steady-state production rate. Parameters like temperature, pH, oxygen consumption and carbon dioxide formation are measured and controlled to optimize the fermentation process.

Submerged fermentation process provide several advantages like process parameters can be easily measured and monitored in comparison to solid state fermentation, very even distribution of bacterial and yeast cell in the fermentation medium, sufficiently high amount of water content is available. Some limitations of the process include high cost of the medium used, use of very large reactors where at times monitoring and prediction of microbial growth behavior becomes difficult.

During harvesting the enzymes from the fermentation medium, firstly the insoluble products like microbial cells are removed. This is normally done by centrifugation. As most industrial enzymes are extracellular (secreted by cells into the external environment), they remain in the fermented broth after the biomass has been removed. The biomass can then be treated with lime to inactivate the microorganisms and stabilise it during storage and they can be then recycled and used as a fertilisers.

The enzymes in the remaining broth are then concentrated by evaporation, membrane filtration or crystallization depending on their intended application. If pure enzyme preparations are required, they are usually isolated by gel or ion exchange chromatography.

Certain applications require solid enzyme products, so the crude powder enzymes are made into granules to make them more convenient to use. Sometimes liquid formulations are preferred because they are easier to handle and works well along with other liquid ingredients. Enzymes used in starch conversion to convert glucose into fructose are immobilised, typically on the surfaces of inert granules held in reaction columns or towers. This is carried out to prolong their working life as these enzymes normally go on working for over a year.

The enzyme production process by a microorganism at industrial level for commercial applications by using fermentation techniques generally consists of following stages: (i) Selection of the best microbial strain producing enzyme of interest, (ii) Optimization and standardization of culture medium and production conditions for the enzyme by the microbial population, (iii) Optimization of recovery process for the enzyme from the fermentation medium, and (iv) Formulation of a stable and highly active enzyme from the recovered product.

Mutagenesis and Enzyme Engineering

Enzymes have all the properties of true catalysts. In the presence of an appropriate enzyme, a chemical reaction occurs at a much higher rate but the enzyme is not consumed during the reaction process. Their ability to perform very specific chemical transformations (biotransformations) has made enzymes increasingly popular in industries. The use of enzymes in industry is often limited by lack of stability under extreme conditions. Most of the enzymes are often not well suited for harsh reaction conditions required in industrial processes due to the lack of structural stability, which limits their use in industry.

Enzymes have evolved over billions of years to operate most effectively under physiological conditions, on a narrow range of natural substrates, and usually at very low concentrations. By contrast, an efficient industrial synthetic process may require a biocatalytic enzyme to operate on non-natural substrates, and under conditions in which the enzyme becomes unstable or inactive, such as very extreme temperatures, high pressure, broad pH range, a very prolonged use or repeated use, or in the presence of organic solvents which facilitate substrate solubility or product extraction. As a result of these requirements, by far the majority of naturally occurring enzymes are not suitable for industrial-scale biocatalytic processes without further modification of the enzyme itself. Hence in order to overcome these limitations the process of enzyme engineering is practiced which helps in enhancing the enzyme activity, improving its stability, modify its specificity and alter its pH or temperature optima (Jaenicke and Bohm, 1998; Arnold and Volkov, 1999).

The conformation of enzyme proteins must be maintained in order for them to function at optimal activity. Enzyme stability is dependent on maintaining a balance of forces that include hydrophobic interactions, hydrogen bonding, and electrostatic interactions. Therefore, understanding and maintaining enzyme stability are critical if enzymes are to be widely used in industrial processes. Enzyme engineering is used to construct and analyze modified proteins using tools of molecular biology, genetic engineering, biochemical, and traditional chemical methods (Hellinga, 1998). The generation of enzymes with improved activity and stability is feasible by adopting enzyme engineering methods. Advancements in molecular biology have enabled a rapid development in the technologies associated with protein and enzyme engineering (Nicholson *et al.,* 1988; Kidokoro *et al.,* 1995; Martin *et al.,* 2001; Wang *et al.,* 2006).

Two broad approaches namely rational designing and directed evolution have been followed in practice to engineer the amino-acid sequences of enzymes for production of more industry oriented enzymes (Bornscheuer and Pohl, 2001; Adamczak and Krishna, 2004).

Rational Designing of Enzymes

In rational enzyme design, detailed knowledge of the structure and function of the enzyme is used to make desired changes. Such knowledge is often based upon the bioinformatical analysis of protein sequences or amino-acid predispositions, generalised rules derived by characterising the effect of mutations upon enzyme properties, and by implementation of molecular potential functions that enable the effect of mutations upon structure to be predicted (Voigt *et al.,* 2001; Askenazi *et al.,* 2003; Prather and Martin, 2008). Rational designing is done by employing the method of site-directed mutagenesis. As the technique of site-directed mutagenesis is well-developed rational enzyme designing is advantageous in being inexpensive and technically easy (Lee *et al.,* 2009).

The process of site-directed mutagenesis was described long back in 1978 by Hutchinson *et al.,* and since then it had become a powerful tool to study the molecular structure and function of proteins including enzymes. The purpose of site-directed mutagenesis is to alter a protein or enzyme by introducing, replacing, or deleting a specific amino acid. The technique enables a desired modification to be achieved with exquisite precision. Site-directed mutagenesis has been used to change the activity and stability of enzymes, as well as substrate specificity and affinity. The first step of site-directed mutagenesis involves cloning the gene for the enzyme of interest into a vector. In the next step, an oligonucleotide is designed and synthesized which contains a centrally located desired mutation that is flanked by sequences of DNA which are complementary to a specific region of interest. In this way the oligonucleotide is designed to bind to a single region of the target gene. The mutation is introduced into the gene by hybridizing the oligonucleotide to the single-stranded template of the target gene. In order to obtain the single-stranded templates of a target gene, either cloning of the gene is carried out in a single-stranded vector like bacteriophage M13, or alternatively phagemids are used. Another approach to obtain a single-stranded template is by digesting the double-stranded DNA with exonuclease III following nicking of the target DNA with DNase or a restriction endonuclease to generate a single stranded DNA template. The second strand of the DNA is synthesized by using DNA polymerase and the oligonucleotide containing the desired mutation designed in the first step is used as a primer, and the DNA thus obtained can then be circularized by using DNA ligases. The vector that carries the newly synthesized DNA with one mutated strand is then introduced into a bacterial host, where along with DNA replication half of the newly synthesized cell population contains the DNA with desired mutation or change in the enzyme.

Enzymatic activity of many proteases, cellulases and hemicellulases used in several industrial processes has been enhanced by the rational designing (Gupta *et al.*, 2002; Mika *et al.*, 2009). Detergent enzymes are made more bleach-stable using site-directed mutagenesis. By employing site directed mutagenesis a protease from *Bacillus stearothermophilus* was increased in heat tolerance from 86°C to 100°C and was made resistant to boiling (van den Burg *et al.*, 1998). For this purpose eight amino acids were modified which resulted in a 340-fold increase in temperature stability of the enzyme at 100°C without causing any decrease in its activity at lower temperatures. All eight mutations carried out were located very far from the active site of the enzyme.

Directed Evolution

Directed evolution is another method used for enzyme engineering to exploit the power of natural selection to evolve enzymes with desirable properties not found in nature (Jaeger and Reetz, 2000; Jaeger *et al.*, 2001; Turner, 2003; Besenmatter *et al.*, 2004; Otten and Quax, 2005; Romero and Arnold, 2009). The two key steps of directed evolution are generating molecular diversity and identifying the improved variants.

The most widely used approaches to generating diversity are random point mutagenesis and *in vitro* recombination of the gene encoding the enzyme of interest to create a sufficiently large library of gene variants. The random mutagenesis is accomplished by using techniques like error-prone PCR, DNA shuffling, cassette mutagenesis, synthetic shuffling and many other such processes (Stemmer, 1994; Lutz and Patrick, 2004; Kaur and Sharma, 2006; Reetz and Carballeira, 2007). Next to this the constructed library is tested for the presence of mutants possessing the desired changes in enzyme properties using a screen or a defined selection method. After successful screening the obtained mutant strain of the microorganism is exploited for enzyme production at industrial levels. The method of directed evolution mimics the process of natural evolution and generally produces superior results to rational design.

The great advantage of directed evolution is that it requires no prior structural knowledge of an enzyme, nor is it necessary to be able to predict what effect a given mutation will have (Cherry and Fidantsef, 2003). Several proteases, cellulases and hemicellulases with altered enzymatic activity have been modified by employing the technique of directed evolution and are widely applied in several industrial processes (Gupta *et al.*, 2002; Maki *et al.*, 2009). Green fluorescent protein of Clontech (Crameri *et al.*, 1996) and LipoPrime® lipase of Novo Nordisk's are produced by directed evolution technique (Tobin *et al.*, 2000).

Genetically Engineered Microbes and Their Enzymes

Enzymes are naturally occurring proteins that when present enhances up a biochemical process or reaction. Enzymes from genetically modified microorganisms play an advantageous role in all the industrial sectors where microbial enzymes are employed. They are used to produce everything from wine and cheese to corn syrup and baked goods (Zeman and McCrea, 1985; Durand *et al.,* 1988; Punt *et al.,* 2002; Olepska-Beer *et al.,* 2006).

Genetic engineering involves taking the relevant gene from the microorganism that naturally produces a particular enzyme (donor) and inserting it into another microorganism that will produce the enzyme more efficiently (host). The first step involves cleavage of the donor cell DNA into fragments using restriction enzymes. The DNA fragments with the genetic code for the desired enzyme are then placed, with the help of ligases, in a natural vector called a plasmid that can be transferred to the host bacteria or fungi. The DNA added to the host in this way divides along with the cell, leading to a growing population of cloned cells each containing exact replicas of the gene coding for the enzyme of interest. Genetically modified microbes allow production of industrially important enzymes, which are used in dairy, pharmaceuticals and textile industries (Falch, 1991; Adrio and Demain, 2010).

Genetic engineering technology has been used beneficially in the enzyme industry in the following ways: (i) Enzymes naturally occuring in other organisms can be produced in large-scale fermentation processes using genetically modified microbes. Even enzymes of animal or plant origin may be produced independently of the supply of animal and plant tissue. Enzymes with a higher specificity and purity are produced using genetically engineered microbes, (ii) Enzymes found in very less concentrations in exotic microorganisms and in microorganisms which are often difficult to grow may be produced by selecting host microorganisms which are easy to cultivate and from which the enzyme can be easily purified, (iii) Productivity may be boosted by selecting a highly efficient gene construction. Higher production efficiency results in an environmental benefit through reducing energy consumption and waste from the production plants, (iv) Genetic engineering enables to produce in a safe host useful enzyme obtained from a pathogenic or toxin-producing microorganism and to select cultivation conditions that are safe to the manufacturing personnel, to the user of the product, and to the environment at large, and (v) Enzymes with improved stability, activity or specificity can be produced by means of genetic engineering. By employing changes in the sequence of the structural gene, one or more amino acids in the enzyme molecule may be substituted by other amino acids thus changing the charges and the structure of the enzyme.

Many microbial genes encoding enzymes of industrial importance have been cloned and the enzymes expressed at levels hundreds of times higher than those naturally produced. More than 60% of the enzymes used in the present day detergent, food and starch processing industry are recombinant proteins.

The industrial enzymes have been produced to very high levels from industrially-unknown microorganisms in industrial organisms such as *Aspergillus* sp., *Trichoderma* sp., *Saccharomyces cerevisiae*, *Yarrowia lipolytica* and *Bacillus licheniformis* using recombinant DNA technology.

Filamentous fungi like *Aspergillus niger, Aspergillus oryzae, Aspergillus awamori* and *Aspergillus chrysogenum* produce very high levels of recombinant proteins and are one of the main sources of enzymes for industrial applications.

Asparaginase is an enzyme that catalyses the hydrolysis of the amino acid L-asparagine to L-aspartic acid and ammonia. Asparaginase is manufactured by fermentation of pure culture of a genetically modified strain of *Aspergillus niger* that contains multiple copies of the asparaginase gene derived from wild type *Aspergillus niger.* The production observed from the genetically modified strain is significantly higher than that of the wild type. Asparaginase is secreted in the fermentation broth and is subsequently purified and concentrated. For commercial purposes, the enzyme concentrate is formulated and standardized into either a liquid or a granulated preparation using appropriate food-grade substances.

There are three fungal recombinant lipases which are produced by *Aspergillus oryzae* and the donor organisms for these three are *Rhizomucor miehei, Thermomyces lanuginosus* and *Fusarium oxysporum.* These lipases produced through genetic engineering are widely used in the food industry.

Chymosin is the enzyme used for coagulation of milk and it is most commonly used for cheese making. The genome of *Aspergillus niger* is modified by inserting a prochymosin cDNA via an expression vector. Chymosin is secreted as a fusion protein with glucoamylase and processed to the active protein during fermentation (Ward *et al.,* 1990). Species of *Trichoderma* and *Kluyveromyces* have also been employed for chymosin production (Harkki *et al.,* 1989; van den Burg *et al.,* 1990).

In order to be effective in detergents, lipases need to remain functional under harsh conditions such as the presence of surfactants and oxidants, temperatures above 45°C, highly alkaline conditions and therefore the enzyme should be alkalophilic. Recombinant DNA technology has improved the activity of proteases and lipases in washing powders (Wackett, 1997).

Lipolase was the first commercial recombinant lipase introduced by Novo Nordisk for use in a detergent. This was produced by cloning the *Humicola lanuginosa* lipase gene into the *A. oryzae* genome. Applications of these lipases include use in laundry cleaning, interest-erification of lipids, and esterification of glucosides producing glycolipids which are used as biodegradable non-ionic surfactants for detergents, skin care products, contact lenses and as food emulsifiers.

A significantly high level of α-amylase production is obtained by cloning the α-amylase gene from *Bacillus amyloliquefaciens* in *Bacillus subtilis* using multicopy plasmid pUB110 (Keggins *et al.,* 1978; Palva, 1982). The enzyme production obtained was significantly higher in comparison to wild type *Bacillus subtilis* and with the donor *Bacillus amyloliquefaciens.*

Pullulanase is a very potent enzyme for degradation of starch to glucose or maltose. A novel type of pullulanase which mainly produce panose from pullulan is found in *Bacillus stearothermophilus.* This enzyme hydrolyzes pullulan efficiently and it also hydrolyzes a small amount of starch. By using pTB522 as a vector plasmid, the enzyme gene were cloned and expressed in *Bacillus subtilis* to produce a thermostable pullulanase which converts pullulan into not only panose but also glucose and maltose.

A very noteworthy overproduction for an exoglucanase from the cellulolytic *Cellulomonas fimi* was observed after following its cloning in *Escherichia coli* (O'Neill *et al.,* 1986).

Cellobiohydrolase I gene of *Trichoderma reesei* and the endo-β-glucanase components of the cellulase complexes from *Thermomonospora* and *Clostridium thermocellum* were cloned in *Escherichia coli* to achieve a better production (Adrion and Demain, 2010).

A 30-fold increase in production of aspartase was achieved by cloning in *Escherichia coli* (Kombatsubara *et al.,* 1986). Similarly a 38-fold increase in activity of captopril esterase of *Pseudomonas putida,* used in preparing the chiral captopril side chain, was observed by cloning in *Escherichia coli.* Phytase production was observed to increase by 1,000-fold in *Aspergillus niger* by use of recombinant DNA technology (Adrion and Demain, 2010).

Conclusion

With the use of enzymes in industrial processes a significant reduction in high temperatures, organic solvents and extremes of pH can be achieved. Enzyme application increases reaction specificity, product purity and also reduces the amount of environmental waste left after industrial use. The market for microbial enzymes is growing steadily. A plethora of microorganisms are being screened, evaluated and exploited for their newer, specific and important enzymes which have novel applications. The known enzymes are being modified for more diverse applications. The producing microbes are being engineered for better enzymes and production processes are being scaled for more efficient production. Engineering enzymes for specific applications will be a future trend with continuously improving tools and understanding of structure-function relationships and increased search for enzymes from exotic environments and their microbial populations. Development of enzymes to act as crystalline catalysts, having ability to recycle cofactors, and also to function in extremes of pH and temperature and in various solvent systems with enhanced activity and specificity are important technological challenges for the future, the success gained in these aspects of enzymes is likely to create their newer and wider applications which will undeniably improve the living of mankind.

References

Acuna-Arguelles, M. E., M. Gutierrez-Rojas, G. Viniegra-Gonzalez and E. Favela-Torres. 1995. Production and properties of three pectinolytic activities produced by *Aspergillus niger* in submerged and solid-state fermentation. *App. Microbiol. Biotechnol.* 43:808–814.

Adamczak, M. and S. H. Krishna. 2004. Strategies for improving enzyme for efficient biocatalysis. *Food Technol. Biotechnol.* 42:251–264.

Adeyanju, M. M., F. K. Agboola, B. O. Omafuvbe, O. H. Oyefuga and O. O. Adebawo. 2007. A thermostable extracellular α- amylase from *Bacillus Licheniformis* isolated from cassava steep water. *Biotechnol.* 6:473-480.

Adrio, J. L. and D. L. Demain. 2010. Recombinant organisms for production of industrial products. *Bioeng. Bugs* 1:2 116-131.

Ahlawat, S., B. Battan, S. S. Dhiman, J. Sharma and R. P. Mandhan. 2007. Production of the thermostable pectinase and xylanase for their potential application in bleaching of Kraft pulp. *J. Ind. Microbiol. Biotechnol.* 34:763-770.

Ahmed, A., P. Delphine, D. C. Alain, L. Yves and C. Frederic. 2007. A comparative study on two fungal lipases from *Thermomyces lanuginosus* and *Yarrowia lipolytica* shows the combined effects of detergents and pH on lipase adsorption and activity. *Biochem. Biophys. Acta.* 1771: 1446-1456.

Ahmed, A. A. and M. I. Hanan. 2011. A potential new isolate for the production of a thermostable extracellular α- amylase. *J. Bact. Res.* 3:129-137.

Aiyer, P. V. 2005. Amylases and their applications. *Afr. J. Biotechnol.* 4:1525-1529.

Alexander, M. M. and G. A. Sulebele. 1980. Characteristics of pectins from Indian citrus peels. *J. Food Sci. Technol.* 17:180–182.

Alkorta, I., G. Garbisu, M. J. Llama and J. L. Serra. 1998. Industrial applications of pectic enzymes: a review. *Proc. Biochem.* 33:21–28.

Amorim, A. M., M. D. G. Gasques, J. Andreaus and M. Scharf. 2002. The application of catalase for the elimination of hydrogen peroxide residues after bleaching of cotton fabrics. *Ann. Br. Acd. Sci.* 74:433-436.

Andree, H., Muller, W. R. and Schmid, R. D. 1980. Lipases as detergent components. *J. Appl. Biochem.* 2:218-219.

Antier, P., A. Minjares, S. Roussos, M. Raimbault and G. Viniegra-Gonzalez. 1993. Pectinase-hyperproducing mutants of *Aspergillus niger* C28B25 for solid-state fermentation of coffee pulp. *Enz. Microb. Tech.* 15:254–260.

Aravindan, R., P. Anbumathi and T. Viruthagiri. 2007. Lipase applications in food industry. *Ind. J. Biotechnol.* 6:141-158.

Arnold, F. H. and A. A. Volkov. 1999. Directed evolution of biocatalysts. *Curr. Opin. Chem. Biol.* 3:54–59.

Asghar, M., M. J. Asad, S. Rehman and R. L. A. Legge. 2006. Thermostable α-amylase from a moderately thermophilic *Bacillus subtilis* strain for starch processing. *J. Food Eng.* 38:1599-1616.

Askenazi M., E. M. Driggers, D. A. Holtzman, T. C. Norman, S. Iverson, D. P. Zimmer, M. E. Boers, P. R. Blomquist, E. J. Martinez, A. W. Monreal, T. P. Feibelman, M. E. Mayorga, M. E. Maxon, K. Sykes, J. V. Tobin, E. Cordero, S. R. Salama, J. Trueheart, J. C. Royer and K. T. Madden. 2003. Integrating transcriptional and metabolite profiles to direct the engineering of lovastatin-producing fungal strains. *Nat. Biotechnol.* 21:150–156.

Asselin, B. L., M. Y. Lorenson, J. C. Whitin, D. J. Coppola, A. S. Kende, R. L. Blakley and H. J. Cohen. 1991. Measurement of serum L-asparagine in the presence of L-asparaginase requires the presence of an L-asparaginase inhibitor. *Cancer Res.*51:6568-6573.

Babu, K. R. and T. Satyanarayana. 1995. α-Amylase production by thermophilic *Bacillus* coagulans in solid state fermentation. *Proc. Biochem.* 30:305–309.

Bajpai, P. 1999. Application of enzymes in the pulp and paper industry. *Biotechnol. Prog.* 15:147-157.

Baker, R. A. and L. Wicker. 1996 Current and potential applications of enzyme infusion in the food industry. *Trends Food Sci. Technol.* 7:279–284.

Bamforth, C. 2008. The ultimate enzymology: making beer. *Food Sci. Tech.* 22:12-14.

Banerjee, A., Y. Chisti and U. C. Banerjee. 2004. Streptokinase - a clinically useful thrombolytic agent. *Biotechnol. Adv.* 22: 287–307.

Bankar, S. B., M. V. Bule, R. S. Singhal and L. Anathanarayan. 2009. Glucoseoxidase – an overview. *Biotechnol. Adv.* 27:489-501.

Basketter, D. A., J. S. English, S. H. Wakelin and I. R. White. 2008. Enzymes, detergents and skin: facts and fantasies. *Br. J. Dermatol.* 158:1177-1181.

Bedford, M. R. 1995. Mechanism of action and potential environmental benefits from the use of feed enzymes. *Anim. Feed Sci. Tech.* 53:145-155.

Berovic, M. and H. Ostroversnik. 1997. Production of *Aspergillus niger* pectinolytic enzymes by solid state bioprocessing of apple pomace. *J. Biotechnol.* 53:47–53.

Besenmatter, W., P. Kast and D. Hilvert. 2004 New Enzymes from combinatorial library modules. *Meth. Enzymol.* 388:91–102.

Bhat, M. K. and Bhat, S. 1997. Cellulose degrading enzymes and their potential industrial applications. *Biotechnol. Adv.* 15:583–620.

Bhat, M. K. 2000. Cellulases and related enzymes in biotechnology. *Biotechnol. Adv.*18:355–383.

Bhatia, R. P. 1990. Contact lens cleaning composition containing an enzyme and a carboxylvinyl polymer. United States Patent, 4: 630-921.

Bhoopathy, R. 1994. Enzyme technology in food and health industries. *Ind. Food Ind.* 13:22–31.

Bhosale, S. H., M. B. Rao and V. V. Deshpande. 1996. Molecular and industrial aspects of glucose isomerase. *Microbiol. Rev.* 60:280-300.

Bornscheuer, U. T. and M. Pohl. 2001. Improved biocatalysts by directed evolution and rational protein design. *Curr. Opin. Chem. Biol.* 5:137–143

Buchert, J., M. Ranua, A. Kantelinen and L. Viikari. 1992. The role of two *Trichoderma reesei* xylanases in the bleaching of pine Kraft pulp. *Appl. Microbiol. Biotechnol.* 37:825–829.

Buchert, J., M. Ranua, M. Siika-Aho, J. Pere and L. Viikari. 1994. *Trichoderma reesei* cellulases in the bleaching of Kraft pulp. *Appl. Microbiol. Bitechnol.* 40:941–945.

Canay, S., S. Erguven and N. Yulug. 1991. The function of enzymes in removing Candida accumulated on denture plaque. *J. Is. Acd. Sci.* 4:87-89.

Castilho, L. R., T. L. M. Alves and R. A. Medronho. 2000. Production and extraction of pectinases obtained by solid state fermentation of agro-industrial residues with *Aspergillus niger. Biores. Tech.* 71:45–50.

Chandel, A. K., L. V. Rao, M. L. Narasu and O. M. Singh. 2008. The realm of penicillin G acylase in β lactam antibiotics. *Enz. Micro. Tech.* 42:199–207.

Chen, H. Z. 1992. Advances in solid-state fermentation. *Res. App. Microbiol.* (China), 3:7–10.

Chen, Q., H. Guoqing and W. Jinling. 2007. Acid shock of elastase-producing *Bacillus licheniformis* ZJUEL31410 and its elastase characterization evaluation. *J. Food Eng.* 80:490-496.

Cherry, J. R. and A. L. Fidantsef. 2003. Directed evolution of industrial enzymes: an update. *Curr. Opin. Biotechnol.* 14:438–443.

Chesson, A. 1993. Feed enzymes. *Anim. Feed Sci. Tech.* 45:65-69.

Choudhary, R. B., A. K. Jana and M. K. Jha. 2004. Enzyme technology applications in leather processing. *Ind. J. Chem. Tech.* 11:659-671.

Corredig, M. and L. Wicker. 2002. Juice clarification by thermostable fractions of marsh grapefruit pectinmethylesterase. *J. Food Sci.* 67:1668–1671.

Coughlan, M. P. 1985. Cellulases: production, properties and applications. *Biochem. Soc. Trans.* 3:405–406.

Cowan, D. 1996. Industrial enzyme technology. *Trends Biotechnol.* 14:177–178.

Crameri, A., A. Whitehorn and W. P. C. Stemmer. 1996. Improved green fluorescent protein by molecular evolution using DNA shuffling. *Nat. Biotechnol.* 14:315–319.

Das, S., S. Singh, V. Sharma and M. L. Soni. 2011. Biotechnological applications of industrially important amylase enzyme. *Int. J. Pharma Biosci.* 2:486-496.

Dayanandan, A., J. Kanagaraj, L. Sounderraj, R. Govindaraju and G. S. Rajkumar. 2003. Application of an alkaline protease in leather processing: an ecofriendly approach. *J. Clean. Prod.* 11:533-536.

Demir, N., J. Acar, K. Sarioglu and M. Mutlu. 2001. The use of commercial pectinase in fruit juice industry. Part 3: Immobilized pectinase for mash treatment. *J. Food Eng.* 47: 275-280.

Demuner, B. J., N. P. Junior and A. M. S. Antunes. 2011. Technology prospecting on enzymes for the pulp and paper industry. *J. Technol. Manag. Innov.* 6:148-158.

Dewdney, P. A. 1973. Enzymes in food processing. *Nutri. Food Sci. J.* 73:20–23.

Dhawan, S. and J. Kaur. 2007. Microbial mannanases: an overview of production and applications. *Crit. Rev. Biotechnol.* 27:197-216.

Dibenedetto, S. P., A. Di Caltado, R. Ragusa, C. Meli and L. Lo-Nigro. 1995. Levels of L-aspapargine in CSF after intramuscular administration of asparginase from *Erwina* in children with acute lymphoblastic leukemia. *J. Clin. Onc.* 13:339-344.

Dominguez, A., I. Rivela, S. R. Couto and M. A. Sanroman. 2001. Design of a new rotating drum bioreactor for ligninolytic enzyme production by *Phanerochaete chrysosporium* grown on an inert support. *Proc. Biochem.* 37:549–554.

Dominguez, A., M. Costas, M. A. Longo and A. Sanroman. 2003. A novel application of solid state culture: production of lipases by *Yarrowia lipolytica. Biotechnol. Lett.* 25:1225–1229.

Dunn-Coleman, N. S., P. Bloebaum, R. M. Berka, E. Bodie, N. Robinson, G. Armstrong, M. Ward, M. Przetak, G. L. Carter, R. C. La, L. J. Wilson, K. H. Kodama, E. F. Baliu, B. Bower, M. Lamsa and H. Heinsohn. 1991. Commercial levels of chymosin by *Aspergillus. Biotechnol.* 9:976–981.

Durand, A., R. Renaud, S. Almanza, J. Maratray, M. Diez and C. Desgranges. 1993. Solid-state fermentation reactors: from lab scale to pilot plant. *Biotechnol. Adv.* 11:591–597.

Durand, H., M. Clanet and G. Tiraby. 1988. Genetic improvement of *Trichoderma reesei* for large scale cellulase production. *Enz. Microb. Technol.* 10:341–345.

El-Safory, N. S., A. E. Fazary and C. K. Lee. 2010. Hyaluronidases, a group of glycosidases: Current and future perspectives. *Carb. Poly.* 81:165-181.

Falch, E. 1991. Industrial enzymes-developments in production and application. *Biotech. Adv.* 9:643-658.

Fox, P. F. 1998. Exogenous enzymes in dairy technology – a review. *J. Food Biochem.* 17:173–175.

Fredurek, J. and Z. Ilczuk. 1983. Synthesis of pectinolytic enzymes by forced heterokaryons of *Aspergillus niger* in submerged culture. *Acta Alimenta. Pol.* 9:101–107.

Freiermuth, B., M. Garrett and O. Jokinen. 1994. The use of enzymes in the production of release papers. *Pap. Technol.* 25:21–23.

Fukuda, H., A. Kondo and H. Noda. 2001. Biodiesel fuel production by transesterification of oils. *J. Biosci. Bioeng.* 92:405-416.

Gaffar, H. M. 2009. Multifunctional modification of wool using an enzymatic process in aqueous-organic media. *J. Biotechnol.* 141:47-59.

Galante, Y. M., R. Monteverdi, S. Inama, C. Caldini, A. De Conti, V. Lavelli and F. Bonomi. 1993. New applications of enzymes in wine making and olive oil production. *Ita. Biochem. Soc. Trans.* 4:34.

Gandhi, N. N. 1997. Application of lipase. *J. Am. Oil Chem. Soc.* 74:621-634.

Garcia-Carreno, F. L. 1991 Proteases in food technology. *Biotechnol. Edu.* 2:150-153.

Gekas, V. and M. Lopez-Levia. 1985. Hydrolysis of lactose, a literature review. *Pro. Biochem.* 20: 2–12.

Germano, S., A. Pandey, C. A. Osaku, S. N. Rocha and C. R. Soccol. 2003. Characterization and stability of proteases from *Penicillium* sp. produced by solid-state fermentation. *Enz. Microb. Technol.* 32:246–251.

Geweely, N. S. and L. S. Nawar. 2011. Production, optimization, purification and properties of uricase isolated from some fungal flora in Saudi arabian soil. *Aust. J. Basic Appl. Sci.* 5: 220-230.

Gilbert, H. J. and G. P. Hazlewood. 1993. Bacterial cellulases and xylanases. *J. Gen. Microbiol.* 139:187–194.

Gormsen. E., D. Aaslyng and H. Malmos. 1991. Mechanical studies of proteases and lipases for detergent industry. *J. Chem. Technol. Biotechnol.* 50:321-330.

Graham, H., W. Lowgren, D. Pettersson and P. Aman. 1988. Effect of enzyme supplementation on digestion of a barley/pollard based pig feed. *Nutri. Rep. Int.* 38:1073–1079.

Gujral, H. S. and C. M. Rosell. 2004. Improvement of the bread making quality of rice flour by glucose oxidase. *Food Res. Int.* 37:75-81.

Gupta, R., Q. K. Beg and P. Lorenz. 2002. Bacterial alkaline proteases: molecular approaches and industrial applications. *Appl. Microbiol. Biotechnol.* 59:15–32.

Gutierrez, A., J. C. del Rio and A. T. Martinez. 2009. Microbial and enzymatic control of pitch in the pulp and paper industry. *App. Microbiol. Biotechnol.* 82:1005-1018.

Hagedorn, S. and B. Kaphammer. 1994. Microbial biocatalysis in the generation of flavor and fragrance chemicals. *Ann. Rev. Microbiol.* 48:773-800.

Hamelinck, C. N. and A. P. C. Faaij. 2006. Outlook for advanced biofuels. *Ener. Pol.* 34:3268-3283.

Hammond, J. R. M. 1988. Brewery fermentation in the future. *J Appl. Bacteriol.* 65:169–177.

Harkki, A., J. Uusitalo, M. Bailey, M. Penttila and J. K. C. Knowles. 1989. A novel fungal expression system: secretion of active calf chymosin from the filamentous fungus *Trichoderma reesei*. *Biotechnol.* 7:596–603.

Hasan, F., A. A. Shah and A. Hameed. 2006. Industrial applications of microbial lipases. *Enz. Microbiol. Technol.* 39:235-251.

Hasan, F., A. A. Shah, S. Javed and A. Hameed. 2010. Enzymes used in detergents: Lipases. *Afr. J. Biotechnol.* 9:4836-4844.

Hebeish, A. and N. A. Ibrahim. 2007. The impact of frontier sciences on textile industry. *Col.* 54: 41–55.

Hellinga, H. W. 1998. Computational protein engineering. *Nature Struct. Biol.* 5:525–527.

Hemachander, C. and R. Puvanakrishnan. 2000. Lipase from *Ralstonia pickettii* as an additive in laundry detergent formulations. *Proc. Biochem.* 35:809-814.

Herrera-Lopez, E. J. 2012. Lipase and phospholipase biosensors: a review. *Meth. Mol. Biol.* 861:525-543.

Hesseltine, C. W. 1977. Solid-state fermentation. Part 1. *Proc. Biochem.* 12:24–27.

Holker, U., M. Hofer and J. Lenz. 2004. Biotechnology advantages of laboratory-scale solid-state fermentation with fungi. *App. Microbiol. Biotechnol.* 64:175–186.

Holsinger, V. H. and K. H. Kilgerman. 1991. Application of lactase in dairy foods and other foods containing lactose. *Food Tech.* 45:94-95.

Hoondal, G. S., R. P. Tiwari, R. Tiwari, N. Dahiya and Q. K. Beg. 2002. Microbial alkaline pectinases and their industrial applications: A review. *App. Microbiol. Biotechnol.* 59:409-418.

Houde, A., A. Kademi and D. Leblanc. 2004. Lipases and their industrial applications: an overview. *Appl. Biochem. Biotechnol.* 118:155-170.

Hutchison, C. A., S. Philips, M. H. Edgell, S. Gillam, P. Jahnke and M. Smith. 1978. Mutagenesis at a specific position in a DNA sequence. *J. Bol. Chem.* 253:6551-6560.

Imada, A., S. Igarasi, K. Nakahama and M. Isono. 1973. Asparaginase and glutaminase activities of microrganisms. *J. Gen. Microbiol.* 76:85-99.

Iso, M., B. Chen, M. Eguchi, T. Kudo and S. Shrestha. 2001. Production of biodiesel fuel from triglycerides and alcohol using immobilized lipase. *J. Mol. Catal. B: Enz.* 16:53-58.

Jaeger, K. and M. Reetz. 1998. Microbial lipases form versatile tools for biotechnology. *Trends Biotecnol.* 16:396-403.

Jaeger, K. E. and M. T. Reetz. 2000. Directed evolution of enantioselective enzymes for organic chemistry. *Curr. Opin. Chem. Biol.* 4:68-73.

Jaeger, K. E., T. Eggert, A. Eipper and M. T. Reetz. 2001. Directed evolution and the creation of enantioselective biocatalysts. *Appl. Microbiol. Biotechnol.* 55:519-530.

Jaenicke, R. and G. Bohm. 1998. The stability of proteins in extreme environments. *Curr. Opin. Struct. Biol.* 8:738–748.

Janssens, L., H. L. de Pooter, E. J. Vandamme and N. M. Schamp. 1992. Production of flavours by microorganisms. *Process Biochem.* 27:195–215.

Jatavathu, M., S. Jatavathu, M. V. R. Rao and K. R. S. S. Rao. 2011. Efficient leather dehairing by bacterial thermostable protease. *Int. J. Biosci. Biotechnol.* 3:11-26.

Kamini, N. R., C. Hemachander, J. G. S. Mala and R. Puvanakrishnan. 1999. Microbial enzyme technology as an alternative to conventional chemicals in leather industry. *Curr. Sci.* 77:80-86.

Kapoor, M. and R. C. Kuhad. 2002. Improved polygalacturonase production from *Bacillus* sp. MG-CP-2 under submerged and solid state fermentation. *Lett. Appl. Microbiol.* 34:317-322.

Kashyap, D. R., S. K. Soni and R. Tiwari. 2003. Enhanced production of pectinase by *Bacillus* sp. DT7 using solid state fermentation. *Biores. Technol.* 88:251-254.

Kashyap, D. R., P. K. Vohra, S, Chopra and R. Tiwari. 2001. Applications of pectinase in the commercial sector: a review. *Biores. Technol.* 77:215–227.

Kaur, J. and R. Sharma. 2006. Directed Evolution: An approach to engineer enzymes. *Crit. Rev. Biotechnol.* 26:165–199.

Keggins, K. M., P. S. Lovett and E. J. Duvall. 1978. Molecular cloning of genetically active fragments of *Bacillus* DNA in *Bacillus subtilis* and properties of the vector plasmid pUB110. *Proc. Nat. Acad. Sci. US* 75:1423–1427.

Kelo, E., T. Noronkoski and I. Mononen. 2009. Depletion of L-asparagine supply and apoptosis of leukemia cells induced by human glycosylasparaginase. Leukemia 23:1167-1171.

Kidokoro, S., Y. Miki, K. Endo, A. Wada, H. Nagao, T. Miyake, A. Aoyama, T. Yoneya, K. Kai and S. Ooe. 1995. Remarkable activity enhancement of thermolysin mutants. *FEBS Lett.* 367:73–76.

Kirk, O., T. V. Borchert and C. C. Fuglsang. 2002. Industrial enzyme applications. *Curr. Opin. Biotechnol.* 13:345–351.

Koeller, K. M. and C. H. Wong. 2001 Enzymes for chemical synthesis. *Nature.* 409:232-240.

Komatsubara, S., T. Taniguchi and M. Kisumi. 1986. Overproduction of aspartase of *Escherichia coli* K-12 by molecular cloning. *J. Biotechnol.* 3:281-291.

Krishna, C. 1999. Production of bacterial cellulase by solid state bioprocessing of banana wastes. *Biores. Technol.* 69:231–239.

Kuhad, R. C., R. Gupta and A. Singh. 2011. Microbial cellulases and their industrial applications. *Enz. Res.* 1-10.

Kuhad, R. C., M. Kapoor and R. Rustagi. 2004. Enhanced production of an alkaline pectinase from *Streptomyes* sp. RCK-SC by whole cell immobilization and solid state cultivation. *World J. Microbiol. Biotechnol.* 20:257-263.

Kumar, C. G. and H. Takagi. 1999. Microbial alkaline proteases: from a bioindustrial viewpoint. *Biotechnol. Adv.* 17:561-594.

Kumar, C. G., R. K. Malik and M. P. Tiwari. 1998. Novel enzyme-based detergents: An Indian perspective. *Curr. Sci.* 75: 1312-1318.

Kumar, G. V. N. S. 2007. Scope of biotechnology in textiles. *J. Text. Asso.* 263-266.

Kumar, S. S., L. Kumar, V. Sahai and R. Gupta. 2009. A thiol-activated lipase from *Trichosporon asahii* MSR 54: detergent compatibility and presoak formulation for oil removal from soiled cloth at ambient temperature. *J. Ind. Microbiol. Biotechnol.* 36:427-432.

Kumar, V. S., S. Meenakshisundaram and N. Selvakumar. 2008. Conservation of cellulase enzyme in biopolishing application of cotton fabrics. *J. Text. Inst.* 1:339-346.

Kunzelmann, U. and G. Bottcher. 1997. Biosensor properties of glucoseoxidase immobilized within SiO_2 gels. *Sens. Actu. B: Chem.* 39:222-228.

Lee, S. C., Y. J. Chang, D. M. Shin, J. Han, M. H. Seo, H. Fazelinia, C. Maranas and H.S. Kim. 2009. Designing the substrate specificity of D-hydantoinase using a rational approach. *Enz. Micro. Techn.* 44:170–175.

Leon, A. E., E. Duran and C. B. Barber. 2002. Utilization of enzyme mixtures to retard bread crumb firming. *J. Agri. Food Chem.* 50:1416-1419.

Longo, M. A. and M. A. Sanroman. 2006. Production of food aroma compounds: microbial and enzymatic methodologies. *Food Technol. Biotechnol.* 44:335–353.

Lonsane, B. K., G. Saucedo-Castuneda and M. Raimbault. 1992. Scale-up strategies for solid-state fermentation systems. *Proc. Biochem.* 27:259–273.

Lutz, S. and W. M. Patrick. 2004. Novel methods for directed evolution of enzymes: quality, not quantity. *Curr. Opin. Biotechnol.* 15:291–297.

Maki, M., K. T. Leung and W. Qin. 2009. The prospects of cellulase-producing bacteria for the bioconversion of lignocellulosic biomass. *Int. J. Biol. Sci.* 5:500-516.

Mantovani, C. F., M. P. Geimba and A. Brandelli. 2005. Enzymatic clarification of fruit juices by fungal pectin lyase. *Food Biotechnol.* 19:173-181.

Martin, A., V. Sieber and F. X. Schmid. 2001. *In vitro* selection of highly stabilized protein variants with optimized surface. *J. Mol. Biol.* 309:717–726.

Martins, E. S., D. Silva, R. Da Silva and E. Gomes. 2002. Solid state production of thermostable pectinases from thermophilic *Thermoascus aurantiacus*. *Proc. Biochem.* 37:949–954.

Medeiros, A., A. Pandey, P. Christen, P. S. G. Fontoura, R. J. S. Freitas and C.R. Soccol. 2001. Aroma compounds produced by *Kluyveromyces marxianus* in solid-state fermentation on packed bed column bioreactor. *World J. Microbiol. Biotechnol.* 17:767–771.

Metzger, J. O. and U. Bornscheuer. 2006. Lipids as renewable resources: current state of chemical and biotechnological conversion and diversification. *Appl. Microbiol. Biotechnol.* 71:13–22.

Milichova, Z. and M. Rosenberg. 2006. Current trends of β-galactosidase application in food techonology. *J. Food Nutri. Res.* 45:47-54.

Mitidieri, S., A. H. S. Martinelli, A. Schrank and M. H. Vainstein. 2006. Enzymatic detergent formulation containing amylase from *Aspergillus niger*: A comparative study with commercial detergent formulations. *Biores. Technol.* 97:1217–1224.

Muir, D. D. 1996. Production and use of microbial enzymes for dairy processing. *J. Soc. Dairy Technol.* 49:24–32

Nagayasu, T., M. Miyanaga, T. Tanaka, T. Sakiyama and K. Nakanishi. 1994. Synthesis of aspartame precursor with an immobilized thermolysin in *tert*-amyl alcohol. *Biotechnol. Bioeng.* 43:1118-1123.

Najafpour, G. D. and C. P. Shan. 2003. Enzymatic hydrolysis of molasses. *Biores. Technol.* 86:91-94.

Nicholson, H., W. J. Becktel and B. W. Matthews. 1988. Enhanced protein thermostability from designed mutations that interact with alpha-helix dipoles. *Nature* 336:651–656.

Noe, P., J. Chevalier, F. Mora and J. Comtat. 1986. Action of enzymes in chemical pulp fibres. Part II: enzymatic beating. *J. Wood Chem. Technol.* 6:167–184.

Noureddini, H., X. Gao and R. S. Philkana. 2005. Immobilized *Pseudomonas cepacia* lipase for biodiesel fuel production from soybean oil. *Biores. Technol.* 96:769-777.

O'Neill, G. P., D. G. Kilburn, R. A. J. Warren and R. C. Miller Jr. 1986. Overproduction from a cellulase gene with a high guanosine-plus-cytosine content in *Escherichia coli*. *Appl. Environ. Microbiol.* 52:737-743.

Olempska-Beer, Z. S., R. I. Merker, M. D. Ditto and M. J. DiNovi. 2006. Food-processing enzymes from recombinant microorganisms—a review. *Regul. Toxicol. Pharmacol.* 45:144–158.

Olsen, H. S. and P. P. Falholt. 1998. The role of enzymes in modern detergency. *J. Surf. Deter.* 1:555-567.

Otten, L. G. and W. J. Quax. 2005. Directed evolution: selecting today's biocatalysts. *Biomol. Eng.* 22:1–9.

Palva, I. 1982. Molecular cloning of α-amylase gene from *Bacillus amyloliquefaciens* and its expression in *Bacillus subtilis*. *Gene.* 19:81-87.

Pandey, A., P. Nigam, C. R. Soccol, V. T. Soccol, D. Singh and R. Mohan. 2000. Advance in microbial amylases: review. *Biotechnol. Appl. Biochem.* 31:135-152.

Pandey, A., P. Selvakumar, C. R. Soccol and P. Nigam. 1999. Solid state fermentation for the production of industrial enzymes. *Curr. Sci.* 77:149–162.

Pandey, A., C. R. Soccol and D. Mitchell. 2000. New developments in solid state fermentation: I—bioprocesses and products. *Proc. Biochem.* 35:1153–1169.

Pandey, A. 1991. Aspects of fermenter design for solid-state fermentations. *Proc. Biochem.* 26:355–361.

Pederson, G. L., G. A. Screws and D. M. Cedroni. 1992. Biopolishing of cellulosic fabrics. *Can. Text. J.* 109:31-35.

Peper, K. W. and K. G. E. Wyatt. 1989. Enzymatic unhairing of heavy hides. *J. Ind. Leather Technol. Asso.* 36:214-233.

Pere, J., M. Siika-Aho, J. Buchert and L. Viikari. 1995. Effects of purified *Trichoderma reesei* cellulases on the fibre properties of Kraft pulp. *Tappi J.* 78:71–78.

Plomp, P. J. A. M., L. Boer, R. J. Rooije and R. B. Meima. 2011. Asparginase and its use in food production. *United States Patent.* Patent No. 8105815B2.

Prasad, D. Y., J. A. Heitmann and T. W. Joyce. 1992. Enzyme de-inking of black and white letterpress printed newsprint waste. *Prog. Pap. Recy.* 1:21–30.

Prasad, D. Y., J. A. Heitmann and T. W. Joyce. 1993. Enzymatic de-inking of coloured offset newsprint. *Nord. Pulp Pap. Res. J.* 8:284.

Prather, K. L. J. and C. H. Martin. 2008. De novo biosynthetic pathways: rational design of microbial chemical factories. *Curr. Opin. Biotechnol.* 19:468–474.

Puchart, V., P. Katapodis, P. Biely, L. Kremnicky, P. Christakopoulos, M. Vrsanska, D. Kekos, B. J. Macris and M. K. Bhat. 1999. Production of xylanases, mannanases, and pectinases by the thermophilic fungus *Thermomyces lanuginosus*. *Enz. Microb. Technol.* 24: 355–361.

Punt, P. J., N. van Viesen, A. Conesa, A. Albers, J. Mangnus and C. van den Hondel. 2002. Filamentous fungi as cell factories for heterologous protein production. *Trends Biotechnol.* 20:200–206.

Rajasekhar, A., V. Ravi, M. Neerja, M. N. Reddy and K. R. S. S. Rao. 2011. Thermostable bacterial protease - A new way for quality silk production. *Int. J. Biosci. Biotechnol.* 3:43-58.

Ranganathan, S. V., A. L. Narasimhan and K. Muthukumar. 2008. An overview of enzymatic production of biodiesel. *Bioresour. Technol.* 99: 3975- 3981.

Rani, K., R. Rana and S. Datt. 2010. Review on latest overview of proteases. *Int. J. Curr. Life Sci.* 2:12–18.

Rao, M. B., A. M. Tanksale, M. S. Ghatge and V. V. Deshpande. 1998. Molecular and biotechnological aspect of microbiol protease. *Microbiol. Mol. Biol. Rev.* 62:597-635.

Rasiah, I. A., K. H. Sutton, F. L. Low, H. M. Lin and J. A. Gerrard. 2005. Crosslinking of wheat dough proteins by glucose oxidase and the resulting effects on bread and croissants. *Food Chem.* 89: 325-332.

Reetz, M. T. and J. D. Carballeira. 2007. Iterative saturation mutagenesis (ISM) for rapid directed evolution of functional enzymes. *Nature Prot.* 2:891–903.

Rexen, B. 1981. Use of enzymes for the improvement of feed. *Anim. Feed Sci. Technol.* 6:105–14.

Ribeiro, D. S., S. M. B. Henrique, L. S. Oliveira, G. A. Macedo and L. F. Fleuri. 2010. Enzymes in juice processing: a review. *Int. J. Food Sci. Tech.* 45:635-641.

Rivera-Munoz, G., J. R. Tinoco-Valencia, S. Sanchez and A. Farres. 1991. Production of microbial lipases in a solid-state fermentation system. *Biotechnol. Lett.* 13:277–280.

Rize, A., S. Ortolan and A. Brandelli. 2003. Dehairing activity of extracellular proteases produced by keratinolytic bacteria. *J. Chem. Technol. Biotechnol.* 78:855–859.

Rombouts, F. M. and W. Pilnik. 1978. Enzymes in fruit and vegetable juice technology. *Proc. Biochem.* 13:9–13.

Romero, P. A. and F. H. Arnold. 2009. Exploring protein fitness landscapes by directed evolution. *Nat. Rev. Mol. Cell Biol.* 10:866-876.

Ryu, D. D. and M. Mandels. 1980. Cellulases: biosynthesis and applications. *Enzy. Micro. Technol.* 2:91–101.

Sandhya, C., A. Sumantha, G. Szakacs and A. Pandey. 2005. Comparative evaluation of neutral protease production by *Aspergillus oryzae* in submerged and solid-state fermentation. *Proc. Biochem.* 40:2689–2694.

Saxena R. K., L. Dutt and P. N. Agarwal. 2007. A highly thermostable and alkaline amylase from *Bacillus* sp. PN5. *Bioresour. Technol.* 98:260-265.

Saxena, R. K., P. K. Ghosh, R. Gupta, W. S. Davidson, S. Bradoo and R. Gulati. 1999. Microbial lipases, potential biocatalysts for the future industry. *Curr. Sci.* 77: 101-115.

Schmid, A., J. S. Dordick, B. Hauer, A. Kiener, M. Wubbolts and B. Witholt. 2001. Industrial biocatalysis today and tomorrow. *Nature* 409:258-268.

Sedlak, M. and N. W. Y. Ho. 2004. Production of ethanol from cellulosic biomass hydrolysates using genetically engineered saccharomyces yeast capable of co-fermenting glucose and xylose. *App. Biochem. Biotechnol.* 116: 403-405.

Serrat, M., O. Rodriguez, M. Camacho, J. A. Vallejo, J. M. Ajeitos and T. G. Villa. 2011. Influence of nutritional and environmental factors on ethanol and endopolygalacturonase co-production by *Kluyveromyces marxianus* CCEBI 2011. *Int. Microbiol.* 14:41-49.

Servili, M., A. L. Begliomini, G. Montedoro, M. Petruccioli and F. Federici. 1992. Utilisation of a yeast pectinase in olive oil extraction and red wine making processes. *J. Sci. Food Agr.* 58:253-260.

Setzu, S., S. Salis, V. Demontis, A. Salis, M. Monduzzi and G. Mula. 2007. Porous silicone-based potentiometric biosensors for triglycerides. *Phys. Stat. Sol.* A 204:1434-1438.

Sharma, D. C. and T. Satyanarayana. 2005. A marked enhancement in the production of a highly alkaline and thermostable pectinase by *Bacillus pumilus* dcsrl in submerged fermentation by using statistical methods. *Biores. Technol.* 97:727-733.

Shimada, Y., Y. Watanabe, A. Sugihara and Y. Tominaga. 2002. Enzymatic alcoholysis for biodiesel fuel production and application of the reaction to oil processing. *J. Mol. Cat. B: Enz.* 17:133-142.

Shimizu, S., J. Ogawa, M. Kataoka and M. Kobayashi. 1997. Screening of novel microbial enzymes for the production of biologically and chemically useful compounds. *Adv. Biochem. Eng. Biotechnol.* 58:45-87.

Sivaramakrishnan, S., D. Gangadharan, K. M. Nampoothiri, C. R. Soccol and A. Pandey. 2006. α-amylases from microbial sources. *Food Technol. Biotechnol.* 44:173–184.

Soares, M. M. C. N., R. Silva, E. C. Carmona and E. Gomes. 2001. Pectinolytic enzymes production by *Bacillus* species and their potential application on juice extraction. *World J. Microbiol. Biotechnol.* 17:79-82.

Starodub, N. F. 2006. Biosensors for the evaluation of lipase activity. *J. Mol. Cat. B: Enz.* 40:155-160.

Stemmer, W. P. 1994. Rapid evolution of a protein *in vitro* by DNA shuffling. *Nature* 370: 389–391.

Stern, R., G. Kogan, M. J. Jedrzejas and L. Soltes. 2007. The many ways to cleave hyaluronan *Biotechnol. Adv.* 25:537–557.

Sukumaran, R. K., R. R. Singhania and A. Pandey. 2005. Microbial cellulasase – productions, applications and challenges. *J. Sci. Indus. Res.* 64:832-844.

Sunnotel, O. and P. Nigan. 2002. Pectinolytic activity of bacteria isolated from soil and two fungal strains during submerged fermentation. *World J. Microbiol. Biotechnol.* 18:835-839.

Suphatharaprateep, W., B. Cheirsilp and A. Jongjareonrak. 2011. Production and properties of two collagenases from bacteria and their application for collagen extraction. *N. Biotechnol.* 28:649-55.

Taylor, M. M., D. G. Bailey and S. H. Feairheller. 1987. A review of the uses of enzymes in the tannery. *J. Am. Leath. Chem. Assoc.* 82:153–165.

Thanikaivelan, P., J. R. Rao, B. U. Nair and T. Ramaswami. 2004. Progress and recent trends in biotechnological methods for leather processing. *Trends Biotechnol.* 22:181–188.

Thippeswamy, S., K. Girigowda and H. V. Mulimami. 2006. Isolation and identification of α-amylase producing *Bacillus* sp. from dhal industry waste. *Ind. J. Biochem. Biophys.* 43:295-298.

Thom, D., T. Swarthoff and J. Maat. 1990. Detergent formulations containing alkaline lipase derived from *Pseudomonas plantarii. Int. J. Syst. Bacteriol.* 87: 144-152.

Tobin, M. B., C. Gustafsson and G. W. Huisman. 2000. Directed evolution: the rational basis for irrational design. *Curr. Opin. Struct. Biol.* 10:421-427.

Turner, N. J. 2003. Directed evolution of enzymes for applied biocatalysis. *Trends Biotechnol.* 21:474-478.

Turowski, G. A., Z. Rashid, H. Fu, J. A. Madri and M. D. Basson. 1994. Glutamine modulates phenotype and stimulates proliferation in human colon cancer cell lines. *Cancer Res.* 54: 5974–5979.

Tyndall, R. M. 1996. Application of cellulase enzymes to cotton fabrics and garments. *Text. Chem. Color.* 24:23-26.

Tyrell, M. 1995. Advances in natural flavors and materials. *Perf. Flav.* 20:13-21.

Underkofler, L. A., R. R. Barton and S. S. Rennert. 1957. Production of microbial enzymes and their applications. *Microbiol. Proc. Rep.* 6:212-221.

Van Beilen, J. B. and Z. Li. 2002. Enzyme technology: an overview. *Curr. Opin. Biotechnol.* 13:338–344.

Van den Berg, J. A., K. J. van der Laken, A. J. J. van Ooyen, T. C. H. M. Renniers, K. Rietveld, A. Schaap, A. J. Brake, R. J. Bishop, K. Schultz, D. Moyer, M. Richman and J. R. Shuster. 1990. *Kluyveromyces* as a host for heterologous gene expression: expression and secretion of prochymosin. *Biotechnol.* 8:135–139.

Van den Burg, B., G. Vriend, O. Veltman, G. Venema and V. G. H. Eijsink. 1998. Engineering an enzyme to resist boiling. *Proc. Nat. Acad. Sci. US.* 95:2056-2060.

Van der Maarel, M. J. E. C., B. van der Veen, J. C. M. Uitdehaag, H. Leemhuis and L. Dijkhuizen. 2002. Properties and applications of starch converting enzymes of α-amylase family. *J. Biotechnol.* 94:137-155.

Van Rensburg, P. and I. S. Pretorius. 2000. Enzymes in winemaking: Harnessing natural catalysts for efficient biotransformation: a review. *South Afr. J. Enol. Viticul.* 21:52-73.

Vigneshwaran, C., N. Anbumani and M. Ananthasubramanian. 2011. Biovision in textile wet processing industry – technological challenges. *J. Text. Appar. Tech. Manag.* 7:1-13.

Voigt, C. A., S. Kauffman and Z. G. Wang. 2001. Rational evolutionary design: the theory of *in vitro* protein evolution. *Adv. Prot. Chem.* 55:79–160.

Voragen, A. G. J. 1992. Tailor-made enzymes in fruit juice processing. *Fruit Process.* 7:98–102.

Wackett, L. P. 1997. Bacterial biocatalysis: stealing a page from nature's book. *Nat. Biotechnol.* 15:415-416.

Walsh, G. A., R. F. Power and D. R. Headon. 1993. Enzymes in animal feed industry. *Trends Biotechnol.* 11:424–430.

Wang, H. Y., D. M. Liu, Y. Liu, C. F. Cheng, Q. Y. Ma, Q. Huang and Y. Z. Zhang 2006. Screening and mutagenesis of a novel *Bacillus pumilus* strain producing alkaline protease for dehairing. *Lett. Appl. Microbiol.* 44:1–6.

Ward, M., L. J. Wilson, K. H. Kodama, M. W. Rey and R. M. Berka. 1990. Improved production of chymosin in *Aspergillus* by expression as a glucoamylase chymosin fusion. *Biotechnol.* 8:435–440.

Winayanuwattikun, P., C. Kaewpiboon, K. Piriyakananon, W. Chulalaksananukul, T. Yongvanich and J. Svasti. 2011. Immobilized lipase from potential lipolytic microbes for catalyzing biodiesel production using palm oil as feedstock. *Afr. J. Biotechnol.* 10:1666-1673.

Wua, H., J. Wanga, X. Kanga, C. Wanga, D. Wanga, J. Liua, I. A. Aksayb and Y. Lina. 2009. Glucose biosensor based on immobilization of glucose oxidase in platinum nanoparticles/graphene/chitosan nanocomposite film. *Talanta* 80:403–406.

WuDunn, D. 1997. Intracameral urokinase for dissolution of fibrin or blood clots after glaucoma surgery. *Am. J. Ophthalmol.* 124:693-695.

Wyman, C. E. 1999. Biomass ethanol: technical progress, opportunities, and commercial challenges. *Annu. Rev. Energy Environ.* 24:189–226.

Yamada, H. and S. Shimizu. 1988. Microbial and enzymatic processes for the production of biologically and chemically useful compounds. *Angew Chem. Int. Ed. Engl.* 27:622-642.

Zeman, N. W. and J. M. McCrea. 1985. α-amylase production using a recombinant DNA organism. *Cer. Food World.* 30:777–780.

Zhang, D., G. Du and J. Chen. 2010. Fermentation production of microbial catalase and its application in textile industry. *Chin. J. Biotechnol.* 26:1473-1481.

In: Applications of Microbial Genes in Enzyme Technology ISBN: 978-1-62417-808-5
Editors: V.K.Gupta, M.G.Tuohy, G.D.Sharma et al.

Chapter 11

Filamentous Fungi Cellobiohydrolase Genes in Biotechnology

Marcio José Poças-Fonseca*, Fabiana Brandão Alves Silva, Robson Willian de Melo Matos and Thiago Machado Mello-de-Sousa
Department of Genetics and Morphology, Institute of Biological Sciences, Darcy Ribeiro University Campus, Brasilia-DF, Brazil

Abstract

Filamentous fungi cellobiohydrolase genes have been extensively studied aiming the high-level heterologous expression of optimized enzymes which could be employed for vegetal residues conversion in useful products at the industrial level. The generation of biofuels, and of biostoning or biopolishing agents for the textile industry, are of particular interest. In this chapter, we review the main aspects of fungal cellobiohydrolase genes structure and regulation, as well as the most promising studies on their biotechnological applications.

Introduction

Particular interest in cellulolytic microorganisms began during World War II, in the Salomon Islands (Southeast Pacific), when the troops' clothes, tents and other cellulosic fabrics were often degraded by the fungus later classified as *Trichoderma reesei*. Soon, what was initially seen as an economical problem became a promising scientific research field, aiming the conversion of cellulose in products such as recycled paper, animal feed and plant fertilizers. In the textile industry, cellulases have been employed in the formulation of detergents and in the biostoning and biopolishing processes.

---

* Corresponding author: E-mail: mpossas@unb.br, Phone: + 55 (61) 3107-3090; 3107-2916. Fax: +55 (61) 3107-2923.

The crude oil crisis in the mid-1970s drew the attention to the studies on alternative and renewable energy sources. Second generation bioethanol production from lignocellulosic residues is at the moment the main driving force for cellulolytic microorganisms research. The biofuel ethanol industry has been expanding worldwide, particularly in the United States, Brazil, Canada, India and in many European Union countries (Ragauskas, 2006). Vegetal biomass offers a renewable, abundant and inexpensive source of carbon. The use of lignocellulosic residues represents a suitable petroleum substitute which enhances energy security, can reduce greenhouse gas emissions, improves the economy and diminishes the problematic accumulation of sugarcane bagasse, corn stover, wheat and rice straw wastes. In this view, industrial residues, such as pulp and paper processing wastes, are also important (Wyman, 2003).

At the present days, the major problem of using lignocellulosic biomass for biofuel production is the process high cost. Biomass conversion to fuel ethanol comprises stages such as transportation of the biomass material to the site of treatment, pre-treatment of the biomass (chemical and/or physical), hydrolysis of the raw material into fermentable sugars (saccharification) and its subsequent transformation into innumerable fuels and chemicals (Knauf and Moniruzzaman, 2004). Due to the costs, the production of hydrolytic enzymes is still a hindrance to the large scale use of vegetal biomass for producing energy, chemicals or fuel. The discovery of new microbial hydrolytic enzymes is of great interest for the bioethanol industry. A suitable enzyme for this purpose should be resistant to the pre-treatment stages and to pH and temperature oscillations which occur during the fermentation process. It should also be accessible, cheap and must present a good catalytic efficiency. In this view, the search for new genes and the research on heterologous expression systems optimization can lead to an economically feasible bioconversion process.

The Fungal Cellulolytic System

Cellulose is the most abundant biopolymer in nature. It is composed of glucose units linked by β-1,4-glycosidic bonds. In spite of this simple chemical composition, the physical structure is highly complex. From 100 to 15000 linear chains are held together by hydrogen bonds and by Van der Waals forces, thus creating rigid and insoluble microfibrils. In nature, cellulose occurs associated with xylan and lignin, and often presents a heterogeneous structure, with amorphous segments immersed in highly ordered crystalline regions (for review, see Klemm *et al.*, 2005; Shen and Gnanakaram, 2009; Park *et al.*, 2010). Due to this complex physical structure, different enzyme activities are necessary in order to achieve the cellulose complete saccharification into glucose molecules. Although several microorganisms -particularly eubacteria and filamentous fungi- produce cellulases, relatively few are capable of completely saccharifying it into glucose molecules. Filamentous fungi are much more efficient than bacteria in producing and secreting cellulases. Some *Trichoderma reesei* (teleomorph: *Hypocrea jecorina*) mutants can secrete up to 40 g of cellulases per litre of culture medium (Durand *et al.* 1988). In light of such production and secretion potential, of their growth conditions versatility, of the available genetic manipulation tools and of the metabolic products variety, filamentous fungi have been extensively studied as agents for vegetal biomass conversion at the industrial level.

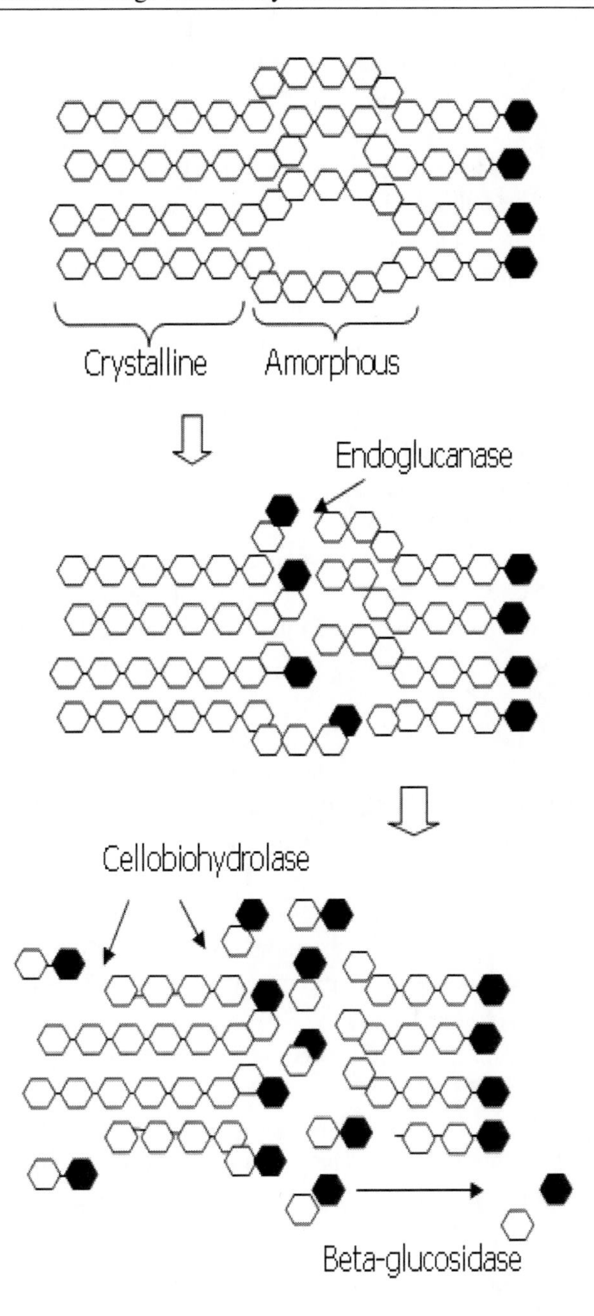

Figure 1. Cellulolytic enzymes synergism. Glucose residues are shown as hexagons and reducing ends are black. The arrows show cellulases action in degrading cellulose (modified from Béguin and Aubert 1994).

Notwithstanding the occurrence of cellulolytic members across the entire kingdom, from the protist-like chytridiomycetes to the advanced basidiomycetes (Lynd *et al.,* 2002), information on cellulolytic fungi is much more extensive for some groups than for others. It is commonly accepted that cellulose degradation by fungi is achieved by the synergistic action of three major classes of enzymes: endoglucanases (3.2.1.4), exoglucanases or cellobiohydrolases (EC 3.2.1.91) and β-glucosidases (3.2.1.21). These enzymes act in combination to hydrolyze crystalline cellulose to smaller oligosaccharides and finally to glucose. Endoglucanases (EGs) normally catalyse random cleavage of internal bonds of the amorphous regions of the cellulose chain, thus providing new chain ends for the action of cellobiohydrolases (CBHs). These late enzymes act in a processive manner from the reducing or non-reducing ends of the polysaccharide chains, as they progress along the polymer, thus liberating either glucose or cellobiose as the major products. β–glucosidases complete the process through the hydrolysis of cellobiose and other cello-oligosaccharides to glucose monomers (Eriksson, 1981; Knowles *et al.*, 1987; Ilmén *et al.*, 1997). Most fungal EGs and CBHs present a modular structure, revealing a tadpole like shape: the catalytic domain as the head, with a flexible long O-glycosylated region, similar to a tail, connecting it to a wedge-shaped cellulose-binding domain (reviewed by Bhat and Bhat 1997). CBH processivity was physically demonstrated by atomic force microscopy by Igarashi *et al.* (2009): the authors presented real time observations of *T. reesei* CBH I sliding in crystalline cellulose with an average velocity of 3.5 nm/s. Praestgaard *et al.* (2011) proposed a mathematical model to describe *T. reesei* Cel7A (CBH I) processivity kinetics: the enzyme maximum activity would be achieved through a balance between a rapid movement, mainly detected at the beginning of the hydrolysis, and a slower movement, hampered by physical obstacles found along the cellulose fiber. CBH processivity as a process dependent on the physical nature of the substrate was also reported by Kurašin and Väljamäe (2011).

In association to CBHs, EGs and beta-glucosidases, oxidative enzymes seem to cooperate in cellulose hydrolysis by basidiomycetes such as *Phanerochaete chrysosporium* (Bao and Renganathan, 1992; Igarashi *et al.* 1998) and *Trametes versicolor* (Tanaka *et al.* 1999). More recently, genes encoding swollenins, proteins which are homologous to plant expansins, were described for saprophytic fungi such as *T. reesei* (Saloheimo *et al.*, 2002), *Trichoderma pseudokoningii* S38 (Yao *et al.*, 2008), *Aspergillus fumigatus* (Chen *et al.*, 2010) and for the biocontrol agent *Trichoderma asperellum* (Brotman *et al.*, 2008). These proteins present a cellulose-binding domain and they weaken the interactions amongst the cellulose microfibers without breaking the β-1,4-glycosidic bonds. Swollenins seem to cooperate with cellulose break-down by deagglomerating cellulose complexes, dispersing cellulose microfibrils, decreasing the particle size and the crystallinity of the cellulosic substrate, thus leading to a significantly accelerated cellulose hydrolysis (Jäger *et al.*, 2011). In 2009, Martinez and collaborators described the genome, transcriptome and secretome analysis of the wood decay basidiomycete *Postia placenta*. This fungus cellulolytic system is unique in the sense that it does not code for CBHs.

Fungal Cellobiohydrolase Genes Structure

T. reesei is by far the most studied cellulolytic fungus. It produces several EGs, one beta-glucosidase and two CBHs. The cellobiohydrolase I gene (*cbh*1) was the first fungal CBH gene to be characterized (Schoemaker *et al.*, 1983) and it encodes a classic architecture cellulase: an N-terminal tunnel-shaped catalytic domain separated from a cellulose-binding domain, or carbohydrate-binding module (CBM), by a flexible hinge region. CBH I is now known as Cel7, although the former denomination is still the most employed in the scientific literature. Cel7A acts preferably on the reducing end of the cellulose chain (Barr *et al.*, 1996).

T. reesei second cellobiohydrolase (Cel6A, formerly CBH II) encodes an N-terminal CBM, a hinge region and a C-terminal catalytic domain (Teeri *et al.*, 1987) and it seems to be more effective on cellulose non-reducing ends (Barr *et al.*, 1996).

The isolation of the *T. reesei* CBH-encoding genes paved the way for the cloning and characterization of several fungi homologous sequences (genes and cDNA molecules), amongst them: a) the saprophytic *P. chrysosporium* (Sims *et al.*, 1988; Covert *et al.*, 1992; van den Wymelenberg *et al.*, 1993; Tempelaars *et al.*, 1994), *Trichoderma koningii* (Wey *et al.*, 1994), *Aspergillus aculeatus* (Takada *et al.*, 1998), *Trichoderma viride* (Cheng *et al.*, 1990; Song *et al.*, 2010), *Penicillium janthinellum* (Koch *et al.*, 1993), *Neurospora crassa* (Taleb and Radford, 1995), *Agaricus bisporus* (Yagüe *et al.*, 1997), *Aspergillus niger* (Gielkens *et al.*, 1999), *Volvariella volvacea* (Jia *et al.*, 1999) and *Corprinopsis cinerea* (Yoshida *et al.*, 2009); b) the phytopathogens *Cryphonectria parasitica* (Wang and Nuss, 1995), *Cochiobolus carbonum* (Sposato *et al.*, 1995), *Claviceps purpurea* (Müller *et al.*, 1997), *Irpex lacteus* (Hamada *et al.*, 1999a; 1999b and 1999c), *Leptosphaeria maculans* (Sexton *et al.*, 2000), *Corticium rolfsii* (Yasokawa *et al.*, 2003) and *Magnaporthe oryzae* (Takahashi *et al.*, 2010); c) the ruminal fungi *Neocallimastix patriciarum* (Denman *et al.*, 1996), *Piromyces* sp E2 and *Piromyces equi* (Harhangi *et al.*, 2003); d) the thermophilic *H. grisea* var. *thermoidea* (Azevedo *et al.*, 1990; Poças-Fonseca *et al.*, 1997), *Melanocarpus albomyces* (Haakana *et al.*, 2004), *Talaromyces emersonii* (Murray *et al.*, 2003; Grassick *et al.*, 2004), *Acremonium thermophilum*, *Thermoascus aurantiacus* and *Chaetomium thermophilum* (Voutilainen *et al.*, 2008); e) the endophytic *Fusicoccum* sp. (BCC4124) (Kanokratana *et al.*, 2008) and f) the marine fungus *Penicillium chrysogenum* FS010 (Hou *et al.*, 2007). Multigenic CBH families were described for *P. chrysosporium* BKM-1767 (Covert *et al.*, 1992), *P. chrysosporium* (Broda *et al.*, 1995), *H. grisea* var. *thermoidea* (Poças-Fonseca *et al.*, 1997), *M. oryzae* (Takahashi *et al.*, 2010) and *C. cinerea* (Tamura *et al.*, 2012). The bimodular structure (catalytic domain and carbohydrate-binding module) is not universal for fungal CBHs. *P. chrysosporium* BKM-1767 *cbh*1.1 (Covert *et al.*, 1992), *C. carbonum cel*1 (Sposato *et al.*, 1995), *C. parasitica cbh*1 (Wang and Nuss, 1995), *H. grisea* var. *thermoidea cbh*1.2 (Poças-Fonseca *et al.*, 1997), *C. purpurea cel*1 (Müller *et al.*, 1997), *A. niger cbh*A (Gielkens *et al.*, 1999), *L. maculans cel*1 and *cel*2 (Sexton *et al.*, 2000), *M. albomyces cel*7B (Haakana *et al.*, 2004), *T. aurantiacus cel*7A (Voutilainen *et al.*, 2008), *Fusicoccum* sp. (BCC4124) *cbh*1 (Kranokratana *et al.*, 2008) genes do not encode a substrate-binding domain. Enzymes presenting such a CBM-less structure tend to display an endoglucanase-like mode of action. Igarashi *et al.* (2009) showed that a *T. reesei* CBH I CBM-less version, obtained by papain digestion, moved along the cellulose fiber with a velocity similar to that of the intact enzyme.

The CBH genes addressed above present some general features. In the regulatory region, the “CAAT-box” consensus motif (GCC$_{A/T}$CAATCT, or similar derivations) is normally found at a maximum distance of about 400 base pairs (bp) upstream to the translation initiation codon. The “TATA-box” consensus (TATAA$_{A/T}$AA$_{A/T}$) tends to be more conserved and it can be found between 250 and 40 bp upstream to the first AUG. There is no consensus for the possible transcription initiation sites (between one and four in the listed genes, when this information is available), although they tend to co-localize with pyrimidine rich regions. The motif 5′-SYGGR3′ (S = cytosine or guanine, Y = pirimidine, R = purine), described by Cubero and Scazzochio (1994), represents the binding site for the CreA/Cre1 repressor protein and can be found in the regulatory region of several fungal CBH genes. CreA mediates glicosyl-hydrolase genes transcription repression when the fungus is grown in the presence of glucose or another readily metabolizable carbon source. Besides CreA, *H. grisea* var. *thermoidea* CBH genes (Mello-de-Sousa *et al.*, 2011) also present binding sites for the PacC transcription factor, which regulates gene expression in response to alkaline pH (Espeso *et al.*, 1997).

The coding region is usually interrupted by one or two introns. Nonetheless, *T. emersonii cbh*2 gene presents 7 introns (Murray *et al.*, 2003), followed by *P. chrysosporium* ME446 *cbh*2 and *C. parasitica cbh*1 genes, presenting 6 introns each (Tempelaars *et al.*, 1994; Wang and Nuss, 1995). On the other hand, *A. aculeatus cbh*1 and *P. janthinellum cbh*1 genes coding regions do not present introns (Takada *et al.*, 1998; Koch *et al.*, 1993). Introns are normally smaller than 100 bp and there is a striking conservation of the 5´-GT…AG-3` flanking sites. The lariat consensus sequence for filamentous fungi genes ($CTA_{/G}AC_{/T}$; reviewed by Turner, 1993) can be found in the majority of the described CBH genes. Introns position is not normally conserved, except for the closely related genes from the basidiomycetes *P. chrysosporium*, *A. bisporus* and *I. lacteus* (Hamada *et al.*, 1999a). There is a clear codon bias in fungal CBH genes: "C" is always favoured at the third position; when this is not possible, the position is occupied by a "G". NTA codons, where N is any nucleotide, are uncommon. A typical polyadenilation signal for eukaryotic mRNAs 3´ end (AATAAA) is not normally found.

Some fungi were reported as producers of active cellobiohydrolases but the corresponding genes were never cloned, as far as we know. The ascomycetes *Penicillium pinophilum* (Clayessens *et al.*, 1989), *Chrysosporium lucknowense* (Bukhtojarov *et al.*, 2004), *Penicillium echinulatum* (Camassola and Dillon, 2010) and *Mamillisphaeria* sp. (Laothanachareon *et al.*, 2011), as well as the brown-rot basidiomycete *Coniophora puteana* (Schum ex Fr) Karst (Schmidhalter and Canevascini, 1993) and the white-rot softwood-degrading basidiomycete *Phanerochaete carnosa* (Mahajan and Master, 2010) illustrate this situation. *Humicola insolens* is a potent producer of industrial cellulases (Schulein, 1997). Although there are several reports on this fungus cellulases hydrolysis mechanism (e.g. Boisset *et al.*, 2000; Boisset *et al.*, 2001) and on the proteins tridimentional structure (e.g. Varrot *et al.*, 1999a; Varrot *et al.*, 1999b), there is no information on the fungus cellulase genes architecture, since the processes for industrial enzymes production is protected by patents.

Basic Aspects of Fungal Cellulase Genes Regulation

Cellulase production by fungi is mainly regulated at the transcriptional level. Substrates as cellulose, lactose, cellobiose and sophorose normally act as inducers, while glucose normally acts as gene repressor. The presence of a low-level constitutive cellulase is required to initiate cellulose degradation, thus generating soluble inducers that can enter the cell and activate major cellulase genes transcription (Kubicek *et al.*, 1988; El-Gogary *et al.*, 1989). Seiboth *et al.* (1997) demonstrated that, in *T. reesei*, CBH II and EG II enzymes are of pivotal importance to generate the soluble inducer from cellulose. In 2000, Saloheimo and collaborators observed that the disruption of the *T. reesei ace*1 gene impaired the fungus capacity of growing on a cellulose-containing medium, thus suggesting that the ACEI zinc finger protein could be the first positive activator of fungal cellulase genes. Nonetheless, Aro *et al.* (2003) demonstrated that rather an activator, ACEI was actually a repressor of cellulase and xylanase genes expression. In the light of this study, ACEII, whose gene cloning and functional characterization had been published in 2001 by the same group, was confirmed as the true responsible for *T. reesei* cellulase and xylanase genes induction in the presence of cellulose. More recently, Portnoy *et al.* (2011) described a complex regulatory network for *T. reesei* cellulases upon growth on lactose, involving the transcription factors XYR1, ACE1 and ACE2-encoding genes differential expression. Those genes expression pattern varied in distinct low-, high- and hyper-producer strains. Also concerning the *T. reesei* cellulolytic system regulation, Seiboth *et al.* (2005) demonstrated that cellulases production on lactose depended on a low level beta-galactosidase activity. The same group concluded that D-galactose induces cellulases when the fungus grows at a low rate, although in the same conditions lactose is still a better inducer (Karaffa *et al.*, 2006). In regard of new information on cellulase genes regulation in fungi other than *T. reesei*, Suzuki *et al.* (2010) showed that the cellooligosaccharides cellotriose and cellotetraose are the most potent cellulose-derived inducers for *P. chrysosporium* CBH genes expression. Sun and Glass (2011) have identified a glucose repression cellulolytic regulon in *N. crassa*: in a *cre*1 deletion strain, the authors observed that not only cellulase genes transcription was increased, but also a higher cellulolytic activity was achieved. This study could also identify new genes involved in cellulases production and secretion in *N. crassa*. Recently, our research group demonstrated that the themophilic deuteromycete *H. grisea* var. *thermoidea* cellulase genes expression is regulated by a cross-talk mechanism involving the carbon source and the culture medium pH in which the fungus grows on (Mello-de-Sousa *et al.*, 2011).

Fungal Cellobiohydrolase Genes Biotechnological Applications

The progress of the Recombinant DNA Technology, and the cloning and characterization of fungal CBH genes from 1983, led to an increasing impact in strains optimization and heterologous protein production aiming diverse industrial applications. *T. reesei cbh*1 promoter functional characterization employing the *Escherichia coli lac*Z gene as reporter (Ilmén *et al.*, 1996) revealed sites whose removal abolished glucose repression without affecting sophorose induction. This study set the basis for the employment of the *cbh*1 promoter as a strong and finely regulated signal for heterologous proteins expression in *T. reesei* and other fungi. Since then, different studies focused the design of optimized versions of this promoter aiming academic research and industrial application. As an example, we highlight the work reported by Liu *et al.* (2008), who inserted additional copies of the CCAAT box and of the Ace2 transcription activator binding site, thus creating a series of modified promoters which were capable of increasing the glucoronidase reporter gene mRNA accumulation. CBH genes and regulatory sequences have been widely employed for heterologous expression purposes. Nyyssönen and Keränen (1995) obtained high level of antibodies light and heavy chains by fusing the respective coding sequences with the CBH I catalytic domain coding region. The fusion strategy seemed to increase the protein passage through the endoplasmic reticulum and the secretion efficiency. *T. reesei cbh*1 promoter and signal peptide coding region have been successfully employed for the expression of several industrial proteins, some relevant examples are listed below:

- *Aspergillus niger* acid phosphatase, which was produced up to 240 times more in the *T. reesei* heterologous host than in the native species (Miettinen-Oinonen *et al.*, 1997);
- Barley cysteine endopeptidase B and barley cellobiohydrolase I (Nykänen *et al.*, 1997);
- *H. grisea* var. *thermoidea* xylanase 2 (Faria *et al.*, 2002);
- *Dictyoglomus thermophilum* xylanase B (Bergquist *et al.*, 2004);
- *M. albomyces* laccase (Kiiskinen *et al.*, 2004);
- the thermostable *T. aurantiacus* CBH I (Benkó *et al.*, 2007);
- different neutral thermostable cellulases from *M. albomyces,* presenting potential applications in the textile industry as biostone-washing agents for denim fabric and cotton biofinishing (Haakana *et al.*, 2004; Szijártó *et al.*, 2008);
- *Aspergillus nidulans* class I hydrophobin (Schmoll *et al.*, 2010);
- the ethylene-forming enzyme from *Pseudomonas syringae* pv. *glycinea* and human erythropoietin (Zhong *et al.*, 2011);
- *Trametes* sp. AH28-2 laccase A (Zhang *et al.*, 2012).

Recently, Qin *et al.* (2012) described an innovative experimental approach to increase the *A. niger* Lip lipase in *T. reesei* as heterologous host under control of the *cbh*1 promoter: the authors employed interference RNA (iRNA) to silence the endogenous *cbh*1 gene and thus achieved some 1.8 – 3.2 fold increase in the recombinant lipase production. Lv *et al.* (2012) constructed two *T. reesei* expression vectors, harbouring the *cbh*1 promoter and terminator, which were efficiently inserted into the *T. reesei* genome with an *Agrobacterium*-mediated transformation system. These vectors present the advantage of allowing gene expression and gene knock-out at a specific chromosomal location by homologous or random recombination.

The *Agrobacterium* transformation system was also employed for the expression of *Peniclillium decumbens* beta-glucosidase in the *T. reesei* cellulase hyperproducer strain Rut-C30 under control of the native *cbh*1 promoter (Ma *et al.*, 2011). Since *T. reesei* beta-glucosidase activity is not pronounced, complete cellulose saccharification requires additional enzyme supplementation; by expressing the *P. decumbens* beta-glucosidase, the authors achieved an increase of about 30% in *T. reesei* total cellulase activity. Furthermore, when the purified recombinant enzyme was employed to complement a *T. reesei* cellulases cocktail, the glucose production from pre-treated cornstalk increased by 80%, pointing out to a promising application at the production of biofuel ethanol form lignocellulosic residues.

Besides *T. reesei*, *T. viride cbh*1 gene promoter and/or signal peptide encoding region have also been employed for the heterologous expression of industrial enzymes such as the *Aspergillus oryzae* Taka-amilase (Cheng and Udaka, 1991) and the saponin hydrolases from *Neocosmospora vasinfecta* var. *vasinfecta* (Watanabe *et al.*, 2004), *A. oryzae* and *Eupenicillium brefeldianum* (Watanabe *et al.*, 2005). Saponins are antifungal compounds thought to protect plants from phytopathogenic fungi and have been used as hepatoprotective, anticarcinogenic and anti-inflammatory drugs. The *T. viride* CBH I signal peptide was also used to achieve *Neocallimastix frontalis* endoxylanase 3 efficient production and secretion in *Penicillium roqueforti* as heterologous host (Durand *et al.*, 1999).

As an alternative to *T. reesei* as heterologous host for fungal cellulase genes expression, *A. oryzae* has been occasionally used. Schülein (1997) cloned seven cellulase genes from the thermophilic saprophytic *H. insolens* in *A. oryzae*, amongst them *cbh*1 and *cbh*2. Recombinant CBH I and CBH II retained their remarkable thermostability and activity peak was determined as pH 5.5 and pH 9, respectively. *A. oryzae* was also employed for *T. reesei* (Takashima *et al.*, 1998a) and *H. grisea* (Takashima *et al.*, 1996; Takashima *et al.* 1998b) cellobiohydrolase genes expression, but recombinant proteins presented different biochemical properties when compared to the native ones, especially concerning the molecular masses, due to divergent glycosilation patterns. More recently, Takahashi *et al.* (2010) produced the *M. oryzae* Cel6A cellobiohydrolase in *A. oryzae*: in the presence of 292 mM cellobiose, the recombinant enzyme displayed increased cellopentaose hydrolysis at pH 4.5 and pH 6.0. Nonetheless, this effect was not detected at pH 9.0, suggesting that the effect of cellobiose on enzyme activity regulation is pH-dependent.

Due to the cultivation versatility, the large production and secretion ability and to the well established industrial processes, yeasts have been successfully employed for the production of filamentous fungi cellobiohydrolases at large scale. The first report of such initiative dates back to 1988, when Penttilä and collaborators described the expression of *T. reesei* CBH I and CBH II in *Saccharomyces cerevisiae*. In spite of presenting molecular mass differences when compared to the native proteins, due to a distinct glycosilation pattern, the recombinant enzymes where able to degrade amorphous cellulose and around 100 micrograms/mL of CBH II were recovered from the yeast culture supernatant. The methylotrophic yeast *Pichia pastoris* was also employed for the expression of *T. reesei* Cel7A (CBH I; Boer *et al.*, 2000).

The recombinant protein was also overglycosilated when compared to the native one, but not to the same extent as in *S. cerevisiae*. Although k_{cat} and K_m values were not significantly altered, cellulose degradation was reduced in comparison to the native enzyme.

Heinzelman *et al.* (2009) employed a protein structure-guided recombination strategy to generate a library of chimeric enzymes secreted by *S. cerevisiae*. The authors recombined CBH II enzymes from the thermophilic fungi *H. insolens* and *C. thermophilum*, as well as the *T. reesei* CBH II, and obtained a series of chimeric CBHs presenting a higher thermostability and broader pH/activity profiles.

The *S. cerevisiae* structure-guided protein engineering approach was also used to obtain a version of the *T. emersonii* Cel7A cellobiohydrolase presenting an improved thermostability (Voutilainen *et al.*, 2010). *T. viride* CBH I and CBH II were also expressed in *S. cerevisiae* under control of the *GAL1* promoter (Song *et al.*, 2010). Both recombinant enzymes presented acidic optimum pH and optima temperatures above 60°C.

With the aim of obtaining a *S. cerevisiae* recombinant strain which could efficiently generate glucose from cellulose, van Wyk *et al.* (2010) co-expressed the thermophilic actinomycete *Thermobifida fusca cel9A* endoglucanase gene with one of the following *T. reesei* genes: *egl*1, *egl*2 (endoglucanases), *cbh*1 or *cbh*2 (cellobiohydrolases). Enzyme activity on amorphous cellulose was not affected by co-expression, while the activity on the crystalline form of the substrate was increased particularly with the Cel9A/CBH I binary reaction.

Recently, our research group has successfully expressed *H. grisea* var. *thermoidea cbh*1.2 gene (Poças-Fonseca *et al.*, 1997) in *P. pastoris* (Oliveira *et al.*, submitted). Recombinant enzyme (rCBH1.2) was secreted as a functional enzyme, presenting a molecular mass of 47 kDa, compatible to the one of the native protein (De-Paula *et al.*, 2003). rCBH1.2 exhibited an optimum activity at 60 °C, at pH 8.5, and presented a remarkable thermostability, particularly at alkaline pH. Interestingly, rCBH1.2 presents both endoglucanase and exoglucanase activities. The biochemical properties of rCBH1.2 indicate that this enzyme represents a potential biocatalyst for the textile industry. As pointed out before, the main driving force for the research on fungal cellobiohydrolases described above has been the generation of soluble sugars for fermentation to bioethanol.

In this view, some very promising studies with cellulase-expressing yeasts have been published in the recent years. Yanase *et al.* (2010) achieved direct ethanol fermentation from phosphoric acid swollen cellulose by expressing *T. reesei* EGs and CBHs, as well as beta-glucosidases from *A. aculeatus* attached to the *S. cerevisiae* cell wall surface, or secreted in the culture medium supernatant.

Maximum ethanol yield was 2.1 g/L for cellulases cell wall-displaying recombinant yeasts. Ilmén *et al.* (2011) have engineered *S. cerevisiae* strains expressing combinations of 14 different *cbh*1 and 10 distinct *cbh*2 genes of fungal origin. The authors concluded that some particular genes are more compatible to high-level expression in *S. cerevisiae* than others. Although the stress response in the endoplasmic reticulum and the regulation of the unfolded protein response is involved, the underlining reason for such a difference is not clear.

Nonetheless, CBH I and CBH II were expressed at high levels (0.3 g/L and 1.0 g/L, respectively) and the addition of beta-glucosidase to the CBH-expressing strains cultures led to the fermentation of microcystalline cellulose to ethanol. *S. cerevisiae* cell-surface display of heterologous enzymes, in combination with a novel fermentation system and the addition of 10 filter paper units/g-biomass of industrial cellulases, was employed by Matano *et al.* (2012) to achieve high-level ethanol production from rice straw. In this study, the authors simultaneously expressed *T. reesei* EG II and CBH II, as well as the *A. aculeatus* beta-glucosidase. The fermentation vessel was rotated under controlled temperature and rice straw was agitated by gravity in order to increase the mixing with the added cellulases. This combined process resulted in an 89% theoretical conversion of solid rice straw to bioethanol.

Conclusion

Filamentous fungi cellobiohydrolase genes have been studied for more than three decades now. The saprophytic *T. reesei* is the model cellulolytic fungus and has provided much of the information on cellobiohydrolase genes structure and regulation, as well on the enzymes architecture and reaction mechanism. This information paved the way to the exploitation of several other cellulolytic fungi, including other saprophytic, thermophilic, phytopathogenic and wood-rot fungi. Fungal cellobiohydrolase genes and/or regulatory signals have been widely employed in biotechnology for the production of industrial enzymes, focusing on paper recycling, textiles processing and bioethanol generation. The first results on ethanol production from lignocellulosic residues have recently been reported.

Acknowledgments

We are grateful to FINEP (Research and Projects Financing, Brazil)/MCT (Ministery of Science and Technology - Bioethanol Network, Brazil), to CNPq (National Council for Scientific and Technological Development-Brazil) and to FAP-DF (Research Support Foundation of the Federal District-Brazil) for financial support for our scientific research activities.

References

Aro, N., A. Saloheimo, M. Ilmén and M. Penttilä. 2001. ACEII, a novel transcriptional activator involved in regulation of cellulase and xylanase genes of *Trichoderma reesei*. *J. Biol. Chem.* 276: 24309-24314.

Aro, N., M. Ilmén, A. Saloheimo and M. Penttilä. 2003. ACEI of *Trichoderma reesei* is a repressor of cellulase and xylanase expression. *Appl. Environ. Microbiol.* 69: 56-65.

Azevedo, M.O., M.S.S Felipe, S. Astolfi-Filho and A. Radford. 1990. Cloning, sequencing and homologies of the *cbh* 1 (exoglucanase) gene of *Humicola grisea* var. *thermoidea*. *J. Gen. Microbiol.* 136: 2569-2576.

Bao, W. and V. Renganathan. 1992. Cellobiose oxidase of *Phanerochaete chrysosporium* enhances crystalline cellulose degradation by cellulases. *FEBS Letters* 302: 77-80.

Barr, B.K., Y.L Hsieh, B. Ganem and D.B. Wilson. 1996. Identification of two functionally different classes of exocellulases. *Biochem.* 35: 586-592.

Béguin, P. and J.P. Aubert. 1994. The biological degradation of cellulose. *FEMS Microbiol. Rev.* 13: 25-58.

Benko, Z., E. Drahos, Z. Szengyel, T. Puranen, J. Vehmaanperä and K. Réczey. 2007. *Thermoascus aurantiacus* CBHI/Cel7A production in *Trichoderma reesei* on alternative carbon sources. *Appl. Biochem. Biotechnol.* 137-140(1-12): 195 – 204.

Bergquist, P.L., V.S. Te'o, M.D. Gibbs, N.C. Curach and K.M. Nevalainen. 2004. Recombinant enzymes from thermophilic micro-organisms expressed in fungal hosts. *Biochem. Soc. Trans.* 32: 293-297.

Bhat, M.K. and S. Bhat. 1997. Cellulose degrading enzymes and their potential applications. *Biotechnol. Adv.* 15: 583-620.

Boer, H., T.T. Teeri and A. Koivula. 2000. Characterization of *Trichoderma reesei* cellobiohydrolase Cel7A secreted from *Pichia pastoris* using two different promoters. *Biotechnol Bioeng*. 69: 486-94.

Boisset, C., C. Fraschini, M. Schülein, B. Henrissat and H. Chanzy. 2000. Imaging the enzymatic digestion of bacterial cellulose ribbons reveals the endo character of the cellobiohydrolase Cel6A from *Humicola insolens* and its mode of synergy with cellobiohydrolase Cel7A. *Appl. Environ. Microbiol.* 66: 1444-1452.

Boisset, C., C. Pétrequin, H. Chanzy, B. Henrissat and M. Schülein. 2001. Optimized mixtures of recombinant *Humicola insolens* cellulases for the biodegradation of crystalline cellulose. *Biotechnol. Bioeng.* 72: 339–345.

Broda, P., P.R.J. Birch, P.R. Brooks and P.F.G Sims. 1995. PCR-mediated analysis of lignocellulolytic gene transcription by *Phanerochaete chrysosporium*: substrate-dependent differential expression within gene families. *Appl. Environ. Microbiol.* 61: 2358-2364.

Brotman, Y., E. Briff, A. Viterbo and I. Chet. 2008. Role of Swollenin, an Expansin-Like Protein from *Trichoderma*, in Plant Root Colonization. *Plant. Physiol.* 147: 779-789.

Bukhtojarov, F.E., B.B. Ustinov, T.N. Salanovich, A.I. Antonov, A.V. Gusakov, O.N. Okunev and A.P. Sinitsyn. 2004. Cellulase complex of the fungus *Chrysosporium lucknowense:* isolation and characterization of endoglucanases and cellobiohydrolases. *Biochemistry (Mosc).* 69: 542-51.

Camassola, M. and A.J. Dillon. 2010. Cellulases and xylanases production by *Penicillium echinulatum* grown on sugar cane bagasse in solid-state fermentation. *Appl. Biochem. Biotechnol.* 162: 1889 – 1900.

Chen, X., Y. Liang, J. Hua, L. Tao, W. Qin and S. Chen. 2010. Overexpression of bacterial ethylene-forming enzyme gene in *Trichoderma reesei* enhanced the production of ethylene. *Int. J. Biol. Sci.* 6: 96-106.

Chen, X.A., N. Ishida, N. Todaka, R. Nakamura, J. Maruyama, H. Takahashi and K. Kitamoto. 2010. Promotion of efficient Saccharification of crystalline cellulose by *Aspergillus fumigatus* Swo1. *Appl. Environ. Microbiol.* 76: 2556-2561.

Cheng, C., N. Tsukagoshi and S. Udaka. 1990. Nucleotide sequence of the cellobiohydrolase gene from *Trichoderma viride. Nucleic Acids Res.* 18: 5559.

Cheng, C. and S. Udaka. 1991. Efficient production of Taka-amylase A by *Trichoderma viride. Agric. Biol. Chem.* 55: 1817-1822.

Claeyssens, M., H. Van Tilbeurgh, P. Tomme, T. M. Wood and S. I. McRae. 1989. Fungal cellulase systems: Comparison of the specificities of the cellobiohydrolases isolated from *Penicillium pinophilum* and *Trichoderma reesei. Biochem J.* 261: 819–825.

Covert, S. F., A.V. Wymelenberg and D. Cullen. 1992. Structure, organization and transcription of a cellobiohydrolase gene cluster from *Phanerochaete chrysosporium. Appl. Environ. Microbiol.* 58: 2168-2175.

Cubero, B. and C. Scazzochio. 1994. Two different, adjacent and divergent zinc finger binding sites are necessary for CREA-mediated carbon catabolite repression in the proline gene cluster of *Aspergillus nidulans. EMBO J.* 13: 407-415.

Denman, S., G.P. Xue and B. Patel. 1996. Characterization of a *Neocallimastix patriciarum* cellulase cDNA (*cel*A) homologous to *Trichoderma reesei* cellobiohydrolase II. *Appl. Environ. Microbiol.* 62: 1889–1896.

De-Paula, E.H., M.J. Poças-Fonseca, and M.O. Azevedo. 2003. The product of *Humicola grisea* var. *thermoidea cbh*1.2 gene is the major expressed protein under induction by lignocellulosic residues. *World J. Microbiol. Biotechnol.* 19: 631-635.

Durand, H., M. Clanet and G. Tiraby. 1988. Genetic improvement of *Trichoderma reesei* for large scale production. *Enzyme Microb. Technol.* 10: 341-346.

Durand, R., C. Rascle and M. Fèvre. 1999. Expression of a catalytic domain of a *Neocallimastix frontalis* endoxylanase gene (*xyn*3) in *Kluyveromyces lactis* and *Penicillium roqueforti. Appl. Microbiol. Biotechnol.* 52: 208-214.

El-Gogary, S., A. Leite, O. Crivellaro, D.E. Eveleigh and H. El-Dorry. 1989. Mechanism by which cellulose triggers cellobiohydrolase I gene expression in *Trichoderma reesei. Proc. Natl. Acad. Sci. USA* 86: 6138-6141.

Eriksson, K.-E. 1978. Enzyme mechanisms involved in cellulose hydrolysis by the rot fungus *Sporotrichum pulverulentum. Biotechnol. Bioeng.* 70: 317-332.

Espeso, E.A., J. Tilburn, L. Sanches-Pulido, C.V. Brown, A. Valencia, H.N. Arst Jr. and M.A Peñalva. 1997. Specific DNA recognition by the *Aspergillus nidulans* three zinc finger transcription factor PacC. *J. Mol. Biol.* 274: 466-480.

Faria F.P., V.S. Te'O, P.L. Bergquist, M.O. Azevedo and K.M. Nevalainen. 2002. Expression and processing of a major xylanase (XYN2) from the thermophilic fungus *Humicola grisea* var. *thermoidea* in *Trichoderma reesei. Lett. Appl. Microbiol.* 34: 119-123.

Gielkens, M.M.C., E. Dekkers, J. Visser and L.H. de Graaff. 1999. Two Cellobiohydrolase-Encoding Genes from Aspergillus niger Require D-Xylose and the Xylanolytic Transcriptional Activator XlnR for Their Expression. *Appl. Environ. Microbiol.* 65: 4340-4345.

Grassick, A., P.G. Murray, R. Thompson, C.M. Collins, L. Byrnes, G. Birrane, T.M. Higgins and M.G. Tuohy. 2004. Three-dimensional structure of a thermostable native cellobiohydrolase, CBH IB, and molecular characterization of the *cel7* gene from the filamentous fungus *Talaromyces emersonii. Eur. J. Biochem.* 271: 4495-4506.

Haakana, H., A. Miettinen-Oinonen, V. Joutsjoki, A. Mäntylä, P. Suominen and J. Vehmaanperä. 2004. Cloning of cellulase genes from *Melanocarpus albomyces* and their efficient expression in *Trichoderma reesei. Enzyme Microb. Technol.* 34: 159 – 167.

Hamada, N., R. Okumura, N. Fuse, R. Kodaira, M. Shimosaka, T. Kanda, and M. Okazaki. 1999a. Isolation and transcriptional analysis of a cellulase (*cel*1) from the basidiomycete *Irpex lacteus. J. Biosci. Bioeng.* 87: 97-102.

Hamada, N., K. Ishikawa, N. Fuse, R. Kodaira, Y. Amano, M. Shimosaka, T. Kanda and M. Okazaki. 1999b. Purification, characterization and gene analysis of exo-cellulase II (Ex-2) from the white rot basidiomycete *Irpex lacteus. J. Biosci. Bioeng.* 87: 442-451.

Hamada, N., N. Fuse, M. Shimosaka, R. Kodaira, Y. Amano, T. Kanda and M. Okazaki. 1999c. Cloning and characterization of a new exo-cellulase gene, *cel*3, in *Irpex lacteus. FEMS Microbiol. Lett.* 172: 231-237.

Harhangi, H.R., A.C.J. Freelove, W. Ubhayasekera, M. van Dinther, P.J.M. Steenbakkers, A. Akhmanova, C. van der Drift, M.S.M. Jetten, S.L. Mowbray, H.J. Gilbert and H.J.M. Op den Camp. 2003. Cel6A, a major exoglucanase from the cellulosome of the anaerobic fungi *Piromyces sp.* E2 and *Piromyces equi. Biochim. Biophys. Acta.* 1628: 30-39.

Heinzelman, P., C.D. Snow, I. Wu, C. Nguyen, A. Villalobos, S. Govindarajan, J. Minshull and F.H. Arnold. 2009. A family of thermostable fungal cellulases created by structure-guided recombination. *PNAS* 106: 5610 – 5615.

Hou, Y., T. Wang, H. Long and H. Zhu. 2007. Cloning, sequencing and expression analysis of the first cellulase gene encoding cellobiohydrolase 1 from a cold-adaptive *Penicillium chrysogenum* FS010. *Acta. Biochim. Biophys. Sin.* 39: 101-107.

Igarashi, K., M. Samejima and K-E.L. Eriksson. 1998. Cellobiose dehydrogenase enhances *Phanerochaete chrysosporium* cellobiohydrolase I activity by relieving product inhibition. *Eur. J. Biochem.* 253: 101-106.

Igarashi, K., A. Koivula, M. Wada, S. Kimura, M. Penttila and M. Samejima. 2009. High Speed Atomic Force Microscopy Visualizes Processive Movement of *Trichoderma reesei* Cellobiohydrolase I on Crystalline Cellulose. *J. Biol. Chem.* 284: 36186–36190.

Ilmén, M., M.-L.Onnela, S. Klemsdal, S. Keränen and Penttilä, M. 1996. Functional analysis of the cellobiohydrolase I promoter of the filamentous fungus *Trichoderma reesei. Mol. Gen. Genet.* 253: 303-314.

Ilmén, M., A. Saloheimo, M-L. Onnela and M.E. Penttilä. 1997. Regulation of cellulase in the filamentous fungus *Trichoderma reesei*. *Appl. Environ. Microbiol.* 63: 1298-1306.

Ilmén, M., R. den Haan, E. Brevnova, J. McBride, E. Wiswall, A. Froehlich, A. Koivola, S.P. Voutilainen, M. Siika-aho, D. C. la Grange, N. Thorngren, S. Ahlgren, M. Mellon, K. Deleault, V. Rajgarhia, W.H. van Zyl and M. Penttilä. 2011. High level secretion of cellobiohydrolases by *Saccharomyces cerevisiae*. *Biotechnol Biofuels* 4: 30.

Jäger, G., M. Girfoglio, F. Dollo, R. Rinaldi, H. Bongard, U. Commandeur, R. Fischer, A. C. Spiess and J. B. Rainer. 2011. How recombinant swollenin from *Kluyveromyces lactis* affects cellulosic substrates and accelerates their hydrolysis. *Biotechnol. Biofuels*. 4: 33.

Jia, J., P.S. Dyer, J.A. Buswell and J.F. Peberdy.1999. Cloning of the *cbh*I and *cbh*II genes involved in cellulose utilization by the straw mushroom *Volvariella volvacea*. *Mol. Gen. Genet.* 261: 985-993.

Kanokratana, P., D. Chantasingh, V. Chamreda, S. Tanapongpipat, K. Pootanakit and L. Eurwilaichitr. 2008. Identification and expression of cellobiohydrolase (CBHI) gene from an endophytic fungus *Fusicoccum sp.* (BCC4124) in *Pichia pastoris*. *Protein Expr. Purif.* 58: 148-153.

Karaffa, L., E. Fekete, C. Gamauf, A. Szentirmai, C.P. Kubicek and B. Seiboth. 2006. D-Galactose induces cellulase gene expression in *Hypocrea jecorina* at low growth rates. *Microbiology*. 152: 1507-1514.

Kiiskinen, L.L., K. Kruus, M. Bailey, E. Ylösmäki, M. Siika-Aho and M. Saloheimo. 2004. Expression of *Melanocarpus albomyces* laccase in *Trichoderma reesei* and characterization of the purified enzyme. *Microbiology*.150: 3065-3074.

Klemm, D., B. Heublein, H-P. Fink and A. Bohn, 2005. Cellulose: fascinating biopolymer and sustainable raw material. *Angew. Chem. Int. Ed. Engl.* 44: 3358 – 3393.

Knauf, M. and M. Moniruzzaman, 2004. Lignocellulosic biomass processing: A perspective. *International Sugar Journal* 106: 147-150.

Knowles, J., P. Lehtovaara and T.T. Teeri. 1987. Cellulase families and their genes. *TIBTECH*. 5: 255 – 261.

Koch, A., C.T.O. Weigel and G. Schulz. 1993. Cloning, sequencing, and heterologous expression of a cellulase encoding cDNA (*cbh*1) from *Penicillium janthinellum*. *Gene* 124: 57-65.

Kubicek, C.P., G. Mühlbauer, M. Klotz, E. John and E.M. Kubicek-Pranz. 1988. Properties of a conidial-bound cellulase enzyme system from *Trichoderma reesei*. *J. Gen. Microbiol.* 134: 1215-1222.

Kurašin, M and P. Väljamäe. 2011. Processivity of cellobiohydrolases is limited by the substrate. *J. Biol. Chem.* 286: 169-177.

Laothanachareon, T., P. Khonzue, N. Rattanaphan, P. Tinnasulanon, S. Apawasin, A. Paemanee, V. Ruanglek, S. Tanapongpipat, V. Champreda and L. Eurwilaichitr. 2011. Production of multi-fiber modifying enzyme from *Mamillisphaeria* sp. for refining of recycled paper pulp. *Biosci. Biotechnol. Biochem*. 75: 2297 – 2303.

Liu, T., T. Wang, X. Li and X. Liu. 2008. Improved heterologous gene expression in *Trichoderma reesei* by cellobiohydrolase I gene (*cbh*1) promoter optimization. *Acta. Biochim. Biophys. Sin.* 40: 158-165.

Lv, D., W. Wang and D. Wei. 2012. Construction of two vectors for gene expression in *Trichoderma reesei*. *Plasmid*. 67: 67-71.

Lynd, L.R., P.J. Weimer, W.H. van Zyl and I.S. Pretorius. 2002. Microbial cellulose utilization: Fundamentals and biotechnology *Microbiol. Mol. Biol. Rev.* 66:506-577.

Ma, L., J. Zhang, G. Zou, C. Wang and Z. Zhou. 2011. Improvement of cellulase activity in *Trichoderma reesei* by heterologous expression of a beta-glucosidase gene from *Penicillium decumbens*. *Enzyme Microb. Technol.* 49: 366-371.

Mahajan, S. and E.R. Master. 2010. Proteomic characterization of lignocellulose-degrading enzymes secreted by *Phanerochaete carnosa* grown on spruce and microcrystalline cellulose. *Appl. Microbiol. Biotechnol.* 86: 1903-1914.

Martinez, D., J. Challacombe, I. Morgenstern and D. Cullen. 2009. Genome, transcriptome, and secretome analysis of wood decay fungus *Postia placenta* supports unique mechanisms of lignocellulose conversion. *Proc. Natl. Acad. Sci. U.S.A.* 106: 1954-1959.

Matano, Y., Hasunuma, T. and A. Kondo. 2012. Display of cellulases on the cell surface of *Saccharomyces cerevisiae* for high yield ethanol production from high-solid lignocellulosic biomass. *Biores. Technol.* 108: 128 – 133.

Mello-de-Sousa, T.M., I. Silva-Pereira and M.J. Poças-Fonseca. 2011. Carbon source and pH-dependent transcriptional regulation of cellulase genes of *Humicola grisea* var. *thermoidea* grown on sugarcane bagasse. *Enzyme and Microbial Technology* 48: 19-26.

Miettinen-Oinonen, A., T.Torkkeli, M. Paloheimo and H. Nevalainen. 1997. Overexpression of the *Aspergillus niger* pH 2.5 acid phosphatase gene in a heterologous host *Trichoderma reesei*. *J. Biotechnol.* 58: 13-20.

Müller, U., K.B. Tenberge, B. Oeser and P.Tudzynski. 1997. *Cel*1, probably encoding a cellobiohydrolase lacking the substrate binding domain, is expressed in the initial infection phase of *Claviceps purpurea* on Secale cereale. *Mol. Plant. Microbe. Interact.* 10: 268-279.

Murray, P.G., C.M. Collins, A. Grassick and M.G. Tuohy. 2003. Molecular cloning, transcriptional, and expression analysis of the first cellulase gene (*cbh*2), encoding cellobiohydrolase II, from the moderately thermophilic fungus *Talaromyces emersonii* and structure prediction of the gene product. *Biochem. Biophys. Res. Commun.* 301: 280-286.

Nykänen, M., R. Saarelainen, M. Raudaskoski, H.K. Nevalainen and A. Mikkonen. 1997. Expression and Secretion of Barley Cysteine Endopeptidase B and Cellobiohydrolase I in *Trichoderma reesei*. *Appl. Environ. Microbiol.* 63: 4929–4937.

Nyyssönen, E. and S. Keränen.1995. Multiple roles of the cellulase CBHI in enhancing production of fusion antibodies by the filamentous fungus *Trichoderma reesei*. *Curr. Genet.* 28:71-79.

Park, S.; J. O´Baker, M. E. Himmel, P. A. Parilla and D. K. Johnson, 2010. Cellulose crystallinity index: measurement techniques and their impact on interpreting cellulase performance. *Biotechnol. Biofuels* 3: 10.

Penttilä, M.E., L. André, P. Lehtovaara, M. Bailey, T.T. Teeri and J.K. Knowles. 1988. Efficient secretion of two fungal cellobiohydrolases by *Saccharomyces cerevisiae*. *Gene.* 63: 103-112.

Poças-Fonseca, M.J., B.D. Lima, M.M. Brígido, I.S. Pereira, M.S.S. Felipe, A. Radford and M.O. Azevedo. 1997. *Humicola grisea* var. *thermoidea cbh*1.2: a new gene in the family of cellobiohydrolases is expressed and encodes a cellulose-binding domain-less protein. *J. Gen. Appl. Microbiol.* 43: 115-120.

Portnoy, T., A. Margeot, V. Seidl-Seiboth, S.L. Crom, F.B. Chaabane, R. Linke, B. Seiboth and C.P. Kubicek. 2011. Differential Regulation of the Cellulase Transcription Factors XYR1, ACE2, and ACE1 in *Trichoderma reesei* Strains Producing High and Low Levels of Cellulase. *Eukaryot. Cell.* 10: 262–271.

Praestgaard, E., J. Elmerdahl, L. Murphy, S. Nymand, K.C. McFarland, K. Borch and P. Westh. 2011. A kinetic model for the burst phase of processive cellulases. *FEBS J.* 278: 1547-1560.

Qin, L.N., F.R. Cai, X.R. Dong, Z.B. Huang,Y. Tao, J.Z. Huang and Z.Y. Dong. 2012. Improved production of heterologous lipase in *Trichoderma reesei* by iRNA mediated gene silencing of an endogenic highly expressed gene. *Bioresour. Technol.* 109: 116-122.

Ragauskas A.J., C.K. Williams, B.H. Davison, G. Britovsek, J. Cairney, C.A. Eckert, W.J. Frederick Jr, J.P. Hallett, D.J. Leak, C.L. Liotta, Jonathan R. Mielenz, Richard Murphy, Richard Templer and T. Tschaplinski. 2006. The Path Forward for Biofuels and Biomaterials. *Science* 311: 484–489.

Saloheimo, A., N. Aro, M. Ilmén and M. Penttilä. 2000. Isolation of the *ace*1 gene encoding a Cys_2-Hys_2 transcription factor involved in regulation of activity of the cellulase promoter *cbh*1 of *Trichoderma reesei. J. Biol. Chem.* 275: 5817-5825.

Saloheimo, M., M. Paloheimo, S. Hakola, J. Pere, B. Swanson, E. Nyyssönen, A. Bhatia, M. Ward and M. Penttilä. 2002. Swollenin, a *Trichoderma reesei* protein with sequence similarity to the plant expansins, exhibits disruption activity on cellulosic materials. *Eur. J. Biochem.* 269: 4202-4211.

Schmidhalter, D.R. and G. Canevascini. 1993. Purification and characterization of two exo-cellobiohydrolases from the brown-rot fungus *Coniophora puteana* (Schum ex Fr) Karst. *Arch. Biochem. Biophys.* 300: 551-558.

Schmoll, M., C. Seibel, C. Kotlowski, F.W.G. Vendt, B. Liebmann and C.P. Kubicek. 2010. Recombinant production of an *Aspergillus nidulans* class I hydrophobin (DewA) in *Hypocrea jecorina* (*Trichoderma reesei*) is promoter-dependent. *Appl. Microbiol. Biotechnol.* 88: 95-103.

Schülein. M. 1997. Enzymatic properties of cellulases from *Humicola insolens. J. Biotechnol.* 57: 71-81.

Seiboth, B., S. Hakola, R.L. Mach, P.L. Suominen and C.P. Kubicek. 1997. Role of four major cellulases in triggering of cellulase gene expression by cellulose in *Trichoderma reesei. J. Bacteriol.* 179: 5318–5320.

Seiboth, B., L. Hartl, N. Salovuori, K. Lanthaler, G.D. Robson, J. Vehmaanperä, M.E. Penttilä and C.P. Kubicek. 2005. Role of the *bga*1-encoded extracellular beta-galactosidase of *Hypocrea jecorina* in cellulase induction by lactose. *Appl. Environ. Microbiol.* 71: 851-857.

Sexton, A.C., M. Paulsen, J. Woestemeyer and B.J. Howlett. 2000. Cloning, characterization and chromosomal location of three genes encoding host-cell-wall-degrading enzymes in *Leptosphaeria maculans*, a fungal pathogen of *Brassica* spp. *Gene* 248: 89-97.

Shen, T. and S. Gnanakaram, 2009. The Stability of Cellulose: A Statistical Perspective from a Coarse-Grained Model of Hydrogen-Bond Networks. *Biophys. J.* 96: 3032 – 3040.

Shoemaker, S., V.Schweickart, M. Ladner, D. Gelfand, S. Kwok, K. Myambo and M. Innis. 1983. Molecular cloning of exo-cellobiohydrolase I derived from *Trichoderma reesei* strain L27. *BIO/TECHNOLOGY* 1: 691-696.

Sims, P., C. James and P. Broda. 1988. The identification, molecular cloning and characterization of a gene from *Phanerochaete chrysosporium* that shows strong homology to the exo-cellobiohydrolase I gene from *Trichoderma reesei*. *Gene* 74: 411-422.

Song, J., B. Liu, Z. Liu and Q. Yang. 2010. Cloning of two cellobiohydrolase genes from *Trichoderma viride* and heterogenous expression in yeast *Saccharomyces cerevisiae*. *Mol. Biol. Rep*. 37: 2135-2140.

Sposato, P., J.-H. Ahn and J.D. Walton. 1995. Characterization and disruption of a gene in the maize pathogen *Cochliobolus carbonum* encoding a cellulase lacking a cellulose binding domain and hinge region. *MPMI* 8: 602-609.

Sun, J. and N.L. Glass. 2011. Identification of the CRE-1 Cellulolytic Regulon in *Neurospora crassa*. *PLoS ONE*. 6: e25654.

Suzuki, H., K. Igarashi and M. Samejima. 2010. Cellotriose and cellotetraose as inducers of the genes encoding cellobiohydrolases in the basidiomycete *Phanerochaete chrysosporium*. *Appl. Environ. Microbiol.* 76: 6164-6170.

Szijártó, N., M. Siika-Aho, M. Tenkanen, M. Alapuranen, J. Vehmaanperä, K. Réczey and L. Viikari. 2008. Hydrolysis of amorphous and crystalline cellulose by heterologously produced cellulases of *Melanocarpus albomyces*. *J. Biotechnnol*. 136: 140-147.

Takada, G., T. Kawaguchi, J-I. Sumitani and M. Arai, 1998. Cloning, nucleotide sequence and transcriptional analysis of *Aspergillus aculeatus* n^{o} F-50 cellobiohydrolase I (*cbhI*) gene. *J. Ferment. Bioeng*. 85: 1-9.

Takahashi, M., H. Takahashi, Y. Nakano, T. Konoshi, R. Terauchi and T. Takeda. 2010. Characterization of a cellobiohydrolase (MoCel6A) produced by *Magnaporthe oryzae*. *Appl. Environ. Microbiol.* 76: 6583-6590.

Takashima, S., A. Nakamura, M. Hidaka, H. Masaki, and T. Uozumi. 1996. Cloning, sequencing and expression of the cellulase genes of *Humicola grisea* var. *thermoidea*. *J. Biotechnol.* 50: 137-147.

Takashima S., H. Iikura, A. Nakamura, M. Hidaka, H. Masaki and T. Uozumi. 1998a. Overproduction of recombinant *Trichoderma reesei* cellulases by *Aspergillus oryzae* and their enzymatic properties. *J. Biotechnol*. 65: 163-171.

Takashima, S., H. Iikura, A. Nakamura, M. Hidaka, H. Masaki and T. Uozumi. 1998b. Isolation of the gene and characterization of the enzymatic properties of a major exoglucanase of *Humicola grisea* without a cellulose-binding. *J. Biochem.* (Tokyo) 124: 717-725.

Taleb, F. and A. Radford. 1995. The cellulase complex of *Neurospora crassa*: *cbh*1 cloning, sequencing and homologies. *Gene* 161: 137-138.

Tamura, M., T. Miyazaki, Y.Tanaka, M. Yoshida, A. Nishikawa and T. Tonozuka. 2012. Comparison of the structural changes in two cellobiohydrolases, CcCel6A and CcCel6C, from *Coprinopsis cinerea*: a tweezer-like motion in the structure of CcCel6C. *FEBS J.* "Accepted Article" doi: 10.1111/j.1742-4658.2012.08568.x.

Tanaka, H., S. Itakura and A. Enoki. 1999. Hydroxyl radical generation by an extracellular low-molecular-weight substance and phenol oxidase activity during wood degradation by the white-rot basidiomycete *Trametes versicolor*. *J. Biotechnol*. 75: 57-70.

Teeri T.T., P. Lehtovaara, S. Kauppinen, I. Salovuori and J. Knowles. 1987. Homologous domains in *Trichoderma reesei* cellulolytic enzymes: gene sequence and expression of cellobiohydrolase II. *Gene* 51: 43-52.

Tempelaars, C.A.M., P.R.J. Birch, P.F.G. Sims and P. Broda. 1994. Isolation, characterization and analysis of the expression of the *cbh*II gene of *Phanerochaete chrysosporium. Appl. Environ. Microbiol.* 60: 4387-4393.

Turner, G. 1993. Gene organization in filamentous fungi. In: The Eukaryotic Genome Organization and Regulation. Broda, P. M. A. ; Oliver, S. G. and Sims, P. F. G. (eds). Society for General Microbiology Symposium 50. Cambridge University Press. pp.107-125.

Van den Wymelenberg, A.V., S. Covert and D. Cullen. 1993. Identification of the Gene Encoding the Major Cellobiohydrolase of the White Rot Fungus *Phanerochaete chrysosporium. Appl. Environ. Microbiol.* 59: 3492-3494.

Van Wyk, N., R. den Haan and W.H. van Zyl. 2010. Heterologous co-production of *Thermobifida fusca* Cel9A with other cellulases in *Saccharomyces cerevisiae. Appl. Microbiol. Biotechnol.* 87: 1813-1820.

Varrot, A., S. Hastrup, M. Schülein and G.J. Davies. 1999a. Crystal structure of the catalytic core domain of the family 6 cellobiohydrolase II, Cel6A, from *Humicola insolens*, at 1.92 Å resolution. *Biochem. J.* 337: 297–304.

Varrot, A., M. Schülein and G.J. Davies.1999b. Structural changes of the active site tunnel of *Humicola insolens* cellobiohydrolase, Cel6A, upon oligosaccharide binding. *Biochemistry.* 38: 8884-8891.

Voutilainen, S.P., P.G. Murray, M.G. Tuohy and A. Koivula. 2010. Expression of *Talaromyces emersonii* cellobiohydrolase Cel7A in *Saccharomyces cerevisiae* and rational mutagenesis to improve its thermostability and activity. *Protein Eng. Des. Sel.* 23: 69 – 79.

Wang, P. and D.L. Nuss. 1995. Induction of a *Cryphonectria parasitica* cellobiohydrolase I gene is supressed by hypovirus infection and regulated by a GTP-binding-protein-linked signaling pathway involved in fungal pathogenesis. *Proc. Natl. Acad. Sci. USA* 92: 11529-11533.

Watanabe, M., N. Sumida, K. Yanai and T. Murakami. 2004. A Novel Saponin Hydrolase from Neocosmospora vasinfecta *var.* vasinfecta. *Appl. Environ. Microbiol.* 70: 865–872.

Watanabe, M., N. Sumida, K. Yanai and T. Murakami. 2005. Cloning and characterization of saponin hydrolases from *Aspergillus oryzae* and *Eupenicillium brefeldianum. Biosci. Biotechnol. Biochem.* 69: 2178-2185.

Wey, T.T., T.H. Hseu and L. Huang. 1994. Molecular cloning and sequence analysis of the cellobiohydrolase I gene from *Trichoderma koningii* G-39. *Curr. Microbiol.* 28: 31-39.

Wyman, C.E. 2003. Potential Synergies and Challenges in Refining Cellulosic Biomass to Fuels, Chemicals and Power. *Biotechnol. Progress* 19: 254–262.

Yagüe, E., M. Mehak-Zunic, L. Morgan, D. A. Wood and C.F. Thurston. 1997. Expression of CEL2 and CEL4, two proteins from *Agaricus bisporus* with similarity to fungal cellobiohydrolase I and β-mannanase, respectively, is regulated by the carbon source. *Microbiol.* 143: 239-244.

Yamada, R., N. Taniguchi, T. Tanaka, C. Ogino, H. Fukuda and A. Kondo. 2011. Direct ethanol production from cellulosic materials using a diploid strain of *Saccharomyces cerevisiae* with optimized cellulase expression. *Biotechnol. Biofuels* 4: 8.

Yanase, S., R. Yamada, S. Kaneko, H. Noda, T. Hasunuma, T. Tanaka, C. Ogino, H. Fukuda and A. Kondo. 2010. Ethanol production from cellulosic materials using cellulase-expressing yeast. *Biotechnol. J.* 5: 449 – 455.

Yao, Q., T.T. Sun, W.F Liu and G.J. Chen. 2008. Gene cloning and heterologous expression of a novel endoglucanase, swollenin, from *Trichoderma pseudokoningii* S38. *Biosci. Biotechnol Biochem.* 72: 2799-2805.

Yasokawa, D., T. Shimizu, R. Nakagawa, T. Ikeda and K. Nagashima. 2003. Cloning, sequencing and heterologous expression of a cellobiohydrolase cDNA from the basidiomycete *Corticium rolfsii. Biosci. Biotechnol. Biochem.* 67: 1319-1326.

Yoshida, M., K. Sato, S. Kaneko and K. Fukuda. 2009. Cloning and transcript analysis of multiple genes encoding the glycoside hydrolase family 6 enzyme from *Coprinopsis cinerea. Biosci. Biotechnol. Biochem.* 73: 67-73.

Zhang, J., Y. Qu, P. Xiao, X. Wang, T. Wang and F. He. 2012. Improved biomass saccharification by *Trichoderma reesei* through heterologous expression of *lac*A gene from *Trametes* sp. AH28-2. *J. Biosci. Bioeng.* doi:10.1016/j.jbiosc.2012.01.016.

Zhong, Y., X. Liu, P. Xiao, S. Wei and T. Wang. 2011. Expression and secretion of the human erythropoietin using an optimized *cbh*1 promoter and the native CBH I signal sequence in the industrial fungus *Trichoderma reesei. Appl. Biochem. Biotechnol.* 165: 1169-1177.

Zhou, J., Y.H. Wang, J. Chu, Y.P. Zhuang, S.L. Zhang and P. Yin. 2008. Identification and purification of the main components of cellulases from a mutant strain of *Trichoderma viride* T 100-14. *Bioresour. Technol.* 99: 6826-6833.

In: Applications of Microbial Genes in Enzyme Technology ISBN: 978-1-62417-808-5
Editors: V.K.Gupta, M.G.Tuohy, G.D.Sharma et al.

Chapter 12

Microbial Beta-Galactosidase and Its Use in Enzyme Technology

*A. G. Lydon**
Molecular Glycobiotechnology Group, Discipline of Biochemistry,
School of Natural Sciences, National University of Ireland Galway, Galway, Ireland

Abstract

β -Galactosidase (EC 3.2.1.23), is an exo-acting glycosyl hydrolase that cleaves single β-linked galactose residues from the non-reducing ends of carbohydrate polymers or other galactose containing molecules. β -Galactosidase is one of the most commonly used industrial enzymes due to a variety of suitable applications in the food and dairy sectors. The thermophilic saprophytic fungus *Talaromyces emersonii* produces an array of cellulose, hemicellulose and pectin hydrolysing activities. This chapter provides an overview of the characterisation of the β-galactosidase component of this system. The *β-galactosidase* gene is encoded by a 3533 bp open reading frame interrupted by 8 introns encoding a1008 amino acid protein with a secretory signal peptide and high identity to other fungal *β-galactosidase* genes. Expression profiling by Northern analysis indicated induction of *β-galactosidase* expression by pectin and pectin composite sugars. Expression was repressed in the presence of glucose and addition of glucose to pectin induced cultures abolished transcription after 4 h.

Introduction

Plant cell wall polysaccharides are the most abundant organic compounds found in nature (Enari, 1983), (Margolles-Clark et al., 1997). Degradation of these polysaccharides is of considerable ecological, agricultural and commercial importance. Carbohydrate degradation occurs in a variety of ecological niches where plant residues accumulate. Thus, carbohydrate hydrolysing microorganisms include a variety of aerobes and anaerobes, mesophiles, and

* Corresponding author: A. G. Lydon. E-mail: annlydon@yahoo.co.uk.

thermophiles. Fungi and bacteria are the main natural agents of carbohydrate degradation. These microorganisms have evolved multi-component enzyme systems, consisting of a number of different enzymes with different specificities. These enzymes, which are natures own biocatalysts, facilitate the use of plant cell wall polysaccharides by the microorganism for a multitude of functions, from energy storage and structure to highly specific roles in molecular recognition. Therefore, polysaccharide hydrolysis is crucial for energy uptake, cell wall expansion and degradation and the turnover of signalling molecules. β-Galactosidase, also known as lactase (EC 3.2.1.23), is an exo-acting glycosyl hydrolase that cleaves single β-linked galactose residues from the non-reducing ends of carbohydrate polymers or other galactose containing molecules. β-Galactosidases are distributed widely in nature, being produced by both prokaryotic and eukaryotic organisms (Gekas et al, 1985). The role of microbial β-galactosidase most likely involves the removal of β-linked galactose residues from plant-derived oligo- and polysaccharides, for example, the hemicellulose xylan and pectin. β-Galactosidase is one of the most commonly used industrial enzymes due to a variety of suitable applications in the food and dairy sectors (Shaikh et al., 1999). It is commonly used to cleave lactose into glucose and galactose, which is of clinical importance in the preparation of lactose free milk and milk products for lactose intolerant individuals (Shukla, 1975). Furthermore, the enzyme can be utilised in the treatment of whey permeate which is an abundant effluent produced in cheese and casein manufacture. The biotechnological utilization of this economically valuable feedstock is largely limited by the high concentrations of lactose due to its poor solubility and insufficient sweetness. Hydrolysis of lactose to glucose and galactose by β-galactosidase would overcome some of these limitations and permit greater use of whey permeates, eg. as a substitute for corn syrup in soft drinks, fermented beverages and confectionary products (Szczodrak, 2000). Whilst a number of non-pathogenic, 'generally regarded as safe' microorganisms are used as producers of enzymes, the filamentous fungi are significantly important. Filamentous fungi are extremely efficient cell factories due to their secretion of a variety of enzymes at a high level (Punt et al., 2002). It has been well documented that the use of thermostable enzymes offers many advantages including reduced risk of microbial contamination during enzyme-catalyzed reactions, higher reaction rates and greater product yields (Haki and Rakshit, 2003). This has prompted the search for thermophilic sources of enzymes. To date, relatively little is known about β-galactosidases from filamentous fungi, especially thermophilic fungi.

In addition, few β-galactosidase genes have been cloned from filamentous fungi, and until now, none have been cloned and characterized from a thermophilic fungal species. Examples in the databases to date include gene sequence data from a number of *Aspergillus* species (*A. fumigatus*, GenBank BX649607; *A. nidulans*, GenBank AACD01000005; *A. oryzae* GenBank E12172 and *A. niger* GenBank L06037), *Hypocrea jecorina* (GenBank AJ549427) and *Penicillium sp.* (GenBank AJ629057). *Talaromyces emersonii* is a saprophytic, aerobic, thermophilic, fungus, originally isolated from composting plant biomass. *Talaromyces* species typically grow between a maximum temperature of 70°C and a minimum of 30°C with an optimal growth temperature of 45°C (Moloney et al., 1983). *T. emersonii* produces a wide spectrum of plant cell wall polysaccharide degrading enzymes including β-galactosidase. The majority of these enzymes isolated to date have displayed noteworthy thermostability (Moloney *et al.*, 1985; Tuohy *et al.*, 1993; Tuohy *et al.*, 2002; Murray *et al.*, 2003, Maloney et al., 2004). This has resulted in the investigation of this eukaryote as a source of thermozymes for key biotechnological applications. This chapter reports on the molecular cloning, characterisation and expression analysis of the β-galactosidase gene.

Materials and Methods

Microorganism and Growth Conditions

T. emersonii strain IMI 392299 was obtained from laboratory stocks. Mycelia harvested from cultures grown at 45°C on Sabouraud dextrose agar were used to inoculate mineral salt liquid media containing corn steep liquor (0.5 % v/v), yeast extract (0.1 % w/v), KH_2PO_4 (0.5 % w/v), $(NH_4)_2SO_4$ (1.5 % w/v), $FeSO_4.7H_2O$ (62.5 mg/L); and $ZnSO_4.7H_2O$, H_3BO_3, $MnSO_4.4H_2O$, Na_2MoO_4, $CoCl_3.6H_2O$, KI (all at 12.5 mg/L), $MgSO_4.7H_2O$ (0.05 % w/v), $CaCl_2.2H_2O$ (0.05 % w/v), anhydrous Na_2SO_4 (0.10 % w/v) carbon source, (2 % w/v), pH 4.5. Liquid cultures were grown at 45°C with shaking at 220 rpm.

After appropriate timed intervals mycelia were harvested by filtration through several layers of fine grade muslin, washed with 75 mM sodium citrate, pH 7.5, and frozen immediately under liquid nitrogen.

Culture filtrate was concentrated using an Amicon ultrafiltration device with a 10 kDa cut-off and used as enzyme solution. *E. coli* strains JM109 (Promega) and DH5α were used as plasmid hosts and the strain KW251 was used as a host for the LambdaGEM-11 (Promega) *T. emersonii* genomic library. Plasmid pGEM-T easy (Promega) was used for sub-cloning and sequencing of PCR products according to the manufacturer's instructions.

Construction of Genomic Library

Total genomic DNA was isolated from *T. emersonii* mycelia cultivated on 2 % glucose for 24 h by the method of Raeder and Broda (1985). *T. emersonii Sau* 3A genomic library was prepared in LambdaGEM-11 (Promega). *Escherichia coli* KW251 was used as host strain in preparation and screening of the genomic library. Single plaque forming units were purified using Qiagen Lambda purification system according to the manufacturer's instructions.

Genomic DNA PCR Amplification

Amplification of the DNA fragment encoding a portion of the *β-gal* gene was performed using the polymerase chain reaction (PCR). *T. emersonii* genomic DNA was amplified with degenerate primers based on existing *β-gal* sequences present in the databases using sense 5'-GAYATYTTCSAVAAGTTC-3' and antisense 5'-RTTNCCCCARTTSGTNCC-3' (Y=C or T; S= G or C; V=G, C or A; R = G or A; N = A, C or T) primers. Reactions contained 2.5 units of Qiagen HotStart™ Taq DNA polymerase (15 min activation at 95°C), 1X buffer (Qiagen), 200 μM of each deoxynucleotide triphosphate, 1.5 mM $MgCl_2$ and 1 μM primers.

Reaction conditions for PCR amplification were 94°C for 1 min, 45°C for 1 min and 72°C for 1 min, for 30 cycles followed by a final extension of 10 min. PCR products were separated by electrophoresis on a 1.2 % agarose gel and products were purified by Wizard PCR preps DNA purification system (Promega) and cloned into pGEM-T easy vector (Promega), following the manufacturers' protocols. Plasmids were purified from *E. coli* cultures using Qiaprep spin miniprep kit (Qiagen) and sequenced. The purified fragment (984 bp) was confirmed by sequencing and similarity searches (BLAST) to encode part of the *T. emersonii* *β-gal* gene. This fragment was labeled with Digoxigenin (DIG) and purified probe used to screen the genomic library as described in Sambrook *et al.,* (1989).

Rapid Amplification of cDNA Ends (RACE)

T. emersonii was grown in a basic medium described earlier containing 2 % citrus pectin as inducing carbon source. Total RNA was isolated from frozen mycelia as described by Chomczynski and Sacchi (1987) after 72 h growth. RNA (10 μg) was used as template for RACE using a modification of the Ambion (Manufacturer) RACE protocol.

Reverse transcriptions were carried out in 20 μL reaction mixtures containing 6 units of *C. therm.* polymerase™ (Roche Molecular Biochemicals), 1X RT buffer (Roche), 5 % DMSO, 5 mM DTT, 200 μM each deoxynucleotide triphosphates, 5 mM $MgCl_2$ and 1 μM of the 3' RACE adapter 5'-GCGAGCACAGAATTAATACGACTCACTATAGGT_{20}TVN-3' to make first strand cDNA.

Reactions were performed at 55°C for 1 h. One μL of this reaction was then used as template to perform 5' and 3' RACE PCR using the outer and inner RACE primers supplied by the manufacturer and outer and inner gene specific primers designed from the genomic fragment for *β-gal*; 5' RACE primers, outer, 5'-GAGGATATGAATCATGCC-3' and inner, 5'-AGTTCTTCGTTGCAGCCATATAG-3' and 3' RACE primers, outer, 5'-GATGTATCTTCCACTCGTCGCA-3' and inner, 5'-TGCTCGATCGCAACTCTGCCTAT-3'. Reaction conditions for RACE PCR were as follows 95°C for 15 min (1 cycle), 94°C for 1 min, 60°C for 1 min, 72°C for 1 min (35 cycles) and 72°C for 10 min. PCR products were cloned as described earlier.

Isolation of β-gal cDNA and Genomic Genes

The full length *β-gal* cDNA and genomic genes were amplified from *T. emersonii* first-strand cDNA and genomic DNA respectively using primers, corresponding to the putative amino-terminal and carboxyl-terminal sequences from the the 5' and 3' RACE products; *β-gal* sense primer 5'-ATGAAGCTTCTCTCCTCGTTTGCCGCCGCC-3' and the *β-gal* anti-sense primer 5'-CTAGTACGCCCCCTCACGCTTTGTATACTTTGG-3'. The following PCR cycling parameters were used 95°C for 15 min (1 cycle), 94°C for 1 min, 65°C for 1 min and 72°C for 3.5 min. (35 cycles) and 72°C for 10 min. PCR products were cloned as described earlier.

Southern and Northern Analysis

Sau3A genomic library from *T. emersonii* was screened independently with 984 bp Digoxygenin labeled *β-gal* probe as described in Sambrook *et al.* Hybridisation was carried out overnight at 65°C in 5X SSC, 0.1 % (w/v) N-lauroylsarcosine, 0.02 % (w/v) SDS, 1 % (w/v) blocking reagent (Roche Molecular Biochemicals).

Initial screening of 30,000 phage clones identified three positively hybridizing plaques. Detection was performed after incubation of the membrane with the conjugate antibody and using CDP-Star (Roche Molecular Biochemicals) as the chemiluminescent substrate according to the manufacturers' instructions.

DNA from these clones was purified using a Qiagen Lambda DNA purification kit. The presence of the full length *β-gal* gene in these clones was confirmed by PCR. Insert DNA from independent clones was sequenced directly using a *β-gal* specific primer to direct sequencing upstream of the start codon. RNA (10 μg) from *T. emersonii* mycelia cultivated on various inducing substrates were separated electrophorectically on 1.2 % formaldehyde-agarose gel and blotted as described above.

Hybridisation was carried out overnight at 60°C in 7 % SDS, 50 % deionised formamide, 5X SSC, 50 mM sodium phosphate, pH 7.0, N-lauroylsarcosine and 2 % (w/v) blocking reagent. A concentration of 20 ng of DIG labelled full-length cDNA probes per ml of hybridisation buffer was used in all cases. Detection is as described above.

Sequence Analysis

All sequencing was carried out in both directions to eliminate read errors. Sequencing reactions were carried out by Altabiososcience laboratories, University of Birmingham, England. Cycle sequencing reactions are done on a PE Biosystems 877 robotic system.

Database similarity searches were performed using the National Centre for Biotechnological Information (NCBI) online program BLAST (Altschul et al., 1990) against protein (BlastX) and nucleotide (BlastN) sequences stored in GenBank.

Results and Discussion

Characterisation of *β-Galactosidase*

Using degenerate primers, a PCR product of 984 bp was amplified from the *T. emersonii* genomic DNA. Sequence analysis of the product revealed a high degree of similarity with other eukaryotic β-galactosidase genes in the database. Full length *β-gal* gene is encoded by a 3533 bp open reading frame interrupted by 8 introns with consensus 5' and 3' splice sites, varying in length from 55 bp to 80 bp, encoding a 1008 amino acid protein (GenBank AF439737). Comparison of the deduced β-galactosidase amino acid sequence from *T. emersonii* with those of β-galactosidase genes from *A. niger* (GenBank AF156268), *H. jecorina* (GenBank AF478686), *Penicillium sp.* (GenBank AJ629057), *A. candidus* (GenBank

CAD24293) and *A. oryzae* (GenBank E12172) revealed identity values (ClustalW) of 66%, 68%, 55%, 70% and 70% respectively (Figure 1).

The *N*-terminal domain of the deduced protein product contains a putative signal secretory peptide of 19 amino acids. Other fungal β-Galactosidases from *A. niger*, *A. oryzae*, and *P. canescens*, also contain signal secretory peptides (Ito et al., 2002).

The calculated molecular mass of the deduced amino acid sequence was 108.6 kDa. Nine putative *N*-glycosylation sites were identified in the deduced protein sequence by the PHD server prosite pattern search. *β-gal* gene product belongs to glycosyl hydrolase family 35 (EC 3.2.1.23) with a GH family 35 signature pattern GGPVILYQPENEY between amino acid 189 and 201 inclusive.

The putative amino acid active site residues identified in *Penicillium sp* β-galactosidase (Rojas et al., 2004) are also conserved in the *T. emersonii β-gal* gene at aa 200 (glutamate) and aa 297 (glutamate) in the deduced amino acid sequence. Sequencing of the region upstream of the *β-gal* start codon revealed several putative regulatory elements.

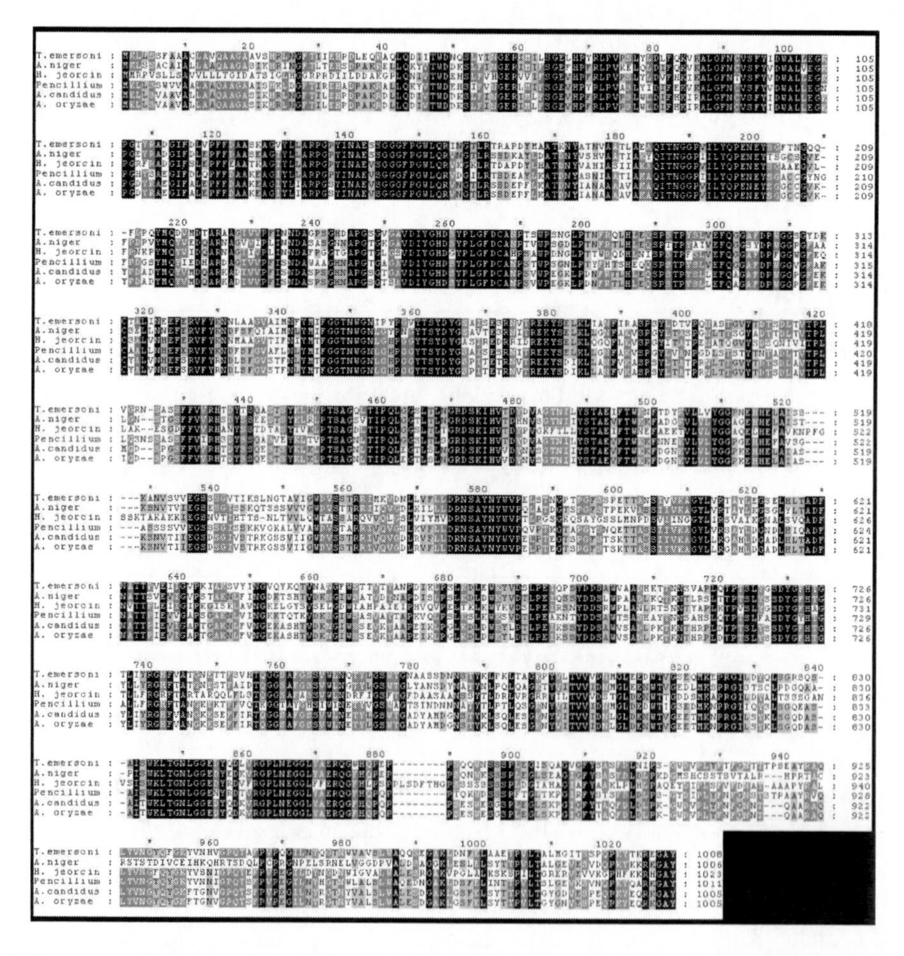

Figure 1. Sequence alignment of the deduced amino acid sequences of the *T. emersonii β-galactosidase* with those of β-galactosidases from *A. niger, H. jecorina, Penicillium sp., A. candidus* and *A. oryzae*. Residues identical in all sequences are printed in white a on black background. Residues identical in five of the six sequences are printed in white on grey background. Residues identical in four of the six sequences are printed in black on grey background.

A TATA box-like motif was present at position –114 bp and one CAAT box was identified at position –223 bp. Three putative Cre (catabolite repressor element) binding sites (Ilmen et al., 1996) at –92, –159, and –232 and three potential sites for the cellulase and xylanase repressor ACE 1 (Aro et al., 2003) at positions –108, –120, and –294 are also present.

Analysis of the promoter region of *H. Jecorina* β-galactosidase identified six sites for the CCAAT-binding Hap 2/3/5 complex. The promoter region of *H. Jecorina* β-galactosidase gene also contained three single sites and one double site for the carbon catabolite repressor Cre1 and one site each for the cellulose and xylanase repressor Ace 1. No consensus binding sites for XlnR were found (Seiboth et al. 2005).

Northern Analysis

Northern analysis of the *β-gal* transcription (Figure 2) showed expression was induced by the heteropolysaccharide pectin and its monomers, L-arabinose and D-galacturonic acid. *β-gal* inductions on pectin are initially low but increase with cultivation time. Evidence has been obtained for the role of galacturonic acid as a general inducer of pectinolytic enzymes in *A. niger* (de Vries et al., 2002). Genes encoding pectin main-chain cleaving enzymes (*pelA, plyA, pgaX*, and *rglA*) and a gene encoding pectin methylesterase (*pmeA*) are expressed in the presence of D-galacturonic acid (Parenicova, 2000). D-Galacturonic acid also induces expression of genes encoding arabinofuranosidases (*abfA* and *abfB*), endoarabinase (*abnA*), endogalactanase (*galA*), and β-galactosidase (*lacA*) in *A. niger*, all of which act on pectin side-chains (de Vries et al., 2002). Induction of *T. emersonii β-gal* by D-galacturonic acid suggests a similar induction mechanism in *T. emersonii*. L-Arabinose also induced expression of *T. emersonii β-gal* but at a lower level than pectin and D-galacturonic acid. β-Galactosidase from *A. niger* (*lac A*) (de Vries and Visser, 2001) and *Trichoderma reesei bga 1* (Seiboth et al., 2005) are also expressed in the presence of arabinose. No detectable levels of *β-gal* expression were evident in glucose induced cultures until 120 h suggesting relief from glucose repression when the glucose has been consumed.

The addition of 2% glucose to *T. emersonii* mycelia previously cultured on pectin (72 h) resulted in abolition of the *β-gal* signal within 4 h indicative of carbon catabolite repression. Similarly, neither *A. niger lac A* nor *T. reesei bga 1* were expressed in the presence of glucose (de Vries et al., 1999), (Seiboth et al., 2005).

Indeed, carbon catabolite repression, mediated by the *T. reesei* regulatory protein Cre 1, interferes with *bga 1* expression depending on the carbon source at either the basal or induced level of transcription (Seiboth et al., 2005). The sequence gene encoding the catabolite repressor element (Cre) gene from *T. emersonii* has been published (GB: AF440004).

Glucose repression of *β-gal* expression and identification of putative Cre binding sites in the upstream regulatory region of the gene suggests that this catabolite repressor element may bind to specific target sequences in the promoter of *β-galactosidase* and downregulate its transcription on glucose. However, no binding of the *T. emersonii* Cre protein to the putative Cre binding sites within 472 bp upstream region of the *β-gal* was detected in electrophoretic mobility shift assays (Unpublished results). However, additional sites for Cre binding may exist further upstream in the *β-gal* promoter.

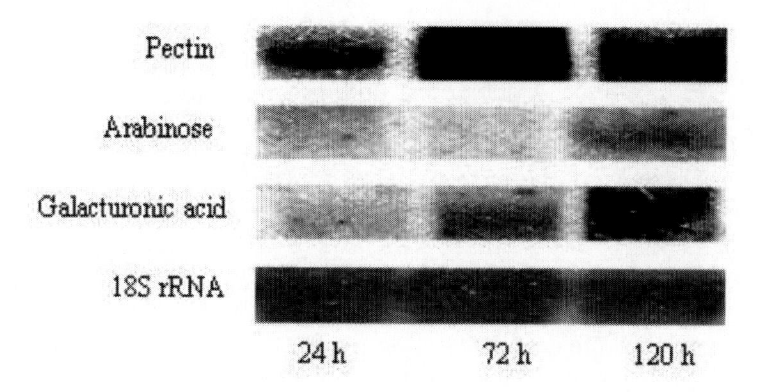

Figure 2. Northern analysis of total RNA samples isolated after harvesting *T. emersonii* cultures at different timepoints during growth on Pectin Arabinose and Galacturonic Acid. Loading control was performed by probing the membrane with 18S ribosomal RNA (lower section of panel).

It has also been suggested that Cre may enforce carbon catabolite repression by an indirect mechanism repressing a gene encoding a transcriptional activator (Orejas et al., 1999), (Orejas et al., 2001). Three putative ACE (Activator of Cellulase Expression) binding sites were also identified in the cloned upstream sequence, and as ACE has also been shown to act as a repressor protein in regulating the expression of certain cellulases (Aro et al., 2003), and could function as an alternative mediator of carbon catobolite repression in the *β-gal* gene promoter.

Lactose induced cultures did not display *β-gal* transcription. Similar *lac A* from *A. niger* which is not expressed in the presence on this disaccharide (de Vries et al., 1999). However, low levels of T. *reesei bgal* were detected on lactose (Seiboth et al., 2005). No detectable levels of *β-gal* transcription were observed on D-galactose and galactose containing oligosaccharides melibiose and raffinose.

Conclusion

β-Galactosidase is one of the most commonly used industrial enzymes due to a variety of suitable applications in the food and dairy sectors. β-Galactosidase catalyzes the hydrolysis of β-1,4-galactosyl linkages (also β-1,2, β-1,3 and β-1,6-linkages in many cases), removing β-linked galactose residues from a range of substrates including plant derived oligo- and polysaccharides, galactose-containing glycoproteins and lactose. β-Galactosidases also cleave synthetic substrates, such as 4-nitrophenol-β-D-galactose (4NP-β-Gal) and 2-nitrophenol-β-D-galactose (2NP-β-Gal). Additionally β-galactosidase displays transglycosylation activity lending the enzyme to enormous potential for synthesis of novel oligosaccharides in food, pharmaceutical and medical applications. This chapter represents the first report at the molecular level, of a β-galactosidase from a thermophilic fungus, *Talaromyces emersonii*. Fungal species generally produce extracellular glycosidases which have broad stability profiles, and acidic pH optima, unlike the bacterial and yeast enzymes which usually operate best around neutral pH. To date, only mesophilic bacterial and fungal enzymes have been used industrially to treat lactose and there is increasing interest in thermostable enzymes.

Talaromyces emersonii produces an extracellular β-galactosidase. This enzyme would therefore offer key advantages in a number of biotechnological applications.

Acknowledgments

Research for this chapter was conducted under the supervision of Dr. Maria G Touhy, Molecular Glycobiotechnology group, Discipline of Biochemistry, School of Natural Sciences, National University of Ireland Galway, University Road, Galway, Ireland.

References

Altschul, S. F, W. Gish, W. Miller, E. W. Myers and D. J. Lipman. 1990. Basic local alignment search tool. *J. Mol. Biol.* 215: 403-410.

Aro, N., M. Ilmen, A. Saloheimo, and M. Penttila. 2003. ACEI of Trichoderma reesei is a repressor of cellulase and xylanase expression. *Appl. Environ. Microbiol.* 69: 56-65.

Chomczynski, P. and N. Sacchi 1987. Single-step method of RNA isolation by acid guanidinium thiocyanate-phenol-chloroform extraction. *Anal. Biochem.* 162: 156-159.

De Vries, R. P., J. Jansen, A. Guillermo, L. Parenicova, V. Joosten, F. Wulfert J. A. Benen and V. Jaap. 2002. Expression profiling of pectinolytic genes from *Aspergillus niger. FEBS Lett.* 530: 41-47.

De Vries, R. P., H. C. van den Broeck, E. P. M. Dekkers, L. H. de Graaff and J. Visser 1999a. Differential expression of three α-galactosidase genes and a single β-galactosidase from *Aspergillus niger. Appl. Environ. Microbiol.* 65: 2453-2460.

De Vries, R. P., J. Visser and L. H. de Graaff L. H. 1999. CreA modulates the XlnR-induced expression on xylose of *Aspergillus niger* genes involved in xylan degradation. *Res. Microbiol.* 150: 281-285.

De Vries, R. P. and J. Visser 2001. *Aspergillus* enzymes involved in degradation of plant cell wall polysaccharides. *Microbiol. Mol. Biol. Revs.* 65: 497-522.

De Vries, R. P., J. Jansen, A. Guillermo, L. Parenicova, V. Joosten, F. Wulfert, J. A. Benen and V. Jaap 2002. Expression profiling of pectinolytic genes from *Aspergillus niger. FEBS Lett.* 530: 41-47.

Enari, T. M. 1983. Microbial cellulases. In: W. M. Fogarty, ed., *Microbial enzymes and biotechnology*. Elsevier applied science, London, pp 183-223.

Gekas. V. 1985. Hydrolysis of lactose: a literature review. *Process Biochem.* 2–11.

Haki, G. D. and S. K. Rakshit 2003. Developments in industrially important thermostable enzymes: a review. *Bioresource Technology* 89: 17-34.

Ilmen, M., C. Thrane and M. Penttila. 1996. The glucose repressor gene cre1 of *Trichoderma:* isolation and expression of a full-length and a truncated mutant form. *Mol. Gen. Genet.* 251: 451-460.

Ito, Y., T. Sasaki, K. Kitamoto, C. Kumagai, K. Takahashi, K. Gomi and G. Tamaru. 2002. Cloning, nucleotide sequencing, and expression of the b-galactosidase-encoding gene (lacA) from *Aspergillus oryzae. J. Gen. Microbiol.* 48: 135-142.

Maloney, A. P., S. M. Callan, P. G. Murray and M. G. Tuohy. 2004. Mitochondrial malate dehydrogenase from the thermophilic, filamentous fungus Talaromyces emersonii Purification of the native enzyme, cloning and overexpression of the corresponding gene. *Eur. J. Biochem.* 271, 3115-3126.

Margolles-Clark, E., M. Ilmen and M. Penttila. 1997. Expression patterns of ten hemicellulase genes of the filamentous fungus *Trichoderma reesei* on various carbon sources. *J. Biotechnol.* 57: 167-179.

Moloney, A., P. J. Considine and M. P. Coughlan. 1983 Cellulose Hydrolysis by *Talaromyces emersonii* grown on different substrates. *Biotechnology Bioengeneering* 25: 1169-1173.

Moloney, A. P., S. I. McCrae, T. M. Wood and M. P. Coughlan. 1985. Isolation and characterization of the endoglucanases of *Talaromyces emersonii*. *Biochem. J.* 225: 365-374.

Murray, P. G., C. M. Collins, A. Grassick and M. G. Tuohy. 2003. Molecular cloning, transcriptional, and expression analysis of the first cellulase gene (*cbh2*), encoding cellobiohydrolase II, from the moderately thermophilic fungus *Talaromyces emersoni*i and structure prediction of the gene product. *Biochem. Biophys. Res. Commun.* 301: 280-286.

Orejas, M., A. P. MacCabe, J. A. Perez Gonzalez, S. Kumar and D. Ramon. 1999. Carbon catabolite repression of the *Aspergillus nidulan*s xlnA gene. *Mol. Microbiol.* 31: 177-184.

Orejas, M, A. P. MacCabe, J. A. Perez-Gonzalez, S. Kumar, D. Ramon. 2001. The wide-domain carbon catabolite repressor CreA indirectly controls expression of the *Aspergillus nidulans* xlnB gene, encoding the acidic endo-beta-(1,4)-xylanase X(24). *J. Bacteriol.* 183: 1517-1523.

Parenicova, L. 2000. Pectinases of *Aspergillus niger:* a molecular and biochemical characterization. *Ph.D. Thesis*. Wageningen University, Wageningen, The Netherlands.

Punt, P. J., N. van Biezen, A. Conesa, A. Albers, J. Mangnus and C. van den Hondel. 2002. Filamentous fungi as cell factories for heterologous protein production. *Trends Biotechnol.* 20: 200-206.

Raeder, U. and P. Broda. 1985. Rapid preparation of DNA from filamentous fungi. *Lett. Appl. Microbiol.* 1: 17-20.

Sambrook, J., E. F. Fritsch and T. Maniatis. 1989. *Molecular Cloning: A Laboratory Manual*, Ed. 2nd. Cold Spring Harbor Laboratory Press, New York.

Seiboth, B., L. Hartl, N. Salovuori, K. Lanthaler, G. D. Robson, J. Vehmaanpera, M. E. Penttila and C. P. Kubicek. 2005. Role of the bga1-encoded extracellular {beta}-galactosidase of *Hypocrea jecorina* in cellulase induction by lactose. *Appl. Environ. Microbiol.* 71: 851-857.

Shaikh, S. A., J. M., Khire and M. I. Khan. 1999. Characterization of a thermostable extracellular ß-galactosidase from a thermophilic fungus *Rhizomucor* sp. *Biochim. Biophys. Acta* 1472: 314-322.

Shukla, T. P., 1975. Beta-glactosidase technology: a solution to the lactose problem. *CRC. Crit. Rev. Food Technol.* 5:325.

Szczodrak, J. 2000. Hydrolysis of Lactose in Whey Permeate by Immobilized β-galactosidase from *Kluyveromyces fragilis*. *J. Mol. Catal. B: Enzymatic* 10: 631-637.

Tuohy, M. G., J. Puls, M. Claeyssens, M. Vrsanska and M. P. Coughlan. 1993. The xylan-degrading enzyme system of *Talaromyces emersonii*: novel enzymes with activity against aryl beta-D-xylosides and unsubstituted xylans. *Biochem. J.* 290 (Pt 2): 515-523.

Tuohy, M. G., D. J. Walsh, P. G. Murray, M. Claeyssens, M. M. Cuffe, A. V. Savage and M. P. Coughlan. 2002. Kinetic parameters and mode of action of the cellobiohydrolases produced by *Talaromyces emersonii*. *Biochim. Biophys. Acta* 1596: 366-380.

In: Applications of Microbial Genes in Enzyme Technology ISBN: 978-1-62417-808-5
Editors: V.K.Gupta, M.G.Tuohy, G.D.Sharma et al.

Chapter 13

Genetics and Genetic Engineering Aspects of Bacterial ACC Deaminases: New Insights in Stress Agriculture

Manoharan Melvin Joe and Tongmin Sa*
Department of Agricultural Chemistry, Chungbuk National University,
Cheongju, Chungbuk, Republic of Korea

Abstract

Plant growth-promoting bacteria are known to stimulate plant growth and development through different direct and indirect mechanisms. One among the key mechanisms employed by plant growth-promoting bacteria in facilitating plant growth is by lowering the plant ethylene levels in developing or stressed plants through the enzyme 1-aminocyclopropane-1-carboxylate (ACC) deaminase. Genes encoding this enzyme have been isolated from strains of *Pseudomonas* spp., *Rhizobium leguminosarum,* the yeast *Hansenula saturnus*, and the fungus *Penicillium citrinum.*

Although a number of different plant genomes encode genes that bear sequence homology to bacterial ACC deaminase, this pathway has never been proved in plants. Moreover, genes encoding this enzyme are also absent in most of the microorganisms. Recent landmark advances in the field of genetic engineering allow us the ease of manipulation of this enzyme to modulate plant growth and development and thereby creating more robust plants with desirable traits.

This article reviews the published works on this enzyme, with emphasis on alterations or modifications of this gene sequence with insights into the changes in plants and their possible consequences in plant-microbe interactions.

Keywords: ACC deaminase, Abiotic and Biotic stress, Plant Growth Promoting Rhizobacteria, Ethylene, Genetic Engineering

* Corresponding author: E-mail: tomsa@chungbuk.ac.kr, Phone: +8243263447.

Introduction

Ethylene is essential for proper plant development, growth and survival and for signaling changes during seed germination, flowering and fruit development (Mattoo and Shuttle, 1991; Abeles *et al.,* 1992). However, ethylene has the ability to exacerbate an environmental pressure that may be deleterious to plant growth and health (Saleem *et al.,* 2007). The enzyme 1-aminocyclopropane-1-carboxylate (ACC) deaminase found in various plant growth-promoting rhizobacteria degrades ACC, the immediate precursor of ethylene, thereby reducing ethylene biosynthesis in higher plants (Ma *et al.,* 2004).

ACC-deaminase containing bacteria treated plants are known to promote plant growth and development under both normal and stressed conditions through reduced plant ethylene levels (Glick *et al.* 1998). Recently, genetic manipulation of cultivars or other microorganisms to express genes for this enzyme has attracted much attention among scientists (Stearns and Glick, 2003). In this review emphasis would be laid on recent developments in this extremely important area of genetic engineering of ACC deaminase genes in microorganisms and plants.

ACC Deaminase

Pyridoxal 5'- phosphate (PLP) 1-dependent enzyme, ACC deaminase, was first reported in *Pseudomonas* sp. strain ACP (Honma and Shimomura (1978). This enzyme degrades a cyclopropanoid amino acid: 1-aminocyclopropane- 1-carboxylic acid (ACC) to α-ketobutyrate and ammonia and is known to participate in propanoate metabolism (Yao *et al.,* 2000).

Although the systematic name of this enzyme is 1-aminocyclopropane-1-carboxylate aminohydrolase, this enzyme is also called 1-aminocyclopropane-1-carboxylate endolyase (Wakatsuki *et al.,* 2000).

Ethylene Biosynthesis

According to Grichko and Glick (2001) stress ethylene is often reported to be synthesized in two peaks, a smaller one occurring within several hours of any imposed physiological stress and larger peak generally observed around 72 h after the imposition of the stress. These authors also added that the first stress ethylene peak acts as a trigger, to initiate a number of plant defense hormones, while the second peak may be deleterious for the plant. Ethylene is produced by most plant tissues and biosynthesis of this hormone begins with the compound S-adenosylmethionine (SAM) that is also required as the precursor in many other pathways.

The ethylene biosynthetic pathway, illustrated in Figure 1 along with the Yang cycle, begins with the enzyme ACC synthase that converts SAM to 1-aminocyclopropane-1-carboxylic acid (ACC) and 5′-methylthioadenosine (MTA), which is recycled to L-methionine. This allows for levels of L-methionine to remain relatively unchanged even during high rates of ethylene production (Abeles *et al.,* 1992). Formation of L-methionine is the rate limiting step in the ethylene biosynthesis pathway, since the extremely labile ACC synthase enzyme has been shown to: (a) be rate limiting and (b) to rise proportionally to ethylene levels within the tissues of some plants (Abeles *et al.,* 1992).

The gene for this enzyme is part of a multigene family and considerable evidence indicates that the transcription of different forms is induced under different environmental or physiological conditions (Theologis, 1992). The next step is the conversion of ACC to ethylene by ACC oxidase, an enzyme present in most tissues at very low levels (Yang and Hoffman, 1984). Like ACC synthase, several isoforms of ACC oxidase have been identified and found to be active under different physiological conditions (Hamilton et al. 1990; Abeles *et al.,* 1992). ACC oxidase genes are also part of a multigene family, and the proteins are thought to be post-translationally modified, giving rise to different isoforms (Arshad and Frankenberger, 2002).

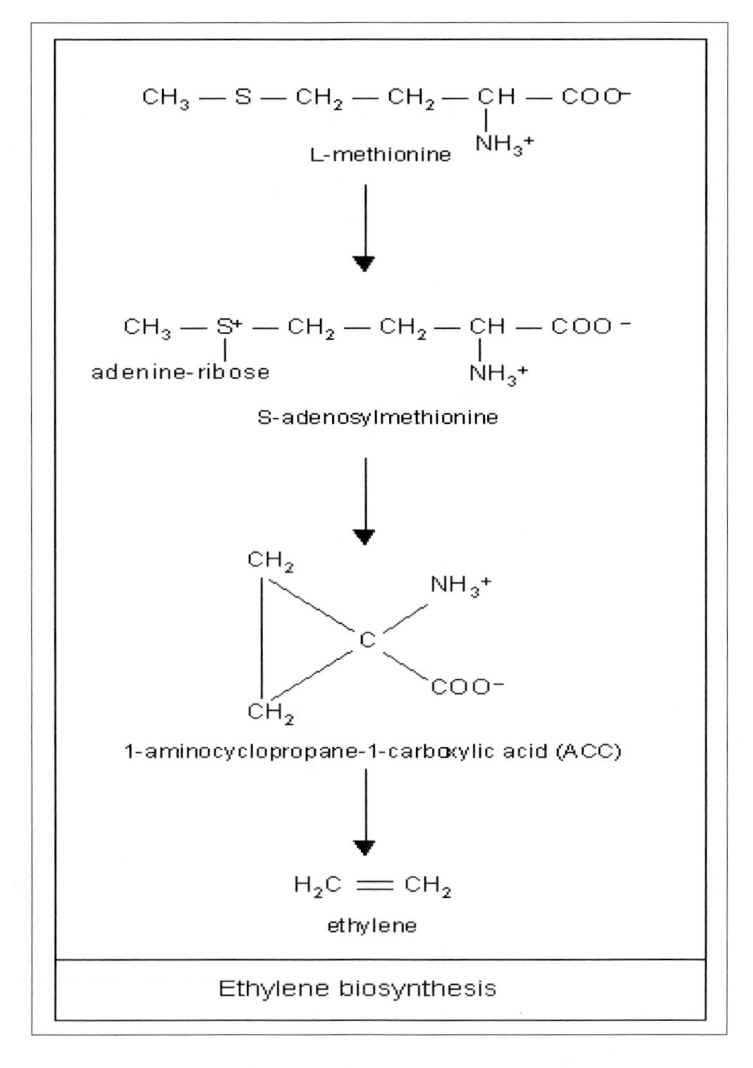

Figure 1. Schematic diagram depicting the biosynthes of Ethylene. In higher plants, ethylene biosynthesis starts with the *S*-adenosylation of methionine in order to give *S*-adenosylmethionine. This step is followed by the closing a cyclopropane ring to form ACC, which is then oxidatively cleaved to give ethylene. From Bleecker and Kende (2000).

Biochemistry

Honma and Shimomura (1978) were the first to provide evidence for the presence of this pyridoxal-phosphate (PLP) dependent enzyme, 1-aminocyclopropane-1-carboxylate deaminase (ACCD) and this enzyme has an estimated molecular mass of 110 kDa and is composed of three identical subunits, each with a molecular mass of about 36.5 kDa (Honma and Shimomura, 1978).

ACC deaminase utilizes pyridoxal 5'-phosphate, which acts as a cofactor in catalyzing the cleavage of ACC to α-ketobutyrate and ammonia (Walsh *et al.* 1981). Like other polymeric enzymes, ACC deaminase demonstrates a vast array of biochemical and physical characteristics depending on the microbial species. The molecular mass of ACC deaminase is up to 105000 Da and its subunit molecular mass ranges from 35000 to 41800 Da (Honma and Shimomura, 1978; Walsh *et al.,* 1981; Honma, 1985; Minami *et al.,* 1998; Jia, 1999; Ose *et al.,* 2003).

Generally, ACC deaminase exhibits an optimum activity at a pH close to 8; however, this might vary depending on the microbial species (Walsh *et al.,* 1981; Honma, 1985; Honmam *et al.,* 1993; Minami *et al.,* 1998). The Km values of this enzyme in any chemical reaction range from 1.5 to 4.6 mM, and the kcat values range from 146 to 290 min^{-1} (Jacobson *et al.,* 1994; Minami *et al.,* 1998; Jia *et al.,* 1999; Hontzeas *et al.,* 2004; Karthikeyan *et al.* 2004).

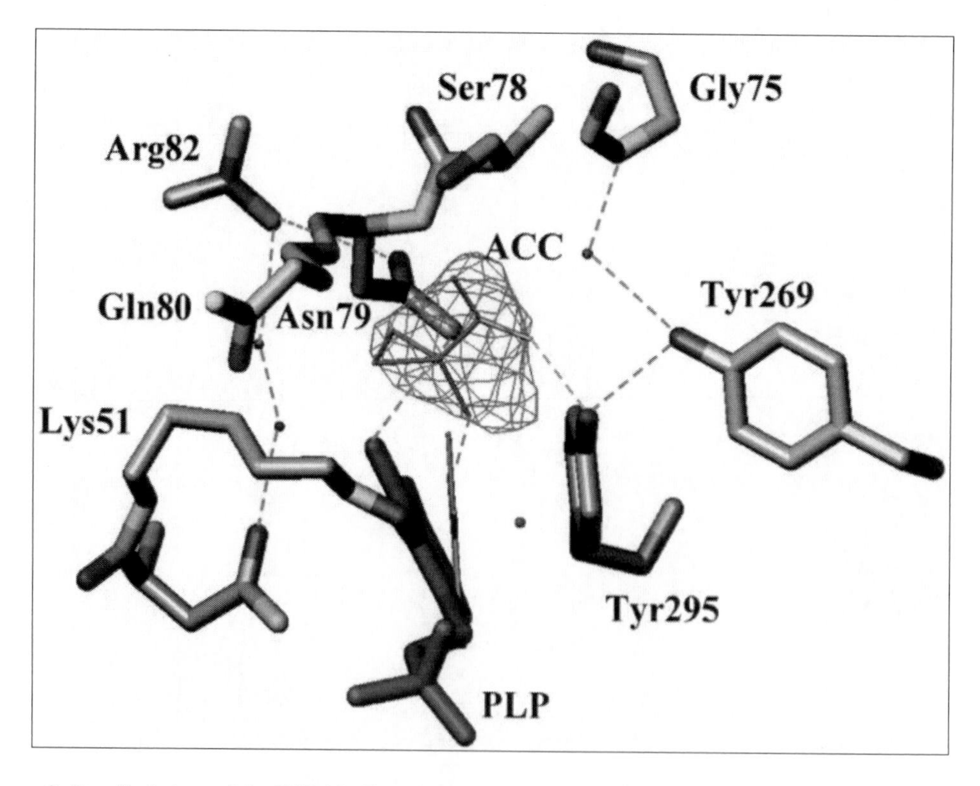

Figure 2. Detailed view of the PLP-binding site and proposed substrate complex. ACC is modeled on the electron density for the bound sulfoxide ion. Thin bonds are hypothetical drawings of PLP and the bound substrate. From Yao *et al.* (2000).

The ACC deaminases from the bacterium *Pseudomonas* sp. (bACCD; EC 4.1.99.4) (Honma, 1993) and the yeast *Hansenula saturnus* (yACCD; EC 4.1.99.2 (Minami *et al.*, 1998) were the most commonly studied ACC deaminases.

Yao *et al.* (2000) based on multiple wavelengths anomalous diffraction method using mercury atoms as anomalous scatters determined the crystal structure of ACCD from *Hansenula saturnus* Based on this structure it was found ACCD folds into two domains, each of which has an open twisted α/β structure similar to the β-subunit of tryptophan synthetase. ACCD, unlike in other members of the β family of PLP-dependent enzymes, PLP is buried deep in the molecule.

The structure provides the first view of the catalytic center of the cyclopropane ring opening.

ACC Deaminase Genes and Their Distribution

The gene encoding ACC deaminase has been isolated from a few strains of *Pseudomonas* spp., *Rhizobium leguminosarum*, the yeast *Hansenula saturnus*, and the fungus *Penicillium citrinum* (Hontzeas *et al.,* 2005).

The first documented evidence for the presence of ACC deaminase in *Rhizobium* spp. was provided by Sebastianova *et al.* (2003), who observed ACC deaminase genes from *R. leguminosarum* bv. *viciae* 128C53K and 99A1 strains have 64% identity to the gene of *Pseudomonas putida* UW4. Jacobson *et al.* (1994) reported induction of ACC deaminase gene expression requires the addition of ACC to the growing cells and this suggests the induced nature of ACC deaminase enzyme and mode of regulation in this bacterium, is relatively complex.

In fact, analysis of DNA sequence data for the region upstream of the ACC deaminase structural gene (*acdS*) from *Pseudomonas putida* UW4 indicates that this DNA segment contains a CRP (cyclic AMP receptor protein) binding site, an FNR (fumarate– nitrate reduction regulatory protein) binding site (a known anaerobic transcriptional regulator), an Lrp (leucine-responsive regulatory protein) binding site, an open reading frame encoding an Lrp protein and three putative promoter sequences, one controlling the ACC deaminase regulatory gene (acdR; encoding Lrp) and two controlling acdS (Grichko and Glick 2000; Li and Glick 2001).

All of these features were shown to be involved in the transcriptional regulation of acdS. More recently, in this same bacterium, a protein (AcdB) that interacts directly with ACC, the Lrp protein and the region of DNA upstream of *acdS* was identified and characterized (Cheng *et al.* 2007).

Based on a combination of published works Glick *et al.* (2007) developed a model on the transcriptional regulation of *acdS* as given in Figure 3. In addition to *P. putida* UW4, genes encoding Lrp proteins have been found immediately upstream from a number of bacterial ACC deaminase structural genes, and in every instance *acdS* and *acdR* were oriented in opposite directions (Hontzeas *et al.* 2004). On the other hand, neither the CRP nor the FNR binding site were found to be present in some instances.

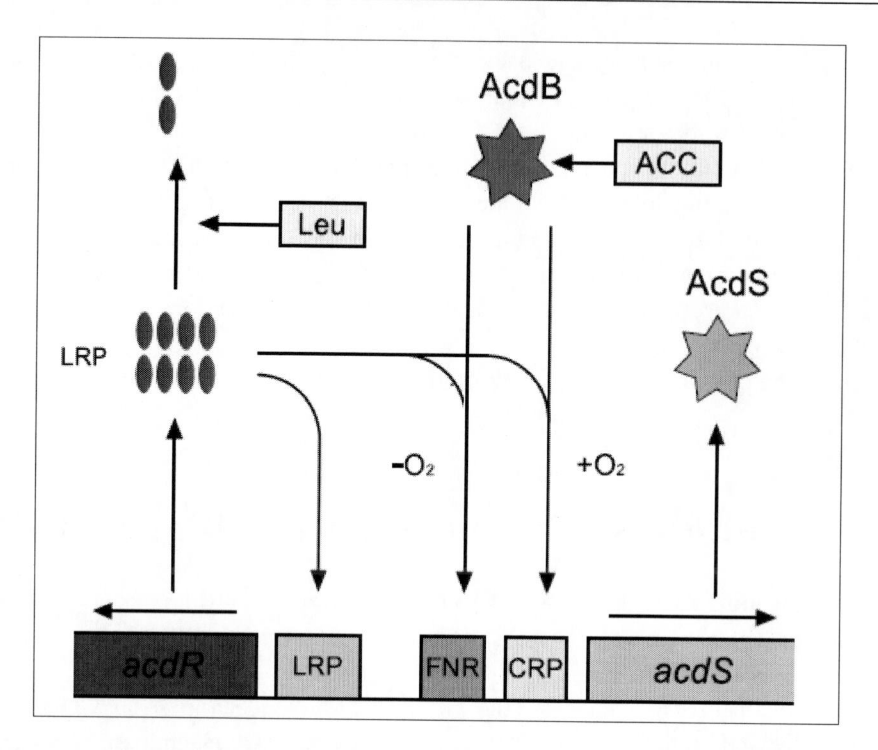

Figure 3. Model of the transcriptional regulation of ACC deaminase expression in *Pseudomonas putida* UW4. The acdR gene encodes an Lrp protein which is thought to function as an octamer according to Leonard et al. (2001). This protein can either bind to a DNA sequence known as an LRP box, preventing further transcription of this gene, or it can bind to a complex of ACC and the AcdB protein, encoding glycerophosphoryl diester phosphodiesterase, and together Lrp and AcdB can bind to either an FNR or CRP box on the DNA. Binding to FNR is favoured under anerobic conditions while binding to CRP is favoured under aerobic conditions. The binding of these factors facilitates transcription of acdS by RNA polymerase. The newly synthesized ACC deaminase (= AcdS) cleaves ACC to form ammonia and α-ketobutyrate, the latter compound being a precursor of branched chain amino acids including leucine. Finally, in the presence of high levels of leucine in the cell, the Lrp octamer is dissociated into an inactive dimeric form thereby shutting down further transcription of acdS. From Glick *et al.* (2007).

These data suggest that *acdS* and *acdR* are usually inherited together and the mode of transcriptional regulation is a central feature of the functioning of many bacterial ACC deaminases (Hontzeas *et al.* 2004). Holguin and Glick (2001) cloned ACC deaminase structural gene (*acd*S) from *Enterobacter cloacae* UW4 in plasmid pRK415 under the control of the *lac* promoter and then transferred into *Azospirillum brasilense* Cd and Sp245.

Azospirillum transformants thus obtained showed a high ACC deaminase activity, similar to that observed in *Enterobacter cloacae* UW4. Hontzeas *et al.* (2004) used the technique of RNA arbitrarily primed-polymerase chain reaction (RAP-PCR) to study the changes in gene expression over time in canola roots treated with the 1-aminocyclopropane-1-carboxylate (ACC) deaminase-containing plant-growth promoting bacterium *Enterobacter cloacae* UW4. These authors compared the changes with those in a mutant of *E. cloacae* UW4 in which the ACC deaminase structural gene *acdS* was replaced by homologous recombination with *acdS* with an intentional knockout containing a tetracycline resistance gene.

Results based on this study showed that the genes were either up- or down-regulated over a three-day period in canola plants treated with wild-type or mutant bacteria. Further isolation, cloning, and sequencing of this gene sequence showed a high homology with *Arabidopsis thaliana* genes.

Hontzeas et al. (2005) reported that ACC deaminase genes have evolved through horizontal transfer and not in the same manner as 16S ribosomal RNA genes, which have transmitted vertically.

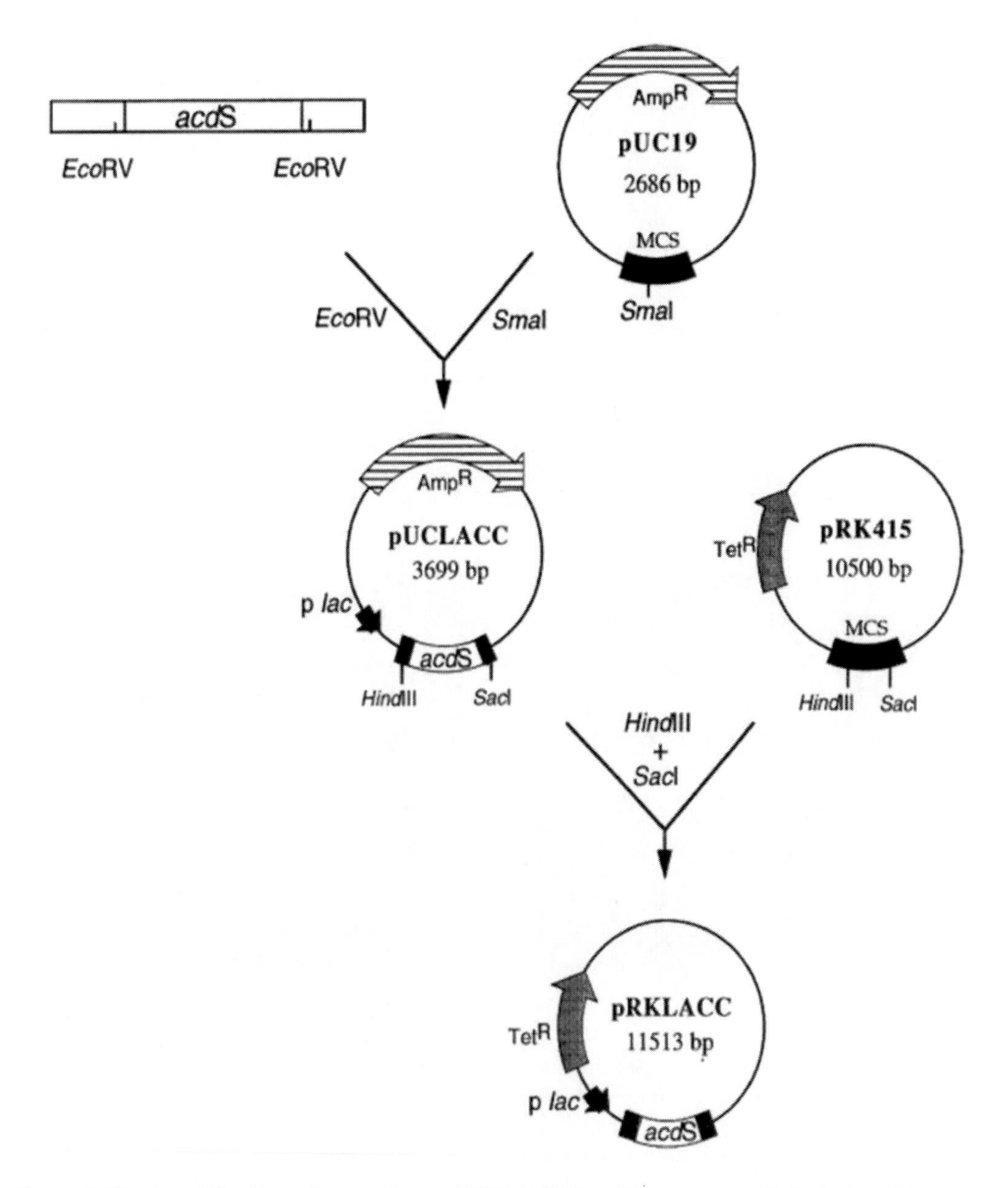

Figure 4. Cloning of the *Enterobacter cloacae* UW4 ACC deaminase gene, *acd*S, in the broad host range plasmid pRK415 under the control of the *Escherichia coli lac* promoter. MCS stands for multiple cloning sites. From Holguin and Glick (2001).

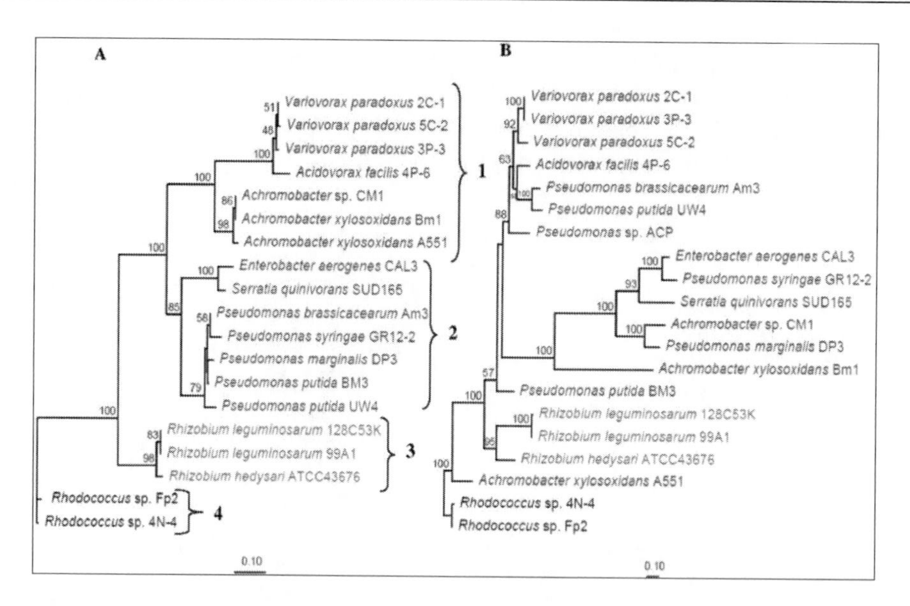

Figure 5. ML phylogenetic tree with bootstrap values of 16S rRNA gene sequences (500 bp) of soil bacteria used to isolate ACC deaminase (A). Consensus phylogenetic tree with bootstrap values of partial ACC deaminase DNA (750 bp) sequences (B).1, species of the order *Burkholderiales*; 2, members of the class *Gammaproteobacteria*; 3, species of the class *Alphaproteobacteria*; 4, gram-positive *Rhodococcus* spp. (Phylum *Actinobacteria*). From Hontzeas *et al.* (2005).

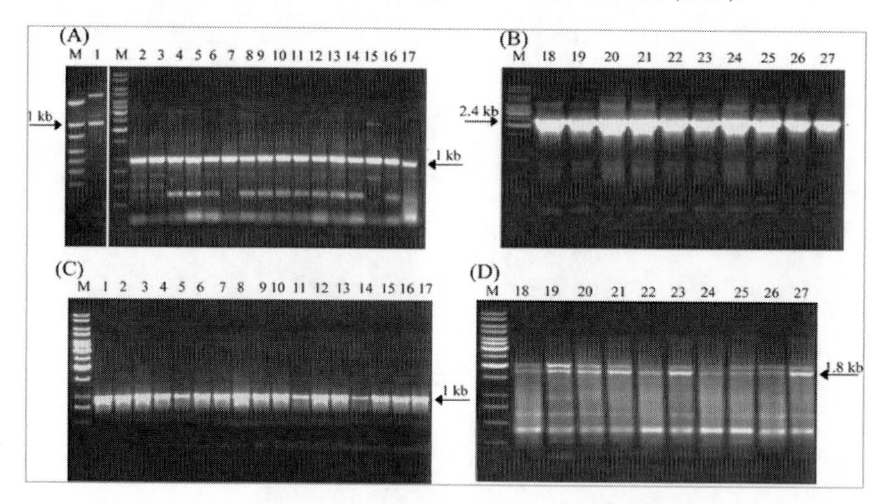

Figure 6. Agarose gel electrophoresis of the (a, b) PCR-amplified ACC deaminase gene and the (c, d) 5' upstream regulatory region of the ACC deaminase gene. M: 1-kb DNA Ladder. 1. *R. gallicum* PB2; 2. *R. leguminosarum*PB45; 3. *R. leguminosarum* PB61; 4. *R. leguminosarum* PB62; 5. *R. leguminosarum* PB126; 6. *R. leguminosarum* PB129; 7. *R. leguminosarum* PB130; 8. *R. leguminosarum* PB131; 9.*R. leguminosarum* PB141; 10. *R.leguminosarum* PB142; 11. *R. leguminosarum* PB154; 12. *R. leguminosarum* PB170; 13. *R. leguminosarum* PB171; 14. *R. leguminosarum* PB173; 15. R. *leguminosarum* PB180; 16. *R. leguminosarum* PB194; 17. *R.leguminosarum* PB223; 18. *R. leguminosarum* PB161; 19. *R. leguminosarum* PB162; 20. *R. leguminosarum* PB163; 21. *R. leguminosarum* PB164; 22. *R. leguminosarum* PB165; 23. *R. leguminosarum* PB166; 24. *R.leguminosarum* PB167; 25. *R. leguminosarum* PB168; 26. *R. leguminosarum* PB169; 27. *R. leguminosarum* PB172 From Duan (2009).

These authors added that the pattern cannot be explained by a single transfer, and suggested the possibility for a multiple transfer. Duan *et al.* (2009) based on polymerase chain reaction (PCR) from 27 rhizobium strains collected from different sites across Saskatchewan, Canada found that 17 strains have 99% identities with the previously characterized ACC deaminase structural gene (*acdS*) from *R. leguminosarum* bv. *viciae* 128C53K, whereas the others are 84% identical (864~866/1,020 bp) compared to the acdS from strain 128C53K. Todorovic and Glick (2008) isolated putative ACC deaminase cDNAs from tomato plants with the objective of establishing whether the product of this gene is a function of ACC deaminase gene. These authors demonstrated that the enzyme encoded by the putative ACC deaminase cDNA does not have the ability to break the cyclopropane ring of ACC, but utilized D-cysteine as a substrate, and encoded for the enzyme D-cysteine desulfhydrase.

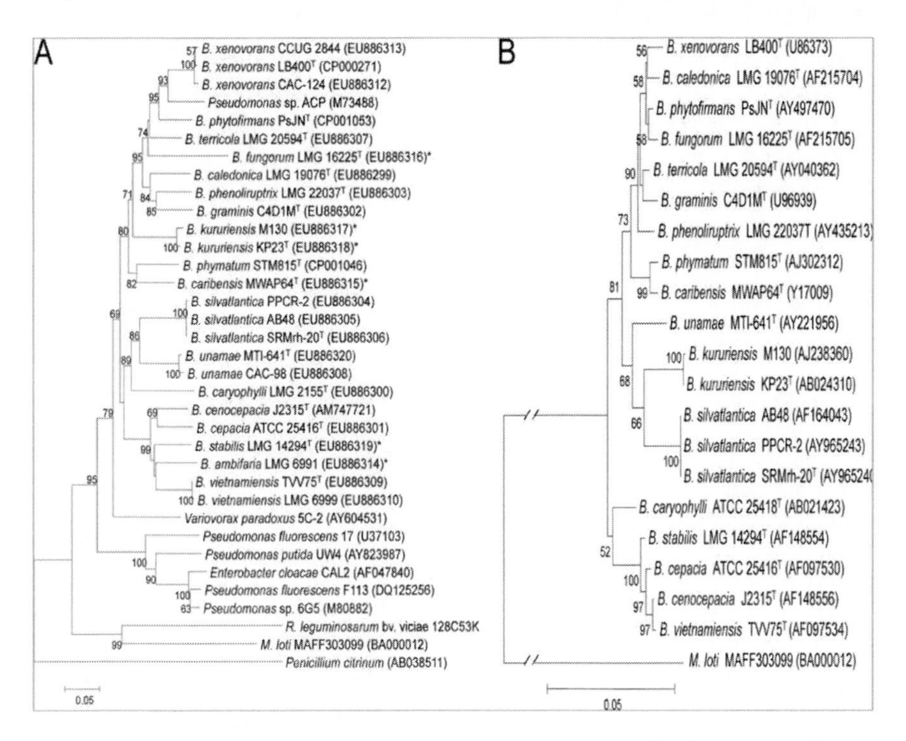

Figure 7. Phylogenetic tree based on complete *acdS* gene sequences (1,017 bp) of *Burkholderia* species and *acdS* gene partial sequences (785 bp) (indicated by an asterisk) (A). Phylogenetic tree based on 16S rRNA gene sequences (1,310 bp) of *Burkholderia* species. The trees were constructed using the neighbor-joining method (B). The nodal robustness of the trees was assessed using 1,000 bootstrap replicates. For both phylogenetic trees the bar indicates 5 nucleotide substitutions per 100 nucleotides. The NCBI GenBank accession number for each strain is shown in parentheses. From Onofre-Lemus *et al.* (2009).

Using site-directed mutagenesis, it was shown that altering two amino acid residues within the predicted active site served to change the enzyme from D-cysteine desulfhydrase to ACC deaminase. Alternatively, changing two amino acid residues at the same positions within the ACC deaminase site converts this enzyme into D-cysteine desulfhydrase. These authors believe that it is possible that a change in these two residues might have occurred in an ancestral protein resulting in two different enzymatic activities. No ACC deaminase pathway has ever been proven in plants, even with the fact that the number of different plant genomes encodes genes which have sequence homology to bacterial ACDs.

Recently McDonnell *et al.* (2009) reported that Arabidopsis and Populus have inherent ACC deaminase activity, and we showed that this activity in Arabidopsis is due, in part, to the product of *ACC deaminase1* (*AtACD1*) (At1g48420).

Onofre-Lemus *et al.* (2009) investigated the presence of *acdS* gene in 45 strains, most of which, representing 20 well-known plant associated *Burkholderia* species. The results demonstrated that ACC deaminase activity is a widespread feature in this genus since the *acdS* gene sequences were highly conserved (76 to 99% identity). Phylogenetic analysis of *acdS* gene sequences in *Burkholderia* showed tight clustering, which were clearly distinct from diazotrophic plant-associated *Burkholderia* species. Yim *et al.* (2009) isolated ACC positive 19 strains and identified by 16S rRNA gene sequence analysis found to be the members of the genera *Pseudomonas* and *Agrobacterium* belonging to α - and γ - Proteobacteria groups. Kamala-Kannan *et al.* (2010) based on Polymerase chain reaction (PCR) for *acdS* gene showed that the isolated *P. entomophila* strain PS-PJH carry sequences similar to known *acdS* genes.

These authors based on the results of the multiple sequence alignment revealed >99% identity (nucleotide and amino acid) with *acdS* gene of *Pseudomonas putida* strains AM15 and UW4. Based on the 16S– 23S internal transcribed spacer region sequences, the isolate was identified as *P. entomophila*.

Role of Bacterial ACC Deaminase in Stress Agriculture

The production of ethylene in response to abiotic and biotic stresses leads to root growth inhibition and ultimately disturbing the plant growth. ACC deaminase containing PGPR boost plant growth in general and in particular under stressed conditions. They do so by regulation of ethylene production in response to various abiotic and biotic stresses like salinity, drought, water logging, temperature, pathogenicity and contaminants. The role of PGPR containing ACC deaminase in relation to the nature of stress is described below in a genetic perspective. The different genetic manipulations carried out with the structural gene for ACC deaminase (*acdS*) and its consequences are provided in Table 1.

Table 1. Genetic manipulation with the structural gene for ACC deaminase (*acdS*) and its consequences

Plant	Manipulation	Consequences	Reference
Tomato	ACC deaminase genes transferred from *P. chloraphis* 6G5 with CaMV 35S	Ethylene was decreased by 90% with no observed phenotypic differences	Klee *et al.* (1991)
Tomato	ACC deaminase genes expressed under the control of the 35*S* promoter from cauliflower mosaic virus	Ethylene levels increased from mature green to orange stage by 50–97%.	Reed *et al.* (1995)
Tomato	Transfer of ACC deaminase from *E. cloacae* UW4	Increased accumulation of metals and higher shoot/root ratio.	Grichko *et al.* (2000)

Plant	Manipulation	Consequences	Reference
Tomato	Three different promoters: CaMV 35S, rolD and PRB-1b were used to transfer ACC deaminase from *E. cloacae* UW4	Up to 70% decrease in ethylene concentration in transgenic plants compared to non-transformed subjected to flooding stress	Grichko and Glick (2001)
Tomato	Transfer of ACC deaminase from *E. cloacae* UW4	Reduction in disease symptoms with no decrease in the fungal infection or progression.	Robison *et al.* (2001)
Tomato and Canola	ACC deaminase structural gene (*acd*S) from *Enterobacter cloacae* UW4 to *Azospirillum brasilense* Cd and Sp245.	Transformed *Azospirillum* strains were able to increase the length of tomato and canola seedlings	Holguin and Glick (2001)
Canola	Transfer of ACC deaminase from *E. cloacae* UW4	Transgenic plants had a 40% higher germination rate, increased biomass and a higher arsenic uptake than non-transformed plants	Nie *et al.* (2002)
Tomato	ACC deaminase gene (*acdS*) under the transcriptional control of either the *rolD* promoter or the PRB-1*b* promoter	transgenic tomato plants were more healthy and have productive phenotype	Grichko *et al.* (2004)
Alfaalfa	Structural gene (*acdS*) leucine-responsive regulatory protein like gene (*lrpL*), from *R. leguminosarum* bv. *viciae* 128C53K into *Sinorhizobium meliloti*	Transformants showed 35 to 40% greater nodulation efficiency	Ma *et al.* (2004)
Lotus	Expression of *acdS* gene in *Mesorhizobium loti* MAFF303099	Matured root nodules showed the expression of *acdS*	Nukui *et al.* (2006)
Lomandra leucocephala	*acdS* genes from *Rhizobium* sp. strain TAL1145 and *Sinorhizobium* sp. BL3 transferred to strain TAL1145.	Enhancement in growth and nodulation of inoculated plants.	Tittabutr *et al.* (2008)
Lotus	*acdS* into the *M. loti* chromosome under a constitutive promoter activity	Transconjugant had higher nodule formation and were more competitiive	Conforte *et al.* (2010)
Canola	RNAi silencing of the ACCD gene in *T. asperellum*	Promote root elongation and growth in pouch assays	Vitrbo *et al.* (2010)
Red pepper	ACC deaminase possessing CBMB20 was tagged with green fluorescent protein (*gfp*)	Increase in plant height, fruit dry weight and total biomass	Lee *et al.* (2011)

Heavy Metal Stress

Phytoremediation to clean up heavy metal contaminated soil has gained more attention than conventional technology since earlier method has been regarded as environmental friendly and cost effective (Haque *et al.*, 2006; Chehregani *et al.*, 2009; Kotrba *et al.*, 2009). The success of the phytoremediation process depends on an adequate plant yield and high heavy metal concentrations in above-ground tissues of plants (Rajkumar *et al.*, 2009). This has prompted researchers to explore the possibilities of enhancing the plant biomass and metal uptake using PGPB as bioinoculants (Abou-Shanab *et al.*, 2006; Sheng and Xia, 2006; Madhaiyan et al. 2007; Rajkumar *et al.*, 2009). Grichko *et al.* (2000) evaluated the efficiency of transgenic tomato plants *Lycopersicon esculentum* cv. Heinz 902 expressing the bacterial gene 1-aminocyclopropane-1-carboxylic acid (ACC) deaminase, under the transcriptional control of either two tandem 35*S* cauliflower mosaic virus promoters (constitutive expression), the *rolD* promoter from *Agrobacterium rhizogenes* (root specific expression) or the pathogenesis related PRB-1*b* promoter from tobacco. Their ability to grow in the presence of Cd, Co, Cu, Mg, Ni, Pb, or Zn and to accumulate these metals was studied in detail.

Figure 8. Morphological comparison between transgenic petunia and tobacco plants and PCR confirmation of T1 transgenic tobacco plant lines. (A) Comparison of transgenic petunia from different constructs. Left: growth comparison of transgenic petunia plants from pBI101 control (left) and iaaM/ACC (right) after planted in mixed commercial soil for 4 weeks. (B) T1 transgenic tobacco plants of pBI101 empty vector (C) T1 transgenic tobacco plants of iaaM/ACC. Both plants of B and C were grown after planted in sand for 2 weeks. (D) PCR analysis of T1 kanamycin-resistant transgenic tobacco lines. 1, DNA marker; 2, pBI-iaaM/ACC plasmid control; 3, plant from pBI101 control; 4–7: four independent iaaM/ACC transgenic plants. From Grichko *et al.* (2000).

These authors examined the parameters such as metal concentration, ACC deaminase activity in both plant shoots and roots and leaf chlorophyll content. Based on these studies these authors concluded that the transgenic tomato plants expressing ACC deaminase have acquired a greater amount of metal within the plant tissues, and were less subject to the deleterious effects of the metals on plant growth compared with normal plants. As part of a phytoremediation strategy, transgenic plants expressing bacterial ACC deaminase genes were constructed in tobacco and canola (Nie et al. 2002). Stearns et al. (2005) reported resistance in transgenic plants towards nickel, arsenic and high salt. Nie *et al.* (2002) and Stearns *et al.* (2005) reported that the transgenic tomato plants expressing the ACC deaminase gene under the control of the rolD promoter were significantly protected from the growth inhibition due to heavy metal stress. Plants inoculated with *Pseudomonas putida* HS-2 strain produced an increased plant biomass as well as in nickel (Ni) uptake in shoots and roots of both transformed (expressing a bacterial ACC deaminase gene in its roots) and nontransformed plants Rodriguez *et al.* (2008).

These authors suggest this strain as a potential candidate for both phytoremediation protocols and in plant growth promotion. Stearns *et al.* (2005) in an effort to gain the full advantages of phytoremediation provided by bacterial ACC deaminases from the environment with two transgenic canola lines expressing this enzyme driven by either tandem constitutive cauliflower mosaic virus (CaMV) *35S* promoters or the root specific *rolD* promoter from *Agrobacterium rhizogenes*.

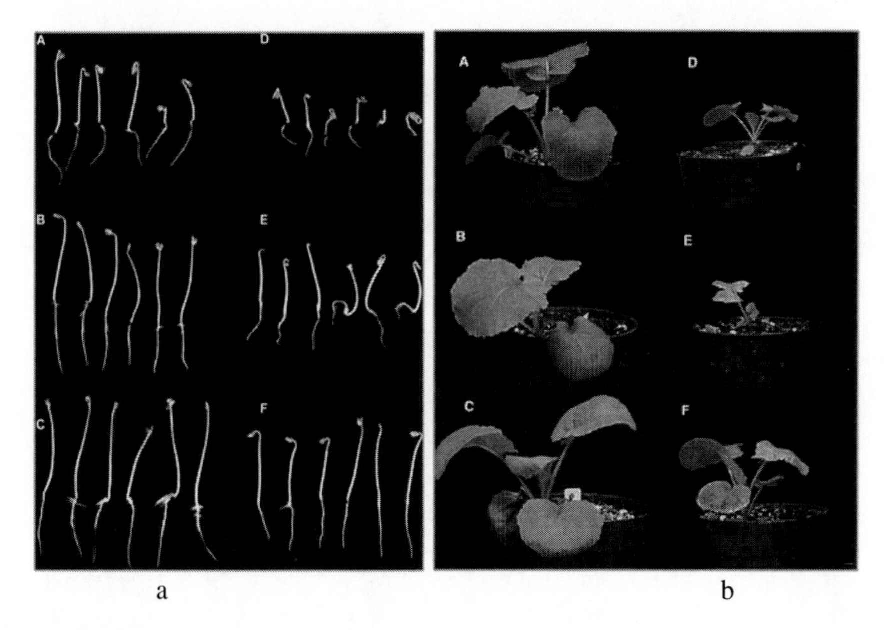

Figure 9. Five-day-old canola seedlings from growth pouch experiment a). (A) non-transformed in water, (B) *35S* in water, (C) *rolD* in water, (D) non-transformed in 6.0 mM $NiSO_4$ solution, (E) *35S* in 6.0 mM $NiSO_4$ solution, (F) *rolD* in 6.0 mM $NiSO_4$ solution. Three-week-old canola plants b). (A) non-transformed plant in unspiked soil, (B) *35S* plant in unspiked soil, (C) *rolD* plant in unspiked soil, (D) non-transformed plant in nickel-spiked soil, (E) *35S* plant in nickel-spiked soil, (F) *rolD* plant in nickel-spiked soil. From: Stearns *et al.* (2005).

Following the growth of transgenic and non transgenic canola plants in nickel contaminated soil, it was observed that the *rolD* plants demonstrated a significant increase in tolerance to nickel compared to the non transformed control plants. Farewell *et al.* (2007) studied the growth of transgenic canola (*Brassica napus*) expressing a gene for the enzyme 1 aminocyclopropane-1-carboxylate (ACC) deaminase and compared its efficiency to non-transformed canola exposed to flooding and elevated soil Ni concentration, in situ. Additionally, the ability of plant growth-promoting bacterium *Pseudomonas putida* UW4, expressing ACC deaminase activity, to facilitate the growth of non-transformed and transgenic canola under the above mentioned conditions was also examined. These authors reported that transgenic canola and/or canola treated with *P. putida* UW4 had greater shoot biomass compared to non-transformed canola roots under low flood-stress conditions. Under high flooded-stress conditions, shoot biomass was reduced and Ni accumulation was increased in all instances relative to low flood-stress conditions. Zhang *et al.* (2008) constructed two binary vectors in which the *Agrobacterium* iaaM gene was studied either under the transcriptional control of a xylem-specific glycine-rich protein promoter alone, or co-expressed with the bacterial ACC deaminase gene, driven by the constitutive CaMV 35S promoter. Transgenic tobacco plants when grown in sand supplemented with either Cu^{2+} or Co^{2+}, or co-expressed with tissue specific both iaaM and ACC deaminase genes showed faster growth with larger biomass with a more extensive root system, and accumulated a greater amount of heavy metals than the empty vector control plants. Transgenic plants co-expressing both genes accumulated more heavy metals into the plant shoots and tolerated up to 150 mg l^{-1} CuSO4, while the growth of the control plants was greatly inhibited.

Cavalca *et al.* (2010) investigated the effect of ACC deaminase producing and arsenic-resistant *Alcaligenes* sp. strain DhalL on the growth and arsenic uptake of sunflower (*Helianthus annuus* L.) under pot culture conditions. Arsenic content was significantly higher in above ground parts of inoculated plants than in uninoculated plants, highlighting the significance of this strain on arsenic uptake by sunflower plants. These authors carried out a Real Time PCR method, based on the quantification of *ACR3(2)* gene carried by DhalL, in order to monitor the presence of this genes in the soil and colonization of sunflower plant by the strain. They found that the *ACR3(2)* gene copy number was one hundred times higher in inoculated compared to the uninoculated pots, especially in the rhizosphere soil, indicating the colonization efficiency of this strain. The results suggest that the presence of arsenic resistant strain such as *Alcaligenes* sp. DhalL in the rhizosphere of sunflower could influence as mobilization and uptake by plant.

Abiotic Stress

Stress ethylene production in response to diverse abiotic stresses such as salinity, drought, water logging, and temperature leads to inhibition of root growth and consequently growth of the plant as a whole. These ACC deaminase PGPR boost plant growth particularly under stressed conditions by the regulation of accelerated ethylene production in response to a multitude of abiotic stresses (Glick *et al.* 1998; Grichko *et al.*, 2000; Sergeeva *et al.*, 2006; Saravanakumar and Samiyappan, 2006; Karthikeyan et al. 2012). Applications of PGPR containing ACC deaminase in relation to the nature of various abiotic stresses are described below. Grichko *et al.* (2000) studied the expression of bacterial gene 1-aminocyclopropane-1-carboxylic acid (ACC) deaminase, under the transcriptional control of either of the two tandem 35*S* cauliflower mosaic virus promoters (constitutive expression), the *rolD* promoter from *Agrobacterium rhizogenes* (root specific expression) or the pathogenesis related PRB-1*b* promoter from tobacco in transgenic tomato plants *Lycopersicon esculentum* (Solanaceae) cv. Heinz 902. These authors also compared the response of transformed plants against non transformed plants in flooding stress. Under flooding stress conditions results suggest that the transgenic tomato plants expressing ACC deaminase showed increased tolerance to flooding stress and have less deleterious effects of root hypoxia on plant growth than non-transformed plants.

Grichko and Glick (2001) studied the inoculation effect of ACC deaminase containing PGPR on tomato plants subjected to flooding stress. For this study they used seeds of wild-type tomato plants inoculated with either ACC deaminase containing *Pseudomonas putida* UW4, *Enterobacter cloacae* CAL2 or *P. putida* (ATCC17399/pRKACC) strain or the strain

P. putida (ATCC17399/pRK415) which is devoid of this gene. Tomato plants (55-day-old) were subjected to flooding stress for nine consecutive days and a number of physiological and biochemical parameters were recorded. Results reveal that the tomato plants inoculated with ACC deaminase containing PGPR strains showed substantial tolerance to flooding stress implying that bacterial ACC deaminase have lowered stress ethylene levels due to flooding stress. Sergeeva *et al.* (2006) transformed Canola, *Brassica napus* cv. Westar, to express a bacterial 1 aminocyclopropane-1-carboxylate (ACC) deaminase (EC 4.1.99.4) gene under the transcriptional control of constitutive 35S promoter from cauliflower mosaic virus, the root-specific promoter of the rolD gene within the T-DNA from Ri plasmid of *Agrobacterium rhizogenes*, and promoter for pathogenesis-related prb-1b gene from tobacco. The ability of both transformed and non transformed canola plants to grow in the presence of 0–200 mM NaCl suggest that the presence of ACC deaminase provided the transgenic canola lines with tolerance ability to inhibitory effects of salt stress, compared to the non-transformed canola plants. Results suggest that the plants transformed with the rolD gene within the T-DNA from the Ri plasmid of *A. rhizogenes* was found to be most effective. These authors suggest improved salt tolerance in these transgenic plants by decreasing stress ethylene biosynthesis. Saravanakumar and Samiyappan (2006) evaluated the efficacy of four plant growth-promoting rhizobacteria (PGPR) strains in groundnut plants against saline stress under in vitro conditions.

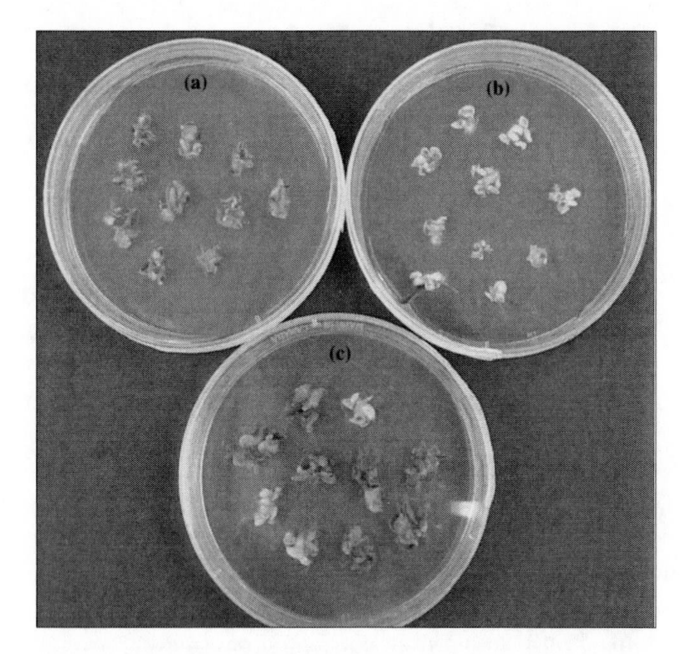

Figure 10. Test of canola plants on selection plates with kanamycin. Embryos from homozygous transgenic canola plants grow all green (a); embryos from non-transformed canola plants are all pale (b); and embryos from heterozygous transgenic canola plants grow a combination of green and pale (c). From Cheng *et al.* (2007).

Biochemical and molecular (PCR) analysis revealed that among the four PGPR strains used, *P. fluorescens* strain TDK1 showed better ACC deaminase activity among the strains, and positive reaction to PCR amplification. *P. fluorescens* strain TDK1 possessing ACC deaminase activity enhanced saline tolerance in groundnut plants, which in turn resulted to increased yield when compared with the groundnut plants treated with *Pseudomonas* strains not having ACC deaminase activity. Cheng *et al.* (2007) studied the growth of canola plants treated with either wild-type *Pseudomonas putida* UW4 or a 1-aminocyclopropane-1-carboxylate (ACC) deaminase minus mutant of this strain in the presence of inhibitory levels of salt and with plants maintained at 10 and at 20 °C. These authors observed a dramatic decrease in plant growth by the addition of salt at 10 °C, while a slight decrease at 20 °C. It was observed that the addition of the wild type but not the mutant strain of *P. putida* UW4 significantly improved plant growth. Jonathan *et al.* (2009) reported that plants can also irreversibly remove ACC from ethylene production through the activity of a plant encoded ACC deaminase in both Arabidopsis and in Poplar. Furthermore, these authors using an antisense construct of *AtACD1* in Arabidopsis investigated the role of ACC deamination during salt stress and reported that this activity varied during tomato ripening in a manner consistent with a factor that is involved in the regulation of ethylene levels.

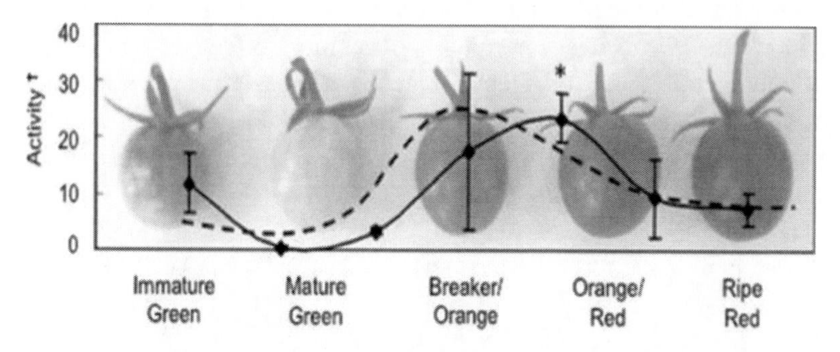

Figure 11. Tomato fruits exhibit ACC deaminase activity during ripening. A plot of ACC deaminase activity (Solid Line) with known levels of ethylene production during ripening (Dashed Line) superimposed over pictures of the corresponding stage of tomato development. *Indicates significant increase in activity (†n mol mg^{-1} hr^{-1}). From Jonathan *et al.* (2009).

Sadrinia *et al.* (2011) investigated the effect of rhizosphere bacteria *Pseudomonas mendocina* containing plasmid carrying the gene encoding ACC deaminase on resistance of tomato plants for resistance to salinity. Amplification of acds gene in *Pseudomonas mendocina* was performed and this gene was cloned in *Escherichia coli* and was subsequently transferred back to *P. mendocina.* The effect of bacterial ACC deaminase genes on the resistance of tomato plants to NaCl was studied under Pot and Greenhouse conditions. In pot culture experiment, tomato plants treated with recombinant *P. mendocina* producing ACC deaminase promoted growth in high salt concentrations and reduced ethylene levels compared to *P. mendocina* treatment (without plasmid) and control group. Based on the study these workers concluded that recombinant *P. mendocina* producing ACC deaminase reduced the ethylene content of tomato plant in high salt concentrations and improved plant resistance to salinity.

Biotic Stress

Currently, plant growth–promoting rhizobacteria (PGPR)—mediated management of pests and diseases are more ecologically sustainable than the use of synthetic chemicals

(Madhaiyan *et al.* 2004; 2006). Ethylene synthesis in plants is enhanced with the severity of pathogenic infection. Aside from reducing plant stress ethylene levels are several reports support the hypothesis that ACC deaminase rhizobacteria have antagonistic effects against microbial pathogens (Robison *et al.* 2001; Belimov *et al.* 2007; Indiragandhi *et al.* (2008). Wang *et al.* (2000) reported that *P. fluorescens* strain CHA0, a root colonizing bacterium, has a broad spectrum of biocontrol activity against plant diseases. However, CHA0 is unable to utilize 1-aminocyclopropane-1-carboxylic acid (ACC), the immediate precursor of plant ethylene, as a sole source of nitrogen. These results suggests that CHA0 does not contain the enzyme ACC deaminase, which cleaves ACC to ammonia and □-ketobutyrate, and was able to promote root elongation of plant seedlings treated with bacteria containing this enzyme. Furthermore, these authors transferred an ACC deaminase gene, together with its regulatory region, into *P. fluorescens* strains CHA0 and CHA96 (a regulatory gacA mutant of CHA0). It was observed that ACC deaminase activity was expressed in both CHA0 and CHA96 strains and the transformed strains with ACC deaminase activity increased root length of canola plants under gnotobiotic conditions, whereas strains without this activity showed no effect. Introduction of ACC deaminase genes into strain CHA0 improved its ability to protect cucumber against *Pythium* damping-off, and potato tubers against *Erwinia* soft rot in small hermetically sealed containers. Robison *et al.* (2001) examined the effects of reduced ethylene synthesis on *Verticillium* wilt caused by *Verticillium dahliae* in tomato by transforming tomato with ACC deaminase. Three promoters that were used to express ACC deaminase in the plant include: (i) CaMV 35S (constitutive expression); (ii) rol D (limits expression specifically to the site of *Verticillium* infection, i.e. the roots); and (iii) prb- 1b (limits expression to certain environmental cues, e.g. disease infection). Significant reductions in the *Verticillium* wilt symptoms were obtained from rol D- and prb- 1b-, but not from 35S-transformants.

The pathogen was detected in stem sections of plants with reduced number and symptoms, suggesting that reduced ethylene synthesis results in increased disease tolerance. Zanetti *et al.* (2002) cloned a cDNA clone encoding an ACC oxidase, ST-ACO3, isolated from potato (*Solanum tuberosum* L.) by differential screening of *Fusarium eumartii* infected-tuber cDNA library. The deduced amino acid sequence exhibited similarity to other ACC oxidase proteins from several plants species. Northern blot analysis revealed that the ST-ACO3 mRNA level increased in potato tubers upon inoculation with *F. eumartii*, as well as after treatment with salicylic acid and indole-3-acetic acid, suggesting a possible cross-talk between different signaling pathways involved in the defense response of potato tubers against *F. eumartii* attack. Hontzeas *et al.* (2003) used the technique of RNA arbitrarily primed-polymerase chain reaction (RAP-PCR) to study the changes in gene expression over time in canola roots treated with the 1-aminocyclopropane-1-carboxylate (ACC) deaminase-containing plant-growth-promoting bacterium *Enterobacter cloacae* UW4. These authors compared the changes with those in a mutant of *E. cloacae* UW4 in which the ACC deaminase structural gene *acdS* was replaced by homologous recombination with *acdS* with an intentional knockout containing a tetracycline resistance gene. Based on these studies they reported that the genes that were either up- or down-regulated over a three-day period in canola plants treated with wild-type or mutant bacteria all appeared to have high homology with *Arabidopsis thaliana* genes.

Figure 12. Visual symptoms of *Verticillium* wilt in (a) rol D-17 and (b) prb-1 plants. Transgenic (Tg) tomato seedlings, and sibling controls (NTg), were mock-inoculated (mock) or inoculated with *V. dahliae* race 2 (+Vd), as described in Experimental procedures. Each quadrant contains four seedlings. Picture was taken 14 days after inoculation. From Robinson *et al.* (2001).

These authors reported that the ACC deaminase-producing *E. cloacae* UW4 up regulate genes involved in cell division and proliferation and down-regulate stress genes. Belimov *et al.* (2007) investigated the role of bacterial 1-aminocyclopropane-1-carboxylate (ACC) deaminase activity using *Pseudomonas brassicacearum* in tomato (*Lycopersicon esculentum=Solanum lycopersicum*) plants. The phytopathogenic strain 520-1 *P. brassicacearum* possessed ACC deaminase activity, an important trait of plant growth-promoting rhizobacteria (PGPR) that stimulates root growth. This strain increased *in vitro* root elongation and root biomass of soil-grown tomato cv. Ailsa Craig at low bacterial concentrations (10^6 cells ml^{-1} *in vitro* and 10^6 cells g^{-1} soil) but had negative effects on *in vitro* root elongation at higher bacterial concentrations. A mutant strain of 520-1 (designated T8-1) that was engineered to be ACC deaminase deficient failed to promote tomato root growth *in vitro* and in soil. Though both the strains showed similar colonization ability either on root surfaces or in wounded stems ACC deaminase containing bacterial strain *P. brassicacearum* Am3 can promote growth in tomato by masking the phytopathogenic properties of this bacterium.

Indiragandhi et al. (2008) reported a significant increase in the activities of pathogenesis-related (PR) proteins and defense enzymes such as β-1,3-glucanase, phenylalanine ammonia-lyase, peroxidase and polyphenol oxidase were observed in ACC deaminase containing

Methylobacterium oryzae CBMB20 pretreated and challenged with *Pseudomonas syringae* pv. tomato (Pst) compared to control plants in both growth chamber and greenhouse conditions. These authors also added that the increased PR proteins and defense enzyme activities were correlated with the reduction of stress ethylene level. Viterbo *et al.* (2010) evaluated the ACC deaminase activity of plant growth-promoting fungus *Trichoderma asperellum* T203 for biocontrol efficiency. Fungal cultures grown with ACC as the sole nitrogen source showed high enzymatic activity. The enzyme encoding gene (Tas-acdS) was isolated, and an average 3.5-fold increase in gene induction by 3mM ACC was detected by real-time PCR. *Escherichia coli* bacteria carrying the intron-free cDNA of Tas-acdS cloned into the vector pAlter-EX1 under the control of the tac promoter revealed specific ACCd activity and ability to promote canola (*Brassica napus*) root elongation in pouch assays. RNAi silencing of the ACCD gene in *T. asperellum* showed decreased ability of the mutants to promote root elongation in canola seedlings. These results suggest a role for ACCd in the plant root growth promotion effect by *T. asperellum.*

Agrobacterium tumefaciens D3 has been previously reported to contain a putative ACC deaminase structural gene (*acdS*) and a regulatory gene (*acdR* = *lrpL*) (Hao *et al.,* 2011). Under gnotobiotic conditions, wild-type *A. tumefaciens* D3 was shown to be able to promote plant root elongation, while the *acdS* and *lrpL* double mutant strain *A. tumefaciens* D3-1 lost this ability. However, when this mutant strain co-inoculated with the virulent strain, *A. tumefaciens* C58, in wounded castor bean plants, both the wild-type *A. tumefaciens* D3 and the mutant *A. tumefaciens* D3-1 were found to be able to significantly inhibit crown gall development induced by *A. tumefaciens* C58. Siddikee *et al.* (2011) isolated three 1-aminocyclopropane-1-carboxylic acid (ACC) deaminase-producing halotolerant bacteria from West Coast soil of Yellow Sea, Incheon, South Korea and these strains RS16, RS656 and RS111 were identified by 16S rRNA gene sequencing as *Brevibacterium iodinum*, *Bacillus licheniformis* and *Zhihengliuela alba*, respectively. Under greenhouse conditions these halotolerant bacterial strains mitigated salt stress in red pepper by reducing salt stress-induced ethylene production.

Nodulation

Nodulation is a very complex process involving a variety of genes that control *NOD* factors essential for the establishment, maintenance, regulation and root nodule development. Although ethylene plays a negative role in nodulation some rhizobial strains can lower the endogenous ethylene levels in roots through their 1-aminocyclopropane-1-carboxylate (ACC) deaminase activity.

Transgenic rhizobia or legume plants with bacterial ACC deaminase expression could alleviate the negative effects of stress ethylene on nodulation. Ma *et al.* (2004) introduced the ACC deaminase structural gene (*acdS*) and its upstream regulatory gene, a leucine-responsive regulatory protein (LRP)-like gene (*lrpL*), from *R. leguminosarum* bv. *viciae* 128C53K into *Sinorhizobium meliloti*, that lack this enzyme. These authors reported that the ACC deaminase-producing *S. meliloti* transformants showed 35 to 40% greater nodulation efficiency in *Medicago sativa* (alfalfa), and also reduced ethylene production in these plants.

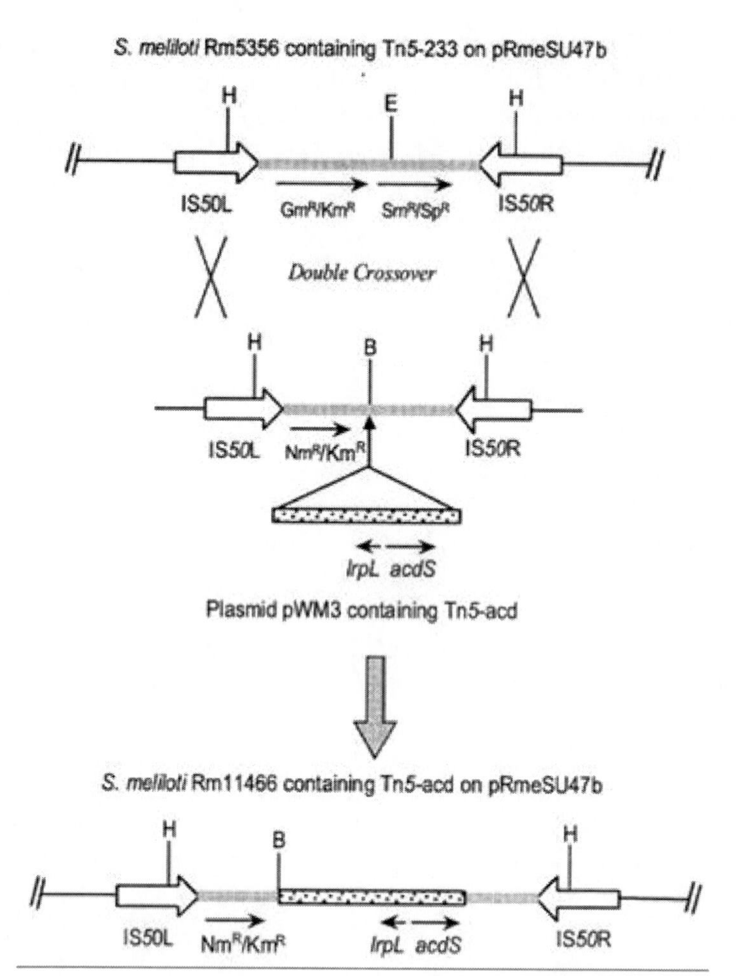

Figure 13. Construction of *S. meliloti* Rm11466 by transposon replacement. A 4-kb DNA fragment containing the *lrpL* and *acdS* genes from *R. leguminosarum* bv. *viciae* 128C53K was inserted into the BamHI site of transposon Tn*5* in pGS220 to construct pWM3. pWM3 is suicidal after being introduced into *S. meliloti* Rm5356. After double crossover between the IS*50* regions of the two transposons, Tn*5*-233 and Tn*5*-acd, the neomycin resistance gene, leucine-responsive regulatory-like gene (*lrpL*), and the ACC deaminase structural gene (*acdS*) were inserted into megaplasmid pRmeSU47b in *S. meliloti* Rm5356. The resulting variant was named Rm11466. Restriction sites: B, BamHI; E, EcoRI; H, HindIII. From Ma *et al.* (2004).

Nukui *et al.* (2006) in order to study the regulation of the *acdS* gene encoding ACC deaminase in *Mesorhizobium loti* MAFF303099 during symbiosis with the host legume *Lotus japonicas* introduced the β-glucuronidase (GUS) gene into *acdS* so that GUS was expressed under control of the *acdS* promoter, and also generated disruption mutants with mutations in the nitrogen fixation regulator gene, *nifA*.

The histochemical GUS assay showed that there was exclusive expression of *acdS* in mature root nodules. Quantitative reverse transcription-PCR demonstrated that *nifA2*disruption resulted in considerably diminished expression of *acdS*, *nifH*, and *nifA1* in bacteroid cells. In contrast, *nifA1* disruption slightly enhanced expression of the *acdS* transcripts and suppressed *nifH* to some extent. These results indicate that the *acdS* gene and other symbiotic genes are positively regulated by the NifA2 protein, but not by the NifA1 protein, in *M. loti*. Tittabutr *et al.* (2008) cloned the *acdS* genes encoding ACC deaminase from *Rhizobium* sp. strain TAL1145 and *Sinorhizobium* sp. BL3 in multicopy plasmids, and transferred it to the strain TAL1145. These authors reported that this BL3-acdS gene enhanced the ACC deaminase activity in TAL1145 compared to the native acdS gene in TAL1145.

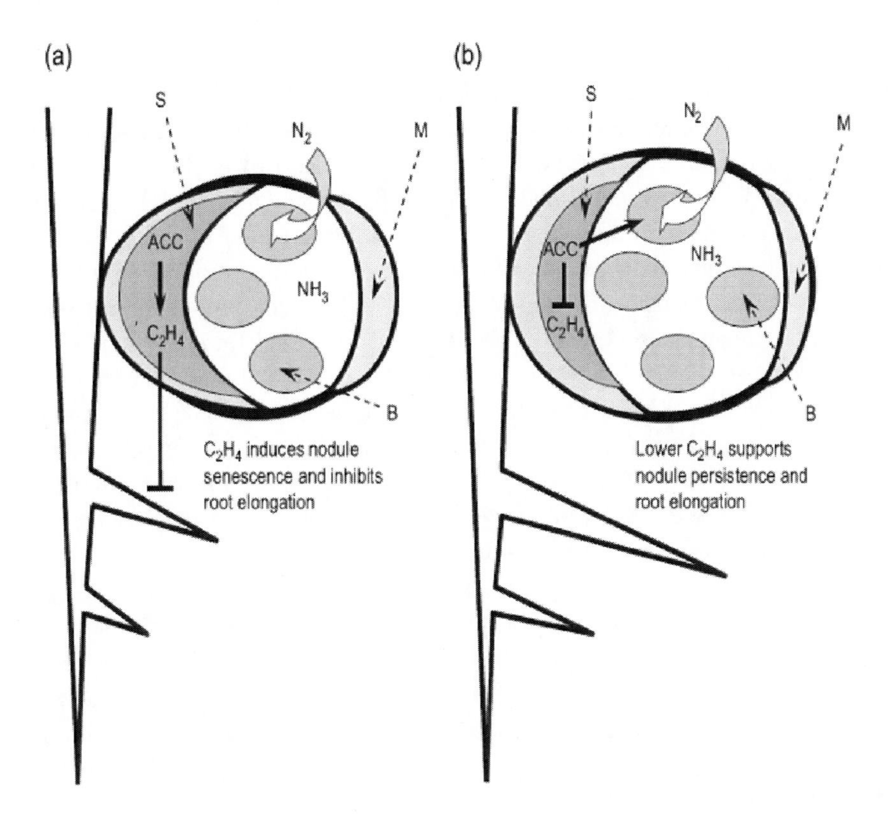

Figure 14. Schematic representation of leucaena nodules formed by AcdS⁻ (a) and AcdS+ (b) rhizobia, highlighting the possible effects of increased ACC deaminase activities on nodule senescence. Ethylene production in nodules formed by $AcdS^+$ rhizobia may be reduced due to ACC deaminase activities. As a result, AcdS+ rhizobia may form bigger nodules with relatively smaller senescence zone and larger nitrogen-fixing bacteroid zone. The increased root size of leucaena seelings inoculated with AcdS+ rhizobia may be caused by either increased nitrogen fixation by AcdS+ bacteroids or direct sequestering of ACC from the growing roots by AcdS+ rhizobia on the root surface. B: bacteroid, M: meristematic zone, S: senescence zone. From Ma *et al.* (2004).

The transconjugants of TAL1145 containing the native- and BL3-acdS genes formed nodules with greater number and sizes, and produced higher root mass in *L. leucocephala* than by TAL1145. This study shows that the introduction of multiple copies of the *acdS* gene can increase the ACC deaminase activities and can enhance the nodulation and growth of inoculated plants. Conforte *et al.* (2010) integrated the structural gene ACC deaminase (*acdS*) into the *M. loti* chromosome under a constitutive promoter activity. Transconjugant *M. loti* thus obtained has a gene encoding ACC deaminase, but this gene is under the activity of the NifA-RpoN-dependent promoter, that could only be expressed inside the nodule. The transformed strain induced a higher nodule formation and was found to be more competitive than the wild-type strain on *Lotus japonicus* and *L. tenuis*. These results suggest that the introduction of the ACC deaminase activity within *M. loti* could be a novel strategy to increase nodulation competitiveness of the bacteria.

Delayed Ripening

The plant hormone ethylene is an essential signaling molecule involved in many plant developmental processes including: germination, flower development, fruit ripening and responses to many environmental stimuli. Moreover, large increases in ethylene levels occur during stress responses in plants including fruit ripening and flower wilting. Manipulation of ethylene biosynthesis allows us to modulate these processes and thereby create plants with more robust and/or desirable traits. DNA Plant Technology (DNAP), Agritope and Monsanto developed tomatoes that delayed ripening by preventing the production of ethylene, a hormone that triggers ripening of fruit (Wood, 1995). Ethylene production in tomatoes was due to ACC, the precursor to ethylene. DNAP's tomato, called Endless Summer, inserted a truncated version of the ACC synthase gene into the tomato that interfered with the endogenous ACC synthase. Monsanto's tomato was engineered with the *ACC* deaminase gene from the soil bacterium *Pseudomonas chlororaphis* that lowered ethylene levels by breaking down ACC (Klee *et al.* 1991). Agritope introduced an S-adenosylmethionine hydrolase (SAMase) encoding gene derived from the *E. coli* bacteriophage T3, which reduced the levels of S-adenosylmethionine, a precursor to ACC (Good *et al.* 1994).

Wang *et al.* (2001) by applying 10 pmol of okadaic acid (OA), a specific inhibitor of type 1 or type 2A serine/threonine protein phosphatases, to the orchid (*Phalaenopsis* sp.) stigma induced a dramatic increase in production of ethylene and an accelerated senescence of the whole flower. OA treatment induced a differential expression pattern for the ACC synthase multigene family. Accumulation of *Phal-ACS1* transcript in the stigma, labelum, and ovary induced by OA were higher than those induced by pollination as determined by "semiquantitative" reverse transcriptase-polymerase chain reaction. In contrast, the transcript levels of *Phal-ACS2* and *Phal-ACS3* induced by OA were much lower than those induced by pollination. Aida *et al.* (1998) demonstrated extended shelf life in flower of torenia (*Torenia fournieri* Lind.) by introducing a fragment of the ACC oxidase gene in sense or in antisense orientation by *Agrobacterium*-mediated gene transfer.

Among primary transformants, 8 sense-gene-introduced plants and 3 antisense-gene-introduced plants showed significantly higher longevity than wild-type plants. Analysis of offspring suggested that the introduced gene has been inherited, and the extended flower longevity was linked to the existence of the gene. Northern blot analysis and measurement of ethylene production demonstrated a reduction in mRNA level and endogenous ethylene production in plants with improved flower longevity. Grichko *et al.* (2004) compared transgenic tomato (*Lycopersicon esculentum* Mill, cv. Heinz 902) plants expressing ACC deaminase with nontransformed plants for a number of traits that are thought to be affected by ACC and ethylene in plant tissues and in transgenic plants, the ACC deaminase gene under the transcriptional control of either two tandem 35S cauliflower mosaic virus promoters (constitutive expression), the *rolD* promoter from *Agrobacterium rhizogenes* (root-specific expression), or the PRB-1*b* promoter from tobacco (stress-induced expression).

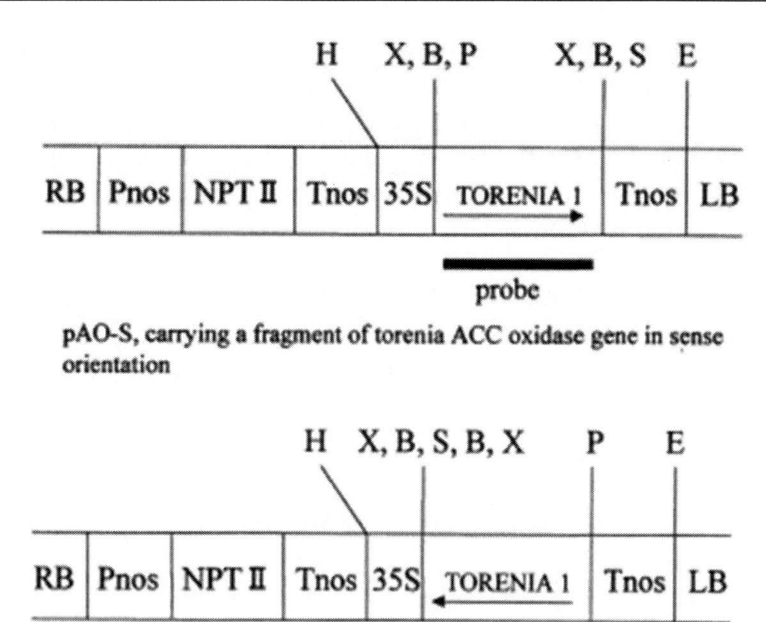

Figure 15. The structure of the binary vector pAO-S and pAO-A. The cloned fragment of torenia ACC oxidase gene (TORENIA-1: ~850 bp) was substituted for the GUS coding region of a binary vector pBI121 (Clontech, CA) with sense (pAO-S) or antisense (pAO-A) orientation. The length in the figure does not correspond to the actual length. RB and LB, right and left border sequences of T-DNA; Pnos and Tnos, promoter and terminator of nopaline synthase gene; 35S, promoter of CaMV 35S RNA gene; NPT II, coding region of neomycin phosphotransferase II gene; B, E, H, P, S and X, restriction sites of *Bam*H, *Eco*R I, *Hin*d III, *Pst* I, *Sma* I and *Xba* I, respectively. From Aida *et al.* (1998).

Figure 16. A flowering transgenic plant harboring ACC oxidase transgene (right) and a wild-type plant (left). The longevity of flowers in the transformant was greater than that of the wild type, which resulted in more flowers blooming simultaneously per stem on the transformant. From Aida *et al.* (1998).

The results presented in this study suggest that the ACC deaminase transgenic tomato plants exhibit a very healthy and more productive phenotype compared to the nontransformed plants since these plants had a large roots and shoot length, higher chlorophyll leaf and protein content.Yu and Bao (2004) transformed ACC oxidase mediated by *Agrobacterium tumefaciens* in the cultivar 'Master' of carnation (*Dianthus caryophyllus* L.) using four T-DNA structures containing sense, antisense, sense direct repeat and antisense direct repeat gene.

Detection based on Southern blotting analysis showed that foreign gene was integrated into the carnation genome with 14 new transgenic lines. During senescence in cut flowers, the ethylene production in the most of the transgenic lines decreased significantly, with ethylene not detected in some transformants.

Plant Growth Promotion

In addition to lowering ethylene levels, the bacteria may also provide a variety of other benefits to the plant. Some of these benefits are discussed here in the light of previous findings. Holguin and Glick (2001) cloned the ACC deaminase structural gene (*acd*S) from *Enterobacter cloacae* UW4 was cloned in the broad host range plasmid pRK415 under the control of the *lac* promoter and transferred into *Azospirillum brasilense* Cd and Sp245. The roots of tomato and canola seedlings were significantly longer in plants inoculated with *A. brasilense* Cd transformants than those in plants inoculated with the nontransformed strains of the same bacterium. Olubukola *et al.* (2003) conducted experiments under pot culture conditions to determine the growth effect of different rhizobacterial strains on maize plants.

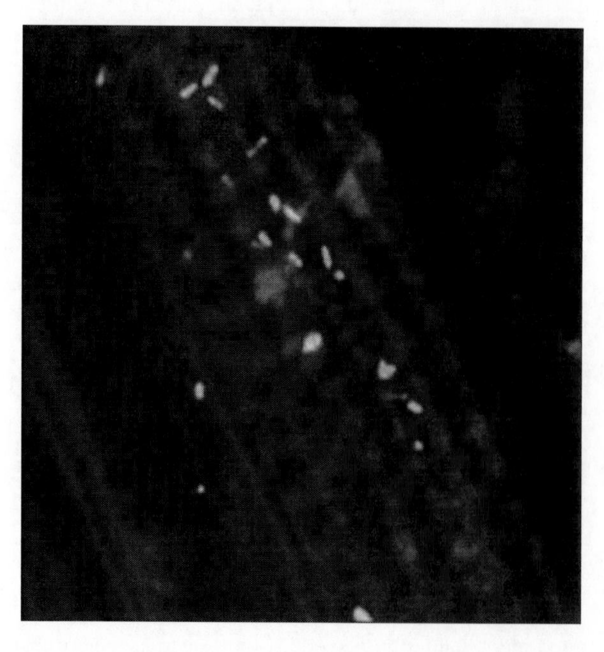

Figure 17. Photographs showing the endophytic colonization of *B. phytofirmans* strain PsJN. From Compant *et al.* (2005).

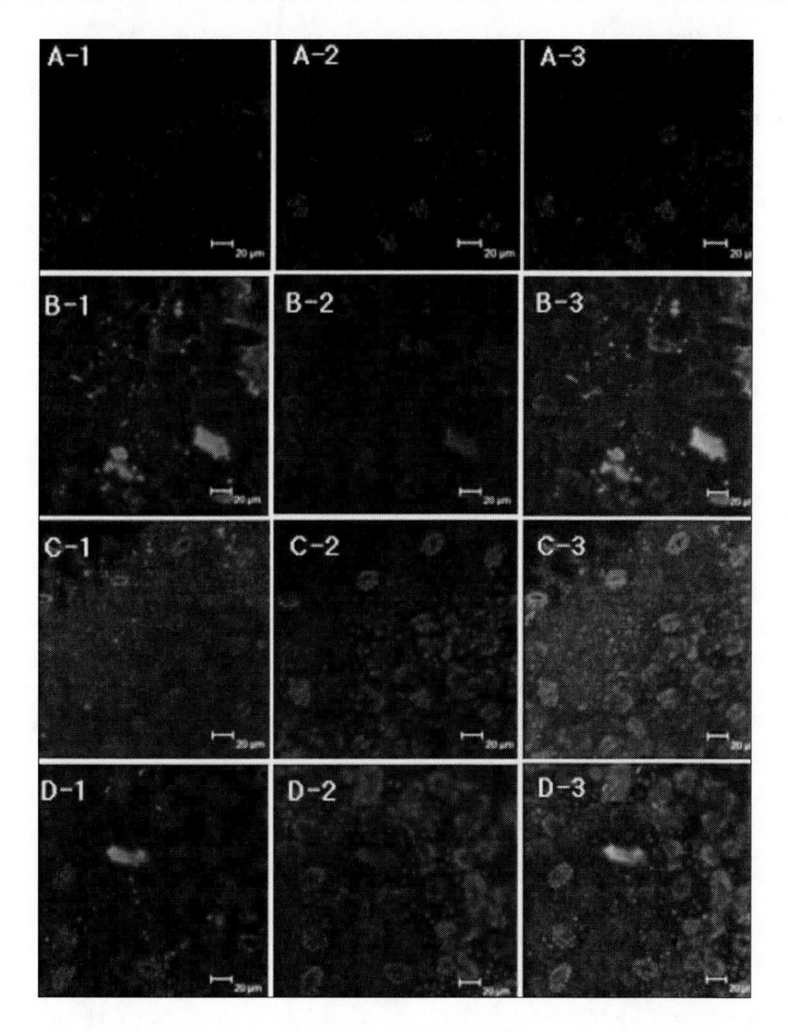

Figure 18. CLSM images showing colonization of gfp-tagged M. oryzae CBMB20 on leaves (at 50 days after transplantation). (A) Non-inoculated;(B) Soil inoculated; (C) Foliar inoculated, (D) Soil+foliar inoculated; (1) Green fluorescence; (2) Red fluorescence; (3) Green and red fluorescence overlapping. From Lee et al. 2011.

Three different bacterial strains were selected based on their plant growth promoting effects and ACC deaminase genes were amplified by polymerase chain reaction (PCR). Though each bacterial inoculation increased agronomic characteristics of maize the increase was not always statistically significant and an ACC deaminase specific product was amplified only from the strains *Pseudomonas* sp. 4MKS8 and *Klebsiella oxytoca* 10MKR7. *Burkholderia phytofirmans* strain PsJN T belonging to the family ß-Proteobacteria (Sessitsch *et al.,* 2005) was isolated from surface-sterilized and *Glomus vesiculiferum* infected onion roots (Nowak *et al.,* 1997). ACC deaminase activity of the strain PsJN probably contributed to the plant growth promoting abilities of this strain. Strain PsJN colonizes various plants endophytically and in the rhizospheres and its plant growth promotion ability has been reported with various plants such as potato, tomato, grapevine (Frommel *et al.,* 1991; Nowak *et al.*, 1995; Pillay and Nowak, 1997; Bensalim *et al.*, 1998; Compant *et al.,* 2005). Conteso et al. (2008) investigated the role of AcdS and the involvement of ethylene signaling pathway in plant development responses to rhizobacteria, using the model plant *Arabidopsis thaliana*. These authors compared the changes in root architecture and root hair length induced by ACC deaminase containing four rhizobacterial strains (*Phyllobacterium brassicacearum* STM196, *Pseudomonas putida* UW4, *Rhizobium leguminosarum* bv. viciae 128C53K, *Mesorhizobium loti* MAFF303099) and by their respective *acdS* deficient mutants. Though all the mutant strains induced similar changes in lateral root development compared to thier counterparts, root hairs of seedlings inoculated with the *acdS* mutant strains were significantly longer. Based on the results these authors suggested that rhizobacterial *acdS* activity affects local regulatory mechanisms in plant roots, and not lateral root development that is under systemic regulation involving shoot–root dialog.

Sun *et al.* (2009) used the structural gene for ACC deaminase (*acdS*) from the endophytic plant growth-promoting bacterium *B. phytofirmans* PsJN to construct a mutant strain *B. phytofirmans* YS2 (*B. phytofirmans* PsJN/Δ*acdS*), in which an internal segment of the *acdS* gene was deleted. The mutant YS2 lost ACC deaminase activity as well as its ability to promote root elongation with canola seedlings. Vitrbo *et al.* (2010) evaluated the plant growth promoting ability in ACC deaminase containing fungi *Trichoderma asperellum* T203. This strain was able to promote canola (*Brassica napus*) root elongation in pouch assays and RNAi silencing of the ACCD gene in *T. asperellum* showed decreased ability to promote root elongation in canola seedlings. Lee et al. (2011) reported increased Plant height, fruit dry weight, and total biomass in all ACC deaminase containing *M. oryzae* CBMB20 inoculation methods as compared to noninoculated control. Furthermore, uptake of mineral nutrients such as N, P, K, Ca, and Mg in red pepper plants in all *M. oryzae* CBMB20 inoculation methods was higher than in non-inoculated control plants.

Conclusion

The present day development in agriculture is hampered with various kinds of stresses that accentuate the biosynthesis of ethylene, inhibiting plant growth through several mechanisms at molecular level. Transgenic plants produced to express ACC deaminase genes are found to more robust than their non-transformed counterparts in the face of pathogen attack, flooding, drought, or high salinity. Moreover, PGPR expressing ACC deaminase genes are helpful in reducing stress responses in cop plants, modulation of nodulation in legumes and in the biological control of plant diseases and could be useful for developing better understanding of mechanisms responsible for induction of tolerance in plants.

Acknowledgment

This research was supported by the Basic Science Research Program through the National Research Foundation of Korea (NRF) funded by the Ministry of Education, Science and Technology (2012R1A2A1A01005294).

References

Abeles, F.B., P.W. Morgan and M.E. Saltveit. 1992. *Ethylene in Plant Biology*. Academic Press, New York. pp: 147-154.

Abou-Shanab, R. A., K. Ghanem and N. Ghanem. 2008. The role of bacteria on heavy-metal extraction and uptake by plants growing on multi-metal contaminated soils. *World J. Microbiol. Biotechnol.*, 24 (2): 253-262.

Aida, R., T. Yoshida, K. Ichimura, R. Goto, and M. Shibata.1998. Extension of flower longevity in transgenic torenia plants incorporating ACC oxidase transgene. *Plant Science* 138 91–101.

Arshad, M and W.T. Frankenberger. 2002. *Ethylene: agricultural sources and applications*. Kluwer Academic / Plenum Publishers, New York.

Belimov, A.A., I.C. Dodd, V.I. Safronova, N. Hontzeas and W.J. Davies.2007. *Pseudomonas brassicacearum* strain Am3 containing 1-aminocyclopropane-1-carboxylate deaminase can show both pathogenic and growth-promoting properties in its interaction with tomato. *J. Exp. Bot.* 24: 1-11.

Bensalim, S., J. Nowak and S.K. Asiedu.1998. Temperature and pseudomonad bacterium effects on *in vitro* and *ex vitro* performance of 18 clones of potato. *Am. J. Potato Res.* 75,145-152.

Bleecker AB, Kende H (2000) Ethylene: a gaseous signal molecule in plants. *Annu. Rev. Cell Dev. Biol.* 16: 1–18.

Cavalca, L., Corsini, A., Bachate, S., and Andreoni, V. 2010. Role of PGP arsenic-resistant bacteria in As mobilization and translocation in *Helianthus annuus* L. 19th World Congress of Soil Science, Soil Solutions for a Changing World. 1 – 6 August 2010, Brisbane, Australia.

Chehregani, A., M. Noori, H. Lari Yazdi, Phytoremediation of heavy-metal polluted soils: screening for new accumulator plants in Angouran mine (Iran) and evaluation of removal ability, *Ecotoxicol. Environ. Saf.* 72 (2009) 1349–1353.

Cheng, Z., E. Park, B.R. Glick. 2007. 1-Aminocyclopropane-1-carboxylate (ACC) deaminase from *Pseudomonas putida* UW4 facilitates the growth of canola in the presence of salt. *Can. J. Microbiol.* 54. 212–219.

Compant, S., Reiter, B., Sessitsch, A., Nowak, J., Clement, C., and Ait Barka, E. (2005). Endophytic colonization of *Vitis vinifera* L. by a plant growth-promoting bacterium, *Burkholderia* sp. strain PsJN. *Appl. Environ. Microbiol.* 71, 1685-1693.

Conforte, V.P., M. Echeverria, C. Sanchez, R.A. Ugalde, A.B. Menendez, V.C. Lepek 2010. Engineered ACC deaminaseexpressing free-living cells of Mesorhizobium loti show increased nodulation efficiency and competitiveness on *Lotus* spp. *J. Gen. Appl. Microbiol.* 56(4):331–338.

Contesto, C., G. Desbrosses, C. Lefoulon, G. Bena, F. Borel, M. Galland, L. Gamet, F. Varoquauxa and B. Touraine.2008. Effects of rhizobacterial ACC deaminase activity on *Arabidopsis* indicate that ethylene mediates local root responses to plant growth-promoting rhizobacteria. *Plant Science* 175:178-189.

Duan, J., K. M. Mu¨ller, T. C. Charles, S. Vesely, and B. R. Glick. 2009. 1-Aminocyclopropane-1-carboxylate (ACC) deaminase genes in rhizobia from southern Saskatchewan. *Microb. Ecol.* 57:423–436.

Farwell, A. J., S. Vesely., V. Nero, K. McCormack, H. Rodriguez, S. Shah, D.G. Dixon, and B.R. Glick. 2007. Tolerance of transgenic canola (*Brassica napus*) amended with ACC deaminase-containing plant growth-promoting bacteria to flooding stress at a metal-contaminated field site. *Environ. Poll.* 147: 540–545.

Glick, B.R., D.M. Penrose, and J. Li. 1998. A model for the lowering of plant ethylene concentrations by plant growth-promoting bacteria. *J. Theoretical Biol.* 190: 63-68.

Glick, B. R., Z. Cheng, J. Czarny and J. Duan. 2007. Promotion of plant growth by ACC deaminase-producing soil bacteria *Eur. J. Plant Pathol.* 119:329–339.

Good, X., J. Kellogg, W. Wagoner, D. Langhoff, W. Matsumura and R.K. Bestwick 1994. "Reduced ethylene synthesis by transgenic tomatoes expressing S-adenosylmethionine hydrolase". *Plant Molecular Biology* 26 (3): 781.

Grichko, V.P., B. Filby, B.R. Glick. 2000. Increased ability of transgenic plants expressing the bacterial enzyme ACC deaminase to accumulate Cd, Co, Cu, Ni, Pb, and Zn. *J. Biotechnol.* 81:45–53.

Grichko, V. P. and B.R. Glick. 2001. Amelioration of flooding stress by ACC deaminase-containing plant growth-promoting bacteria. *Plant Physiol. and Biochem.*, 39, 11–17.

Grichko, V. P., B.R. Glick, V.I. Grishko, and K. P. Pauls. 2004. Evaluation of Tomato Plants with Constitutive, Root-Specific, and Stress-Induced ACC Deaminase Gene Expression. *Russian J. Plant Physiol.* 52 (3): 359–364.

Klee, H. J., M. B. Hayford, K. A. Kretzmer, G. F. Barry and G. M. Kishore 1991. Control of ethylene synthesis by expression of a bacterial enzyme in transgenic tomato plants. *The Plant Cell* 3(11): 1187–1193.

Hamilton, A.J, G.W. Lycett and D. Grierson. 1990. Antisense gene that inhibits synthesis of ethylene in transgenic plants. *Nature* 346: 284-287.

Hao, Y., Charles, T.C., Bernard R. Glick (2011) ACC deaminase activity in avirulent *Agrobacterium tumefaciens* D3. *Can. J. Microbiol.* 57(4): 278-286.

Haque, M. R., M.K. Ahmed, M.A. Mannaf, and M.M. Islam. 2006. Seasonal variation of heavy metals concentrations in *Gudusia chapra* inhabiting the Sunderban mangrove forest. *J. NOAMI.,* 23 (1), 1-21.

Holguin, G. and B.R. Glick. 2001. Expression of the ACC deaminase gene from *Enterobacter cloacae* UW4 in *Azospirillum brasilense. Microb. Ecol.* 41: 281-288.

Honma M. 1993. Stereospecific reaction of 1-aminocyclopropane-1-carboxylate deaminase. In: J.C. Pech, A. Latche, and C. Balague (eds) Cellular and Molecular Aspects of the Plant Hormone Ethylene, pp: 111-116 Kluwer Academic Publishers, Dordrecht, The Netherlands.

Honma, M and T. Shimomura. 1978. Metabolism of 1-aminocyclopropane- 1-carboxylic acid. *Agric. Biol. Chem.* 42:1825–1831.

Honma, M. 1985. Chemically reactive sulfhydryl groups of 1-aminocyclopropane-1-carboxylate deaminase. *Agric. Biol. Chem. 49*: 567-571.

Hontzeas N, Zoidakis J, Glick BR, Abu-Omar MM. 2003. Expression and characterization of 1-aminocyclopropane-1-carboxylate deaminase from the rhizobacterium *Pseudomonas putida* UW4: a key enzyme in bacterial plant growth promotion. *Biochimica. Biophysica. Acta.* 1703: 11-19.

Hontzeas, N., A.O. Richardson, A. Belimov V. Safronova, M.M. Abu-Omar and B.R. Glick. 2005. Evidence for horizontal transfer of 1-aminocyclopropane-1-carboxylate deaminase genes. *J. Bacteriol.* 186: 2439-2448.

Indiragandhi, P., R. Anandham, K.A. Kim, W.J. Yim, M. Madhaiyan and T. Sa. 2008. Induction of defense responses in tomato against *pseudomonas syringae* pv. tomato by regulating the stress ethylene level with *methylobacterium oryzae* CBMB20 containing 1-aminocyclopropane-1-carboxylate deaminase, *World J. Microb. Biotechnol.* 24(7): 1037-1045.

Jacobson, C.B., J.J. Pasternak, and B.R. Glick. 1994. Partial purification and characterization of 1-aminocyclopropane-1-carboxylate deaminase from the plant growth promotion in rhizobacterium *Pseudomonas putida* GR12-2. *Can. J. Microbiol.* 40: 1019-1025.

Jia, Y.J., Y. Kakuta, M. Sugawara, T. Igarashi, N. Oki, M. Kisaki, T. Shoji, Y. Kanetuna, T. Horita, H. Matsui and M. Honma.1999. Synthesis and degradation of 1-aminocyclopropane-1-carboxylic acid by *Penicillium citrinum. Biosci. Biotechnol. Biochem.* 63:542–549.

Jonathan M, L. McDonnell, and S. Regan. 2009. Plant encoded 1-aminocyclopropane-1-carboxylic acid deaminase activity implicated in different aspects of plant development. Plant Signal Behav. 4(12): 1186–1189.

Kamalakannan, S., K. Lee, S. Park, J. Chae, B. Yun, Y. H. Lee, Y. J. Park and O. Byung-Taek. 2010. Characterization of ACC deaminase gene in *Pseudomonas entomophila* strain PS-PJH isolated from the rhizosphere soil. *J. Basic Microbiol.*50, 200–205.

Karthikeyan, S., Q. Zhou, Z. Zhao, C.L. Kao, Z. Tao, H. Robinson, H.W. Liu and H. Zhang. 2004. Structural analysis of *Pseudomonas* 1-aminocyclopropane-1-carboxylate deaminase complexes: insight into the mechanism of a unique pyridoxal-5- phosphate dependent cyclopropane ring-opening reaction. *Biochem.* 43:13328–13339.

Karthikeyan, B., M.M. Joe, R. Islam, and T. Sa. 2012. ACC deaminase containing diazotrophic endophytic bacteria ameliorate salt stress in Catharanthus roseus through reduced ethylene levels and induction of antioxidative defense systems. Symbiosis (In press) DOI: 10.1007/s13199-012-0162-6.

Kotrba, P., J. Najmanova, T. Macek, T. Ruml and M. Mackova. 2009. Genetically Modified Plants in Phytoremediation of Heavy Metal and Metalloid Soil and Sediment Pollution. *Biotechnol. Adv.* 27(6): 799–810.

Leonard, P. M., S.H.J. Smits, S.E. Sedelnikova, A.B. Brinkman, W.M. de Vos, O.J. van der Oost, D.W. Rice and J.B. Rafferty. 2001. Crystal structure of the Lrp-like transcrptional regulator from the archaeon Pyrococcus furiosus. *EMBO Journal,* 20, 990–997.

Lee, M., P.S. Chauhan, W. Yim, G. Lee, Y. S. Kim, K. Park, and T. Sa. 2011. Foliar Colonization and Growth Promotion of Red Pepper (*Capsicum annuum* L.) by *Methylobacterium oryzae* CBMB20 *J. Appl. Biol. Chem.* 54(2): 120-125.

Li, J and B.R. Glick. 2001. Transcriptional regulation of the Enterobacter cloacae UW4 1-aminocyclopropane-1- carboxylate (ACC) deaminase gene (acdS). *Can. J. Microbiol.*, 47, 359–367.

Ma, W., T.C. Charles and B.R. Glick. 2004. Expression of an exogenous ACC deaminase gene in *Sinorhizobium meliloti* increases its ability to nodulate Alfalfa. *Appl. Environ. Microbiol.,* 70: 5891–7.

Mattoo, A.K. and J.C. Suttle. 1991. The Plant Hormone Ethylene. CRC, Press, Boca Raton, FL.

Madhaiyan, M., S. Poonguzhali, M. Senthilkumar, S. Seshadri, H.K. Chung, J.C. Yang, S.P. Sundaram and T. Sa 2004. Growth promotion and induction of systemic resistance in rice cultivar Co-47 (*Oryza sativa* L.) by *Methylobacterium* spp, *Bot. Bull. Acad. Sinica.*, 45: 315-324.

Madhaiyan, M., S. Poonguzhali and T. Sa 2006. Systemic resistance case study with *Methylobacterium* and rice. *In Prospects and applications for plant associated microbes*. Ed by Sorvari, S. and A.M. Pittila. BioBen Innovations, Finland.

Madhaiyan, M., S. Poonguzhali and T. Sa. 2007. Metal tolerating methylotrophic bacteria reduces nickel and cadmium toxicity and promotes plant growth of tomato (*Lycopersicon esculentum* L.). *Chemosphere* 69: 220–228.

McDonnell, L., J.M. Plett, S. Andersson-Gunneras, C. Kozela, J. Dugardeyn, S.D. Van Der, B.R. Glick, Sundberg, B and Regan S. 2009. Ethylene levels are regulated by a plant encoded 1-aminocyclopropane-1-carboxylic acid deaminase. *Physiol. Plant* 136: 94–109.

Minami R, K. Uchiyama, T. Murakami, J. Kawai, K. Mikami, T. Yamada, D. Yokoi, H. Ito, H. Matsui, H. Honm. 1998. Properties, sequence, and synthesis in *Escherichia coli* of 1-aminocyclopropane-1-carboxylate deaminase from *Hansenula saturnus*. *J. Microbiol.* 41: 109-117.

N. Hontzeas, S. Saleh and B.R. Glick. 2004. Changes in gene expression in canola roots induced by ACC-deaminase-containing plant-growth-promoting bacteria. Mol. *Plant-Microbe. Interact.* 12: 951–959.

Nie, L., S. Shah, G.I. Burd, D.G. Dixon and B.R. Glick. 2002. Phytoremediation of arsenate contaminated soil by transgenic canola and the plant growth-promoting bacterium *Enterobacter cloacae* CAL2. *Plant Physiol. Biochem.* 40:355–361.

Nowak, J. 1998. Benefits of *in vitro* "biotization" of plant tissue cultures with microbial inoculants. *In Vitro Cell. Dev. Biol. Plant* 34: 122-130.

Nukui, N., K. Minamisawa, S.I. Ayabe, T. Aoki. 2006. Expression of the 1-aminocyclopropane-1- carboxylic acid deaminase gene requires symbiotic nitrogen-fixing regulator gene nifA2 in *Mesorhizobium loti* MAFF303099. *Appl. Environ. Microbiol.* 72: 4964-4969.

Olubukola, O. B, Osir E. O., Sanni, A.I., Odhiambo, G.D., and Bulimo, W.D. 2003. Amplification of 1-amino-cyclopropane-1-carboxylic (ACC) deaminase from plant growth promoting rhizobacteria in *Striga*-infested soil. *African J. Biotechnol.* 2 (6): 157–160.

Onofre-Lemus, J., I. Hernández-Lucas, L. Girard, J. Caballero-Melladom 2009. ACC (1-aminocyclopropane-1-carboxylate) deaminase activity, a widespread trait in *Burkholderia* species, and its growth promoting effect on tomato plants. *Appl. Environ. Microbiol.* 75:6581–6590.

Osee, T., A. Fujino, M. Yao, N. Watanabe, M. Honma and I. Tanaka. 2003. Reaction intermediate structures of 1-aminocyclopropane-1-carboxylate deaminase: insight into PLP-dependent cyclopropane ring-opening reaction. *J. Biol. Chem.* 278: 41069–41076.

Pillay, V.K and J. Nowak. 1997. Inoculum density, temperature and genotype effects on epiphytic and endophytic colonization and *in vitro* growth promotion of tomato (*Lycopersicon esculentum* L.) by a pseudomonad bacterium. *Can. J. Microbiol.* 43,354-361.

Rajkumar, M., N. Ae and H. Freitas. 2009. Endophytic Bacteria and Their Potential to Enhance Heavy Metal Phytoextraction. *Chemosphere* 77(2): 153- 160.

Robison, M.M., S. Shah, B. Tamot, K.P. Pauls, B.A. Moffatt, and B.R. Glick. 2001. Reduced symptoms of *Verticillium* wilt in transgenic tomato expressing a bacterial ACC deaminase. *Mol. Plant Pathol.* 23: 135–145.

Rodriguez, H., S. Vessely, S. Shah and B.R. Glick. 2008. Effect of a nickel-tolerant ACC deaminase-producing Pseudomonas strain on growth of nontransformed and transgenic canola plants, *Curr. Microbiol.* 57, 170–174.

Sadrnia, M., N. Maksimava, E. Khromsova, S. Stanislavich, P. Owlia and M. Arjomandzadegan. 2011. Study the effect of bacterial 1-aminocyclopropane-1-carboxylate deaminase (acc deaminase) on resistance to salt stress in tomato plant. *Analele Universității din Oradea - Fascicula Biologie*. Tom. XVIII, Issue: 2, 2011, pp. 120-123.

Saleem M., Arshad S. Hussain and A.S. Bhatti 2007. Perspective of plant growth promoting rhizobacteria (PGPR) containing ACC deaminase in stress agriculture. *J. Ind. Microbiol. Biotechnol.* 34: 635–648.

Saravanakumar, D., R. Samiyappan. 2006.ACC deaminase from *Pseudomonas fluorescens* mediated saline resistance in groundnut (*Arachis hypogea*) plants. *J. Appl. Microbiol.,* 102 (2006), pp. 1283–1292.

Sergeeva, E., S. Shah, B.R. Glick. Tolerance of transgenic canola expressing a bacterial ACC deaminase gene to high concentrations of salt. *World J. Microbiol. Biotechnol.,* 22 (2006), pp. 277–282.

Sessitsch, A., Coenye, T., Sturz, A.V., Vandamme, P., Ait Barka, E., Salles, J.F., van Elsas, J.D., Faure, D., Reiter, B., Glick, B.R., Wang-Pruski, G., and Nowak, J. (2005). *Burkholderia phytofirmans* sp. nov., a novel plant-associated bacterium with plant-beneficial properties. *Int. J. Syst. Evol. Microbiol.* 55, 1187-1192.

Sheng, X.F., Xia, J.J., 2006. Improvement of rape (*Brassica napus*) plant growth and cadmium uptake by cadmium-resistant bacteria. *Chemosphere* 64, 1036–1042.

Siddikee, M. A., Glick, B. R., Chauhan, P. S., W. J. Yim and T. Sa. 2011. Enhancement of growth and salt tolerance of red pepper seedlings (*Capsicum annuum* L.) by regulating stress ethylene synthesis with halotolerant bacteria containing 1-aminocyclopropane-1-carboxylic acid deaminase activity. *Plant Physiol. Biochem.* 49(4): 427-434.

Stearns, J.C and B.R. Glick. 2003. Transgenic plants with altered ethylene biosynthesis or perception. *Biotechnnol. Adv.* 21(3): 193-210.

Stearns, J.C., S. Shah, B.M. Greenberg, D.G. Dixon and B.R. Glick. 2005. Tolerance of transgenic canola expressing 1-aminocyclopropane-1-carboxylic acid deaminase to growth inhibition by nickel. *Plant Physiol. Biochem.* 43:701–708.

Sun, J., V. Cardoza, D. M. Mitchell, L. Bright, G. Oldroyd and J. M. Harris. 2006. Crosstalk between jasmonic acid, ethylene and Nod factor signalling allows integration of diverse inputs for regulation of nodulation. *Plant J.* 46: 961–970.

Theologism, A 1992. One rotten apple spoils the whole bushel: the role of ethylene in fruit ripening. *Cell* 70: 181-184.

Tittabutr, P., J. Awaya, Q. Li, and D. Borthakur. 2008. The cloned 1-aminocyclopropane-1-carboxylate (ACC) deaminase gene from *Sinorhizobium* sp. strain BL3 in Rhizobium sp. strain TAL1145 promotes nodulation and growth of Leucaena leucocephala. Syst. Appl Microbiol. 31 (2): 141-50.

Todorovic, B and *B.R.* Glick. 2008. The interconversion of ACC deaminase and d-cysteine desulfhydrase by directed mutagenesis. *Planta* 229*:* 193–205.

Viterbo, A., U. Landau, S. Kim, L. Chernin, and I. Chet. 2010. Characterization of ACC deaminase from the biocontrol and plant growth promoting agent *Trichoderma asperellum* T203. *FEMS Microbiol. Lett.* 305:42–48.

Wakatsuki, T., M. S. Kolodney, G. I. Zahalak, and E. L. Elson. 2000. Cell mechanics studied by a reconstituted model tissue. *Biophys. J.* 79: 2353–2368.

Walsh, C., R.A. Pascal M. Johnston, R. Raines, D. Dikshit, A. Krantz, M. Honma. 1981. In: Molecular Mechanistic studies on the pyridoxal phosphate enzyme 1-aminocyclopropane-1-carboxylate deaminase from *Pseudomonas* sp. Ed: VanLoon, L.C. and B.R. Glick. 2004. Increased plant fitness by rhizobacteria. *Biochemistry* 20:7509–7519.

Wang, C.K.E., B.R. Glick and G. Defago. 2000. Effect of transferring 1- aminocyclopropane-1-carboxylic acid (ACC) deaminase genes into *Pseudomonas fluorescens* strain CHA0 and its gacA derivative CHA96 on their growth-promoting and disease-suppressive capacities. *Can J. Microbiol.* 46:898–907.

Wood, M. 2005. "Tomato Trek Yields Chilean Treasure". United States Department of Agriculture.

Yang, S.F and N.E. Hoffman. 1984. Ethylene biosynthesis and its regulation in higher plants. *Annual Review of Plant Physiol.* 35: 155-189.

Yao, M., Ose, T., Sugimoto, H., Horiuchi, A., Nakagawa, A., Wakatsuki, S., Yokoi, D., Murakami, T., Honma, M., and Tanaka, I. 2000. Crystal structure of 1-aminocyclopropane-1-carboxylate deaminase from *Hansenula saturnus*. *J. Biol. Chem.* 275: 34557–34565.

Yim, W.J., S. Poonguzhali, M. Madhaiyan, P. Palaniappan, M.A. Siddikee and T. Sa. 2009. Characterization of plant-growth promoting diazotrophic bacteria isolated from field grown chinese cabbage under different fertilization conditions, *J. Microbiol.* 47(2): 147-155.

Yu, Y and M. Bao. 2004. Carnation Flower Vase Life Prolonged by Transformation with Antisense *ACC* Oxidase Gene *Acta Horticulturae Sinica*. 34(5):633-636.

Zanetti, M.E., M.C. Terrile, D.A. Arce, A.V. Godoy, B.S. Segundo and C. Casalongue. 2002. Isolation and characterization of a potato cDNA corresponding to a 1-aminocyclopropane-1-carboxylate (ACC) oxidase gene differentially activated by stress *J. Exp. Bot.* 53 (379): 2455-2457.

Zhang, H., M.S. Kim, Y. Sun, S.E. Dowd, H. Shi, P.W. Pare. 2008. Soil bacteria confer plant salt tolerance by tissue-specific regulation of sodium transporter HKT1. *Mol Plant Microbe Interact* 21:737–744.

In: Applications of Microbial Genes in Enzyme Technology ISBN: 978-1-62417-808-5
Editors: V.K.Gupta, M.G.Tuohy, G.D.Sharma et al.

Chapter 14

Variable Expression and Regulation of Genes Encoding Peroxidase: Multiple Applications

Ram Naraian**, *Rajanish Kumar Pandey, Yashvant Patel and V. K. Singh
Department of Biotechnology, Faculty of Science,
Veer Bahadur Singh Purvanchal University, Jaunpur, India

Abstract

The present chapter has summarized current knowledge on differential regulation of genes encoding for different fungal peroxidase enzymes and their isozymes. Peroxidase has been detected in numerous kinds of organism such as plants, animal, insects, bacteria, and more than ever fungi. The peroxidase are mainly produced during the stationary growth phase of the fungi, but current investigations have reported that various factor *viz* situations of carbon, nitrogen, sulphur limitation, oxidative stress, and heat shock trigger the levels of peroxidase gene expression and enzyme production. Two major category of white-rot fungal (WRF) peroxidase: Lignin peroxidase (LiP) and Manganese peroxidase (MnP) have been identified and characterized at the transcript level. Methods allowing the analysis of differential expression and regulation of peroxidase-encoding genes, PCR amplification of peroxidase related nucleotide sequences from cDNA (RT-PCR amplification) prepared by using RNA from ligninolytic cultures. Peroxidase isoforms have potential application in the field of biotechnology and nanotechnology. Both kinds of peroxidase are well known to play important physiological roles such as, morphogenesis, pathogenesis and lignin degradation. Peroxidases are enormously used in many biotechnological processes *viz*., biodegradation, bioremediation, agriculture, medicinal and industrial applications. Currently peroxidase have been also explored to different advanced biotechnological processes including biosensor, beverages, animal feed, cosmetics, immunoassays and transformation of antibiotics and steroids.

* Corresponding author: E-mail: ramnarain_itrc@rediffmail.com, Phone: +919453037072.

Introduction

Mycelium of fungus release extracellular ligninolytic enzymes, which play an important role in lignocellulosics biomass conversion. These ligninolytic enzymes are lignin peroxidase (LiP) and manganese peroxidase (MnP) (Kersten and Kirk, 1987; Kirk and Farrell, 1987). Peroxidase super family classified as heme-containing extracellular fungal peroxidase (Welinder and Gajhede, 1993; Martínez, 2002). Peroxidases are oxidoreductase that utilizes hydrogen peroxide to catalyze oxidation reaction (Everse and Everse, 1991). White-rot fungi are capable to degrade recalcitrant environmental pollutants such as textile dyes, polyaromatic hydrocarbons, polychlorophenols and polychlorinated biphenyls (Asghar *et al.*, 2006). This is achieved by excreting extracellular polyphenol oxidases particularly lignin peroxidases and manganese peroxidases which are effective in degrading lignin (Revankar and Lele, 2007). These peroxidase have been isolated from various white-rot basidiomycete fungi such as *Phaerochaete chrysosporium, Pleurotus ostreatus, Trametes versicolor* (Lundquist and Nyman, 1989; Johansson *et al.*, 1993), *Phlebibia radiate* (Niku-Paavola *et al.*, 1988), *Physisporium rivulosus, Bjerkandera adusta* (Kimura *et al.*, 1990), *Cerviporiopsis subvermispora* (Ruttiman *et al.*, 1992) and *Agricus bisporus* (Bonnen *et al.*, 1994).

These enzymes have an interest in this study for their numerous biotechnological applications in last 20 years. Both MnP and LiP have been characterized by a variety of biochemical and kinetic techniques (Gold and Alic, 1993). Multiple forms (isoforms) of these versatile catalytic enzymes have been isolated and characterized by chromatographic analysis, N-terminal amino acid sequence analysis and molecular cloning techniques. Regulation system of these isozymes performs by the analysis of transcript that shows the change in isozymes production at transcriptional level. For the study of closely related transcript, quantitative reverse transcription PCR (RT-PCR) were used (James *et al.*, 1992; Broda *et al.*, 1995; Brooks *et al.*, 1993).The expression of the peroxidase in the medium is influenced by the several factors and expression of peroxidase genes and can be controlled by different factors. In the present chapter, a detailed account of several peroxidase gene families, their different known isozymes, differential regulation under numerous conditions in presence of the variety of supplements, and broad spectrum of their applications has been discussed.

Gene Families Encoding Peroxidase

During the period of last fifteen years, knowledge of fungal peroxidase encoding genes and their regulation in model system *P. chrysosporium* has increased rapidly (Conesa *et al.*, 2002; Cullen, 1997; Martínez, 2002). The super family of peroxidase can be divided into three subclasses comprising; first: organized localized heme peroxidases (class I), second: secreted fungal heme peroxidase (Class II) and third: secreted plant heme peroxidase (class III). Class I belongs to bacterial and eukaryotic organisms, class II from fungi and class III basically from plants. One of these classes II has major importance due to their microbial secretion and its vast applicability. Vanden *et al.* (2006) reported that *P. chrysosporium* have 10 LiP encoding genes and 5 MnP encoding genes 5 within genomic size 35.1 Mbp, and total proteins 10048 (http://genome.jgipsf.org/Phchr1/Phchr1.home.html). Little information is known about the organization of peroxidase genes other than *P. chrysosporium,* although a cluster containing two LiP and one MnP-encoding gene has been described for *T. versicolor* (Johansson and Nyman, 1996). Very recently, genome sequence data of two other wood-colonizing, white-rot fungi, i.e., *S. commune* and *Pleurotus ostreatus,* became available. Because of the separate functions of subclasse II has been further subcategorized into two major categories Lip and MnP. These subcategories are described separately as below.

Lignin Peroxidase (Lip) Gene Family

Lignin peroxidase (LiP) isozymes were first reported in the cultures of *P. chrysosporium* (Glenn *et al.*, 1983; Tien and Kirk, 1983), and other white-rot fungi including *Phlebia radiata* and *P. tremellosa* (Niku-Paavola *et al.*, 1988; Lundell *et al.*, 1990; Vares *et al.*, 1995), *Trametes* (*T. versicolor* and *T. trogii*) (Jonsson *et al.*, 1987; Vares and Hatakka, 1997), and *Bjerkandera* (*B. adusta* and *Bjerkandera* spp. (Heinfling *et al.*, 1998). High degree of homology at amino acid sequence, nucleotide sequences and intron /exon structure have been clarified that genes are allelic. These LiP isozymes encoded by closely related genes are due to differential post-translational modification (Brown *et al.*, 1988; Zhang *et al.*, 1986). These closely related genes are present in three different linkage groups (Cullen, 1997). Genetic linkage in *P. chrysosporium* has been demonstrated by restriction fragment length polymorphisms (RFLP) and PCR-based segregation analysis (Gaskell *et al.*, 1994). The cluster of *lip* structurally related genes have been designated as *lipA* through *lip J* (Brown *et al.*, 1988). Restriction fragment length polymorphism (RFLP) and allele specific marker demonstrated that linkage of eight genes *lipA, lipB, lipC, lipE, lipG, lipH, lipI and lipJ*, reside within 3% recombination, which corresponds to 96 kb region of scaffold 19 (Martinez *et al.*, 2004). Another two gene *lipD* and *lipF* separated from other eight genes differentially localized by Southern blots of pulsed field gels (D'Souza, 1993; Gaskell *et al.*, 1991, 1994; Stewart, 1992). Furthermore, Stewart and Cullen (1999) also reported that lignin peroxidases of *P. chrysosporium* are encoded by a minimum of 10 closely related genes, designated from A to J. These are *lip*A, *lipB, lipC, lipD, lipE, lipF, lipG, lipH, lipI and lipJ*. Expression and regulation of *lip* genes was also analyzed by Northen blot with gene-specific marker (Gaskel *et al.*, 1991). All genomic sequences of *P. chrysosporium* strain are available for expanding our knowledge about the regulation and expression of peroxidase genes.

Manganese Peroxidase (MnP) Gene Family

Manganese peroxidases are most dominating enzymes among lignin-degrading fungi including white-rot basidiomycets (Hatakka, 2001; Hofrichter, 2002; Steffen *et al.*, 2002; Lankinen *et al.*, 2005). Isozymes encoding MnP genes have been sequenced from a group of several white-rot fungi such as *P. chrysosporium* (Pease *et al.*, 1989; Pribnow *et al.*, 1989; Orth *et al.*, 1994; Alic *et al.*, 1997), *T. versicolor* MPGI (Johansson, 1994), *T. versicolor PGVII* (Johansson and Nyman, 1996), *C. subvermispora* (Lobos *et al.*, 1998; Tello *et al.*, 2000), and *P. ostreatus* (Asada *et al.*, 1995). The *Ceriporiopsis subvermispora* possess several structurally related genes encoding MnP (Lobos *et al.*, 1998; Tello *et al.*, 2000). Like LiP, the MnP isozymes are also encoded by multiple genes (Perie *et al.*, 1991, Pribnow *et al.*, 1989). Previously three MnP genes were characterized as: *mnp1*, *mnp2*, and *mnp3* (Pease *et al.*, 1989; Pribnow *et al.*, 1989; Orth *et al.*, 1994; Alic *et al.*, 1997), in addition two new MnP genes were found by BLAST searches of the genome (Martinez *et al.*, 2004). The genetic analysis revealed two new unrelated MnP encoding genes of *Physisporinus rivulosus*, *mnpA*, and *mnpB*, and similar variability of these two *mnp* genes in *P. rivulosus* and *P. radiata* strain 79 was recently described (Hilden *et al.*, 2005). In addition, the exon/intron structure of the genomic sequences is uniform within this group and was identical in *P. rivulosus mnpA*, *C. subvermispora CS-mnp1-3* genes (Lobos *et al.*, 1998; Tello *et al.*, 2000) and *mnp1*, *mnp2* genes of *Dichomitus squalens* (Li *et al.*, 1999). The promoter region of *mnp* has heat shock elements and putative metal response elements (MREs) (Gold and Alic, 1993; Johansson and Nyman, 1996; Gold *et al.* 2000; Tello *et al.*, 2000; Hildén *et al.*, 2005). That MREs sequences are identical to *cis*-acting, responsible for heavy metal induction. Gold and colleagues have found several regions of the *mnpl* promoter with strong homology to the mouse metallothionein MRE consensus (Gold and Alic, 1993). In *P. chrysosporium*, the *mnp3* promoter lacks paired putative MREs (Alic *et al.*, 1997). In contrast, the *mnp1* promoter has two pairs of putative MREs (Godfrey *et al.*, 1990) and the *mnp2* promoter has one pair (Mayfield *et al.*, 1994). In recent years, different peroxidases have been purified from *Pleurotus* species, and their genes have been sequenced and analyzed. These include *mnp1* (Asada, 1995), *mnp2* (Giardina, 2000), and *mnp3* (Irie, 2000) *mnp4* (Cohen et al., 2002) from oyster mushroom *P. ostreatus*.

Differential Regulation of Peroxidase Genes

Ligninolytic activity in culture of microbes is a secondary metabolic function which is triggered by defined medium. Influencing factors for the isoenzyme production and its isoenzyme profile in white-rot fungi depends on culture conditions, substrate composition and period of incubation (Cullen, 1997). Expression of lignolytic genes is also triggered by the level of carbon, nitrogen, sulphur limitation (Gold and Alic, 1993), oxidative stress, and heat shock (Stewart *et al.*, 1992; Gold and Alic, 1993; Li *et al.*, 1994; Belinky *et al.*, 2003). It was speculated by several other workers (Holzbaur and Tien, 1988; Stewart *et al.*, 1992; Reiser *et al.*, 1993; Janse *et al.*, 1998; Vallim *et al.*, 1998; Stewart and Cullen, 1999) regulation of LiP genes are transcribed and their expression is dramatically regulated by culture conditions. Differential regulation of MnP isozymes has been observed with response to media composition in *C. subvermispora* and *P. chrysosporium* (Pease and Tien, 1992; Lobos *et al.*, 1994). No clear relationship between genomic organization and transcriptional regulation has been observed by Stewart *et al.* (1992). Several workers reported that *P. chrysosporium* LiP genes are tightly clustered and structurally similar (Stewart *et al.*, 1992; Stewart and Cullen, 1999). Transcriptional control of MnP expression is complex and possible transcriptional control elements are particularly metal response elements (MREs), which have been identified in 5'-untranslated regions (Godfrey *et al.*, 1990, 1994; Alic and Gold, 1991; Brown *et al.*, 1993; Alic *et al.*, 1997). During recent years, several investigations have been conducted to observe the influence of chemical and biological inducers for better peroxidase expression. Few of them, which were considered playing important role in the expression of peroxidase including lignocellulosic substrates, nitrogen supplements, manganese ions, different aromatic compounds, H_2O_2, heat shock and co-culturing.

Regulation by Ligninocellusic Substrates

In general, basal substrate basically lignocellulose available in culture medium plays an important role in the production of lignocellulolytic enzymes and affects their expression at gene level. Therefore, several workers have tried different lignocellulosic substrate for quantitative yields of enzymes. Substrate dependent expression of LiP-encoding genes in *P. chrysosporium* has been performed on aspen wood chips (Janse *et al.*, 1998). Spruce sawdust was shown to have a distinct effect on transcript level of *P. rivulosus* MnP genes (Hakala *et al.*, 2006). Production of multiple isoforms of MnP by *P. rivulosus* T241i grown on spruce wood chips was observed (Hakala *et al.*, 2005). Several other reports have demonstrated that *Dichomitus squalens* under various conditions, efficiently degrades natural lignin from birch (Blanchette, 1987), spruce wood (Chang *et al.*, 1980), wheat straw, barley, and grape straw (Sanchez, 2009). Cellulytic and ligninolytic enzymes were produced by fungal microflora such as *P. chrysosporium* and *Rhizopus stolonifer* on coir waste substrate (Paulraj *et al.*, 2009). Furthermore, Naraian *et al.* (2009) used corn cob as basal substrate and different nitrogen rich oil seed cakes as supplements for cultivation of *P. florida*. The expression of Mn peroxidase found dependent on substrate and its composition in *P. florida, P. sajor-caju and P. eryngii* (Naraian *et al.*, 2010) Other ligninocellusics substrates such as red oak, grape seeds, barley bran, wood chips used for isoenzymes isolation (Sanchez, 2009; Baldrian and Valaskova, 2008; Abbas, 2005). Lixia and colleagues (2011) reported that bioconversion of rape straw into a nutritionally enriched substrate by fungus *Ganoderma lucidum*. Furthermore, in another effort production of ligninolytic enzymes from white-rot fungus *Schizophyllum commune* by using banana stalk as basal substrate through the process of solid state fermentation was also successful (Muhammad and Muhammad, 2011). Pickard *et al.*, 1999 reported to increase ligninolytic enzyme production of the white-rot fungi *Coriolopsis gallica* and *Bjerkandera adusta* in cereal bran supplement. *Agaricus bisporus* cultures with wheat and rye bran favoured MnP production over those with straw (Lankinen *et al.*, 2005).

Regulation by Nitrogen Supplements

Nitrogen concentration (Gold and Alic, 1993; Li *et al.*, 1994; Hakala, 2007) and organic or inorganic nitrogen source (Kaal *et al.*, 1993; Naraian *et al.*, 2010) are major factors that affect fungal lignin-modifying peroxidase expression. In *P. rivulosus*, nutrient nitrogen did not play an essential role for MnP production (Terhi *et al.*, 2006). However, in *Bjerkandera adusta* and *Pleurotus ostreatus*, induction by high nitrogen has been reported (Kaal *et al.*, 1995; Mester *et al.*, 1996). Recently, a manganese repressed, nitrogen induced peroxidase was identified in *Trametes versicolor* (Collins *et al.*, 1999). High nutrient nitrogen does not affect expression of the peroxidases in *Bjerkandera* spp. and *Pleurotus* spp. (Mester *et al.*, 1996; Naraian *et al.*, 2010). LiP transcriptional analysis demonstrated by Tien and Tu, in the presence of nutrient nitrogen *in vitro* used poly (A) RNAs and Northern blot. Northern blot analysis also indicates that MnP is regulated by nutrient nitrogen at the transcript level (Pribnow *et al.*, 1989). In *P. ostreatus* (Kamitsuji *et al.*, 2005) and *T. versicolor* (Collins *et al.*, 1999), some peroxidase isoforms appear to be unaffected by nutrient nitrogen, whereas, some are repressed. In *Dichomitus squalens* degrades lignin under nitrogen-sufficient conditions as well as nitrogen-limiting conditions (Perie and Gold, 1991). In *P.*

chrysosporium, *lip* genes transcribed under conditions of nitrogen sufficiency, Northern blots of total RNA from 5 and 6 days old cultures probed with the cDNA corresponding to LiP isozyme H8 (L18) (Ritch, 1991). Northern blot analyses showed that steady-state levels of *lipD* transcripts are least abundant than those of *lipA* under nitrogen starvation (Holzbaur *et al.*, 1988). Ruiz-Duenas (1999) demonstrated the conditions involving a limited concentration of ammonium; no peroxidase activity was detected in *P. eryngii*. However, when ammonium was replaced by peptone, the induction of gene *mnpl* transcription was strong, and extracellular activity was detected.

Regulation by Manganese (Mn)

Regulation of gene expression by metals is well reported, both in prokaryotes and eukaryotes (O'Halloran, 1993; Thiele, 1992). Most commonly, metals exert their action through transcription factors that specifically interact with sequences present in the upstream region of target genes. Alternatively, proteins may bind to sequences present in mRNA, thus affecting the overall expression of corresponding gene (Haile, 1999). Manganese (Mn^{+2}) is an important metal that plays central role in the regulation and expression of lignocellulolytic genes especially MnP. It has been shown that MnP transcripts level increase considerably upon addition of Mn^{2+} to culture of *P. chrysosporium* (Johansson *et al.*, 2002). The white-rot basidiomycete *Dichomitus squalens* expresses MnP and degrades lignin only in the presence of Mn^{2+}, suggesting that MnP is essential for lignin degradation by this organism (Perie and Gold, 1991). Transcription of MnP genes is additionally, regulated by Mn^{2+} ions. White-rot basidiomycete *P. chrysosporium*, mRNA level from the manganese peroxidase gene (*mnpl*) have been shown to be dramatically elevated in the presence of manganese (Brown *et al.*, 1991). Differential regulation of *mnp* genes by manganese has been also widely shown in *P. ostreatus* (Cohen *et al.*, 2001), *C. subvermispora* (Tello *et al.*, 2000; Manubens *et al.*, 2003), and *T. versicolor* (Collins *et al.*, 1999; Johansson *et al.*, 2002; Kim *et al.*, 2005). The *P. chrysosporium mnp*3 and the *C. subvermispora mnp*3 genes were shown not to respond to Mn^{2+} induction (Gettemy *et al.*, 1998; Tello *et al.*, 2000). Regulation of MnP expression by Mn^{2+} has been observed repeatedly in white-rot fungi. The levels of different *mnp* transcripts vary in response to Mn^{2+} reported in *P. chrysosporium* (Gettemy *et al.*, 1998), *Pleurotus ostreatus* (Cohen *et al.*, 2001), *C. subvermispora* (Manubens *et al.*, 2003), *P. radiate* (Hildén *et al.*, 2005), *P. rivulosus* (Hakala *et al.*, 2006), and *Phlebia* sp. MG-60 (Kamei *et al.*, 2008). *T. versicolor* isozymes designated LiP12, LiP7, and MnP2 (Ritch, 1991), which are encoded by *lip1*, *lip4*, *lip6*, and *mnp1*, respectively (Johansson and Nyman, 1996, 1995). Manganese has a major impact on MnP production and *mnp* gene transcription in the lignin-selective white-rot fungus *Physisporinus rivulosus* (Terhi *et al.*, 2006). In *Bjerkandera* sp. strain BOS55 MnP production is stimulated by manganese nutrients (Tunde and Field, 1998).

Regulation by Different Aromatic Compounds

It has been well established that peroxidase expression in several fungi has been regulated by natural aromatic compounds such as: varatryl alcohol, atropine, syringic acid etc. These aromatic compounds in medium acts as carbon source and differentially regulates the expression of peroxidase. When *P. chrysosporium* is grown on defined media containing limiting amount of carbon, *lip* gene was unregulated. Production of *P. radiata* LiP isozymes has shown to be dependent on the lignocellulosic materials used as carbon source (Niku-Paavola *et al.*, 1990; Vares *et al.*, 1995). *Physisporium rivulosus* seems to possess a similar pattern of enzymes production; *mnp* transcript observed was very low. The *lip* genes are differentially regulated by culture conditions, Northern blot analyzes showed that steady-state levels of *lipD* transcripts are far more abundant than those of *lipA* under carbon starvation (Holzbaur and Tien, 1988). Pease and Tien (1992) reported that carbon limited in *P. chrysosporium* cultures, MnP isozyme H4 appear first, with H3 predominating later. Under these conditions no H5 is produced. Veratryl alcohol is a *de novo* secondary metabolite produced by many white-rot fungi, including *Bjerkandera* sp. strain BOS55 (de Jong *et al.*, 1994).

Their concentrations ranging from 0.01 to 0.80 mM occur in liquid cultures as well as during solid-state fermentation of wood (Mester *et al.*, 1995). Veratryl alcohol promote MnP production in white-rot fungal cultures (Niku-Paavola *et al.*, 1990; Scheel *et al.*, 2000; Hofrichter, 2002; Manubens *et al.*, 2003; Hakala *et al.*, 2006). The veratryl alcohol which is substrate for LiP, is a natural metabolite of white-rot fungi i.e. *P. chrysosporium* (Lundquist and Kirk, 1978), *Pycnoporus cinnabarinus* (Hatakka, 1985) and *Phlebia radiata* (Kantelinen *et al.*, 1989). However, this aromatic compound has been widely used to induce LiP activity in cultures of white-rot fungi but only in few cases, a slight induction of MnP has been observed (Scheel *et al.*, 2000). Terhi *et al.* (2006) reported that veratryl alcohol has an impact to MnP production and *mnp* gene transcription in the lignin-selective white-rot fungus *Physisporinus rivulosus*. In *Nematoloma frowardii* and *Clitocybula dusenii* (Scheel *et al.*, 2000) a rise in MnP production was noted after addition of veratryl alcohol, but the effect was much lower than that of manganese. Moreover, addition of veratryl alcohol enhances transcription of both *mnpA* and *mnpB* in *P. rivulosus* (Terhi *et al.*, 2006).

Atropine is a naturally occurring tropane alkaloid extracted from plants such as *Atropa belladonna*, *Datura stramonium*, *Mandragora officinarum* and few other plants of family solanaceae. It is secondary metabolite of these plants. Although there is no much available data but few workers have tried to observe the effect of this metabolite on the expression of peroxidase enzyme in fungi. In 1992, Boominathan and Reddy reported that atropine can inhibit ligninolytic enzymes production in fungi. Masahiko et al. (2009), also reported gene expression in 3-days old culture of *P. chrysosporium* supplemented with atropine, which inhibits production of lignin degrading enzymes.

Thus, based on the result of these workers, it can be concluded that atropine negatively affects the production and expression of enzymes. Syringic acid is also a naturally occurring o-methylated trihydroxybenzoic acid, a type of chemical compound can be extracted from *Euterpe oleracea*. It has been observed that syringic acid promote MnP production in white-rot fungal cultures (Niku-Paavola *et al.*, 1990; Scheel *et al.*, 2000; Hofrichter, 2002; Manubens *et al.*, 2003; Hakala *et al.*, 2006). This acid compound slightly increased MnP production in *C. subvermispora*, although no induction is observed in the expression of the two investigated MnP encoding genes (Manubens *et al.*, 2003). Augusto Manubens (2003) found that syringic acid at 0.5 mM increased the levels of *mnp1* mRNA in *Ceriporiopsis subvermispora*. Various hydroquinone, as well as quinones can be generated from lignin residues during the ligninolytic process (Martinez *et al.*, 2005). Alejandro *et al.* (2009) found that in the *Ceriporiopsis subvermispora* Cs-mnp2 transcript levels decrease in cultures treated for 3 hours with hydroquinone.

Heat Shock Regulation

In addition to thermal stress, a wide variety of chemical agents are known to induce heat shock proteins (Lindquist, 1986; Nover, 1991; Storz, 1990). These factors include heavy metals, various organic compounds, and oxidants (Lindquist, 1986; Schlesinger, 1990). The expression of *mnp* is transiently induced by a heat shock in nitrogen limited cultures and sequences matching to the consensus heat shock element (CN2GAAN2 TTCN2G) are found in the promoters of *mnp* genes (Godfrey *et al.*, 1990 and 1994). Li *et al.* (1995) found that neither metal response elements nor heat shock elements have been found in the promoter regions of sequenced *lip* genes. Ethanol and arsenite are known to induce the synthesis of heat shock proteins in bacteria and fungi (Nover, 1991; Kapoor, 1990).

Regulation by Hydrogen Peroxide (H_2O_2)

Induction of MnP expression in *P. chrysosporium* cultures by addition of H_2O_2 compounds (Li *et al.*, 1995) has been also reported. Alejandro *et al.*, (2009) performed that *Ceriporiopsis subvermispora* transcript levels of the ligninolytic genes *mnp2* mRNAs are not affected by H_2O_2. However, in *P. chrysosporium*, H_2O_2 compound increases *mnp* transcript levels only in nitrogen-limited cultures (Li *et al.*, 1995). The *mnpl* transcripts in *Pleurotus eryngii,* 0.5mM H_2O_2 increases which revert to normal levels as the concentration of externally added H_2O_2 decreases in the cultures (Ruiz-Duenas *et al.*, 1999). Li *et al.* (1995) investigating the *mnp* promoter elements that are responsible for H_2O_2 induction of *mnp* gene transcription.

Regulation by Oxygen

The positive effect of O_2 on lignin degradation and high atmosphere O_2 enhances ligninolytic activity by *P. chrysosporium* (Kirk, 1978; Keyser, 1978). Li *et al.* (1995) first examined the effects of O_2 on MnP activity and *mnp* gene transcription. Effect of O_2 was, at least in part, at the level of *mnp* gene transcription, O_2 is positively affecting Mn induction of *mnp* gene transcription.

Regulation by Co-Culturing

The effectiveness of individual isolates can be improved by co-culturing with other highly efficient strains. A single species can efficiently act in coordination of other strain to degrade the same substrate (Boddy, 2000). Mixed fungal cultures could lead to a higher enzyme production through synergistic interactions, but the final result seems dependent on the particular species combination or on the mode of interaction between species, and on the microenvironmental or nutritional conditions in the substrate under colonization (Gutierrez-Correa and Tengerdy, 1998). Co-culturing of two or more fungal strains in mixed culture fermentation is widely used in many biological processes including the production of antibiotics, enzymes and fermented food (Gutierrez-Correa, 1998).

But the main drawback of co-culturing however is the complexity of growing multiple microorganisms in the same culture (Lynd *et al.*, 2002). Yujie Chi et al. (2007) reported the potential of co-cultivation of white-rot fungi for biopulping purposes with respect to two efficient biopulping fungi, *C. subvermispora* and *P. rivulosus*, and ligninolytic fungi, *P. chrysosporium* and *Pleurotus ostreatus*. Improving fungal cellulolytic activity of *T. reesei* and *A. niger* by co-culturing was the subject of extensive research including studies done by Maheshwari (Maheshwari, 1994; Juhász, 2003; Ahmad, 2008). Moreover, other fungal strains have been co-cultured to obtain better cellulolytic activity such as co-culturing of *T. reesei* RUT-C30 and *A. phoenicis* (Duff, 1985) or *A. ellipticus* and *A. fumigatus* (Gupte and Madamwar, 1997). Cellulose and hemicelluloses both together hydrolyzed by co-culturing fungal strains *T. reesei* D1-6 and *A. wentii* Pt 2804 in a mixed submerged culture (Panda *et al.*, 1983) and co-culturing *T. reesei* LM-UC4 and *A. phoenicis* QM329 using ammonia-treated bagasse (Duenas *et al.*, 1995). In both cases, enzyme activity for cellulases and hemicellulases was significantly increased. The bioconversion of rape straw by the mixed-strain fermentation of *Ganoderma lucidum* and yeasts (*Saccharomyces cerevisiae, Candida tropicalis and Candida utilis*), into an enriched substrate increased crude protein and digestibility (Lixia *et al.*, 2011). Mixed fungal cultures have many advantages compared to their monocultures, including improving productivity, adaptability and substrate utilization.

Applications

White- rot fungi have complex enzymatic machinery that enables to degrade lignin and other recalcitrant compounds and play important roles in carbon recycling, because lignocelluloses are most abundant organic carbon compound on earth. Fungi are directly applicable in the processes of ligninocellulose bioconversion (Ruggeri and Sassi, 2003; Bosco *et al.*, 1999). Due to their powerful degrading capabilities towards various recalcitrant chemicals, white-rot fungi and their lignin degrading enzymes have long been studied for biotechnological applications (Yeo *et al.*, 2007) such as biobleaching (Takano *et al.*, 2001), biodecolorization (Dias *et al.*, 2003) and bioremediation (Beltz *et al.*, 2001; Cheong *et al.*, 2006). The enzyme peroxidase was first identified as a potential agent to break down lignin and whiten wood pulp for paper production for many years. Later on it was found that is involved in eumelanin breakdown because of eumelanin has a chemical structure similar to lignin. The development of lignin peroxidase as a skin-lightening agent resulted from these discoveries and opened its wide use in cosmetics. Now with advancement of the knowledge LiPs and MnPs have been exploited to numerous other processes such as oxidation of organic pollutants, stabilization of fruit juices, biosensor development, nanobiotechnology, biofuels cells, textile biofinishing, beverage processing, digestion of animal feed stuffs, biobleaching systems, cosmetics, enzyme immunoassays, wastewater detoxification, detergent manufacturing and transformation of antibiotics and steroids (Tien and Kirk, 1998; Ryan *et al.*, 2003; Boer *et al.*, 2006; Papinutti and Forchiassin, 2007; Ravankar and Lele, 2007; Asghar *et al.*, 2008).

Conclusion

Current researches on genomics of white-rot fungus offers significant opportunities for elucidating the roles and interactions of peroxidase and genes involved in degrading ligninocellolosics and their regulation. Our requirement needs more commercial development to achieve a high production of these enzymes at a much lower cost as utilization of cheaper substrate and search of better inducer. Peroxidase isoforms are expressed differentially, and the inducers act both separately and in conjunction. Differential regulation of the peroxidases supports specific biological roles for individual isozyme and related genes expression

References

Abbas, A., H. Koc, F. Liu and M. Tien, 2005. Fungal degradation of wood: initial proteomic analysis of extracellular proteins of *Phanerochaete chrysosporium* grown on oak substrate. *Curr. Genet.* 47: 49-56.

Ahamed, A. and P. Vermette, 2008. Enhanced enzyme production from mixed cultures of *Trichoderma reesei* RUT-C30 and *Aspergillus niger* LMA grown as fed batch in a stirred tank bioreactor. *Biochemical Eng. J.* 42: 41-46.

Alejandro, A., A.M. Rodrigo, G. Bernardo and V. Rafael, 2009. Hydroquinone and H_2O_2 di¡erentiallya¡ect the ultrastructure and expression of ligninolytic genes in the basidiomycete *Ceriporiopsis subvermispora. FEMS Microbiol. Lett.* 294: 232–238.

Alic, M., L. Akileswaran and M.H. Gold, 1997. Characterization of the gene encoding manganese peroxidase isozyme 3 from *Phanerochaete chrysosporium. Biochim. Biophys. Acta* 1338: 1-7.

Asada, Y., A. Watanabe, T. Irie, T. Nakayama and M. Kuwahara, 1995. Structures of genomic and complementary DNAs coding for *Pleurotus ostreatus* manganese (II) peroxidase. *Biochim. Biophys. Acta* 1251: 205-209.

Asgher, M., S. Kausar, H.N. Bhati and M. Ali, 2008. Optimization of medium for decolorization of solar golden yellow R direct textile dye by *Schizophyllum commune* IBL-06. *Int. Biodeter. Biodegr.* 61(2): 189-193.

Baldrian, P. and V. Valaskova, 2008. Degradation of cellulose by basidiomycetous fungi. *FEMS Microbiol. Rev.* 32: 501-521.

Belinky, P.A., N. Flikshtein, S. Lechenko, S. Gepstein and C.G. Dosoretz, 2003. Reactive oxygen species and induction of lignin peroxidase in *Phanerochaete chrysosporium. Appl. Eviron. Microbiol.* 69: 6500-6506.

Beltz, L.A., D. Neira, C. Axtell, S. Iverson, W. Deaton, T. Waldschmidt, J. Bumpus and C. Johnston, 2001. Immunotoxicity of explosive contaminated soil before and after bioremediation. *Arch. Environ. Contam. Toxicol.* 40: 311-317.

Blanchette, R.A., L. Otjen and M.C. Carlson, 1987. Lignin distribution in cell walls of birch wood decayed by white-rot basidiomycetes. *Phytopathol.* 77: 684-690.

Boddy, L., 2000. Interspecific combative interactions between wood-decaying basidiomycetes. *FEMS Microbial. Ecol.* 31: 185-194.

Boer, G.C., L. Obici, C.G.M. De Souza and R.M. Peralta, 2006. Purification and some properties of Mn peroxidase from *Lentinula edodes. Proc. Biochem.* 41: 1203-1207.

Bonnen, A.M., L.H. Anton and A.B. Orth, 1994. Lignin-degrading enzymes of the commercial button mushroom, *Agaricus bisporus*. *Appl. Environ. Microbiol.* 60: 960-965.

Boominathan, K. and C.A. Reddy, 1992. Fungal degradation of lignin: biotechnological applications, Arora DK, Elander RP, Mukerji KG (eds.). In handbook of applied mycology, Vol. 4. Marcel Dekker Inc., New York, pp. 763-822.

Bosco, F., B. Ruggeri and G. Sassi, 1999. Performances of a trickle bed reactor (TBR) for exoenzyme production by *Phanerochaete chrysosporium*: Influence of a superficial liquid velocity. *Chem. Eng. Sci.* 54: 3163-3169.

Broda, P., P. Birch, P. Brooks and P. Sims, 1995. PCR-mediated analysis of lignocellulolytic gene transcription by *Phanerochaete chrysosporium*: substrate-dependent differential expression within gene families. *Appl. Environ. Microbiol.* 61: 2358-2364.

Brooks, P., P. Sims and P. Broda. 1993. Isozyme specific polymerase chain reaction analysis of differential gene expression: a general method applied to lignin peroxidase genes of *Phanerochaete chrysosporium*. *Bio/Technology* 11: 830-834.

Brown, A., P.F.G. Sims, U. Raeder and P. Broda, 1988. Multiple ligninase-related genes from *Phanerochaete chrysosporium*. *Gene* 73: 77-85.

Brown, J.A., M. Alic and M.H. Gold, 1991. Manganese peroxidase gene transcription in *Phanerochaete chrysosporium*: activation by manganese. *J. Bacteriol.* 173: 4101-4106.

Chang, H-M., C.L. Chen and T.K. Kirk, 1980. Chemistry of lignin degraded by white-rot fungi, in lignin biodegradation: Microbiology, chemistry and potential applications, edited by T. K. Kirk, T. Higuchi and H-M. Chang, CRC Press, Inc., Boca Raton, Florida, Vol. I, Pp. 215-229.

Cheong, S., S. Yeo, H.G. Song and H. Choi, 2006. Determination of laccase gene expression during degradation of 2, 4, 6-trinitrotoluene and its catabolic intermediates in *Trametes versicolor*. *Microbiol. Res.* 161: 316-320.

Cohen, R., Y. Hadar and O. Yarden, 2001. Transcript and activity levels of different *Pleurotus ostreatus* peroxidases are differentially affected by Mn^{2+}. *Environ. Microbiol.* 3: 312-22.

Cohen, R., O. Yarden and Y. Hadar, 2002, Lignocellulose affects Mn^{+2} regulation of peroxidase transcript levels in solid-state cultures of *Pleurotus ostreatus*. *Appl. Environ. Microbiol.* 68 (6):3156–3158.

Collins, P.J., M.M. O'Brien and A.D.W. Dobson, 1999. Cloning and characterization of a cDNA encoding a novel extracellular peroxidase from *Trametes versicolor*. *Appl. Environ. Microbiol.* 65: 1343-1347.

Conesa, A., P.J. Punt and C.A.M.J.J. van den Hondel, 2002. Fungal peroxidases: molecular aspects and applications. *J. Biotechnol.* 93: 143-158.

Cullen, D., 1997. Recent advances on the molecular genetics of ligninolytic fungi. *J. Biotechnol.* 53: 273-289.

D'Souza, T.M., S.B. Dass, A. Rasooly and C.A. Reddy, 1993. Electrophoretic karyotyping of the lignin-degrading basidiomycete *Phanerochaete chrysosporium*. *Mol. Microbiol.* 8: 803-807.

de Jong, E., J.A. Field and J.A.M. de Bont. 1994. Aryl alcohols in the physiology of ligninolytic fungi. *FEMS Microbiol. Rev.* 13:153–188.

Dias A, R. Bezerra, P. Lemos and A. Pereiram, 2003. *In-vivo* and laccase characterization of xenobiotic azo dyes by basidiomycetous fungus: characterization of its lignolytic system. *World J. Microbiol. Biotechnol.* 19: 969-975.

Duenas, R., R.P. Tengerdy and M. Gutierrez-Correa, 1995. Cellulase production by mixed fungi in solid-substrate fermentation of bagasse. *World J. Microbiol. Biotechnol.* 11: 333-337.

Duff, S.J.B., 1985. Cellulase and beta-glucosidase production by mixed culture of *Trichoderma reesei* Rut C30 and *Aspergillus phoenicis. Biotechnol. Lett.* 7: 185-190.

Everse, J. and K.E. Everse, 1991. Peroxidases in Chemistry and Biology, vols. 1-2. CRC Press, Boca Raton, Florida.

Gaskell, J., E. Dieperink and D. Cullen, 1991. Genomic organization of lignin peroxidase genes of *Phanerochaete chrysosporium. Nucleic Acids Res.* 19: 599-603.

Gaskell, J., P. Stewart, P. Kersten, S. Covert, J. Reiser and D. Cullen, 1994. Establishment of genetic linkage by allele-specific polymerase chain reaction: application to the lignin peroxidase gene family of *Phanerochaete chrysosporium. Bio. Technol.* 12: 1372-1375.

Gettemy, J.M., B. Ma, M. Alic and M.H. Gold, 1998. Reverse transcription-PCR analysis of the regulation of the manganese peroxidase gene family. *Appl. Environ. Microbiol.* 64: 569-574.

Giardina, P., G. Palmieri, B. Fontanella, V. Rivieccio and G. Sannia, 2000. Manganese peroxidase isoenzymes produced by *Pleurotus ostreatus* grown on wood sawdust. *Arch. Biochem. Biophys.* 376: 171-179.

Glenn, J.K., M.A. Morgan, M.B. Mayfield, M. Kuwahara and M.H. Gold, 1983. An extracellular H_2O_2-requiring enzyme preparation involved in lignin biodegradation by the white rot basidiomycete *Phanerochaete chrysosporium. Biochem. Biophys. Res. Comm.* 114: 1077- 1083.

Godfrey, B.J. and M.H. Gold, 1994. Characterization of the mnp2 gene encoding manganese peroxidase isozyme 2 from the basidiomycete *Phanerochaete chrysosporium. Gene* 142: 231-235.

Godfrey, B.J., M.B. Mayfield, J.A. Brown and M. Gold, 1990. Characterization of a gene encoding manganese peroxidase from *Phanerochaete chrysosporium. Gene* 93: 119-124.

Gold, M.H. and M. Alic, 1993. Molecular biology of the lignin-degrading basidiomycete *Phanerochaete chrysosporium. Microbiol. Rev.* 57: 605-622.

Gold, M.H., H. Wariishi and K. Valli. Extracellular peroxidase involving in lignin degradation by the white rot basidiomycete *Phanerochaete chrysosporium,* Pp.127-140. In J.R.Whitaker and P.E.Sonnet (eds.), Biocatalysis in agricultural biotechnology. ACS Symposium Series 389. American Chemical Society, Washington, D.C.

Gupte, A. and D. Madamwar, 1997. Solid state fermentation of lignocellulosic waste for cellulose and β-glucosidase production by co-cultivation by *Aspergillus ellipticus* and *Aspergillus fumigatus. Biotechnol. Prog.*13: 166-169.

Gutierrez-Correa, M. And R.P. Tengerdy, 1998. Cellulolytic enzyme production by fungal mixed culture solid substrate fermentation. *Biotechnol. Lett.* 20: 45-47.

Haile, D.J., 1999. Regulation of genes of iron metabolism by the iron response elements. *Am. J. Med. Sci.* 318: 230-240.

Hakala, T.K., K. Hilden, P. Maijala, C. Olsson and A. Hatakka, 2006. Differential regulation and characterization of two variable MnP encoding genes in the white-rot fungus *Physisporinus rivulosus. Appl. Microbiol. Biotechnol.* 73: 839-849.

Hakala, T.K., T. Lundell, S. Galkin, P. Maijala, N. Kalkkinen and A. Hatakka, 2005. Manganese peroxidases, laccases and oxalic acid from the selective white-rot fungus *Physisporinus rivulosus* grown on spruce wood chips. *Enzyme Microbiol. Technol.* 36: 461-468.

Hatakka, A., 2001. Biodegradation of lignin. In: Hofrichter M., Steinbüchel A., (eds.). Biopolymers. Vol 1: Lignin, humic substances and coal. Wiley-VCH, Weinheim, Germany, Pp. 129-180.

Hatakka, A.I., 1985. Degradation of veratric acid and other lignin-related aromatic compounds by the white-rot fungus *Pycnoporus cinnabarinus*. *Arch. Microbiol.* 141: 22-28.

Heinfling, A., M.J. Martínez, A.T. Martinez, M. Bergbauer and U. Szewzyk, 1998. Purification and characterization of peroxidases from the dye-decolorizing fungus *Bjerkandera adusta*. *FEMS Microbiol. Lett.* 165: 43-50.

Hilden, K., A.T. Martinez, A. Hatakka and T. Lundell, 2005. The two manganese peroxidases Pr-MnP2 and Pr-MnP3 of *Phlebia radiata*, a lignin-degrading basidiomycete, are phylogenetically and structurally divergent. *Fungal Genet. Biol.* 42: 403-419.

Hofrichter, M., 2002. Review: Lignin conversion by manganese peroxidase (MnP). *Enzyme Microb. Technol.* 30: 454-466.

Holzbaur, E. and M. Tien, 1988. Structure and regulation of a lignin peroxidase gene from *Phanerochaete chrysosporium. Biochem. Biophys. Res. Commun.* 155: 626-633.

Irie, T., Y. Honda, H.H.T. Watanabe and M. Kuwahara, 2000. Isolation of cDNA and genomic fragments encoding the major manganese peroxidase isozyme from the white rot basidiomycete *Pleurotus ostreatus*. *J. Wood Sci.* 46: 230-233.

James, C.M.., M.S.S. Felipe, P.F.G. Sims and P. Broda, 1992. Expression of a single lignin peroxidase-encoding gene in *Phanerochaete chrysosporium* strain ME446. *Gene* 114: 217-222.

Gold, M.H. and M. Alic, 1993. Molecular biology of lignin degradation by *Phanerochaete chrysosporium*. *Microbiol. Rev.* 57: 605-622.

Janse, B., J. Gaskell, M. Ahktar and D. Cullen, 1998. *Phanerochaete chrysosporium* genes encoding lignin peroxidases, manganese peroxidases and glyoxal oxidase in wood. *Appl. Environ. Microbiol.* 64: 3536-3538.

Johansson, T. and P.O. Nyman, 1996. A cluster of genes encoding major isozymes of lignin peroxidase and manganese peroxidase for the white-rot fungus *Trametes versicolor. Gene* 170: 31-38.

Johansson, T. and P.O. Nyman. 1995. The gene from the white-rot fungus isozymes of lignin peroxidase and manganese peroxidase from the white-rot. *Biophys. Acta* 1263: 71-74.

Johansson, T. and P.O. Nyman. 1996. A cluster of genes encoding major isozymes of lignin peroxidase and manganese peroxidase from the white-rot fungus *Trametes versicolor*. *Gene* 170: 31-38.

Johansson, T., 1994. Manganese(II) peroxidase and lignin peroxidase from the white-rot fungus *Trametes versi* color. PhD Thesis, University of Lund, Lund.

Johansson, T., K.G. Welinder and P.O. Nyman, 1993. Isozymes of lignin peroxidase and manganese(II) peroxidase from the white-rot basidiomycete *Trametes versicolor*. II. Partial sequences, peptide maps, and amino acid and carbohydrate compositions. *Arch. Biochem. Biophys.* 300: 57-62.

Johansson, T., P.O. Nymann and D. Cullen. 2002. Differential regulation of mnp2, a new manganese peroxidase-encoding gene from the lignolytic fungus *Trametes versicolor* PRL572. *Appl. Environ. Microbiol.* 68: 2077-2080.

Jönsson, L., T. Johansson, K. Sjostrom and P.O. Nyman, 1987. Purification of ligninase isozymes from the white-rot fungus *Trametes versicolor. Acta Chem. Scand., Ser. B* 41: 766-769.

Juhasz, T., K. Kozma, Z. Szengyel and K. Reczey, 2003. Production of β-glucosidase in mixed culture of *Aspergillus niger* BKMF 1305 and *Trichoderma reesei* RUT C30. *Food Technol. Biotechnol.* 41: 49-53.

Kaal, E.E.J., D.E. Jong and J.A. Field, 1993. Stimulation of ligninolytic peroxidase activity by nitrogen nutrients in the white rot fungus *Bjerkandera* spp. strain BOS55. *Appl. Environ. Microbiol.* 59: 4031-4036.

Kaal, E.E.J., J.A. Field and T.W. Joyce, 1995. Increasing ligninolytic enzyme activities in several white-rot basidiomycetes by nitrogen-sufficient media. *Biosersour. Technol.* 53: 133-139.

Kamei, I., C. Daikoku, Y. Tsutsumi and R. Kondo, 2008. Saline-dependent regulation of manganese peroxidase genes in the hypersaline-tolerant white rot fungus *Phlebia* spp. strain MG-60. *Appl. Environ. Microbiol.* 74: 2709-2716.

Kamitsuji, H., Y. Honda, T. Watanabe and M. Kuwahara, 2005. Mn^{2+} is dispensable for the production of active MnP2 by *Pleurotus ostreatus. Biochem. Biophys. Res. Commun.* 327: 871-876.

Kantelinen, A., A. Hatakkaand and L. Viikari, 1989. Production of lignin peroxidase and laccase by *Phlebia radiata. Appl. Microbiol. Biotechnol.* 31: 234-239.

Kapoor, M., G.M. Sreenivasan, N. Goel and J. Lewis, 1990. Development of thermotolerance in *Neurospora crassa* by heat shock and other stresses eliciting peroxidase induction. *J. Bacteriol.* 172: 2798-2801.

Kersten, P.J. and T.K. Kirk, 1987. Involvement of a new enzyme, glyoxal, in extracellular H_2O_2 production by *Phanerochaete chrysosporium. J.Bectoriol.*169: 2195-2202.

Keyser, P., T.K. Kirk and J.G. Zeikus, 1978. Ligninolytic enzyme system of *Phanerochaete chrysosporium*: synthesized in the absence of lignin in response to nitrogen starvation. *J. Bacteriol.* 135: 790-797.

Kim, Y., S. Yeo, J. Keum, H.G. Song and H. Choi, 2005. Cloning of a manganese peroxidase cDNA gene repressed by manganese in *Trametes versicolor. J. Microbiol.* 43: 569-571.

Kimura, Y., Y. Asada and M. Kuwahara, 1990. Screening of basidiomycetes for lignin peroxidase genes using a DNA probe. *Appl. Microbiol. Biotechnol.* 32: 436-442.

Kirk, T.K. and R.L. Farrell, 1987. Enzymatic “combustion”: the microbial degradation of lignin. *Annu. Rev. Microbiol.* 41: 465-505.

Kirk, T.K., E. Schultz, W.J. Connors, L.F. Lorenz and J.G. Zeikus, 1978. Influence of culture parameters on lignin metabolism by *Phanerochaete chrysosporium. Arch. Microbiol.* 117: 277-285.

Lankinen, P., K. Hilden, N. Aro, M. Salkinoja-Salonen and A. Hatakka, 2005. Manganese peroxidase of *Agaricus bisporus*: grain bran-promoted production and gene characterization. *Appl. Microbiol. Biotehcnol.* 66: 401-407.

Li, D., M. Alic, J.A. Brown and M.H. Gold, 1995. Regulation of manganese peroxidase gene transcription by hydrogen peroxide, chemical stress, and molecular oxygen. *Appl. Environ. Microbiol.* 61: 341-345.

Li, D., N. Li, B. Ma, M.B. Mayfield and M.H. Gold, 1999. Characterization of genes encoding two manganese peroxidases from the lignindegrading fungus *Dichomitus squalens*. *Biochim. Biophys. Acta.* 1434: 356-364.

Lindquist, S., 1986. The heat-shock response. *Annu. Rev. Biochem.* 55: 1151-1191.

Lixia, K., Q. Wu and D. Zhang, 2011. Bioconversion of rape straw into a nutritionally enriched substrate by *Ganoderma lucidum* and yeast. *Afr. J. Biotechnol.* 10(29): 5648-5653.

Lobos, S., L. Larrondo, L. Salas, E. Karahanian and R. Vicuna, 1998. Cloning and molecular analysis of a cDNA and the Cs-mnp1 gene encoding a manganese peroxidase isoenzyme from the lignin-degrading basidiomycete *Ceriporiopsis subvermispora*. *Gene* 206: 185-193.

Lundell, T., A. Leonowicz, J. Rogalski and A. Hatakka, 1990. Formation and action of ligninmodifying enzymes in cultures of *Phlebia radiata* supplemented with veratric acid. *Appl. Environ. Microbiol.* 56: 2623-2629.

Lundquist, K. and T.K. Kirk, 1978. *De novo* synthesis and decomposition of veratryl alcohol by a lignin-degrading basidiomycete. *Phytochem.* 17: 1676.

Lynd, L.R., P.J. Weimer, W.H. van Zyl and I.S. Pretorius, 2002. Microbial cellulose utilization: fundamentals and biotechnology. *Microbiol. Mol. Biol. Rev.* 66: 506-577.

Maheshwari, D.K., S. Gohade, J. Paul and A. Verma, 1994. A paper mill sludge as a potential source for cellulase production by *Trichoderma reesei* QM9123 and *Aspergillus niger* using mixed cultivation. *Carbohydr. Polym.* 23: 161–163.

Manubens, A., M. Avila, P. Canessa and R. Vicuna, 2003. Differential regulation of genes encoding manganese peroxidase (MnP) in the basidiomycete *Ceriporiopsis subvermispora*. *Curr. Genet.* 43: 433-438.

Martinez, A.T., 2002. Molecular biology and structure-function of lignin-degrading heme peroxidases. *Enzyme Microb. Technol.* 30: 425-444.

Martinez, D., L.F. Larrondo, N. Putnam, M.D. Sollewijn Gelpke, K. Huang, J, Chapman, K.G. Helfenbein, R. Ramaiya, J.C. Detter, F. Larimer, P.M. Coutinho, B. Henrissat, R. Berka, D. Cullen and D. Rokhsar, 2004. Genome sequence of the lignocelluloses degrading fungus *Phanerochaete chrysosporium* strain RP78. *Nat. Biotech.* 22: 695-700.

Masahiko, M., S. Kazumi, S. Akifumi, H. Tomohiro, S. Takaiku, O. Naoki, K. Hironori, K. Akiho, I. Kenji and I. Toshikazu, 2009. Changes in the gene expression of the white rot fungus *Phanerochaete chrysosporium* due to the addition of atropine. *Biosci. Biotechnol. Biochem.* 73: 1722-1731.

Mayfield, M.B., B.J. Godfrey and M.H. Gold, 1994. Characterization of the *mnp2* gene encoding manganese peroxidase isozyme 2 from the basidiomycete *Phanerochaete chrysosporium*. *Gene* 142: 231-235.

Mester, T., E. de Jong and J.A. Field, 1995. *Appl. Environ. Microbiol.* 61: 1881-1887.

Mester, T., M. Pena and J.A. Field, 1996. Nutrient regulation of extracellular peroxidases in the white rot fungus, *Bjerkandera* spp strain BOS55. *Appl. Microbiol. Biotechnol.* 44: 778-784.

Muhammad, I. and A. Muhammad, 2011. Production and optimization of ligninolytic enzymes by white rot fungus *Schizophyllum commune* IBL-06 in solid state medium banana stalks. *Afr. J. Biotechnol.* 10(79): 18234-18242.

Naraian, R., R.K. Sahu, S. Kumar, S.K. Garg, C.S. Singh and R.S. Kanaujia, 2009. Influence of different nitrogen rich supplements during cultivation of *Pleurotus florida* on corn cob substrate. *Environmentalist* 29: 1-7.

Naraian, R., D. Singh, A. Verma and S.K. Garg, 2010. Studies on *in vitro* degradability of mixed crude enzyme extracts produced from *Pleurotus* spp. *J. Environ. Biol.* 31: 945-951.

Niku-Paavola, M.L., L. Raaska and M. Itavaara, 1990. Detection of white-rot fungi by a nontoxic stain. *Mycol. Res.* 94: 27-31.

Niku-Paavola, M.L., E. Karhunen, P. Salola and V. Raunio, 1988. Ligninolytic enzymes of the white-rot fungus *Phlebia radiata*. *Biochem. J.* 254:877-884.

Nover, L., 1991. Inducers of HSP synthesis: heat shock and chemical stressors. 5-40. In: L. Nover (ed.), Heat shock response. CRC Press, Boca Raton, Florida.

O'Halloran, T.V., 1993. Transition metals in control of gene expression. *Science* 261: 715-725.

Orth, A., M. Rzhetskaya, D. Cullen, and M. Tien. 1994. Characterization of a cDNA encoding manganese peroxidase from *Phanerochaete chrysosporium*: genomic organization of lignin and manganese peroxidase genes. *Gene* 148: 161–165.

Panda, T., V.S. Bisaria and T.K. Ghose, 1983. Studies on mixed fungal culture for cellulase and hemicellulase production. Part 1. Optimization of medium for the mixed culture of *Trichoderma reesei* D l-6 and *Aspergillus wentii* Pt. 2804. *Biotechnol. Letters* 5: 767-772.

Papinutti, V.L. and F. Forchiassin, 2007. Lignocellulolytic enzymes from *Fomes sclerodermeus* growing in solid-state fermentation. *J. Food Eng.* 8: 54-59.

Paulraj, K., P. Karuppasamy, C. Pothiraj and A. Venkatesan, 2009. Studies on lignocellulose biodegradation of coir waste in solid state fermentation using *Phanerocheate chrysosporium* and *Rhizopus stolonifer*. *Afr. J. Biotechnol.* 8 (24): 6880-6887.

Pease, E.A. and M. Tien, 1992. Heterogeneity and regulation of manganese peroxidases from *Phanerochaete chrysosporium*. *J. Bacteriol.* 174: 3532-3540.

Pease, E.A., A. Andrawis and M. Tien, 1989. Manganese-dependent peroxidase from *Phanerochaete chrysosporium*. Primary structure deduced from complementary DNA sequence. *J. Biol. Chem.* 264: 13531-13535.

Perie, F.H. and M.H. Gold, 1991. Manganese regulation of manganese peroxidase expression and lignin degradation by the white-rot fungus *Dichomitus squalens*. *Appl. Environ. Microbiol.* 57: 2240-2245.

Pickard, M.A., H. Vandertol, R. Roman and R. Vazquez-Duhalt, 1999. High production of ligninolytic enzymes from white rot fungi in cereal bran liquid medium. *Can. J. Microbiol.* 45: 627-631.

Pribnow, D., M.B. Mayfield, V.J. Nipper, J.A. Brown and M.H. Gold, 1989. Characterization of a cDNA encoding a manganese peroxidase, from the lignin-degrading basidiomycete *Phanerochaete chrysosporium*. *J. Biol. Chem.* 264: 5036-5040.

Reiser, J., I.Walther, C. Fraefel and A. Fiechter, 1993. Methods to investigate the expression of lignin peroxidase genes by the white-rot fungus *Phanerochaete chrysosporium*. *Appl. Environ. Microbiol.* 59: 2897-2903.

Revankar, M., S. Desai and K.M. Lele, 2007. Solid-state fermentation for enhanced production of laccase using indigenously isolated *Ganoderma* species. *Appl. Biochem. Biotechnol.* 143: 16-26.

Ritch, T.G., V.J. Nipper, L.A. Akileswaran, J. Smith, D.G. Pribnow and M.H. Gold, 1991. Lignin peroxidase from the basidiomycete *Phanerochaete chrysosporium* is synthesized as a preproenzyme. *Gene* 107: 119-126.

Ruggeri, B. and G. Sassi, 2003. Experimental sensitivity analysis of a trickle bed bioreactor for lignin peroxidases production by *Phanerochaete chrysosporium*. *Process Biochem.* Pp. 1-8.

Ruiz-Duenas, F.J., F. Guillen, S. Camarero, M. Perez-Boada, M.J. Martınez and A.T. Martınez, 1999. Regulation of peroxidase transcript levels in liquid cultures of the ligninolytic fungus *Pleurotus eringii*. *Appl. Environ. Microbiol.* 65: 4458-4463.

Ruttimann, C., E. Schwember, L. Salas, D. Cullen and R. Vicuna, 1992. Lignonolytic enzymes of the white-rot fungus basidiomycetes *Phlebia brevispora* or *Cerviporiopsis subvermispora*. *Biotechnol. Appl. Biochem.* 16: 64-77.

Ryan, S., W. Schnitzhofer, T. Tzanov, A. Cavaco-Paulo and G.M. Gubitzl, 2003. An acid-stable laccase from *Sclerotium rolfsii* with potential for wool dye decolourization. *Enzyme Microbiol. Technol.* 33: 766-774.

Sanchez, C., 2009. Lignocellulosic residues: biodegradation and bioconversion by fungi. *Biotechnol. Adv. 27: 185-194.*

Scheel, T., M. Hofer, S. Ludwig and U. Holker, 2000. Differential expression of manganese peroxidase and laccase in white-rot fungi in the presence of manganese or aromatic compounds. *Appl. Microbiol. Biotechnol.* 54: 686-691.

Schlesinger, M.J., 1990. Heat shock proteins. *J. Biol. Chem.* 265: 12111-12114.

Steffen, K.T., M. Hofrichter and A. Hatakka, 2002. Purification and characterization of manganese peroxidases from the litter-decomposing basidiomycetes *Agrocybe praecox* and *Stropharia coronilla*. *Enzyme. Microb. Technol.* 30: 550-555.

Stewart, P. and D. Cullen, 1999. Organization and differential regulation of a cluster of lignin peroxidase genes of *Phanerochaete chrysosporium*. *J. Bacteriol*. 181: 3427-3432.

Stewart, P., P. Kersten, W.A. Vanden, J. Gaskell and D. Cullen, 1992. The lignin peroxidase gene family of *Phanerochaete chrysosporium:* complex regulation by carbon and nitrogen limitation, and the identification of a second dimorphic chromosome. *J. Bacteriol.* 174: 5036-5042.

Storz, G., L.A. Tartaglia, S.B. Farr and B.N. Ames, 1990. Bacterial defenses against oxidative stress. *Trends Genet.* 6: 363-368.

Takano, M., A. Nishida and M. Nakamura, 2001. Screening of wood-rotting fungi for kraft pulp bleaching by the poly R decolorization test and biobleaching of hardwood kraft pulp by *Phanerochaete crassa* WD1694. *J. Wood Sci.* 47: 63-68.

Tello, M., G. Corsini, L.F. Larrondo, L. Salas, S. Lobos and R. Vicuna, 2000. Characterization of three new manganese peroxidase genes from the ligninolytic basidiomycete *Ceriporiopsis subermispora*. *Biochim. Biophys. Acta.* 1490: 137-144.

Terhi, K., H.K. Hakala, P. Maijala, C. Olsson and A. Hatakka, 2006. Differential regulation of manganese peroxidases and characterization of two variable MnP encoding genes in the white-rot fungus *Physisporinus rivulosus*. *Appl. Microbiol. Biotechnol.*, 73: 839-849.

Thiele, D.J., 1992. Metal-regulated transcription in eukaryotes. *Nucleic Acids Res.* 20: 1183-1191.

Tien, M. and T.K. Kirk, 1998. Lignin peroxidase of *Phanerochaete chyrosprium*. *Methods Enzyme* 161: 238-248.

Tien, M. and T.K. Kirk, 1983. Lignin-degrading enzyme from the hymenomycete *Phanerochaete chrysosporium* burds. *Sci.* 221: 661-663.

Tunde, M. and J.A. Field, 1998. Characterization of a novel manganese peroxidase-lignin peroxidase hybrid isozyme produced by *Bjerkandera* species strain BOS55 in the absence of manganese. *J. Biological Chemistry* 273: 15412-15417.

Vallim, M., B. Janse, J. Gaskell, A. Pizzirani-Kleiner and D. Cullen, 1998. *Phanerochaete chrysosporium* cellobiohydrolase and cellobiose dehydrogenase transcripts in wood. *Appl. Environ. Microbiol.* 64: 1924-1928.

Vares, T. and A. Hatakka, 1997. Lignin-degrading activity and ligninolytic enzymes of different white-rot fungi: Effects of manganese and malonate. *Can. J. Bot.* 75: 61-71.

Vares, T., M. Kalsi and A. Hatakka, 1995. Lignin peroxidases, manganese peroxidases, and other ligninolytic enzymes produced by *Phlebia radiata* during solid-state fermentation of wheat straw. *Appl. Environ. Microbiol.* 61: 3515-3520.

Welinder, K.G. and M. Gajhede, 1993. Structure and evolution of peroxidases. In: Greppin, H., S.K. Rasmussen, K.G. Welinder and C. Penel (eds.), plant peroxidases biochemistry and physiology. University of Copenhagen and University of Geneva, Geneva, Pp. 35-42.

Yeo, S., N. Park, H. Song and H.T. Choi, 2007. Generation of a transformant showing higher manganese peroxidase (Mnp) activity by overexpression of Mnp gene in *Trametes versicolor. J. Microbiol.* 45 (3): 213-218.

Yujie, C., A. Hatakka and P. Maijala, 2007. Can co-culturing of two white-rot fungi increase lignin degradation and the production of lignin-degrading enzymes? *Intl. Biodeter. and Biodeg.* 59(1): 32-39.

Zhang, Y.Z., G.J. Zylstra, R.H. Olsen and C.A. Reddy, 1986. Identification of cDNA clones for ligninase from *Phanerochaete chrysosporium* using synthetic oligonucleotide probes. *Biochem. Biophys. Res. Commun.* 137: 649-656.

In: Applications of Microbial Genes in Enzyme Technology ISBN: 978-1-62417-808-5
Editors: V.K.Gupta, M.G.Tuohy, G.D.Sharma et al.

Chapter 15

Microbial Cold-Active Proteases: Fundamental Aspects and Their Biotechnological Potential

Mohammed Kuddus[1*] and Athar Ali[2]
[1]Protein Research Laboratory,
Department of Biotechnology and Microbiology Integral University, Lucknow, India
[2]Center for Transgenic Plant Development,
Department of Biotechnology Jamia Hamdard (Hamdard University),
New Delhi, India

Abstract

Proteases are the single class of hydrolytic enzymes, which occupy a key position with respect to their applications in both physiological and commercial fields. These enzymes are found in all living organisms and perform both synthetic and degradative functions. Although, there are many microbial sources available for producing proteases, only a few are recognized as producers of cold-active proteases. Cold-adapted microorganisms are the potential source of chilled-active proteases, and these microorganisms have been isolated from the cool environments of the Earth. Cold-active proteases are of commercial value and find multiple applications in various industrial and biotechnological sectors such as additives in detergents, additives in food industries, environmental bio-remediation, biotransformation and molecular biology applications. Consequently, for the last couple of years cold-active microbial proteases have been the enzyme of choice for many biotechnologists, microbiologists, biochemical process engineers, biochemists and environmentalists.

In recent years, the search of microbial sources for cold-active protease in natural diversity has been targeting the undiscovered wealth of molecular diversity. However, there are many possibilities to get novel cold-active proteases through metagenomics and

* E-mail: kuddus_biotech@yahoo.com, atharbiotech@gmail.com; Phone: +91 522 2890730; Fax: +91 522 2890809.

modify the properties of proteases through molecular approach such as the recombinant DNA technology.

In this chapter, we will discuss some novel sources and structure of cold-active microbial proteases; molecular approach to cold adaptation, purification and properties; methods for developing novel cold-active proteases and their various applications in industrial and biotechnological sectors.

Introduction

Hydrolases, which cleave peptide bonds in polypeptides/proteins, are generally known as proteases, proteinases, peptidases or proteolytic enzymes. The International Union of Biochemistry and Molecular Biology (1992) has recommended to use the term peptidase for the subset of peptide bond hydrolases (Subclass E.C. 3.4). However, proteases do not comply easily with the general system of enzyme nomenclature due to their huge diversity of action and structure.

At present, proteases are classified based on of three major criteria: (I) type of reaction catalyzed, (ii) chemical nature of the catalytic site, and (iii) evolutionary relationship concerning to structure (Barett, 1994). Microbial proteases are also classified into acidic, neutral or alkali proteases depending upon whether they are active under acidic, neutral or alkali conditions, respectively. However, proteases are grossly subdivided into two major groups, *viz.* exopeptidases andEndopeptidases, depending on their site of action. Exopeptidases cleave the peptide bond proximal into the amino or carboxy termini of the substrate, whereas endopeptidases cleave peptide bonds from the termini of the substrate. Based on the functional group present at the active site, proteases are further classified into four prominent groups, i.e., serine proteases, aspartic proteases, cysteine proteases and metalloproteases (Hartley, 1960).

Proteases represent one of the largest groups of industrial enzymes and account for about 60% of the total worldwide sale of enzymes (Rao *et al.*, 1998). The current estimated value of the worldwide sales of industrial enzymes is more than $ 1 billion and expected to increase further in coming years (Godfrey and West, 1996). The vast diversity of proteases, in contrast to the specificity of their action, has attracted worldwide attention in attempts to exploit their physiological and biotechnological applications (Fox *et al.*, 1991). In the past two decays microbial enzymes replaced many plant and animal enzymes and used in various industries (Sanchez and Demain, 2011). Cold-active proteases function effectively at low temperatures with high rates of catalysis in comparison to the protease from mesophiles or thermopiles. These proteases have evolved a range of molecular and structural features and high specific activity at low temperatures.

The knowledge of chilled-functioning microbial proteases is increasing globally at an exciting rate to explore cool-enterprising proteases, its producing microorganisms and their industrialapplications. (Margesin *et al.*, 2002; Feller and Gerday, 2003; Georlette *et al.*, 2004.). Unfortunately, the literatures on cold-active proteases are very much scattered and unorganized.

In this chapter, we tried to compile all the related information on the sources, habitats, molecular and structural adaptation, production, characteristics and biotechnological and industrial applications of cold-active microbial proteases.

Source of Cold-Active Microbial Proteases

Proteases are essential constituents of all forms of life on the Earth, including prokaryotes, fungi, plants and animals. The inability of the plant and animal proteases to meet current world demands has led to an increased interest in microbial proteases. Microbial proteases account for approximately 40% of the total worldwide enzyme sales (Godfrey and West, 1996) and preferred from plant and animal sources since they possess almost all the characteristics desired for their biotechnological and industrial applications (Rao *et al.*, 1998).

Also, the commercial application of microbial proteases is attractive due to the relative ease of large-scale production as compared to proteases from plants and animals. Most commercial proteases, mainly neutral and alkaline, are produced by bacteria belonging to the genus *Bacillus* (Rao *et al.*, 1998). Bacterial alkaline proteases are characterized by their high activity at alkaline pH, e.g. pH 10, and their broad substrate specificity. Fungi elaborate a wider variety of enzymes than do bacteria. For example, *Aspergillus oryzae* produces acid, neutral, and alkaline proteases. The fungal proteases also are active over a wide pH range (pH 4 to 11) and exhibit broad substrate specificity. Viral proteases have gained importance due to their functional involvement in the processing of proteins of viruses that cause certain fatal diseases. Cold-active proteases can be produced by prokaryotic as well as eukaryotic organisms. Thus far, most of them originate from psychrophilic (cold-loving) or psychrotolerant (cold-adapted) bacteria and fishes living in Polar regions especially in Antarctic sea water (Feller *et al.*, 1996). Some microbial culture depositories in the world are presented in table 1.

Table 1. Microbial culture depositories

Microbial culture collection centre	Website
American Type Culture Collection (ATCC)	http://www.atcc.org
Belgian Co-ordinated Collections of Microorganisms (BCCM)	http://www.belspo.be/bccm
Common Access to Biological Resources and Information (CABRI)	http://www.cabri.org
Culture Collection, University of Goteborg	http://*www.ccug.se*
Czech Collection of Microorganisms (CCM)	http://www.sci.muni.cz/ccm
European Culture Collections Organisation (ECCO)	http://www.eccosite.org
German National Resource Centre for Biological Material (DSMZ)	http://www.dsmz.de
Japan Collection of Microorganisms (JCM)	http://www.jcm.riken.jp
Microbial Culture Collection (MCC)	http://www.nccs.res.in/mcc
Microbial type culture collection (MTCC)	http://mtcc.imtech.res.in
National Collections of Industrial and Marine Bacteria (NCIMB)	http://*www.ncimb.com*
Netherlands Culture Collection of Bacteria (NCCB)	http://www.cbs.knaw.nl/NCCB
World Federation for Culture Collections (WFCC)	http://*www.wfcc.info*

Cold-Adapted Microorganisms

According to the definition given by Ingraham and Stokes (1959), psychrophilic bacteria should show visible growth at 0°C after 14 days of incubation. This definition has been renewed by Morita (1975) who identified specific physiological group of microorganisms based on their growth temperature as follows:

Psychrophile : T_{min}: <0°C, T_{opt}: <15°C, T_{max}: <20°C
Psychrotolerant : T_{min}: <0°C, T_{opt}: >15°C, T_{max}: >20°C

Further reviews and publications (Baross and Morita, 1978; Inniss and Ingraham, 1978; Herbert, 1986; Russell, 1990; Friedmann, 1994; Deming, 2002) has also set the frame for defining psychrophilic/psychrotolerant organisms and their environments.

However, the classical definition of Morita is frequently used in the literature. This definition proposes that psychrophiles have optimum growth temperatures of <15°C and upper cardinal temperatures of ~20°C. Morita (1975) further distinguished psychrophiles from psychrotolerants (psychrotrophs) on the basis of their cardinal temperatures, in that the psychrotrophs have a minimum growth temperature which is at or just above zero, and optimum and maximum growth temperatures above 20°C. The definition of psychrophilic microorganisms is ambiguous for three main reasons.

First, the temperature limits have been arbitrarily selected and do not correspond to any clear separation of biological processes or environmental conditions.

Second, Morita's definition does not apply to most eukaryotes. Finally, and most important, microorganisms behave as thermodynamic units: increasing the culture temperature increases reaction rates and the growth rate. However, they also behave as biological units: at a given temperature, key metabolic steps that are heat labile impair the functioning of some pathways. It has been shown, for instance, that although the growth rate of some cold-adapted bacteria increases with a temperature shift from 5°C to 25°C, the physiological state is strongly altered, as judged by the decrease in viable counts, exoenzyme production, protein synthesis and membrane permeability (Feller, 1994; Orange, 1994).

This emphasizes that the use of growth rates to define the optimum growth temperature is inappropriate.

Habitats of Cold-Adapted Microorganisms

Most of our planet is cold because nearly three-quarters of the Earth is covered by deep oceans, where the temperature is permanently about 3°C (Austin, 1988). Cold-adapted microbes are major contributors of the nutrient cycle in the deep-oceans (Morita, 1975). The deep-sea is also a high-pressure environment so many microbial isolate are not only psychrophilic but also barophilic or barotolerant (Yayanos, 1995; Russel and Hamamoto, 1998). The continent of Antarctica as well as the land masses in the Arctic provides permanently cold terrestrial environments (Vishniac, 1993). Psychrophilic microorganisms, including bacteria, yeasts, fungi and micro algae, can be found in soils, waters (fresh and saline, still and flowing) and associated with plants and cold-blooded animals. Some psychrotolerant bacteria are pathogenic; they include strains of *Clostridium botulinum* and *Bacillus cereus,* which can grow and produce toxins in food stored in chill-cabinets. In the plant world, a number of psychrotolerant *Pseudomonads* are pathogenic. As part of the pathogenic mechanism, the *Pseudomonads* also produce ice-nucleation proteins, which have biotechnological potential (Li and Lee, 1995).

Molecular Adaptations to Cold

The ability to survive at low temperatures, even below zero, has been evolved by different types of organisms using a wide range of strategies. Cold environments of the Earth's biosphere are successfully colonized by psychrophiles or cold-loving organisms. Psychrophiles have developed adaptive mechanisms to perform their metabolic functions at low temperatures by incorporating unique features in their proteins and membranes. To survive with the reduction of chemical reaction rates induced by low temperatures, these organisms synthesize low temperatures associated enzymes, however, with low thermal stability. Moreover, the ability to synthesize cold-shock or antifreeze proteins, alterations in enzyme kinetics and the stabilization of microtubules enable the psychrophiles to continue their activities at low temperature (Georlette *et al.*, 2004). Instead of cold-active enzymes, cold-acclimation proteins (CAPs) seem to be another important feature of cold-adapted microorganisms. These proteins are permanently synthesized during steady-state growth at low temperatures and are essential for the maintenance of both growth and the cell cycle at low temperatures (Hebraud *et al.*, 1994; Berger *et al.* 1996; Hebraud and Potier, 2000). In psychrophiles, the maintenance of membrane fluidity and permeability has typical roles in low temperatures adaptation. The temperature-dependent changes in membrane lipid composition, fluidity and their biochemical basis have been reviewed (Russell, 1993; Chintalapati *et al.*, 2004). It was found that decrease in bacterial growth temperature leads to increase in fatty acid unsaturation, or decrease in average chain length, or increase in methyl branching, or to some combination of these changes (Russell, 1990). Regarding cold adaptation, improvement of enzyme turnover number (k_{cat}) is also an important physiological parameter, because it offsets the inhibitory effect of low temperatures on reaction rates. In principle, cold-adapted enzymes can optimize the k_{cat}/K_m ratio by increasing k_{cat}, decreasing K_m or by changes in both k_{cat} and K_m (Feller, 2003). Psychrophilic enzymes have a fragile molecular edifice that is uniformly unstable and is stabilized by fewer weak interactions than heat-stable proteins (Feller *et al.*, 1999; D'Amico *et al.*, 2003; Georlette *et al.*, 2003). At present, directed evolution experiments are important in improving our understanding of the structure-function relationships of enzymes. In the laboratory, it is possible to obtain an enzyme with increased cold activity while maintaining, or even improving, its stability by a limited number of mutations (Wintrode and Arnold, 2000).

Accordingly, it has been proposed that the low stability of cold-adapted enzymes is the result of genetic drift that is related to the lack of selection for stable proteins in cold environments (Miyazaki *et al.*, 2000; Wintrode *et al.*, 2000). To define the properties of a cold-active enzyme, the effect of temperature on the activity of psychrophilic and mesophilic enzymes must be evaluated. Some standard reviews have been published on this aspect (D'Amico *et al.*, 2002; Margesin *et al.*, 2002; Feller, 2003) but other excellent reviews should also be consulted for a complete exposure of this topic (Somero, 1995; Lonhienne *et al.*, 2000; Russell, 2000; Sheridan *et al.*, 2000; Smalas *et al.*, 2000; Georlette et. al., 2001; Zecchinon *et al.*, 2001).

Structural Features of Proteases

General Proteases Structure

Microbial proteases may consist of longer single polypeptides or be composed of two or even more identical subunits. The molecular mass of simple monomeric microbial proteases can vary from 9 kDa to 135 kDa but it may have much larger and more complex structures (Rivett, 1989). Among proteases, subtilisins (EC 3.4.21.62) are most important because they work efficiently in alkaline medium. Subtilisin, alkaline serine proteases that initiate nucleophilic attack on the peptide bond, is a non-specific protease initially obtained from *Bacillus subtilis*. Till date more than 200 subtilisin-like proteases have been characterized and sequenced (Siezen and Leunissen, 1997). For the first time three-dimensional structure of the subtilisin BPN' has been refined by Wright *et al.* (1969). Moreover, the three-dimensional structures of subtilisin Novo (Drenth *et al.*, 1972), subtilisin Carlsberg (Bode *et al.*, 1987), subtilisin (Bott *et al.*, 1988), proteinase K (Betzel *et al.*, 1988), thermitase (Gros *et al.*, 1989) and subtilisin Savinase (Betzel *et al.*, 1992) have been reported. The large amount of data available for subtilisins, as illustrated by over 450 site-directed mutants constructed (Davail *et al.*, 1994), and their industrial importance make them attractive model enzymes for structure-stability studies.

Modifications in Protease Structure for Cold Adaptation

In comparison to proteins from mesophiles, psychrophilic proteins has decreased ionic interactions and hydrogen bonds, possess less hydrophobic groups and more charged groups on their surface (Cavicchioli *et al.*, 2002; Deming, 2002; Margesin *et al.*, 2002; Feller and Gerday, 2003; Georlette *et al.*, 2004). Due to these modifications, psychrophilic proteins lose their rigidity and gain increased structural flexibility for enhanced catalytic function. Now on the basis of reviewed literature it is clear that the basis of psychrophily resided in protein structure. For the first time, an enzyme from a psychrophilic bacterium has been crystallised and paving the way for direct structural observations (Aghajari *et al.*, 1996). Thus far, crystal structures of only some microbial psychrophilic enzymes/proteins have been determined by X-ray crystallography (Villeret *et al.*, 1997; Aghajari *et al.*, 1998; Alvarez *et al.*, 1998; Russell *et al.*, 1998; Kim *et al.*, 1999; Leiros *et al.*, 2001; Mandelman *et al.*, 2001). Unfortunately, very few structures have been compared with mesophilic or thermophilic homologues, for instance bacterial α-amylase (Aghajari *et al.*, 1998a), and analyzed in detail with regards to the structural parameters related to cold activity.

However, this limited set of data has already provided valuable insights into the molecular basis of cold adaptation (Leiros *et al.*, 1999; Russell, 2000; Gianese *et al.*, 2002). As far as the active site of psychrophilic enzymes is concerned, all reactive side chains as well as most side chains pointing towards the catalytic cavity are strictly conserved. The differences in electrostatic potentials in and around the active site of psychrophilic enzymes appear to be a crucial parameter for activity at low temperatures. Interestingly, the cold-active trypsin is characterized by marked differences in electrostatic potentials near the active-site region when compared with mesophilic or thermophilic counterparts (Brandsdal *et al.*, 2001). Calculations of the electrostatic potential revealed in some cases an excess of negative charges at the surface of the molecule and, indeed, the pI of cold-active enzymes is frequently more acidic than that of their mesophilic or thermophilic homologues. This has been related to improved interactions with the solvent, which could be of prime importance in the acquisition of flexibility near zero degrees (Feller *et al.*, 1999). Besides the balance of charges, the number of salt bridges covering the protein surface is also reduced.

Definitely, all these factors are not found in every cold-active enzyme and each enzyme adopts its own strategy by using one or a combination of these altered structural factors to improve the local or global mobility of the protein edifice. A recent comparative structural analysis of psychrophilic, mesophilic and thermophilic enzymes reports that each protein family displays a different structural strategy to adapt the temperature. However, some common trends are observed such as number of ion pairs, side chain contribution to the exposed surface and apolar fraction of the buried surface show a consistent decrease with decreasing optimal temperature (Gianese *et al.*, 2002).

Structure of Cold-Active Protease from Psychrophilic *Bacillus* Spp

As per literature reviews it is evident that the Antarctic *Bacillus* spp. is the most extensively studied microorganism with respect to its cold-active protease production and characterization. The psychrophilic bacterium, *Bacillus* TA41, was originally isolated from sea water of Dumont d'Urville Antarctic station which expressed an alkaline protease, subtilisin S41 (Davail *et al.*, 1994). The gene of subtilisin S41 encodes for a pre-proenzyme of 419 amino acids residues.

The nucleotide sequence and NH_2- and COOH- terminal amino acid sequencing of the purified enzyme indicate that the mature subtilisin S41 is composed of 309 residues with a molecular weight of 31,224 Da. Subtilisin S41 shares most of its properties with mesophilic subtilisins (Davail *et al.*, 1994).

However, this enzyme displays a higher specific activity, a shift of the optimum of activity toward low temperatures, and a weak thermal stability, which are all common properties of cold adapted enzymes. The result concluded that the psychrophilic enzyme possesses more flexible molecular structure when compared to mesophilic and thermophilic subtilases in order to compensate for the reduction of reaction rates at low temperatures. Subtilisin S41 model reveals several features able to induce a more flexible, heat-labile conformation such as occurrence of four extended surface loops, a very hydrophilic surface through 11 extra Asp residues, and lack of several salt bridges and aromatic-aromatic interactions (Davail *et al.*, 1994).

Subsequently, Narinx *et al.* (1997) have also purified subtilisin from another Antarctic *Bacillus* TA39. It was isolated from sea water in the coastal area of the French Antarctic base J.S. Dumont d'Urville. The strain displays the characteristics of a microorganism permanently adapted to cold i.e. it does not grow at temperature higher than 25°C. The strain produces two subtilisins coded by two different genes. The gene *subt2* is apparently not expressed in the culture conditions used, in contrast to what happens in the case of *Bacillus* TA41 (Davail *et al.*, 1994) which expresses only *subt2* significantly. The enzyme also displays the usual characteristics of cold enzymes i.e. a high catalytic efficiency at low and moderate temperatures (0-45°C) and a higher thermosensitivity.

As far as the 3D structure of the enzyme is concerned, the analysis corroborates the conclusions already drawn by Davail *et al.* (1994) for *subt2*. When compared with mesophilic subtilisins, the cohesion of the 3D structure appears significantly reduced through a decrease in the number of salt bridges and disappearance of all aromatic interactions. This is in accordance with what has been already found in the case of other cold-active extracellular enzymes (Davail *et al.*, 1994; Feller *et al.*, 1994).

Production of Cold-Active Proteases

A diverse range of psychrophilic/psychrotolerant microorganisms, belonging to bacteria, archaea, yeast and fungi have been isolated from cold environments of Earth, including polar regions, high mountains, glaciers, ocean deeps, caves, the upper atmosphere, refrigerated appliances and the surfaces of plants and animals living in cold environments (Cavicchioli *et al.*, 2002; Deming, 2002; Margesin *et al.*, 2002; Feller and Gerday, 2003; Georlette *et al.*, 2004). Out of these cold environments, deep oceans that cover over 70% of the Earth's surface represent the major ecosystem on the planet.

Many psychrophiles live in biotopes having more than one stress factors, such as low temperature and high pressure in deep seas (piezo-psychrophiles), or high salt concentration and low temperature in sea ice (halo-psychrophiles). These psychrophiles are able to degrade a wide range of polymeric substances by producing their respective enzymes (Demirjian, *et al.*, 2001; Eichler, 2001; Cavicchioli *et al.*, 2002; Deming, 2002; Margesin *et al.*, 2002; Burg, 2003; Feller and Gerday, 2003; Georlette *et al.*, 2004). Some cold-active protease producing microorganisms and their source are given in Table 2.

Fermentation Technology

Enzyme production plays a crucial role in the present biotechnology industry. The environmental conditions of the fermentation play a vital role in microbial growth and enzyme production.

Cold-active proteases are mostly extra-cellular and are extremely influenced by media composition and physicochemical parameters such as incubation period, temperature, pH, agitation, dissolved oxygen, nitrogen source, carbon source, inducers and metal ions. Most of the cold-adapted microorganisms showed good growth rate at low temperature with different carbon and nitrogen sources.

To meet the demand of industries, low-cost medium is required for the production of proteases. Both solid state and submerged fermentation could be used for cold-active protease production, but submerged fermentation is most common method because of greater control of environmental factors.

Table 2. Cold-active proteases producing microorganisms

Microorganism	Source of isolation	Reference
Bacillus sp.	Antarctic soil	Park and Cho, 2011
Serratia marcescens	Kashmir soil	Tariq et al., 2011
Pseudomonas	Uruguayan Antarctic Base	Rosales and Sowinski, 2011
Pseudoalteromonas haloplanktis TAC125	Antarctic marine habitat	Pascale *et al.*, 2010
Pseudomonas lundensis	Sediment of Yellow sea (Eastern China)	Yang *et al.*, 2010
S. maltophilia MTCC 7528	Gangotri glacier (Western Himalaya)	Kuddus and Ramteke, 2009
C. lutium MTCC 7529	Gangotri glacier (Western Himalaya)	Kuddus and Ramteke, 2008
Pseudoalteromonas sp. NJ276	Antarctic sea ice	Wang *et al.*, 2008
Colwellia sp. NJ341	Antarctic habitat	Wang *et al.*, 2008a
Aspergillus ustus	Central Indian Basin	Damare *et al.*, 2006
Clostridium sp.	Schirmacher oasis, Antarctica	Alam *et al.*, 2005
Vibrio sp. PA-44	Marine habitat	Arnorsdottir *et al.*, 2005
Pedobacter cryoconitis	Alpine cryoconite	Margesin *et al.*, 2005
Bacillus cereus SYP-A2-3	Glacier of China	Shi *et al.*, 2005
Colwellia sp. NJ341	Antarctic sea ice	Wang *et al.*, 2005
Pseudomonas sp.	Antarctic habitat	Vazquez *et al.*, 2004
Pseudomonas sp	Antarctic habitat	Aghajari *et al.*, 2003
Bacillus amyloliquefaciens S94	Intestinal flora of rainbow trout	Son and Kim, 2003
Flavobacterium psychrophilum	Fish	Secades *et al.*, 2003
Flavobacterium limicola	Freshwater sediments	Tamaki *et al.*, 2003
Leucosporidium antarcticum	Antarctic habitat	Turkiewicz *et al.*, 2003
Pseudomonas strain DY-A	Deep-sea	Zeng *et al.*, 2003
Pseudoaltermonas sp.	Deep-sea	Chen *et al.*, 2002
Psychrophilic bacterium PA-43	Sub-Arctic habitat	Irwin *et al.*, 2001
Shewanella strain Ac10	Antarctic sea water	**Kulakova *et al.***, 1999
Azospirillum sp.	Mountain soil, Korea	Kun-Hee *et al.*, 1999
Sphingomonas paucimobilis	Antarctic krill	Marianna *et al.*, 1999
Flavobacterium balustinum	Salmon intestine	Morita *et al.*, 1998
Bacillus TA39	Antarctic habitat	**Narinx *et al.***, 1997
Alteromonas sp.	Marine habitat	Shibata *et al.*, 1997
Alteromonas haloplanktis	Marine habitat	Suzuki and Odagami, 1997

A list of some cold-active protease producing bacteria and their production parameters are given in Table 3.

Purification and Characterization

Almost the entire cold-active protease purification is based on multistep process. However, pretty recently, some new techniques have been developed to increase yield and fold purification.

There are also various methods in which protease can be purified in one-step. On the basis of isolated microbial protease properties, one has to design the protocol for downstream processing which depends on the market need, processing cost, final quality and available technology.

Table 3. Fermentation conditions for cold-active proteases production

Microbes	Incubation period	Optimum temp./pH	Substrate used	Reference
Bacillus sp.	60 h	28/7.4	Skim milk	Park and Cho, 2011
Serratia marcescens	48 h	28/7.2	Yeast extract	Tariq et al., 2011
Pseudomonas lundensis	Nm	25/Nm	Nm	Yang *et al.*, 2010
Enterococcus Faecalis TN-9	18 h	30/Nm	Nm	Yuan *et al.*, 2009
S. maltophilia MTCC 7528	128 h	20/9	Casein	Kuddus and Ramteke, 2009
C. lutium MTCC 7529	120 h	15/7	Skim milk	Kuddus and Ramteke, 2008
Colwellia sp. NJ341	Nm	7.96 /Nm	Casein	Wang *et al.*, 2008a
Aspergillus ustus	7 days	30/Nm	Nm	Damare *et al.*, 2006
Clostridium sp.	Nm	10-20/7.5	Casein	Alam *et al.*, 2005
Pedobacter cryoconitis	72 h	15/7	Wheat flour	Margesin *et al.*, 2005
Bacillus cereus SYP	Nm	15/6.5-7	Casein	Shi *et al.*, 2005
Bacillus amyloliquefaciens S94	20 h	25/Nm	Skim milk	Son and Kim, 2003
Pseudomonas DY-A	Nm	10/Nm	Nm	Zeng *et al.*, 2003
Azospirillum sp.	15 h	30/Nm	Skim milk	Kun-Hee *et al.*, 1999
Sphingomonas paucimobilis	72 h	5-10/	Nm	**Turkiewicz** *et al.*, 1999

Nm: Not mentioned.

The significance of purified cold-active protease is widely recognized in a number of applications such as the synthesis of fine chemicals, cosmetics and in pharmaceutical industries; however, homogeneous preparation is not required for all industrial applications. Few purification techniques that produce homogeneous protease are given in Table 4.

The properties of purified protease along with its specific catalytic activity are important factor for their introduction into industrial processes and products (Koeller and Wong, 2001).The characterization of cold-active proteases can be studied in terms of optimum pH and stability, optimum temperature and thermo-stability, effect of metal ions and chelating agents, nature and concentration of substrate, solvents and stabilizing agents, inhibitors etc.

Table 4. Purification of cold-active proteases

Microorganism	Chromatography techniques	Purification fold/ yield (%)	Reference
Serratia marcescens	DEAE cellulose chromatography	9.9/51	Tariq *et al.*, 2011
Pseudomonas lundensis	Fast protein liquid chromatography	14/20	Yang *et al.*, 2010
Enterococcus Faecalis TN-9	Ion-exchange chromatography	492/23	Yuan *et al.*, 2009
S. maltophilia MTCC 7528	DEAE cellulose chromatography	55/4.5	Kuddus and Ramteke, 2009
C. lutium MTCC 7529	DEAE cellulose chromatography	34.1/5.13	Kuddus and Ramteke, 2008
Pseudoalteromonas sp. NJ276	Sephadex column chromatography	22.5/Nm	Wang *et al.*, 2008
Aspergillus ustus	Column chromatography	4.05/21	Damare *et al.*, 2006
Clostridium sp	Column chromatography	12.7/26.6	Alam *et al.*, 2005
Bacillus amyloliquefaciens S94	Sephadex column chromatography	48/3.2	Son and Kim, 2003
Flavobacterium psychrophilum	Fast protein liquid chromatography	829.38/3.54	Secades *et al.*, 2003
Psychrophilic bacterium PA-43	Ion exchange chromatography	25/26.1	Irwin *et al.*, 2001
Shewanella strain Ac10	Affinity chromatography	**Nm**	**Kulakova *et al.***, 1999
Azospirillum sp.	DEAE cellulose chromatography	Nm/3-5	Kun-Hee *et al.*, 1999
Sphingomonas paucimobilis	Affinity chromatography	Nm	**Turkiewicz** *et al.*, 1999
Alteromonas sp.	Sephadex column chromatography	202/13	Shibata *et al.*, 1997

Nm: Not mentioned.

The microbial cold-active proteases have an optimum activity at specific temperature and pH but they are stable at a wide range of temperatures, pH and have broad substrate specificity (Table 5).

Table 5. Properties of cold-active proteases

Microorganism	Mol. wt. (kDa)	Optimum temp/pH	Stability temp/pH	Inhibitors	Reference
Serratia marcescens	56	25/8.5	Nm	EDTA	Tariq *et al.*, 2011
Bacillus sp.	Nm	40/7.4	Nm	EDTA	Park and Cho, 2011
Pseudomonas lundensis	46	30/10.4	25-40/7-10	EDTA	Yang *et al.*, 2010
Enterococcus Faecalis TN-9	30	30/7.5-8	45/6-9.5	EDTA	Yuan *et al.*, 2009
S. maltophilia MTCC 7528	75	20/9	20/10	EGTA	Kuddus and Ramteke, 2009
C. lutium MTCC 7529	115	20/7	4-20/6-8	EDTA	Kuddus and Ramteke, 2008
Pseudoalteromonas sp. NJ276	28	30/8	30-40/8-9	PMSF	Wang *et al.*, 2008
Aspergillus ustus	32	45/9	20-45/6-10	PMSF	Damare *et al.*, 2006
Pedobacter cryoconitis	27	40/8	20-30/7-9	EDTA, EGTA	Margesin *et al.*, 2005
Bacillus cereus SYP-A2-3	34.2	42/7-8.5	Nm	Nm	Shi *et al.*, 2005
Colwellia sp. NJ341	60	35/Nm	Nm/5-12	PMSF	Wang *et al.*, 2005
Bacillus amylo-liquefaciens S94	23	45/10	15-45/Nm	PMSF	Son and Kim, 2003
Flavobacterium psychrophilum	62	24/6-7	Nm	EGTA	Secades *et al.*, 2003
Leucosporidium antarcticum	34.4	25/Nm	0-25/Nm	Nm	Turkiewicz *et al.*, 2003
Pseudomonas strain DY-A	25	40/10	Nm	PMSF	Zeng *et al.*, 2003
Pseudoaltermonas sp.	60.7	30-35/Nm	Nm	Nm	Chen *et al.*, 2003
Psychrophilic bacterium PA-43	76	55/8.3	55-60/Nm	PMSF	Irwin *et al.*, 2001
Shewanella strain Ac10	44	**20/9**	**5-20/9-10**	**Nm**	**Kulakova *et al.*,** 1999
Azospirillum sp.	48.6	40/8.5	30/8-9	EDTA	Kun-Hee *et al.*, 1999
Sphingomonas paucimobilis	116	20-30/7	0-30/6.5-7	EDTA	Turkiewicz *et al.*, 1999
Flavobacterium balustinum P104	70	40/7-9	Nm	PMSF	Morita *et al.*, 1998
Alteromonas sp.	28	40/8.5-9	0-40/7.5-8	EDTA	Shibata *et al.*, 1997
Alteromonas haloplanktis	74	20/8-9	20-30/Nm	PCMB	Suzuki and Odagami, 1997

Nm: Not mentioned.

Due to these broad ranges of temperature, pH and substrate stability cold-active proteases have potentials in biotechnological and industrial applications. There are also several other advantages and disadvantages of cold-active proteases for industrial applications because they are easily deactivated when subjected to extreme heat, pH or in organic solvents.

A numbers of strategies have been proposed to overcome such limitation including the use of soluble additives, immobilization and protein/enzyme engineering (Eijsink *et al.*, 2004; Joseph *et al.*, 2008).

Gene Cloning/Enzyme Engineering

When a prospective microorganism producing a desired enzyme activity has been identified, several steps are required to convert it into a strain that is suitable for commercial use. Therefore, in addition to microbiological screening at low temperature, various molecular approaches including r-DNA technology, protein engineering, directed evolution and metagenomic approach may be established to develop radically different and novel cold-active proteases. As an emerging area of research in the field of enzyme technology it demands extension of biotechnological approach in terms of both quality and quantity. Already established r-DNA technology and protein engineering can be used in restructuring of cold-active protease gene and its protein to achieve qualitative improvements.

Quantitative enhancement of cold-active protease needs strain improvement, especially through site-directed mutagenesis, and standardizing the nutrient medium for the overproduction. Thus far, a small number of cold-active protease genes are isolated and the related studies have been carried out. In this context, gene encoding serine alkaline protease (SapSh) of the psychrotrophic bacterium *Shewanella* strain Ac10 was cloned in *Escherichia coli* (Kulakova *et al.*, 1999). The recombinant SapSh (rSapSh) was characterized by its high level of activity at low temperatures and was five times more active than subtilisin Carlsberg at temperatures ranging from 5 to 15 °C. However, rSapSh was far less stable than the subtilisin (Kulakova *et al.*, 1999). Cloning and expression of another cold-active protease gene (pro-2127) from *Pseudoalteromonas sp* QI-1 has also been reported (Guoying *et al.*, 2011). PRO-2127 showed some structural features common to psychrophilic enzymes such as a decrease in Arg residues and the Arg/(Arg+Lys) ratio.

In the recent years, it is of great interest from an industrial and environmental point of view to design an enzyme which functions with a higher specific activity at low temperatures. Cold-adapted enzymes drew the attention of the scientific community due to their strange properties that render them particularly useful in investigating the possible relationship existing between stability, flexibility and specific activity and as valuable tools for biotechnological purposes. Cold-active proteases could generate avenues for industrial applications. Determination of three-dimensional structures of more cold-active proteases would allow the detailed analysis of protein adaptation to temperatures at molecular level.

Extensive attempts to engineer cold-adapted proteases from subtilisin BPN have previously been made (Kano *et al.*, 1997; Taguchi *et al.*, 2000).

Another strategy to evolve a serine protease with enhanced thermo-stability and activity has been around to use the psychrophilic subtilisin S41 (Miyazaki *et al.*, 2000; Wintrode *et al.*, 2000; Tindbaek *et al.*, 2004). Tindbaek *et al.* (2004) engineered a substrate-specific cold-adapted subtilisin. By site-directed modifications, a highly flexible region of psychrophilic enzyme (TA39 subtilisin) was transferred to the binding region of mesophilic savinase, thus a savinase-S39 hybrid (H5) was constructed. The H5 hybrid showed increased low temperature activity, broader substrate specificity and increased binding region and global flexibility.

Industrial Applications of Cold-Active Proteases

The ability of cold-active proteases to catalyze reactions at low or moderate temperatures offers great industrial and biotechnological potential (Demirjian, *et al.*, 2001; Eichler, 2001; Cavicchioli *et al.*, 2002; Deming, 2002; Margesin *et al.*, 2002; Burg, 2003; Feller and Gerday, 2003; Georlette *et al.*, 2004, Jeseph *et al.*, 2008). For the past few years it has been recognized that cold-adapted proteolytic microorganisms and their products or enzymes provide a large reservoir of potentially novel biotechnological exploitation (Gounot, 1991; Russell, 1992; Margesin and Schinner, 1994; Gerday *et al.*, 2000). In near future, the potential value of cold-adapted enzymes is likely to lead us to a greater annual market than for thermostable enzymes. Some of the more obvious industrial and biotechnological applications of cold-active proteases are described below.

Detergent Additives

The most promising candidates as detergent additive for cold washing are obviously those enzymes that combine cold activity with resistance to alkaline pH values. Reductions in energy consumption due to cold washing are obvious advantages. However, instability of cold-adapted enzymes when added to the final product would be a possible drawback. The recombinant enzymes seem likely to improve the stability of a cold-adapted enzyme, while maintaining its high catalytic efficiency at low temperatures (Narinx, 1997). A recently patented cold-active serine protease (CP70) produced by *Flavobacterium balustinum* has optimum temperature for activity lower by 20°C when compared to classical detergent protease such as Savinase. The enzyme remains stable at 30 °C for 1 h at a pH ranging from 6.5 to 10 and surface-active components/bleaching agents do not affect enzyme activity. Another cold-active alkaline protease was isolated from *Stenotrophomonas maltophilia* with maximum activity and stability at pH 10 and 20 °C. The protease showed excellent stability and compatibility with commercial detergents and exhibited high efficiency for the removal of different types of protein-containing stains at low temperature (Kuddus and Ramteke 2009).

The enzyme completely removed blood and grass stains and increased the reflectance by 26 and 23%, respectively (Kuddus and Ramteke 2011). Using chemical detergents in water at high temperatures and with vigorous mixing, it is possible to remove proteinaceous stains but the cost of water heating is high and lengthy mixing/beating will shorten the life of clothing. The use of cold-active proteases allows lower temperatures to be employed and shorter periods of agitation are needed, often after a preliminary period of soaking. In general, detergents containing cold-active protease remove proteins from clothes soiled with blood, milk, sweat, grass, etc. are far more effective than the non-enzyme detergents.

Food Industry

The applications of cold-adapted enzymes in the food industry can have several advantages not only for their high specific activity, thereby reducing the amount of enzyme needed, but also for their easy inactivation. Food processing at low temperatures minimizes undesirable chemical reactions as well as bacterial contamination, which may indeed be elevated at higher temperatures. When enzymatic activity needs to be controlled, the cold-adapted enzymes are easily inactivated by relatively low heat. Also, cold-adapted proteolytic enzymes are in most cases more economical as their high catalytic efficiencies facilitate the use of smaller amounts of enzymes than are required using analogous mesophilic enzymes. Cold-active proteases from psychrophiles are used extensively in the food industry for the treatment of beer, in bakeries and in the accelerated maturing of cheese (Margesin and Schinner, 1994). Cold-active proteases are also used for tenderization of meat or taste improvement of refrigerated meat (Orange, 1994). Furthermore, proteases facilitate the evaporation of fish/meat stick water, the rendering of fat, and the removal of the membrane from fish roe. Functional food ingredients in the form of soluble protein hydrolysates from protein sources are also being produced using proteases. In the pet food industry, cold-active protease may be used in production of digest, which is coated onto or mixed into dry pet food to improve its palatability. Digest may be produced by using proteases that hydrolyze meat or meat by-products, thus liquefying the raw material and creating a good flavor.

Textile Industry

In textile industry, microbial enzymes have found a wide application for improving production and finishing of fabrics. One can imagine the use of cold-active proteases for beginning threads of raw silk to remove sericin, a proteinaceous substance that covers the silk fiber. In general, degumming is performed in an alkaline solution containing soap. This is a harsh treatment because the fiber itself, the fibrin, is also attacked. It is better to use cold-active proteolytic enzymes because they remove the sericin without attacking the fibrin so there is no fiber damage and the silk threads will be stronger than with that of traditional treatments. Protease treatments can also modify the surface of wool and silk fibers to provide new and unique finishes (Najafi *et al.*, 2005).

Bioremediation

Cold-adapted microbial protease may have great potential in the field of wastewater treatment, bioremediation in protein contaminated cold environment and active compounds synthesis in cold condition. Psychrophilic microorganisms have also been proposed for the bioremediation of polluted soils and waste-waters during the winter in temperate countries, when the degradative capacity of the endogenous microflora is impaired by low temperatures. However, bioaugmentation and inoculation of contaminated environments with specific cold-adapted microorganisms in mixed cultures should help to improve the biodegradation of recalcitrant chemicals. As a result of the high catalytic efficiency of their enzymes and their unique specificity at low and moderate temperatures, cold-adapted microorganisms should be an ideal for bioremediation purposes (Margesin and Schinner, 1999). Psychrophilic anaerobic digestion of human waste at 15°C has been evaluated to pilot-plant scale, using bacterial seed cultures which had been adapted to low-temperature growth. However, little is known about these microorganisms, and the optimum conditions for their use need to be carefully evaluated. The treatment of waste waters contaminated as a result of human activities would probably be the easiest way to start studying the potential applications of cold-adapted microorganisms in lowering the amount of toxic compounds, for example, nitrates, hydrocarbons, aromatic compounds, heavy metals; and biopolymers such as cellulase, chitin, lignin, proteins and triacylglycerols; these efforts have already begun (Margesin and Schinner, 1997; Margesin and Schinner, 1998; Timmis and Pieper, 1999).

Molecular Biology Applications

Cold-active enzymes are ideal candidates for certain applications in molecular biology where high catalytic activity in combination with subsequent fast and efficient inactivation of the enzyme at moderate temperatures is required. In molecular biology, heat-labile enzymes are advantageous to obtain irreversible enzyme inactivation by mild heat treatment without interference with subsequent reactions. Protein expression systems operating at low temperatures are also an important achievement in the field because low temperature can prevent the formation of inclusion bodies and protects heat-sensitive gene products. Remaut and coworkers (1999) designed an efficient expression system by introducing *E. coli* derived controlling elements into psychrotolerant hosts. The most recent example of a protein expression system is the construction of a host-vector system that allows over expression of genes in psychrophilic bacteria (Tutino *et al.*, 2001). One of the protease isolated from the psychrotrophic strain A9 was purified and its application to common molecular biology techniques was demonstrated (Moran *et al.*, 2001). The study highlighted that heat-stable molecular biology enzymes (*Taq* polymerase) was digested by a heat-labile protease, which was then inactivated by a mild heat treatment. The clear benefit of using heat-labile proteases arises in situations where further reactions may be accomplished without an intermediate purification step, thereby saving time and avoiding the possibility of product loss (Moran *et al.*, 2001).

Biocatalysis in Low Water Systems

The commercial synthesis of valuable peptides and other compounds obtained from substrates showing poor solubility in aqueous media can be achieved using enzymes operating under low water conditions. In these systems, the level and distribution of residual water is important because the catalytic efficiency of enzyme preparations is often a strong function of the hydration state (Gerday *et al.*, 2000). Many potentially useful reactions involve reverse hydrolysis and, in this case, the reaction yield will be inversely related to the water activity in the system. Psychrophilic enzymes might therefore have a potential advantage for applications under low water conditions as a result of their inherent greater flexibility, which will be particularly useful in conditions wherein the activity of mesophilic and thermophilic enzymes is severely impaired by an excess of rigidity.

Table 6. Patents in cold-active proteases

Micro- organism	Patented item/process	Patent number	Inventor(s)	Industrial partner
Flavobacterium balustinum P104 strain	Cold-active protease CP70	US6200793 B1 WO9727313A1	AKM Quamrul Hasan and Eiichi Tamiya	Proctor and Gamble, Japan Advance Institute of Sci. and Tech.
Marinomonas protea and Pseudomonas sp.	Process and organism for the production of antifreeze proteins	US20020072108 A1	Mark John Berry, Allen Griffiths, Philip John Hill, Johanna laybourne-Parry, Sarah Victoria Mills	-
Nocardiopsis sp 10R and Nocardiopsis Dassonvillei M58-1	Low temp active alkaline protease and its preparation	WO 8803947	Liu Chi-Li et al.	Novo industry
Paecilomyces marquandii	Low temperature active alkaline protease and its preparation	WO 8803948	Beck, Carol Marie et al.	Novo industry
Serratia marcescencs AP3801	Cold-active protease CP-58 and psychrotrophic bacteria	WO9730172A1	AKM Quamrul Hasan and Eiichi Tamiya	Proctor and Gamble, Japan Advance Institute of Sci. and Tech.
Bacillus sp	Cold alkaline protease producing microorganism and process, application in detergent and food	WO9743406A1	Takaiw Mikio et al.	Kao Corporation
Flavobacterium balustinum	A polynucleotide encoding CP70 cold-active protease	WO9925848A1	Kitado Haruo and Yoshikawa Akikazu	Proctor and Gamble, Japan

Production of Fine Chemicals

Cold-adapted enzymes may be incorporated in the process involving unstable substrates and products. The broader substrate specificity of these biocatalysts coupled with decreased production of byproducts at higher temperatures, are significant advantages that are expected to be exploited for future application in this area. Enzymatic reactions in non-aqueous solvents offer new possibilities for the biotechnological production of many useful chemicals using reactions that are not feasible in aqueous media. The use of enzymes in non-aqueous media has found several applications such as in organic synthesis and synthesis of sugar-based polymers (Joseph *et al.*, 2008).

Application in Peptide Synthesis

Peptides synthesis by using enzymes has attracted worldwide attention in recent years. The proteases from microbial sources have been successfully applied to the synthesis of several small peptides (Kumar and Bhalla, 2005). The enzymatic synthesis of peptide, although offer several advantages, has still been discouraged by some unfavorable factors.

At present, several technologies are being actively explored to overcome these difficulties (Kumar and Bhalla, 2005). The development of new methods suitable for the large-scale production of biologically active peptides may be pursued by understanding the biological functions and properties of cold-active proteases.

Patents in Cold-Active Proteases

Even the cost concerned in pursuing this largely unexplored field is high, number of companies involved in funding cold-active protease research including its preparation and applications.

Some significant developments and their potential commercial applications were made in association with industrial partners (Table 6).

Most of the patents are process, rather than product based, but none of these has led to commercialization to date.

Conclusion

Cold-active enzymes are characterized by high-catalytic efficiency at low and moderate temperatures at which homologous mesophilic enzymes are not active. This property is useful in biotechnology in order to shorten process times, save energy costs, decrease the enzyme concentration and prevent undesired chemical transformations and the loss of volatile compounds. Although, a more extensive effort is required to overcome several bottlenecks such as the high cost of enzyme, low stability, low reaction yields and the low biodiversity of psychrophilic or psychrotrophic microbes. The relatively latest introduction and progress of novel r-DNA technologies such as meta- genomics and site-directed mutagenesis have an intense positive effect on the expression and production of greater amounts of recombinant enzymes, which means more competitive prices, by introducing new or tailored catalytic activities of these enzymes at low temperatures.

Therefore, efforts have to be made in order to achieve economical over production of cold-active proteases in heterologous hosts and their alteration by protein engineering. When compared with chemical reactions, the more specific and cleaner technologies made possible by enzyme-catalyzed processes will promote the continued trend towards natural processes in the production of food and would play an important role in various industrial and biotechnological applications.

References

Aghajari, N., F. Van Petegem, V. Villeret, J.P. Chessa, C. Gerday, R. Haser and J. Van Beeumen. 2003. Crystal structures of a psychrophilic metalloprotease reveal new insights into catalysis by cold-adapted proteases. *Proteins,* 50(4): 636-647.

Aghajari, N., G. Feller, C. Gerda and, R. Haser. 1996. Crystallization and preliminary X-ray diffraction studies of α-amylase from the Antarctic psychrophile *Alteromonas haloplanctis* A23. *Protein Sci.,* 5: 2128–2129.

Aghajari, N., G. Feller, C. Gerday and R. Haser, 1998. Crystal structures of the psychrophilic α-amylase from *Alteromonas haloplanctis* in its native form and complexed with an inhibitor. *Protein Sci.,* 7: 564–572.

Aghajari, N., G. Feller, C. Gerday and R. Haser. 1998a. Structures of the psychrophilic *Alteromonas haloplanctis* α-amylase give insights into cold adaptation at a molecular level. *Structure,* 6: 1503–1516.

Alam, S.I., S. Dube, G.S.N. Reddy, B.K. Bhattacharya, S. Shivaji and L. Singh. 2005. Purification and characterization of extracellular protease produced by *Clostridium* sp. from Schirmacher oasis, Antarctica. *Enz. Micro. Technol.*, 36(5-6): 824-831.

Alvarez, M., J.P. Zeelen, V. Mainfroid, F. Rentier-Delrue, J.A. Martial and L. Wyns. 1998. Triose-phosphate isomerase (TIM) of the psychrophilic bacterium *Vibrio marinus*: kinetic and structural properties. *J. Biol. Chem.*, 273: 2199–2206.

Arnorsdottir, J., M.M. Kristjansson and R. Ficner. 2005. Crystal structure of a subtilisin-like serine proteinase from a psychrotrophic *Vibrio* species reveals structural aspects of cold adaptation. *FEBS J.,* 272(3): 832-845.

Austin, B. 1988. Marine microbiology. Cambridge University Press. Cambridge.

Barett, A.J. 1994. Proteolytic enzymes: serine and cysteine peptidases. *Methods Enzymol.*, 244: 1–15.

Baross, J.A. and R.Y. Morita. 1978. Microbial life at low temperature: Ecological aspects. *In: Microbial Life in Extreme Environments*, Ed. by Kushner, DJ, Acad. Press, London, pp. 9-71.

Berger, F., N. Morellet, F. Menu and P. Potier. 1996. Cold shock and cold acclimation proteins in the psychrotrophic bacterium *Arthrobacter globiformis* SI55. *J. Bacteriol.,* 178: 2999–3007.

Betzel, C., G.P. Pal and W. Saenger. 1988. Three-dimensional structure of proteinase K at 0.15-nm resolution. *Eur J. Biochem.*, 178: 155-171.

Betzel, C., S. Klupsch, G. Papendorf, S. Hastrup, S. Branner and K.S. Wilson. 1992. Crystal structure of the alkaline proteinase Savinase from *Bacillus lentus* at 1.4 Å resolution. *J. Mol. Bio.,* 223: 427-445.

Bode, W., E. Papamokos and D. Musil. 1987. The high-resolution X-ray crystal structure of the complex formed between subtilisin Carlsberg and eglin c, an elastase inhibitor from the leech *Hirudo medicinalis*: Structural analysis, subtilisin structure and interface geometry. *Eur J. Biochem.*, 166: 673-692.

Bott, R., M. Ultsch, A. Kossiakoff, T. Graycar, B. Katz and S. Power. 1988. The three-dimensional structure of *Bacillus amyloliquefaciens* subtilisin at 1.8 Å and an analysis of the structural consequences of peroxide inactivation. *J Biol Chem.*, 263(16):7895-7906.

Brandsdal, B.O., A.O. Smalas and J. Aqvist. 2001. Electrostatic effects play a central role in cold adaptation of trypsin. *FEBS Lett.,* 499: 171–175.

Burg, B.V. 2003. Extremophiles as a source for novel enzymes, *Curr. Opin. Microbiol.,* 6: 213–218.

Cavicchioli, R., K.S. Siddiqui, D. Andrews and K.R. Sowers. 2002. Low-temperature extremophiles and their applications. *Curr. Opin. Biotechnol.,* 13: 253-261.

Chen, X., Y. Zhang, P. Gao and X. Luan. 2003. Two different proteases produced by a deep-sea psychrotrophic bacterial strain, *Pseudoaltermonas* sp. SM9913. *Marine Biol.,* 143: 989-993.

Chen, X.L., C.Y. Sun, Y.Z. Zhang and P.J. Gao. 2002. Effects of different buffers on the thermostability and autolysis of a cold-adapted protease MCP-01. *J. Protein Chem.,* 21(8): 523-527.

Chintalapati, S., M.D. Kiran and S. Shivaji. 2004. Role of membrane lipid fatty acids in cold adaptation. *Cell Mol. Biol.,* 50(5): 631-642.

D'Amico, S., J.C. Marx, C. Gerday and G. Feller. 2003. Activity–stability relationships in extremophilic enzymes. *J. Biol. Chem.* 278: 7891–7896.

D'Amico, S., P. Claverie, T. Collins, D. Georlette, E. Gratia, A. Hoyoux, M. Meuwis, G. Feller and C. Gerday. 2002. Molecular basis of cold adaptation. *Phil. Trans. R. Soc. Lond. B.*, 357: 917–925.

Damare, S., C. Raghukumar, U. Muraleedharan and S. Raghukumar. 2006. Deep-sea fungi as a source of alkaline and cold-tolerant proteases. *Enz. Microb. Technol.*, 39(2): 172-181.

Davail, S., G Feller, E. Narinx and C. Gerday. 1994. Cold adaptation of proteins. Purification, characterization and sequence of the heat-labile subtilisin from the Antarctic psychrophile *Bacillus* TA41. *J. Biol. Chem.,* 269: 17448–17453.

Deming, J.W. 2002. Psychrophiles and polar regions. *Curr. Opin. Microbiol.,* 5: 301–309.

Demirjian, D.C., F. Moris-Varas and C.S. Cassidy. 2001. Enzymes from extremophiles. *Curr. Opin. Chem. Biol.,* 5: 144–151.

Drenth, J., W.G.J. Hol, N. Johan and R. Koekoek. 1972. Subtilisin Novo: The Three-Dimensional Structure and Its Comparison with Subtilisin BPN′. *European J. Biochem.,* 26(2): 177–181.

Eichler, J. 2001. Biotechnological uses of archaeal extremozymes. *Biotechnol. Adv.,* 19: 261–278.

Eijsink, V.G.H., A. Bjork, S. Gaseidnes, R. Sirevag, B. Synstad, B. Burg and G. Vriend. 2004. Rational engineering of enzyme stability. *J Biotechnol.*, 113:105 –120.

Feller, G. 2003. Molecular adaptations to cold in psychrophilic enzymes. *Cell. Mol. Life Sci.,* 60(4): 648-662.

Feller, G. and C. Gerday. 2003. Psychrophilic enzymes: hot topics in cold adaptation, *Nat. Rev. Microbiol.,* 1: 200–208.

Feller, G., D. D'Amico and C. Gerday. 1999. Thermodynamic stability of a cold-active α-amylase from the Antarctic bacterium *Alteromonas haloplanctis*. *Biochem.,* 38: 4613–4619.

Feller, G., E. Narinx, J.L. Arpigny, M. Aittaleb, E. Baise, S. Genicot and C. Gerday. 1996. Enzymes from psychrophilic organisms. *FEMS Microbiol. Rev.,* 18: 189–202.

Feller, G., F. Payan, F. Theys, M. Qian, R. Haser and C. Gerday. 1994. Stability and structural analysis of α-amylase from the Antarctic psychrophile *Alteromonas haloplanctis* A23. *Eur. J. Biochem.,* 222: 441–447.

Fox, J.W., J.D. Shannon and J.B. Bjarnason. 1991. Proteinases and their inhibitors in biotechnology, Enzymes in biomass conversion. *ACS Symp. Ser.,* 460: 62–79.

Friedmann, E.I. 1994. Permafrost as microbial habitat. In: Viable Micro-organisms in Permafrost, Ed. by Gilichinsky D. Russian Academy of Sciences, Pushchino, pp. 21-26.

Georlette, D., M. Bentahir, P. Claverie, T. Collins, S. D'Amico, D. Delille, G. Feller, E. Gratia, A. Hoyoux, T. Lonhienne, M. Meuwis and C. Gerday. 2001. Cold-adapted enzymes. *In*: *Physics and Chemistry Basis of Biotechnology*, Eds. by Bulte J. and DeCuyper M., Kluwer Academic Publ, Netherlands, pp. 177–196.

Georlette, D., V. Blaise, T. Collins, G. Feller and C. Gerday. 2003. Structural and functional adaptations to extreme temperatures in psychrophilic, mesophilic and thermophilic DNA ligases. *J. Biol. Chem.,* 278: 37015–37023.

Georlette, D., V. Blaise, T. Collins, S. D'Amico, E. Gratia, A. Hoyoux, J.C. Marx, G. Sonan, G. Feller and C. Gerday. 2004. Some like it cold: biocatalysis at low temperatures. *FEMS Microbiol. Rev.,* 28: 25–42.

Gerday, C., M. Aittaleb and G. Feller. 2000. Cold–adapted enzymes: from fundamentals to biotechnology. *Trends Biotechnol.,* 18: 103–107.

Gianese, G., F. Bossa and S. Pascarella. 2002. Comparative structural analysis of psychro-, meso- and thermophilic enzymes. *Proteins,* 47: 236–249.

Godfrey, T. and S. West. 1996. Introduction to industrial enzymology. *In: Industrial enzymology*, 2nd edn. Eds. by Godfrey T and West S., Macmillan Press, London, pp. 1–8.

Gounot, A.M. 1991. Bacterial life at low temperature: physiological aspects and biotechnological implications. *J. Appl. Bacteriol.,* 71: 386–397.

Gros, P., C. Betzel, Z. Dauter, K.S. Wilson and W.G.J. Hol. 1989. Molecular dynamics refinement of a thermitase-eglin-c complex at 1.98 Å resolution and comparison of two crystal forms that differ in calcium content. *J. Mol. Biol.*, 210: 347-367.

Guoying, X., C. Shuoshuo and L. Xuezheng. 2011. Cloning and heterologous expression of pro-2127, a gene encoding cold-active protease from *Pseudoalteromonas* sp. QI-1. *Adv. Polar Sci.*, 22: 124–130.

Hartley, B.S. 1960. Proteolytic enzymes. *Annu. Rev. Biochem.*, 29: 45–72.

Hebraud, M. and P. Potier. 2000. Cold acclimation and cold-shock response in psychrotrophic bacteria. In: Cold Shock, Response and Adaptation. Eds. by Inouye M and Yamanaka K, *Horizon Scientific*, UK, pp. 41–60.

Hebraud, M., E. Dubois, P. Potier and J. Labadie. 1994. Effect of growth temperatures on the protein levels in a psychrotrophic bacterium, *Pseudomonas fragi*. *J. Bacteriol.,* 176: 4017–4024.

Herbert, R.A. 1986. The ecology and physiology of psychrophilic microorganisms. In: Microbes in Extreme Environments, Eds. by Herbert RA and Codd GA, SGM Publication, Acad Press, London, pp. 1-23.

Ingraham, J.L. and J.L. Stokes. 1959. Psychrophilic bacteria. *Bacteriol. Rev.*, 23: 97-108.

Inniss, W.E. and J.L. Ingraham. 1978. Microbial life at low temperatures: mechanisms and molecular aspects. In: Microbial Life in Extreme Environments. Ed. by Kushner DJ, Acad. Press, London, pp. 73-104.

International Union of Biochemistry. 1992. Enzyme nomenclature. Academic Press, San Diego, California, ISBN 0-12-227164-5.

Irwin, J.A., G.A. Alfredsson, A.J. Lanzetti, H.M. Gudmundsson and P.C. Engel. 2001. Purification and characterization of a serine peptidase from the marine psychrophile strain PA-43. *FEMS Microbiol Lett.,* 201(2): 285-290.

Joseph, B., P.W. Ramteke and G. Thomas. 2008. Cold-active microbial lipases: Some hot issues and recent developments. *Biotechnol. Adv.*, 26: 457–470.

Kano, H., S. Taguchi and H. Momose. 1997. Cold adaptation of a mesophilic serine protease, subtilisin, by in vitro random mutagenesis. *Appl. Microbiol. Biotechnol.*, 47(1): 46-51.

Kim, S.Y., K.Y. Hwang, S.H. Kim, H.C. Sung, Y.S. Han and Y.J. Cho. 1999. Structural basis for cold adaptation: sequence, biochemical properties, and crystal structure of malate dehydrogenase from a psychrophile *Aquaspirillium arcticum. J. Biol. Chem.,* 274: 11761–11767.

Koeller, K.M. and C.H. Wong. 2001. Enzymes for chemical synthesis. *Nature,* 409: 232-240.

Kuddus, M. and P.W. Ramteke. 2008. A cold-active extracellular metalloprotease from *Curtobacterium luteum* (MTCC 7529): enzyme production and characterization. *J. Gen. Appl. Microbiol.,* 54(6): 385-392.

Kuddus, M. and P.W. Ramteke. 2009. Cold-active extracellular alkaline protease from an alkaliphilic *Stenotrophomonas maltophilia*: Production of enzyme and its industrial applications. *Can. J. Microbiol.,* 55(11): 1294-1301.

Kuddus, M. and P.W. Ramteke. 2011. Production optimization of an extracellular cold-active alkaline protease from *Stenotrophomonas maltophilia* MTCC 7528 and its application in detergent industry. *Afr. J. Microbiol. Res.*, 5(7): 809-816.

Kulakova, L., A. Galkin, T. Kurihara, T. Yoshimura and N. Esaki. 1999. Cold-active serine alkaline protease from the psychrotrophic bacterium *Shewanella* strain ac10: gene cloning and enzyme purification and characterization. *Appl. Environ. Microbiol.,* 65(2): 611-617.

Kumar, D. and T.C. Bhalla. 2005. Microbial proteases in peptide synthesis: approaches and applications. *Appl. Microbiol. Biotechnol.*, 68: 726–736.

Kun-Hee, O., S. Chang, S. Seong, L. Woong, K. O-Seob and S.P. Young. 1999. Isolation of a psychrophilic *Azospirillum* sp. and characterization of its extracellular protease. *FEMS Microbiol. Lett.,* 174: 173-178.

Leiros, H.K., N.P. Willassen and A.O. Smalas. 1999. Residue determinants and sequence analysis of cold-adapted trypsins. *Extremophiles,* 3: 205–219.

Leiros, I., O. Lanes, O. Sundheim, R. Helland, A.O. Smalas and N.P. Willassen. 2001. Crystallization and preliminary X-ray diffraction analysis of a cold-adapted uracil-DNA glycosylase from Atlantic cod (*Gadus morhua*). *Acta Cryst.,* 57: 1706–1708.

Li, J. and T. Lee. 1995. Bacterial ice nucleation and its potential application in the food industry. *Trends Food Sci. Technol.*, 6(8): 259-265.

Lonhienne, T., C. Gerday and G. Feller. 2000. Psychrophilic enzymes: revisiting the thermodynamic parameters of activation may explain local flexibility. *Biochim. Biophys. Acta.*, 1543: 1–10.

Mandelman, D., M. Bentahir, G. Feller, C. Gerday and R. Haser. 2001. Crystallization and preliminary X-ray analysis of a bacterial psychrophilic enzyme, phosphoglycerate kinase. *Acta Cryst.,* 57: 1666–1668.

Margesin, R. and F. Schinner. 1994. Properties of cold adapted microorganisms and their potential role in biotechnology. *J. Biotechnol.,* 33: 1-14.

Margesin, R. and F. Schinner. 1997. Efficiency of indigenous and inoculated cold-adapted soil microorganisms for biodegradation of diesel oil in alpine soils. *Appl. Environ. Microbial.,* 63: 2660-2664.

Margesin, R. and F. Schinner. 1998. Low temperature bioremediation of a waste water contaminated with anionic surfactant and fuel oil. *Appl. Microbiol. Biotechnol.,* 49: 482-486.

Margesin, R. and F. Schinner. 1999. Biodegradation of organic pollutants at low temperature. In: Biotechnological Application of Cold Adapted Organisms. Eds. by Margesin R. and Schinner F., Springer, pp. 271-289.

Margesin, R., G. Feller, C. Gerday and N. Russell. 2002. Cold-Adapted Micro-organisms: Adaptation Strategies and Biotechnological Potential. In: The Encyclopedia of Environmental Microbiology, Vol. 2. Ed. by Bitton G., John Wiley and Sons, New York, pp. 871–885.

Margesin, R., H. Dieplinger, J. Hofmann, B. Sarg and H. Lindner. 2005. A cold-active extracellular metalloprotease from *Pedobacter cryoconitis*: production and properties. *Res. Microbiol.*, 156(4): 499-505.

Marianna, T., G. Ewa, K. Halina and Z. Maria. 1999. Biosynthesis and properties of an extracellular metalloprotease from the Antarctic marine bacterium *Sphingomonas paucimobilis*. *J. Biotechnol.,* 70: 53-60.

Miyazaki, K., P.L. Wintrode, R.A. Grayling, D.N. Rubingh and F.H. Arnold. 2000. Directed evolution study of temperature adaptation in a psychrophilic enzyme. *J. Mol. Biol.,* 297: 1015–1026.

Moran, A.J., M. Hills, J. Gunton and F.E. Nano. 2001. Heat-labile proteases in molecular biology applications. *FEMS Microbiol. Lett.,* 197: 59-63.

Morita, R.Y. 1975. Psychrophilic bacteria. *Bacteriol. Rev.,* 39: 144–167.

Morita, Y., Q. Hasan, T. Sakaguchi, Y. Murakami, K. Yokoyama and E. Tamiya. 1998. Properties of a cold-active protease from psychrotrophic *Flavobacterium balustinum* P104. *Appl. Microbiol. Biotechnol.,* 50(6): 669-675.

Najafi, M.H., D. Deobagkar and D. Deobagkar. 2005. Potential application of protease isolated from *Pseudomonas aeruginosa* PD100. *Electron. J. Biotech.*, 8: 197-203.

Narinx, E., E. Baise and C. Gerday. 1997. Subtilisin from psychrophilic Antarctic bacteria: characterization and site-directed mutagenesis of residues possibly involved in the adaptation to cold. *Protein Eng.,* 10: 1271-1279.

Orange, N. 1994. Growth temperature regulates the induction of β-lactamase in *Pseudomonas fluorescens* through modulation of the outer membrane permeation of a β-lactam-inducing antibiotic. *Microbiol.,* 140: 3125-3130.

Park, I. and J. Cho. 2011. Productions of an extracellular protease by an Antarctic bacterial isolate (*Bacillus* sp. JSP1) as a potential feed additive. *Rev. Colomb. Cienc. Pecu.*, 24: 3-10.

Pascale, D., M. Giuliani, C. De Santi, N. Bergamasco, A. Amoresano, A. Carpentieri, E. Parrilli and M.L. Tutino. 2010. PhAP protease from *Pseudoalteromonas haloplanktis* TAC125: Gene cloning, recombinant production in *E. coli* and enzyme characterization. *Polar Sci.*, 4: 285-294.

Rao, M.B., A.M. Tanksale, M.S. Ghatge and V.V. Deshpande. 1998. Molecular and biotechnological aspects of microbial proteases. *Microbiol. Mol. Biol. Rev.,* 62(3): 597–635.

Remaut, E., C. Bliki, M. Iturriza-Gomara and K. Keymeulen. 1999. Development of regulatable expression systems for cloned genes in cold-adapted bacteria. In: Biotechnological applications of cold adapted organisms. Eds. by Margesin R and Schinner F., Springer Verlag, Heidelberg, pp. 1-16.

Rivett, A.J. 1989. High molecular mass intracellular proteases, *Biochem. J.*, 263: 625-633.

Rosales, C.M. and S.C. Sowinski. 2011. Antarctic bacterial isolates that produce cold-active extracellular proteases at low temperature but are active and stable at high temperature. *Polar Res.*, 30: 7123-7130.

Russell, N.J. 1990. Cold adaptation of microorganisms. *Phil. Trans. R. Soc. Lond., B*. 326: 595–611.

Russell, N.J. 1992. Physiology and molecular biology of psychrophilic micro-organisms. In: Molecular Biology and Biotechnology of Extremophiles. Eds. by Herbert RA and Sharp RJ., Blackie, London, pp. 203–224.

Russell, N.J. 1993. Biochemical differences between psychrophilic and psychro-tolerant microorganisms. In: Trends in microbial ecology. Eds. by Guerrero R and Pedros-Alio C. Spanis Society for Microbiology, Madrid, p. 29.

Russell, N.J. 2000. Toward a molecular understanding of cold activity of enzymes from psychrophiles. *Extremophiles,* 4: 83–90.

Russell, N.J. and T. Hamamoto. 1998. Psychrophiles. In: Extremophiles: Microbial Life in Extreme Environments, Eds. by Horikoshi K and Grant WD, Wiley, New York, pp. 25-45.

Russell, N.J., U. Gerike, M.J. Danson, D.W. Hough and G.L. Taylor. 1998. Structural adaptations of the cold-active citrate synthase from an Antarctic bacterium. *Structure,* 6: 351–361.

Sanchez, S. and A.L. Demain. (2011) Enzymes and bioconversions of industrial, pharmaceutical, and biotechnological significance. *Organic Process Res. Develop.*, 15: 224-30.

Secades, P., B. Alvarez and J.A. Guijarro. 2003. Purification and properties of a new psychrophilic metalloprotease (Fpp2) in the fish pathogen *Flavobacterium psychrophilum. FEMS Microbiol. Lett.,* 226: 273–279.

Sheridan, P.P., N. Panasik, J.M. Coombs and J.E. Brenchley. 2000. Approaches for deciphering the structural basis of low temperature enzyme activity. *Biochim. Biophys. Acta.*, 1543: 417–433

Shi, J.S., Q.F. Wu, Z.H. Xu and W.Y. Tao. 2005. Identification of psychrotrophs SYP-A2-3 producing cold-adapted protease from the No. 1 Glacier of China and study on its fermentation conditions. *Wei Sheng Wu Xue Bao.,* 45(2): 258-263.

Shibata, M., S. Takahashi, R. Sato and K. Oda. 1997. A novel metalloproteinase, almelysin, from a marine bacterium, *Alteromonas* sp. No. 3696: purification and characterization. *Biosci. Biotechnol. Biochem.,* 61(4): 710-715.

Siezen, R.J. and J.A.M. Leunissen. 1997. Subtilases: The superfamily of subtilisin-like serine proteases. *Protein Sci.,* 6: 501-523.

Smalas, A.O., H.K. Leiros, V. Os and N.P. Willassen. 2000. Cold adapted enzymes. *Biotechnol. Annu. Rev.,* 6: 1–57.

Somero, G.N. 1995. Proteins and temperature. *Annu. Rev. Physiol.* 57: 43–68.

Son, E. and J. Kim. 2003. Multicatalytic Alkaline Serine Protease from the Psychrotrophic *Bacillus amyloliquefaciens* S94. *J. Microbiol.*, 41: 58-62.

Suzuki, S. and T. Odagami. 1997. Low-temperature-active thiol protease from marine bacterium *Alteromonas haloplanktis. J. Marine Biotech.,* 5(4): 230-233.

Taguchi, S., S. Komada and H. Momose. 2000. The complete amino acid substitutions at position 131 that are positively involved in cold adaptation of subtilisin BPN'. *Appl. Environ. Microbiol.,* 66(4): 1410-1415.

Tamaki, H., S. Hanada, Y. Kamagata, K. Nakamura, N. Nomura, K. Nakano and M. Matsumura. 2003. *Flavobacterium limicola* sp. nov., a psychrophilic, organic-polymer-degrading bacterium isolated from freshwater sediments. *Int. J. Syst. Evol. Microbiol.,* 53: 519-526.

Tariq, A.L., A.L. Reyaz and J.J. Prabakaran. 2011. Purification and characterization of 56 kDa cold-active protease from *Serratia marcescens. Afr. J. Microbiol. Res.,* 5(32); 5841-5847.

Timmis, K.N. and D.H. Pieper. 1999. Bacteria designated for bioremediation. *Trends Biotechnol.,* 17: 201-204.

Tindbaek, N., A. Svendsen, P.R. Oestergaard and H. Draborg. 2004. Engineering a substrate-specific cold-adapted subtilisin. *Protein Eng. Design Selection,* 17: 149-156.

Turkiewicz, M., E. Gromek, H. Kalinowska and M. Zielińska. 1999. Biosynthesis and properties of an extracellular metalloprotease from the Antarctic marine bacterium *Sphingomonas paucimobilis. Progress Ind. Microbiol.*, 35: 53-60.

Turkiewicz, M., M. Pazgier, H. Kalinowska and S. Bielecki. 2003. A cold-adapted extracellular serine proteinase of the yeast *Leucosporidium antarcticum. Extremophiles,* 7(6): 435-442.

Tutino, M.L., A. Duilio, E. Parrilli, E. Remaut, G. Sannia and G. Marino. 2001. A novel replication element from an Antarctic plasmid as a tool for the expression of proteins at low temperature. *Extremophiles,* 5:257-264.

Vazquez, S.C., S.H. Coria and W.P. MacCormack. 2004. Extracellular proteases from eight psychrotolerant Antarctic strains. *Microbiol Res.,* 159(2): 157-166.

Villeret, V., J.P. Chessa, C. Gerday and J. Van Beeumen. 1997. Preliminary crystal structure determination of the alkaline protease from the Antarctic psychrophile *Pseudomonas aeruginosa. Protein Sci.,* 6: 2462–2464.

Vishniac, H.S. 1993. The microbiology of Antarctic soils. In: Antarctic Microbiology. Ed. by Friedman. Wiley-Liss, New York, p. 297.

Wang, Q., J. Miao, Y. Hou, Y. Ding, G. Wang and G. Li. 2005. Purification and characterization of an extracellular cold-active serine protease from the psychrophilic bacterium *Colwellia* sp. NJ341. *Biotech. Lett.,* 27(16): 1195–1198.

Wang, Q., Y. Hou, Z. Xu, J. Miao and G. Li. 2008. Purification and properties of an extracellular cold-active protease from the psychrophilic bacterium *Pseudoalteromonas* sp. NJ276. *Biochem. Eng.,* 38: 362-368.

Wang, Q., Y. Hou, Z. Xu, J. Miao and G. Li. 2008a. Optimization of cold-active protease production by the psychrophilic bacterium *Colwellia* sp. NJ341 with response surface methodology. *Biores. Technol.,* 99: 1926-1931.

Wintrode, P.L. and F.H. Arnold. 2000. Temperature adaptation of enzymes: lessons from laboratory evolution. *Adv. Protein Chem.,* 55: 161–225.

Wintrode, P.L., K. Miyazaki and F.H. Arnold. 2000. Cold adaptation of a mesophilic subtilisin-like protease by laboratory evolution. *J. Biol. Chem.,* 275: 31635–31640.

Wright, C.S., R.A. Alden and J. Kraut. 1969. Structure of subtilisin BPN at 2.5 A resolution. *Nature* 221: 235-242.

Yang, C., F. Wang, J. Hao, K. Zhang, N. Yuan, M. Sun, 2010. Identification of a proteolytic bacterium, HW08, and characterization of its extracellular cold-active alkaline metalloprotease Ps5. *Biosci. Biotechnol. Biochem.*, 74(6):1220-1225.

Yayanos, A.A. 1995. Microbiology to 10,500 meters in the deep sea. *Annu. Rev. Microbiol.,* 49: 777–805.

Yuan, Q., A. Hayashi, Y. Kitamura, T. Shimada, R. Na and X. Jin. 2009. Purification and characterization of cold-adapted metalloprotease from deep sea water lactic acid bacteria *Enterococcus faecalis* TN-9. *Int. J. Biol.,* 1(2):12-21.

Zecchinon, L., P. Claverie, T. Collins, S. D’Amico, D. Delille, G. Feller, D. Georlette, E. Gratia, A. Hoyoux, M.A. Meuwis, G. Sonan and C. Gerday. 2001. Did psychrophilic enzymes really win the challenge? *Extremophiles,* 5: 313–321.

Zeng, R., R. Zhang, J. Zhao and N. Lin. 2003. Cold-active serine alkaline protease from the psychrophilic bacterium *Pseudomonas* strain DY-A: enzyme purification and characterization. *Extremophiles,* 7(4): 335-337.

In: Applications of Microbial Genes in Enzyme Technology ISBN: 978-1-62417-808-5
Editors: V.K.Gupta, M.G.Tuohy, G.D.Sharma et al.

Chapter 16

Microbial Gene Finding Through Identifying Transcription Factor Binding Sites (TFBS)

Shripal Vijayvargiya[1] and Pratyoosh Shukla[*2]
[1]Department of Computer Science and Engineering,
Birla Institute of Technology, Extension Centre Jaipur, Rajasthan, India
[2]Enzyme Technology and Protein Bioinformatics Laboratory,
Department of Microbiology, M.D. University, Rohtak, Haryana, India

Abstract

The 21st century has seen the announcement of the draft version of the human genome sequence. Model organisms have been sequenced in both the plant and animal kingdoms and, currently, many eukaryotic genome sequencing projects are underway. However, biological interpretation, i.e. annotation, is not keeping pace with this avalanche of raw sequence data. There is still a real need for accurate and fast tools to analyze these sequences and, especially, to find genes and determine their functions. Unfortunately, finding genes in a genomic sequence is far from being a trivial problem. These widely used and recognized approach for genome annotation consists of employing, first, homology methods, also called "Empirical or sequence similarity-based methods," and second, gene prediction methods or "Ab-initio methods." Both kinds of methods are having some limitations. In order to compensate the insufficiency of any individual gene prediction program, the computational methods to construct gene models by multiple evidences is becoming more promising. This chapter focuses on a combined approach for gene prediction through identifying regulatory transcription factor binding sites.

[*] Corresponding author email: Department of Microbiology, M.D. University, Rohtak-124001, Haryana, India. pratyoosh.shukla@gmail.com.

Introduction

The purpose of gene prediction is to identify regions of genomic DNA that encode proteins. Gene finding typically refers to the area of computational biology that is concerned with algorithmically identifying stretches of sequence, usually genomic DNA, that are biologically functional. This, especially, includes protein-coding genes, but may also include other functional elements such as RNA and regulatory regions. Gene finding is one of the first and most important steps in understanding the genome of a species once it has been sequenced.

With the development of genome sequencing for many organisms, more and more raw sequences need to be annotated. One of the primary tasks in deciphering the functional contents of a newly sequenced genome is the identification of its protein coding genes. Generally, genes in human DNA and many other organisms have a relatively regular structure. The beginning of a gene is at the transcription start site (TSS). This is followed by an exon that is a sequence of DNA, which is mostly expressed in the final protein product (or an RNA product). A series of intron-exon pairs may then follow, where introns separate the exons. At the intron-exon boundaries there are splice junctions (or, acceptor/donor sites) that aid the process of RNA-splicing. Figure 1 illustrates the structure of a typical eukaryotic gene.

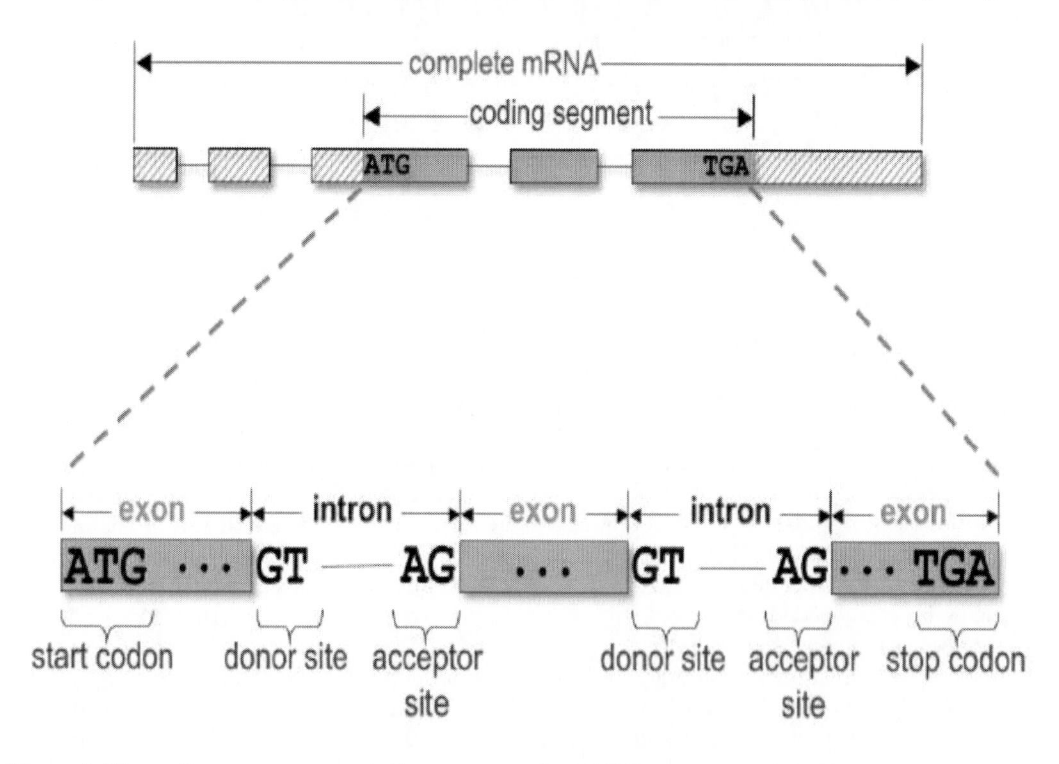

Figure 1. The coding segment extends from a start codon (ATG) to a stop codon (TGA, TAG, or TAA), with one or more introns (GT to AG) in between. Introns are spliced out prior to translation into a protein. Figure adapted from (Majoros, 2007).

It may be noted that our knowledge about the genomic transcription process is limited. For example, in vertebrates, the internal exons are small (typically about 140 nucleotides long), while the introns are much larger (some being more than 100kb long). The mechanism by which the splicing machinery recognizes the exons from within vast stretches of introns is still not fully clear. Accurate information regarding the promoters of most genes is severely limited. There is no strong consensus sequence at the splice junctions. These, and several other issues, make the task of identifying genes extremely challenging.

Computational Techniques for Gene Prediction: A Survey

Computational gene prediction is becoming more and more essential for the automatic analysis and annotation of large uncharacterized genomic sequences.

Gene discovery in prokaryotic genomes is less difficult, due to the higher gene density and the absence of introns in their protein coding regions. DNA sequences that encode proteins are transcribed into mRNA, and the mRNA is usually translated into proteins without significant modification. The longest ORFs (open reading frames) running from the first available start codon on the mRNA to the next stop codon in the same reading frame generally provide a good, but not assured, prediction of the protein coding regions. Several methods have been devised that use different types of Markov models in order to capture the compositional differences among coding regions, “shadow" coding regions (coding on the opposite DNA strand) and noncoding DNA.

In eukaryotic organisms, it is a quite different problem from that encountered in prokaryotes. Transcription of protein coding regions initiated at specific promoter sequences is followed by the removal of noncoding sequences (introns) from pre-mRNA by a splicing mechanism, leaving the protein-encoding exons. Once the introns have been removed and certain other modifications to the mature RNA have been made, the resulting mature mRNA can be translated into the 5’ to 3’ direction, usually from the first start codon to the first stop codon. As a result of the presence of intron sequences in the genomic DNA sequences of eukaryotes, the ORF corresponding to an encoded gene will be interrupted by the presence of introns that usually generate stop codons.

The structural characteristics of eukaryotic genes present several problems with regard to the computational gene identification. The low density of coding regions (3% in human DNA) results in many false positive predictions of non-coding DNA fragments. Small exons (1-20 bp) cannot be recognized using any of the composition-based methods that are successful for prokaryote coding regions. Many *in silico* gene prediction methods have been developed that rely heavily on the recognition of the functional signal encoded within the DNA sequence. These computational methods employ a range of underlying statistical properties of the coding regions. Two types of sensor (content and signal) are routinely used to locate genes in the genomic sequence:

(i) Content sensors classify DNA into coding regions and non-coding regions (introns, intergenic regions and un-translated regions (UTR's)). Content sensors can be further divided into extrinsic and intrinsic sensors. Based on the assumption that coding sequences are more conserved than non-coding ones (Mathe et al., 2002), extrinsic content sensors exploit homology searches to identify highly conserved exons. Using local alignment methods (ranging from he optimal Smith–Waterman algorithm to fast heuristic approaches such as FASTA and BLAST), two approaches can be employed: inter-genomic or cross species comparisons. While these strategies may be effective, they are limited by the constraints of phylogenetic distance. The second approach overcomes this limitation by employing intra-genomic comparisons which (providing data for multigenic families) represents a large percentage of existing genes (e.g. up to 80% for *Arabidopisis*). A significant failing of extrinsic approaches is that they are limited to homologies within the database; if no homologs exist no data can be extracted.

Intrinsic content sensors, on the other hand, focus on specific innate characteristics of the DNA sequence itself, which help to predict the likelihood of whether the sequence in question "codes" for a protein or not. The most obvious indicator of coding versus non-coding sequence identified to date is hexamer frequency (i.e. 6 nucleotide long words) (Mathe et al., 2002). Other useful intrinsic content sensors include nucleotide composition, codon usage and base occurrence periodicity. Coding regions are defined by three Markov models, one for each position inside a codon. These three-periodic MMs are based on the k-mer (especially hexamer) composition of coding sequence and are trained on a set of known sequences before being used to detect a particular content. Region-specific content sensors for coding and non-coding regions or even for different subtypes of non-coding regions have been developed.

(ii) Signal sensors detect the presence of functional sites specific to a gene. To date signals relating to transcription, translation and splicing have all been employed to facilitate gene identification and structure prediction. Transcriptional signal sensors (TSS) include the initiator or cap signal located at the transcriptional start site and the upstream TATA box promoter signal, as well as the polyadenylation signal (a consensus AATAAA hexamer) located 20 to 30 bp downstream of the coding region. Translational signals include the "Kozak signal" located immediately upstream of the start codon (Kozak, 1996). However, given that higher eukaryote genes in particular harbor multiple exons, accurate gene structure prediction in these organisms relies heavily on the identification of splice site signals (Stamm, 2008), specifically donor and acceptor sites (GT-AG on the introns sequence).

Two classes of methods are generally adopted for gene prediction by computational methods: (i) *ab initio* prediction and (ii) similarity based prediction.

Ab-Initio Methods

The majority of *ab- initio* gene-finders are predicated on a range of underlying statistical properties of the coding regions, and use a variety of different mathematical techniques, including neural networks, Markov models, and Fourier transforms. They rely on two sequence information types: signal sensors (consensus) and content sensors (non-consensus). A variety of algorithms can be applied to the modeling of gene structure, including Dynamic Programming (DP), Linear Discriminant Analysis (LDA), the Linguist method, Hidden Markov Models (HMM), and Neural Networks.

Dynamic programming has often been added into gene-finders, in an effort to combine useful features and facilitate the determination of optimum predictions on the basis of internal scoring systems (Stormo, 2000a). HMM-based gene-finders have, thus far, proven the most successful in this regard (Guigó *et al.*, 2000). HMMs represent a DNA sequence as the output of an abstract process that progresses through a series of discrete states, some of which are "hidden" from the observer. These states in the context of gene prediction correspond to exons, introns, and any other classes of desired sequences (including 5′ and 3′ UTRs, promoter regions, intergenic regions, and repetitive DNA). The "hidden" aspect of HMMs dictates that we see only the DNA sequence directly, whereas the state that generated the sequence (such as an exon or intron) remains invisible. The output of a regular HMM exhibits a length of 1 for each state within the hidden state space. By this means, a Generalized Hidden Markov Model (GHMM) was developed, in which subsequent states are generated in accordance with a Markov chain, but exhibit arbitrary length distributions. Gene-finders including GENSCAN, GENIE (Reese *et al.*, 2000), HMMgene (Krogh, 2000), and Phat (Cawley *et al.*, 2001) model genomic sequences via a GHMM approach. In general, they determine the sequence states and durations that maximize the joint probability of the hidden and observed data. One of the more attractive features of a GHMM is that it provides an intuitively "natural" method for the computation of the probability of a predicted exon, given the observed data.

Empirical or Sequence Similarity-Based Methods

Sequence similarity search is a conceptually simple approach that is based on finding similarity in gene sequences between ESTs (expressed sequence tags), proteins, or other genomes to the input genome. This approach is based on the assumption that functional regions (exons) are more conserved evolutionarily than nonfunctional regions (intergenic or intronic regions). Once there is similarity between a certain genomic region and an EST, DNA, or protein, the similarity information can be used to infer gene structure or function of that region. EST-based sequence similarity usually has drawbacks that ESTs only correspond to small portions of the gene sequence, which means that it is often difficult to predict the complete gene structure of a given region. Local alignment and global alignment are two methods based on similarity searches. The most common local alignment tool is the BLAST family of programs, which detects sequence similarity to known genes, proteins, or ESTs. Two more types of software, PROCRUSTES (Gelfand *et al.*, 1996) and GeneWise (Birney and Durbin 2000), use global alignment of a homologous protein to translated ORFs in a genomic sequence for gene prediction. A new heuristic method based on pairwise genome comparison has been implemented in the software called CSTfinder (Mignone *et al.*, 2003). The biggest limitation to this type of approaches is that only about half of the genes being discovered have significant homology to genes in the databases. The underlying principle inherent to the majority of sequence similarity-based gene-finders is the combination of similarity information with signal sensors. Similarity information can be acquired via a variety of sequence comparisons: genomic DNA/protein, genomic DNA/cDNA, or genomic DNA/genomic DNA. These programs align the genomic DNA sequence against a cDNA database, such as AAT (Huang *et al.*, 1997), GeneSeqer (Usuka *et al.*, 2000), or SIM4 (Florea *et al.*, 1998). This method has proven quite reliable with regard to the identification of exons independently of their coding status, particularly in case the genomic sequence is aligned against a cDNA from the same organism, or a closely related organism (Fukunishi *et al.*, 1999). The comparison of two homologous genomic sequences (inter- or intraspecies) also facilitates the identification of conserved exons, and allows for the simultaneous prediction of genes on both sequences. Programs including SLAM (Alexandersson *et al.*, 2003) and TWINSCAN (Flicek *et al.*, 2003) have also been developed, which exploit the sequence conservation between two genomes in order to predict genes. SLAM utilizes a joint probability model for sequence alignment and gene structure to express the different types of expected alignments, for example, in coding regions and introns. In TWINSCAN, alignments are initially conducted using standard tools such as TBLASTX or BLASTN, and then these alignments are used to inform the prediction algorithms.

Combined Gene-Finders

Similarity-based gene-finders are able to detect only a limited number of genes (low sensitivity) due to the lack of known mRNAs, whereas *ab initio* genefinders do not employ sequence similarity, and instead rely on intrinsic gene measures, including coding potentials and splice signals. Two different types of gene-finders, or two or more similar types of genefinders, can be combined. DIGIT (Yada *et al.*, 2003), for example, generates all possible exons from the results of other gene-finders, such as FGENESH (Salamov and Solovyev, 2000), GENSCAN, and HMMgene, and then assigns them their respective exon types, reading frames, and exon scores; finally, it searches a set of exons whose additive scores are maximized under their reading frame constraints. Another example is EuGène (Schiex *et al.*, 2001), which uses NetGene2 (Tolstrup *et al.*, 1997) and SplicePredictor for splice site prediction, NetStar (Pedersen and Nielsen, 1997) for translation initiation prediction, IMM-based content sensors, and similarity information gleaned from protein, EST, and cDNA matches. The tracking of exons shared in common by two or more gene-finders carries an advantage in that it significantly reduces the number of over-predictions, but may also exhibit poor sensitivity and possible inconsistencies at the gene level. Platforms such as Genotator (Harris, 1997), MagPie (Gaasterland and Sensen, 1996), and Ensembl (Hubbard *et al.*, 2002) gather evidence acquired from *ab initio* or homologybased prediction programs, and are considered to be relatively useful tools, which facilitate both humandriven and automated annotations. The increasing availability of complete genome sequences makes it possible to conduct a comparison of all of the proteins encoded by one genome with those of another. All of the comparative genomic methods harbor a theoretical advantage, in that they are not species-specific. In practice, the performance of these methods depends heavily on the evolutionary distance between the compared sequences. In order to retrieve only the relevant information from homology searches against databases, the use of such programs must be combined with other specific programs that can eliminate repeated sequences, which occur with a fair degree of frequency within the human sequence (about one-quarter of the genome).

Transcription Factor Binding Sites (TFBS)

The DNA and genes give only static and general view of the genome. The body of an advanced organism like human is composed of several kinds of different tissues, consisting of cells that are also dynamic and changing over time, although the basic DNA is the same across the body and across time. The dynamics of organisms are handled by the gene regulatory mechanisms. So understanding the process that regulates gene expression and identification of those regulating element is a major challenge of biology. The main idea in gene expression is that every gene contains the information to produce a protein, which performs most of the biological functions of an organism. The main part of regulation is performed by specific proteins called transcription factors (TFs) that regulate the production of RNA and proteins from genes. This regulation is achieved by the TFs binding to DNA near genes, thus influencing the recruitment of RNA polymerase. RNA polymerase is a protein that performs the translation of genes into RNA, the first step in translating genes to proteins. The regions where TFs bind are often called regulatory regions. The region just before the gene, called upstream region, is the most basic regulatory region, but TFs can also bind in regulatory region that are situated after the gene (downstream), within the gene (introns), or further upstream.

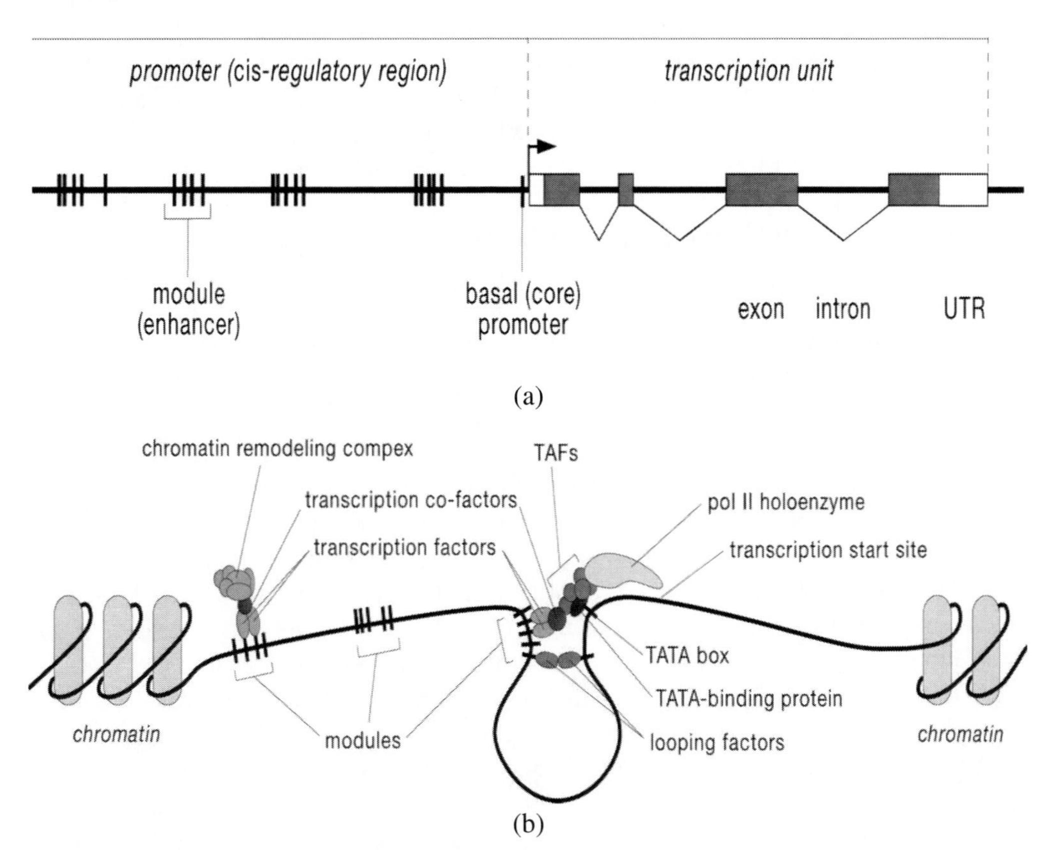

Figure 2. Gene regulations. (a) Promoter region showing distribution of TFBSs in upstream sequence and transcription unit showing exons, introns and UTR. (b) Shows binding of TFs with regulatory factors to initiate transcription. Figure adapted from (Wray *et al.*, 2003).

Gene regulation is a finely controlled mechanism, and the TFs do not attach randomly to the DNA. As both the TFs and the DNA are molecules containing a structured organization of positive and negative charges, binding of a TF to DNA will depend on whether these charges can be aligned in a complementary way that forms strong physical bonds between the molecules. Because of this, each TF will have its own sequence-specific requirement for binding to DNA. Figure 2 illustrates the gene regulation and binding of TFs with regulatory factors to initiate transcription.

Determining where in the DNA each TF can bind is important for several reasons. The regulation of genes by TFs is a basic component of a very complex system of interactions between genes. Knowing the exact locations where TFs can bind is an important step towards determining how genes are regulated by a given TF, and it may also explain how slight sequence variations between individuals in the regulatory regions may influence for instance the risk for a specific disease.

Methods for TFBS Identification

Experimental Methods

Since identification of regulatory regions and binding sites is a prerequisite for understanding gene regulation (Lockhart and Winzeler, 2000; Stormo, 2000b), various experimental and computational techniques have been employed for this purpose. Earlier the experimental techniques of choice to discover and analyze DNA binding sites have been the DNAse footprinting assay and the Electrophoretic Mobility Shift Assay (EMSA). However, the development of DNA microarrays and fast sequencing techniques has led to new, massively parallel methods for in-vivo identification of binding sites, such as ChIP-chip and ChIP-Seq (Elnitski *et al.*, 2006). Following is the brief description of experimental strategies.

Chromatin-immuno-precipitation (ChIP) provides a powerful in vivo strategy to determine its target locations for a known protein. Using formaldehyde, the proteins are cross linked to the DNA, which is then fragmented into 100-500 bp long pieces. A protein-specific antibody coupled to a retrievable tag, is used to pull down (precipitate) the DNA-protein complex from the pool of DNA fragments. Finally, the associated DNA is recovered, sequenced and analyzed – either through amplification or through the use of DNA microarrays.

In a DNA microarray, probe sequences of known DNA molecules are placed on an array of inert substrate thus forming a collection of microscopic spots. By measuring the hybridization levels of target sequences, one can determine their enrichment under different conditions or locations. Using the DNA purified by ChIP, the precise location of the binding regions on the sequence can be identified. This technique known as ChIP-on-chip provides an efficient and scalable way for the identification of binding sites of DNA-binding proteins. Through recently developed genome-wide analyses one can determine the binding sites of a protein throughout the genome. Methods generating higher resolution and coverage (Boyer *et al.*, 2005; Odom *et al.*, 2006) have also been proposed. Although an expensive method, ChIP-chip is gaining popularity due to its ability to identify the TFBSs in an unbiased manner. However, the dependence on a highly TF-specific antibody is usually a major hurdle in performing ChIP-chip experiments.

Experimental identification and verification of such elements is challenging and costly, so much effort has been put into the development of computational approaches.

Computational Techniques for TFBS Identification

Computational discovery of the regulatory elements is possible because they occur several times in the same genome, and they may be evolutionary conserved (Sandve & Drablos, 2006). This means that searching for overrepresented motifs across regulatory regions may discover novel regulatory elements. However this simple looking problem turns out to be a tough problem, made difficult by a low signal-to-noise ratio. This is because of the poor conservation and short length of the transcription factor binding sites in comparison to the length of promoter sequences.

Motif recognition is NP-complete and therefore cannot be solved in polynomial time unless P = NP (Evans et al. 2003). Nonetheless, Numerous methods and tools have been developed for the motif identification problem, including MEME (Bailey *et al.*, 1995), AlignACE (Roth *et al.*, 1998), REDUCE (Bussemaker *et al.*, 2001), Winnower (Pevzner and Sze, 2000), PROJECTION (Buhler and Tompa, 2002), MITRA (Eskin and Pevzner, 2002), MDScan (Liu *et al.*, 2002),YMF (Sinha and Tompa, 2003), pattern driven approaches (Sze *et al.*, 2004), Weeder (Pavesi *et al.*, 2004), DME(Smith *et al.*, 2005), PSM1 (Rajasekaran *et al.*, 2005), VAS (Chin and Leung, 2006), MEME (Bailey *et al.*, 2006), RISOTTO (Pisanti *et al.*, 2006), PMSprune (Davila *et al.*, 2007), the Voting algorithm (Chin and Leung, 2005), MCLWMR (Boucher *et al.*, 2007), Trawler (Ettwiller *et al.*, 2007) and several others. Despite these available tools, the effective and efficient identification of motifs within datasets of interest remains a challenging problem, particularly when studying datasets derived from mammals, such as those from mice and humans. Tompa et al., (2005) have evaluated 13 different motif discovery tools and showed that many of the tools are inefficient when used on datasets derived from organisms higher than yeast.

Gene Prediction Through Identifying TFBS: A Combined Approach

Computational methods for gene prediction work by searching through sequences to locate the most likely ones that encode proteins. These methods are trained to recognize a variety of sequence patterns in a set of known gene sequences of an organism. Once trained, the resulting gene model may then be used to search for similar patterns in newly acquired sequences from the same organism.

Large-scale sequencing projects have motivated the need for a new generation of algorithms for gene recognition. The similarity-based approach to gene prediction is based on the observation that a newly sequenced gene has a good chance of having an already known relative in the database.

The flood of new sequencing data has made this chance even greater. As a result, the trend in gene prediction has been shifted from statistics-based approaches to similarity-based and EST-based algorithms.

In particular, Gelfand *et al.*, (1996) proposed a combinatorial approach to gene prediction, that uses related proteins to derive the exon-intron structure. Instead of employing statistical properties of exons, this method attempts to solve a combinatorial puzzle: to find a set of substrings in a genomic sequence whose concatenation (splicing) fits one of the known proteins.

Snyder and Stormo, (1995) made the first attempts to incorporate similarity analysis into gene prediction algorithms. However, the computational complexity of exploring all exon assemblies on top of sequence alignment algorithms is rather high. Gelfand et al., (1996) proposed a spliced alignment approach to the exon assembly problem that uses related proteins to derive the exon-intron structure.

The Gelfand *et al.*, (1996) approach is based on the following idea. Given a genomic sequence, they first find a set of candidate blocks that contains all true exons. This can be done by selecting all blocks between potential acceptor and donor sites (i.e., between AG and GT dinucleotides).

The resulting set of blocks can contain many false exons, of course, and currently it is impossible to distinguish all actual exons from this set by a statistical procedure. Instead of trying to find the actual exons, they select a related target protein in Gene-Bank and explore all possible block assemblies with the goal of finding an assembly with the highest similarity score to the target protein. The number of different block assemblies is huge, but the spliced alignment algorithm, which is the key ingredient of the method, scans all of them in polynomial time.

In order to compensate the insufficiency of any individual gene prediction program, the computational method to construct gene models by multiple evidences is becoming more promising. For the non annotated genomic sequences, a diverse set of methods can be combined for annotation, including the signal and content sensor approach. Given a sequence and using signal sensors, one can accumulate evidence on the occurrence of signals: translation starts and stops and splice sites are the most important ones since they define the boundaries of coding regions. An important strength of similarity-based approaches is that predictions rely on accumulated preexisting biological data. They should thus produce biologically relevant predictions (even if only partial).

We can integrate the advantages of both signal and content sensor approach for gene prediction to get better results. A combined approach for gene prediction using known motifs is explained in figure 3. The following steps are involved in this approach:

1. First of all search for the known motifs retrieved from promoter sequences of co-regulated genes of closely related organism, in new found genomic sequence.
2. Identify the signals and exons after/between the motifs. This includes identification of start codon just after the motifs, identification of exons using the conserved acceptor and donor sites and identification of stop codons.
3. Assemble the exons and generate the first three 5' to 3' open reading frames.
4. Translate each ORF in corresponding protein sequences.
5. Using the dynamic programming for each translated protein find the length of the longest common subsequence (LCS) with each protein sequence obtained from co-regulated genes.
6. Obtain the LCS that is of maximum alignment score. If the length of this LCS is above threshold this is the probable gene.

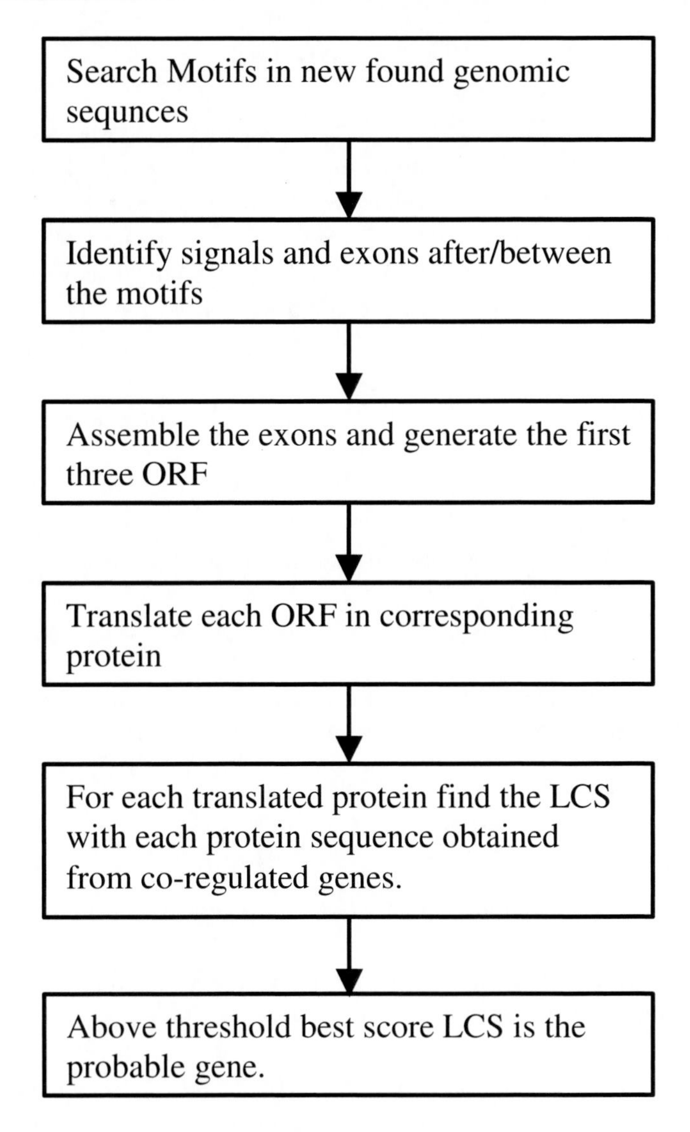

Figure 3. A combined approach for gene prediction using known motifs.

Conclusion

To predict the genes in a given genome using TFBS identification, a combined approach proposed in this chapter can yield good results. The approach combines identification of signal sensors and similarity based methods for gene prediction. In this method, the transcription start sites, transcription factor binding sites, exons, introns and the stop codons can be used as signals to identify gene fragments in a given genomic sequence. These signals can be assembled in an optimum sequence that is representing a possible gene. Further the dynamic programming can be used to identify the most similar known genes with the assembled gene.

References

Alexandersson, M., Cawley S., and Pachter L., 2003. SLAM: cross-species gene finding and alignment with a generalized pair Markov model. *Genome Res.* 13, 496- 502.

Bailey, T. L. and Elkan C., 1995. The value of prior knowledge in discovering motifs with MEME. *In Proc ISMB* 1995, 21–29.

Bailey, T. L., Williams N., Misleh C., Li W. W., 2006. MEME: discovering and analyzing DNA and protein sequence motifs. *Nucleic Acids Res* 34: W369–373.

Birney, E. and Durbin R., 2000. Using GeneWise in the Drosophila annotation experiment. *Genome Res.* 10: 547-548.

Boucher, C., Church P. and Brown D., 2007. A graph clustering approach to weak motif recognition. *In Proc WABI* 2007, 149–160.

Boyer, L.A., Lee T. I. et al., 2005. Core transcriptional regulatory circuitry in human embryonic stem cells. *Cell*, 122(6): 947–56.

Buhler, J. and Tompa M., 2002. Finding motifs using random projections. *J Comput Biol.*, 9: 225-242.

Bussemaker, H.J., Li H., Siggia E.D., 2001. Regulatory element detection using correlation with expression. *Nat Genet*, 27: 167–171.

Cawley, S.E., Wirth A.I., and Speed T.P., 2001. Phat–a gene finding program for Plasmodium falciparum. *Mol. Biochem. Parasitol.* 118, 167-174.

Chin, F. Y. L. and Leung C. M., 2005. Voting algorithms for discovering long motifs. *In Proc APBC* 2005, 261–271.

Chin, F. Y. L. and Leung C. M., 2006. An efficient algorithm for string motif discovery. *In Proc APBC* 2006, 79–88.

Davila, J., Balla S. and Rajasekaran S., 2007. Fast and practical algorithms for planted (l, d) motif search. *TCBB*, 4(4):544–552.

Do, J.H., T.K. Park, and D.-K. Choi., 2005. A computational approach to the inference of sphingolipid pathways from the genome of Aspergillus fumigatus. *Curr. Genet.* 48, 134-141.

Elnitski, L., Jin V.X., Farnham P.J. and Jones S.J., 2006. Locating mammalian transcription factor binding sites: a survey of computational and experimental techniques. *Genome Research* 16 (12): 1455–1464

Eskin, E. and Pevzner P., 2002. Finding composite regulatory patterns in DNA sequences. *Bioinformatics*, 18(Suppl 1):S354-S363.

Ettwiller, L., Paten B., Ramialison M., Birney E., Wittbrodt J., 2007. Trawler: de novo regulatory motif discovery pipeline for chromatin immunoprecipitation. *Nat Methods,* 4: 563–565.

Evans, P. A., Smith A. and Wareham H. T., 2003. On the complexity of finding common approximate substrings. *Theor. Comput. Sci.*, 306 (1-3):407–430.

Flicek, P., E. Keibler, P. Hu, I. Korf, and M.R. Brent., 2003. Leveraging the mouse genome for gene prediction in human: from whole-genome shotgun reads to a global synteny map. *Genome Res.* 13, 46-54.

Florea, L., Hartzell G., Zhang Z., Rubin G.M., and Miller W., 1998. A computer program for aligning a cDNA sequence with a genomic DNA sequence. *Genome Res.* 8, 967-974.

Fukunishi, Y., Suzuki H., Yoshino M., Konno H., and Hayashizaki Y., 1999. Prediction of human cDNA from its homologous mouse full-length cDNA and human shotgun database. *FEBS Lett.* 464, 129-132.

Gaasterland, T. and Sensen C.W., 1996. Fully automated genome analysis that reflects user needs and preferences. A detailed introduction to the MAGPIE system architecture. *Biochimie* 78, 302-310.

Gelfand, M.S., Mironov A.A., and Pevzner P.A., 1996. Gene recognition via spliced sequence alignment. *Proceedings of the National Academy of Sciences USA*, 93:9061–9066.

Guigó, R., Agarwal P. et al., 2000. An assessment of gene prediction accuracy in large DNA sequences. *Genome Res.* 10, 1631-1642.

Harris, N.L., 1997. Genotator: a workbench for sequence annotation. *Genome Res.* 7, 754-762.

Huang, X., Adams M.D., Zhou H., and Kerlavage A.R., 1997. A tool for analyzing and annotating genomic sequences. *Genomics* 46, 37-45.

Hubbard, T., Barker D et al., 2002. The Ensembl genome database project. *Nucleic Acids Res.*30, 38-41.

Kozak, M., 1996. Interpreting cDNA sequences: some insights from studies on translation. *Mamm. Genome* 7, 563–574.

Krogh, A., 2000. Using database matches with HMMgene for automated gene detection in Drosophila. *Genome Res.* 10, 523-528.

Liu, X. S., Brutlag D. L., Liu J. S., 2002. An algorithm for finding protein-DNA binding sites with applications to chromatin-immunoprecipitation microarray experiments. *Nat Biotechnol,* 20: 835–839.

Lockhart, D., Winzeler E., 2000. Genomics, gene expression and DNA arrays, *Nature,* 405, 827-836

Majoros, William H., 2007. Methods for Computational Gene Prediction, Cambridge University Press

Mathe, C., Sagot M.F., Schiex T., Rouze P., 2002. Current methods of gene prediction, their strengths and weaknesses. *Nucleic Acids Res.* 30, 4103–4117.

Mignone, F. et al., 2003. Computational identification of protein coding potential of conserved sequence tags through cross-species evolutionary analysis. *Nucleic Acids Res.* 31: 4639-4645.

Odom, D. T., Dowell R. D. et al., 2006. Core transcriptional regulatory circuitry in human hepatocytes. *Mol. Syst. Biol.*, 2: 0017.

Pavesi, G., Mereghetti P., Mauri G., Pesole G., 2004. Weeder Web: discovery of transcription factor binding sites in a set of sequences from co-regulated genes. *Nucleic Acids Research*, 32: W199–203.

Pedersen, A.G. and H. Nielsen., 1997. Neural network prediction of translation initiation sites in eukaryotes: perspectives for EST and genome analysis, p. 226-233. In *The Fifth International Conference on Intelligence Systems for Molecular Biology.* AAAI Press, Menlo Park, CA.

Pevzner, P. A. and Sze S. H., 2000. Combinatorial approaches to finding subtle signals inDNAsequences. *In Proc. Int. Conf. Intell. Syst. Mol. Biol.*, 8: 269–278.

Pisanti, N., Carvalho A. M., Marsan L., Sagot M. F., 2006. RISOTTO: Fast extraction of motifs with mismatches. In *Proc. LATIN'06, Lecture Notes in Computer Science*, Springer-Verlag, 3887: 757-768.

Rajasekaran, S., Balla S. and Huang C. H., 2005. Exact algorithms for planted motif problems. *J Comput Biol*, 12 (8):1117–1128.

Reese, M.G., Kulp D., Tammana H., and Haussler D., 2000. Genie–gene finding in Drosophila melanogaster. *Genome Res.* 10, 529-538.

Roth, F. P., Hughes J. D., Estep P. W., Church G. M., 1998. Finding DNA regulatory motifs within unaligned noncoding sequences clustered by whole-genome mRNA quantitation. *Nature Biotechnology*, 16:939-945.

Salamov, A.A. and Solovyev V.V., 2000. Ab initio gene finding in Drosophila genomic DNA. *Genome Res.* 10, 391-393.

Sandve, Geir Kjetil and Drabløs Finn, 2006. A survey of motif discovery methods in an integrated framework, *Biology Direct*, 1:11 doi:10.1186/1745-6150-1-11

Schiex, T., Moisan A., and Rouzé P., 2001. EuGène: an eukaryotic gene finder that combines several sources of evidence, p. 111-125. In O. Gascuel and M.-F. Sagot (eds). *Lecture Notes in Computer Science*, Vol. 2006, First International Conference on Biology, Informatics, and Mathematics, JOBIM 2000. Springer-Verlag, Germany.

Sinha, S., Tompa M., 2003. YMF: A program for discovery of novel transcription factor binding sites by statistical overrepresentation. *Nucleic Acids Res* 31: 3586–3588.

Smith, A. D., Sumazin P., Das D., Zhang M. Q., 2005. Mining ChIP-chip data for transcription factor and cofactor binding sites. *Bioinformatics,* 21(Suppl 1): i403–412.

Snyder, E.E. and Stormo G.D., 1995. Identification of protein coding regions in genomic DNA. *Journal of Molecular Biology*, 248:1–18.

Stormo, G.D., 2000a. Gene-finding approaches for eukaryotes. *Genome Res.* 10, 394-397.

Stormo, G.D., 2000b. DNA binding sites: representation and discovery. *Bioinformatics,* vol 16, 16-23.

Sze, S., Lu S. and Chen J., 2004. Integrating sample-driven and pattern driven approaches in motif finding. *In Proc. WABI* 2004, pp. 438–449.

Tolstrup, N., Rouzé P., and Brunak S., 1997. A branch point consensus from Arabidopsis found by non-circular analysis allows for better prediction of acceptor sites. *Nucleic Acids Res.* 25, 3159-3163.

Tompa, M., Li N, Bailey T. L., Church G. M., De Moor B., et al., 2005. Assessing computational tools for the discovery of transcription factor binding sites. *Nat Biotechnol* 23: 137–144

Usuka,, J., Zhu W., and Brendel V., 2000. Optimal spliced alignment of homologous cDNA to a genomic DNA template. *Bioinformatics* 16, 203-211.

Wray, G.A., Hahn M.W., Abouheif E., Balhoff J.P., Pizer M., Rockman M.V., Romano L.A., 2003. The evolution of transcriptional regulation in eukaryotes. *Mol Biol Evol*, 20(9):1377–419.

Yada, T., Takagi T., Totoki Y., and Sakaki Y., 2003. DIGIT: a novel gene finding program by combing gene-finders. *Pac. Symp. Biocomput.* 375-387.

In: Applications of Microbial Genes in Enzyme Technology ISBN: 978-1-62417-808-5
Editors: V.K.Gupta, M.G.Tuohy, G.D.Sharma et al.

Chapter 17

Wild and Engineered Microbes and Proteins in Technical Enzymes: Food for Thought

*Amro A. Amara**
Genetic Engineering and Biotechnology Research Institute,
Mubarak City for Scientific Research and Technology Applications, Alexandria, Egypt
Microbiology Division, Pharmaceutics Department,
College of Pharmacy, King Saud University, Riyadh, Saudi Arabia

Abstract

Two terms are used to distinguish between two kinds of microbes by the microbiologists, wild and engineered microbes. Wild microbes are those microbes isolated from nature, while engineered microbes are genetically modified in the lab. Nature is dynamic and enables a respective level of modification in the genetic materials of the wild type microbes especially in case of the unicellular structures, which are more susceptible to accept and reflect such modifications. Using genetic engineering tools enable many chances for chang and improvement. Actually, those tools are mimicking the modifications that happen naturally to the wild type microbes and their genes. Nowadays, molecular biology tools enable direct change in genes for targeting certain function(s) or modifing the related protein. This is known as "Protein Engineering" in which the newly modified protein is called the "Engineered Protein". Wild type microbes are well adapted creature and though they have existed for an unknown number of years. There are many-missed opportunities concerning the wild type microbes' applications. Scientists investigate the optimum possible production conditions and to mutagenize the wild type microbes to produce products in more quantities. Physical conditions and medium constituents can be optimized to enable better production using single or multiple variable optimization. Such kinds of optimization could lead to a significant product optimization. When genetic engineering tools were not available, scientists used the chemical and the physical mutagens to mutagenize industrial important microbes (for

* Corresponding author e-mail: amroamara@web.de.

a better production of certain products). Scientists used strong screening protocols to pick up the best-mutants. The mutants were then subjected to another cysle(s) of mutagenization or optimization which lead to improvement in the production of enzymes, proteins or antibiotics significantly. Fortunately, with the introduction and advancement in the genetic engineering tools a progress has been achieved to improve the production of many biotechnological products including the enzymes especially those, which have been governed by the role "from gene to protein". The innovation of tools like PCR, DNA isolation, amplification and sequencing, site directed mutagenesis, transformation, plasmid isolation, cloning, sub-cloning, etc., give further chances. The progresses in the science of "Protein Engineering" solve many facts about the protein structure/function. How one can choose and navigate between all those possibilities is endless.

However, in the industrial processes, there are many other factors and concepts that govern the choice between the wild type, mutageneized and the recombinant microbes. Many factors concerned with issues such as the plasmids, the promoters, the expression system, the up-stream and down-stream processes etc., which can influence one's choice as well as give more opportunities to select the most, fitted conditions for a particular process.

One single misunderstanding of the behaviour of the microbe, the gene or the protein and the used conditions could break all the process or gives less products. This chapter discusses crucial issues about wild and engineered microbes/proteins/enzymes. Different examples, experiences from the enzyme history, discussions, questions marks and facts about the technical enzymes will be addressed. Other factors such as the cost, the profit, the consumer and the market demand will also be described. This chapter is recommended for the biotechnologist, molecular biologist, businessperson and industrialists interested in the subject of technical enzymes production, optimization and innovation.

Introduction

Enzymes

Enzymes occur in every cell, hence in all microorganisms (Linderkofler *et al.*, 1958). Enzymes are able to do different types of vital functions. Enzymes are biological catalysts. As proteins, their backbones are mainly made of amino acids in the form of hetero-polymers. Those macromolecules can react spontaneously or after sensing the presence of their substrate(s) and some of them can react with more than one type of substrates. An enzyme could has different levels of specificity for different substrates. As biological catalyst, enzymes show ability to work faster than any other known chemical catalyst whenever there is a substrate and suitable conditions. In general, enzymes have two extraordinary properties: 1) they are highly efficient catalyst able to accelerate reaction by as much as 10^{17} fold 2) and they are exquisitely selective, being able to discriminate between closely related substrates (Hedstrom, 2001).

Although enzymes are proteines in nature and are usually nontoxic, they could harm if they are used incorrectly. Being safe and eco-friendly there is an increasing interest in their use over the chemical catalysts. They can maintain their activities for long time if used correctly. Immobilized enzymes prove that. Enzymes have backbones (which could reach hundreds of amino acids) consisting of twenty amino acids (aa). Few aa (around five) are responsible for catalysis. Those amino acids if changed, the enzyme function could be modified or impaired. In some cases, the change will affect their activity and in other cases, it will affect their specificity. Other changes in one enzyme backbone (aa other than the catalytic ones) could cause change in its activity due to the change in its 3D configuration. This type of changes might have an effect on the enzyme activity but seldom, could affect its specificity. As a dynamic chemical structure, enzymes' surrounding environments are important. Enzymes present in folding 3D forms, can change to uncountable 3D structures.

Enzymes could react singly or with combination with other biological forms including other types of enzymes to produce particular function or product(s). A group of different enzymes could react in a sequence called "pathway", starting by one substrate and ending with one or more than one product. A pathway can be for degrading "catabolic" or for building "anabolic". Enzymes could react inside the cell (*in vivo*) or outside the cell (*in vitro*) whenever the conditions are suitable. Due to their neumerous types, they have been classified based on their functions to six main groups 1) Oxidoreductases 2) Transferases 3) Hydrolases 4) Lyases 5) Isomerases, and 6) Ligases.

Technical enzymes have been used in many important industrial applications such as the paper industry, detergent, drugs, waste degradation, textile, food, pharmaceutical, leather, degumming of silk goods, manufacturing of liquid glue, cosmetics, meat tenderization, cheese production, growth promoters and biodegradable plastic production (PHA, PHB) (Leuschner and Antranikan, 1995; Rao *et al.,* 1998; 2004; Cowan, 1996, Amara 2008, Amara and Salem 2010, Amara and Moawed 2011; Amara and Serour 2008; Gupta *et al.,* 2002a; Gupta *et al.,* 2002b; Poza *et al.,* 2007; Thangam and Rajkumar 2002; Valer, 1975). Proteases are examples about technical enzymes particularly those used in the detergent formulation. These kinds of technical enzymes should have high activity and stability within a broad range of pH and temperature, and should be compatible with various detergent components along with oxidizing and sequestering agents (Ito *et al.,* 1998).

Protein engineering has been used to improve the stability of BPN' from *Bacillus amyfoliquefaciens* in the chelating environment of the detergent by deleting strong calcium-binding site (residues 75-83) and re-stabilizing the enzyme through interactions without involving metal-ion binding. Stability increases of more than 1000-fold in 10 mM EDTA has been reported for this protease (Strausberg *et al.,* 1995). The surface properties of BPN' have also been engineered. Variants of mutants produce negative charges in the active site region of the molecule are adsorbed less strongly and give better laundry performance (Brode *et al.,* 1996). Cold-adapted maturation of thermophilic WF146 protease by mimicking the propeptide binding interactions of *Psychrophilic subtilisin* S41 has been designed by Yang *et al.* (2008).

Microbial Enzymes and the Other Enzymes Producers

Plants, animals and microbes (Eukaryotic or Prokaryotic and Archea) are sources for the enzymes which have been used in different applications, including technical applications. Using enzymes from microbial source is dominant, however, plant and animal are respective sources for some important enzymes. Enzymes from plants and animal sources proved to be of great value.

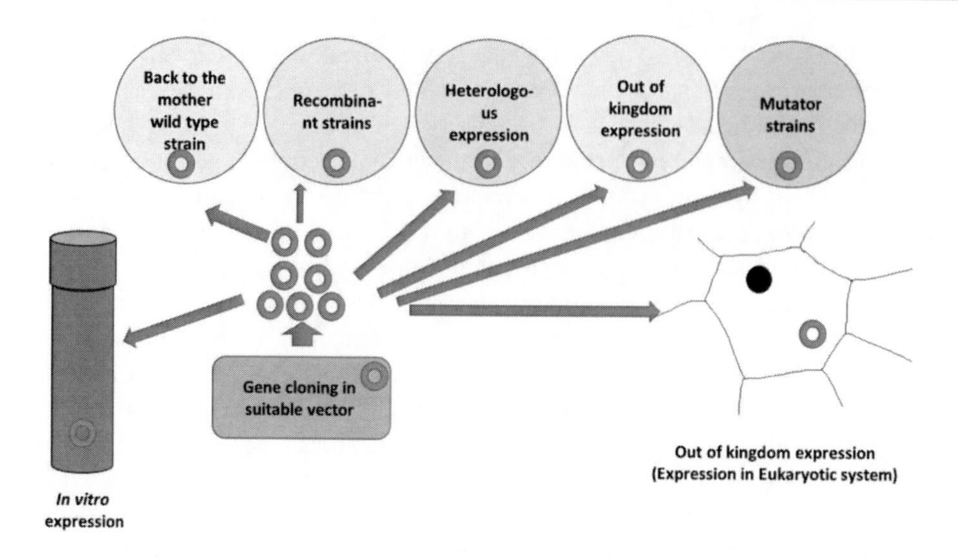

Figure 1. Different expression roots.

Genetic engineering and the molecular biology tools enable the cloning of their relative genes and their expression in different microbial system as in Figure 1 (Out of kingdom expression and production). The different types of technical enzymes used nowadays have been derived from mesophilic and, to less extent, alkalophilic enzymes. An increasing interest on the enzyme produced by the extremophilic microbes have been shown recently. There is a possibility to produce extremophilic enzymes using mesophilic conditions with or without the manipulation of the genetic engineering tools (Amara and Salem 2009; Amara 2011). The biodiversity of the microbes enable the isolation of different kind of enzymes and there are usually more recourses in the nature. Metagenomic is a recent approach that enables and is concerned with the isolation of different kind of genes directly, without the cultivation of their related producer microbes. In fact, most of the microbes are non-cultivable, or in better words we still do not know how to culture them.

Microbes as Producers

In some cases the enzymes that are of value, depending on their applications, produced by the wild strains in relatively low level which have a negative economic value. Additionally, wild type microbes usually produce a mixture of enzymes or exert an unwanted product(s). This is not an invitation to kick-off the wild type microbes, especially those that have been proven historically to be safe or can be easily manipulated to turn to safe ones. Wild type strains have many positive points such as their ability to survive in rate better than the recombinant strains. Wild type strains show ability to utilize large range of substrates and raw materials or degrading complicated substrates. For example wild type *Bacillus spp.*, can utilize more substrates than could wild type *E. coli* do. This will be the same condition in case of recombinant *Bacillus spp* or *E. coli*. There are many routes for establishing or discovering new enzymes or even find better ones than that exists. These routes include i) the different culture collections which have different kinds of identified microbes; ii) natural isolates especially from places where the targeted substrate is exists in excess amounts; iii) known microbes able to produce different kind of enzymes; iv) contamination with unusual properties; v) using minimal medium with the targeted substrate as a single carbon source to enrich and force the correct microbe(s) to utilize such substrate; vi) direct screening for the requested gene without isolating the responsible microbe(s).

Could the Wild Type Produce More?

After the microbial strain has been well identified and the enzyme is well characterized it is now the role of the optimization tools to take place. Here, there are usually some neglected steps made by the researchers where they are normally preferred to go directly to the genetic engineering tools and to clone the responsible gene.

In fact, there are many steps still in need before the use of the molecular biological tools for extra-optimization. But the question is how could we use the genetic tools to optimize the enzymes produced by a wild type if we do not know how much it is able to produce? Surprisingly some wild type microbes could produce amount of enzymes more than one could expected. Cheaper substrates are usually heterogeneous and complicated agricultural or domestic wastes.

In fact, wild type microbes could do more. For optimizing the production conditions of a certain enzyme using certain wild type microbes, there are usually two ways.

The first one is concerned with optimizing the affective variables by changing them one by one. Alternatively collective randomization for all of the variables at once is another way for the optimization. Different experimental design optimization strategies have been used by many scientists with different backgrounds. Using experimental design tools improve the production of certain product ampunt (in some cases) to unexpected levels.

The most logic and easy to use with good results are Plackett Burman and Box-Behnken as well as using the optimization tools in the Excel solver. For revising papers containing detailed description for the three above methods refer to Amara and Salem, (2010), Amara (2011). These three methods are recommended to be used in sequence to enable the highest expected optimization level.

Using experimental design could not only give unexpected level of optimization but also can save substrates and reduce time. Thus the overall cost of the process will be reduced by either eliminating ineffective variables or reducing their amounts during the cultivation processes.

After mapping the best conditions for production, classical mutagenesis enables other chances. Classical mutagenesis is an old tool used historically in strains improvement but in most cases it did not deliver where mutation(s) has/have been happened (Chiang, 2004). Classical mutagenesis is based on using chemical compounds or physical conditions mutagens during mutagenesis. UV and nitrosoguanidin are examples. Unfortionetly, mutation(s) can be happened in any gene (Ermakova-Gerdes *et al.*, 1996).

It is the role of the selection process to select the correct needed mutant (Michel *et al.*, 2000). Moreover, it is important here to state that the mutagenesis should be wisely used. First priority should be for isolating different kinds of enzymes producing microbes or their genes from the nature.

Why traditional mutagenesis is still effective? It is an important step to optimize the production of certain enzyme (using the wild type) to useing the classical mutagenesis. The reason why this step is important is because it is a cheap process for conducting biochemical engineering without useing the genetic engineering tools which might not be available in some places.

Classical mutagenesis could improve the amount/quality of the produced enzyme directly or indirectly as a result of 1) direct mutation in the wild type gene give better activity or new function 2) mutation in another part of the genome (other than the target gene) lead to block one or more of the metabolic pathway(s) which is/are in computation with the enzyme production process 3) improve other pathways lead to product improvement.

After identifying the mutant, it is usually subjected to further cycles of the above kinds of optimization/mutagenesis. We should highlight that the target gene, in some cases could be still un-attacked (wild) and only the metabolic flux has been improved.

Learn Tactics from the Enzyme Research History

The above part describes the important aspect about the enzymes and the wild type microbes. Scaled researchers and the knowledge are crucial factors which are essential for technical enzymes improvement. The best and the most interesting way to build a knowledgeable person is by studying the history of the technical enzymes improvement which include a lot of scientific and technical problems, solutions, inventions and the contribution of the pioneers and their efforts to build this filed.

Those interested in developing enzymes should know the progress of enzyme technology which have been done by the pioneers in this filed. Gaining experiences from the enzyme history is important. For instance, proteases which have been used in technical enzymes were isolated first from mild animal pancreases. The German, Otto Röhm, the founder of the giant chemical laboratory Rohm and Hass, is an example of a famous scientist who has carried out this technique. Moreover, enzymes are globally reacting. In fact, some ethnic groups and old civilizations have used enzymes in many applications extracted from the nature or from traditional technology. The most important experiences from the enzyme technology history are those, which address the principles of the enzymes structure/function and specificity. This has enabled the change of the enzymes using the molecular biology tools and has innovation in the protein engineering as a separate branch of science.

Time for Cloning and the Use of the Evaluable Molecular Biology Tools

Perhaps, ideas and tactic for manipulating wild type microbes have been touched briefly in the above part. This might give the wild type a more space of research in future. Yes, after passing all the above possibility, (using the classical and conventional methods) it is logic to look for further optimization. This will only happened if we build a better understand for our enzyme through its genetic material(s). Or through producing it in a microbial system enable better production and purification. There is still much room for further optimization. The enzymes production follow “one gene one protein” however this molecular concept should be extended to be “one gene one protein in suitable microbe and good production and purification conditions”.

Cloning Vectors and Promoters

Cloning the responsible gene will be the first step to navigate through the molecular biology tools. However, which plasmid and promoter should be used during the factors depends on certain factors. First, whether the enzyme is a producer for a certain product, or the enzyme itself is the product. Also the type and the amount of the expressed enzyme are crucial. If the enzyme under expression is the product the best and the most direct way is to produce it in an optimum amount. This can be happened if its gene is expressed using a strong promoter such as T_7 promoter. Both of the gene and the promoter should be carried in a suitable plasmid which can give several copies (relaxed plasmid) (Figure 2). After transforming the plasmid in a suitable recombinant strain enable over-expression, some other additional conditions should be considered including: i) the kind of the used substrate or its analog ii) the use of an antibiotic marker or another material essential for maintaining the existence of the plasmid iii) the medium constituents and the growth physical conditions. This will distinguish the amount of the produced protein. His_{tag} could be added to the gene (six histidine sequence (amino acids) either at C or N terminal sequences) to improve the purification steps (Hoffmann *et al.*, 2002). Other affinity tools could also be used.

On the other hand and if the enzyme is a producer for a certain product, using a strong promoter will not be the correct choice. If a strong promoter is used, the enzyme will be produced in a large amount (as inclusion bodies) and will exhaust the cell power. This will lead to consume of most of the cell resources which finally will not be able to give the produced enzyme the chance to react with the substrate to produce the targeted product(s). Or a very minute product(s) will be produced. It is important to understand the factors which will lead to optimize the product amount. Nevertheless, in some cases production of inclusion bodies is a good strategy for better purification.

Inclusion bodies can be isolated, ruptured and their content from protein can be further purified. In best case the produced protein has an affinity to a certain matrix.

Gene Expression/Vectors/Recombinant Strains

Cloning gene responsible for production of a particular enzyme gives many production possibilities such as self-expression in the mother wild type strain using suitable multi-copy plasmid. This will enable the existence of more than one copy of the gene. It will also enable heterologous expression in different kinds of hosts. Heterologous expression enables the use of the power of other microbes such as the use of a microbe able to grow on hydrocarbon or utilize complicated waste(s) such as phenol. Or even using a fast growing microbe enable a high cell density. There are many tactics that can be used when the enzyme responsible gene has been cloned. Also it enables the use of genetically modified microbes which usually called recombinant strains. All of the previously mentioned tools and tactics about genes and enzymes are still under the umbrella of the wild type gene/enzyme. Only modified genes give modified protein if amino acid(s) one or more has/have been changed and this change will only be effective if the new protein is able to give a new function or impair an old one.

Nowadays, there are many efficient commercial excellent recombinant strains from different microbes able to produce not only enzymes but any protein (whenever the microbe itself will not be harmed). Those microbes have been manipulated using different genetic engineering tools to match the best use for different applications.

The first approved recombinant protein manufactured using transformed *E. coli* was rDNA Lilly insulin (Humulin) from Eli-Lilly-Co. in the 1970s approved in the early 1980s (Manning *et al.*, 1989). Recently, *Pichia pastoris* has been shown an increasing usage rate (Sørenson, 2010).

There are several factors that affecting the amount of the expressed protein including: 1) the cultivation and the growth conditions, 2) the type of the microbial host strain, 3) the microbes capacity, generation time and their surface/volume ratio, 4) the plasmid copy number, 5) the type of the promoter (Figure 2), 6) the inducer (substrate and/or analog) 7) the RNA degradation rate (some recombinant strains have been impaired in the RNases).

Virus's promoters (e.g. T_7 promoter) are used for strong protein expression. The substrate analog could also change the rate of the expression. This is due to the fact that the expression will not be stopped due to the utilization of the original substrate. As an example, IPTG, the lactose analog is not utilized by the cells. It is important to highlight that the induction of a certain gene to express a certain protein could affect the cell replication.

If the induction starts so early (in lag phase), where the number of the cells is not enough this might give the normal yield/cell but will reduce the yield/liter because of the existence of less cell numbers (Figure 3) (Amara, 2005). In some expression system, the RNAase has been impaired to allow maximum transcription but there is still a need for selecting the correct time for induction.

The expression of a certain cloned gene could be in the mother wild cell (self transformation), in another wild microbes (Heterologous expression), in recombinant strain (transformation), transformation between the eukaryotic and prokaryotic systems and *vice verse* (out of kingdom expression). Introns should be eliminated from any eukaryotic genes going to be expressed in prokaryotic system. Also, there are many shuttle vectors which enable the expression in both of prokaryotic and eukaryotic system (Abd-El-Haleem *et al.*, 2007).

All of these various expression systems are based on genes in their wild type forms or mutagenized ones. However, the overall system will not allow change in the genetic materials during the expression processes. Expression in a mutator strain such as XL1-Red will enable *in vivo* mutagenesis in the targeted gene during the processes of its replication and expression. In tube (*in vitro*) low fidelity DNA polymerases can induce mutation.

This can also happen naturally when a microbe has one or more impaired genes; especially the DNA repairing genes. It is important to highlight that there are currently many perfect expression systems and vectors for different purposes.

These recombinant strains have been improved by scientists and companies to match the exact purposes for their use, either production, purification or even modification and mutagenesis.

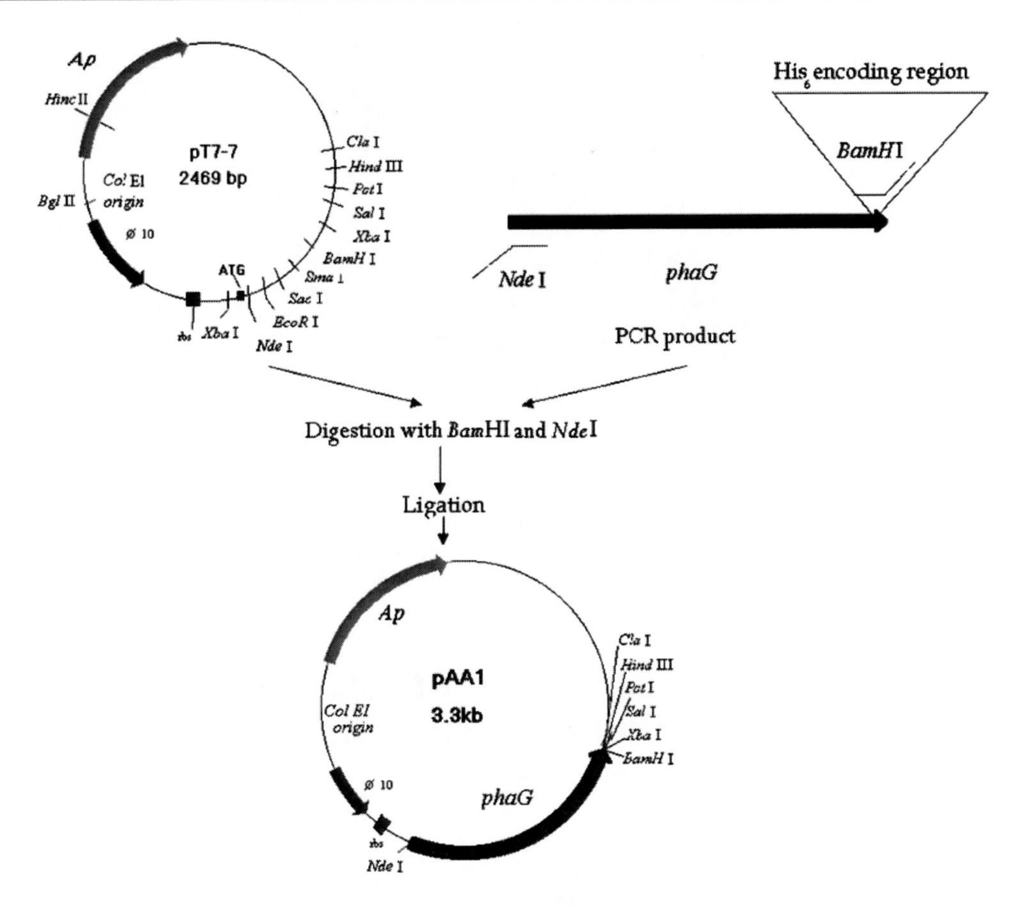

Figure 2. Construction of pAA1, a pT7-7 derivative containing the *phaG* gene from *P. putida* co-linear to the Ø10 promoter in the restriction sites *Nde*I and *BamH*I (Amara 2005).

Their major features include, better transformation efficiency, no DNases, no restriction enzymes, removal of the endotoxin genes, and other special genetic modifications have been introduced such as: adding antibiotic markers or adding gene(s) enabling the expression of virus promoters.

The gene of one of the lysis protein can be added to induce self lysis and product release. As for vectors, they have been improved significantly and can be contain some useful elements such as multiple restriction sites and two promoters (one in each side of the gene(s) insertion sites or near to it). This enables blunt end ligation and expression for the cloned gene in any direction.

There are different types of promoters which selected based on the aim of use and the requested expression level. The vector contains either a strong or normal promoter or both. Different markers can be also used based on the use purposes. Markers include antibiotic markers, fluorescence markers and many others.

His_{tag} or another affinity insertion part can be added to the gene before the stop codon or in the N terminus. Many other useful features have been introduced to the recombinant strains and to the used cloning and expression vectors, which could improve the process, the production, the purification etc.

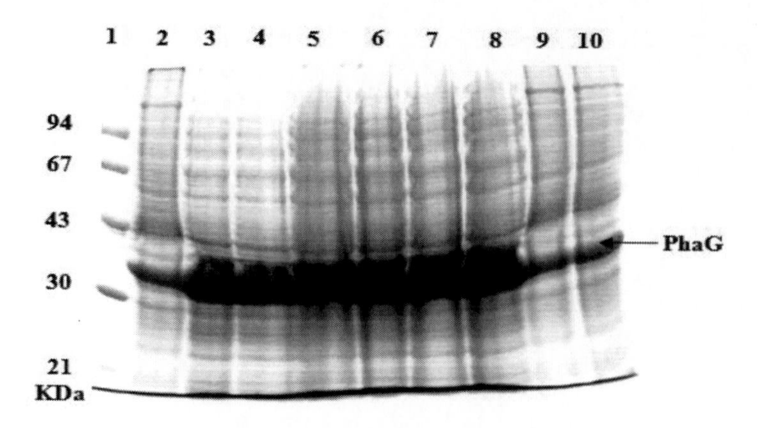

Figure 3. Arrow shows different level of PhaG overproduction; Lane 1, molecular weight standard; lane 2, IPTG added 8 h after the beginning of the cultivation (18 h); lane 3, and 4, IPTG added at the beginning of the cultivation (18 h); lane 5-8, IPTG added at the beginning of the cultivation (26 h); lane 9 and 10, like lane 2 (Amara 2005).

Improvement of Structure, Function and Specificity

Protein Engineering

"Any non nature or induced change for a gene/protein leading to new structures/function(s) is in the frame of protein engineering". Protein engineering is concerned with the modification of the protein structure/function(s) or building protein from scratch. The engineered protein usually has new criteria(s) and can be mediated on the level of the genes or proteins. There is a real need for engineering different types of enzymes to improve their functions. Less pure or completely crude proteins or enzymes could be used in many industrial applications, which do not need high purity. However, they must be contamination free in case of medicinal and pharmaceutical applications. Medically used proteins should be highly pure, active, correctly folded and biocompatible (Degim and Çelebi, 2007; Woods and Hamuro, 2001; Nishijima, 2005; Standley *et al.,* 2008).

Regarding to their activity and stability enzymes have been modified to match perfectly the reason(s) of their usage. New microbes from extreme environments are becoming an important source of new backbones for the engineered proteins. Engineering special protein is a process of build up/modifying what already existed. Technical enzymes such as proteases which are used in Powder-detergent require stability against certain protein stains in tough environment such as hard water or even solvents. Properties, such as stability, high activity (in the case of enzymes) and the ability to fold and interact correctly with surfaces are necessary for a variety of industrially important enzymes (Goodenough 1995; Runbingh 1997; Arulmuthu *et al.,* 2009; Crisman and Randolph 2009). PE should be applied to solve complicated problems and introduce unexplored new properties (Chen *et al.,* 2002; Fowler *et al.,* 2002; Kan, 2002; O'Maille *et al.,* 2002; Best *et al.,* 2003; Kiss *et al.,* 2003; Nielsen *et al.,*

2004b; O'Maille *et al.,* 2004; Sueda *et al.,* 2004; Tandang *et al.,* 2005; Bai *et al.,* 2007; Alahuhta *et al.,* 2008; Evdokimov *et al.,* 2008).

"Success in designing useful proteins is largely a matter of trying over and over again. But protein engineers often found themselves having to choose between trying to make bigger libraries and focusing libraries on sequences most likely to be effective" (Baker 2011).

There are many natural phenomenon that prove that proteins have been modified naturally. As an example: Sickle cell anaemia and Cystic fibrosis (Harris, 1992; Platt and Falcone, 1988). Post-translation modification, which can happen either before the protein is used in the cell, or as a part of control mechanisms is a natural mechanism for modifying protein structure (Caraglial *et al.,* 2004). Pro-insulin consisting of ABC fragments is functionless. After the action of the peptidases and the sulphur bonds linkage, the C fragment will be removed. Without the existence of the C fragment; Pro-insulin becomes as correct insulin.

Proteins, including the enzymes, work together to achieve a particular function, and they often associate to form stable complexes (Anthea, 1993). Insulin was the first protein to be sequenced, by Frederick Sanger, who won the Nobel Prize for this achievement in 1958. He has succeeded in solving the insulin sequence by sequencing its content of amino acids. It was a complicated process especially in the presence of disulfide bonds between A and B fragments. However, Sanger and Thampson (1953 a, b) have highlighted the importance of the insulin 3D structure (for more details about this amazing scientific story refer to Sanger (1988)). This success enables later the production of the recombinant insulin.

The first three-dimensional (3D) structures for haemoglobin and myoglobin have been resolved by Muirhead and Perutz (1963) and Kendrew *et al.,* (1958 a, b) respectively. The 3D structures of both proteins were determined by x-ray diffraction analysis. Based on their pioneering work, they were awarded Nobel Prize in Chemistry in 1962. The Hen egg white lysozyme (HEWL) was the first enzyme atomic structure to be solved by x-ray crystallography in 1965.

The three dimensional structure of the many proteins and enzymes which have been solved by x-ray analysis as well as the well known structure of the 20 amino acids, the configuration between their chemical bonds and their physical properties enable the understanding of many aspects about the protein 3D. Therefore, many hypothetical protein models have been built from the previously solved 3D proteins structures or from the knowledge extracted from the configurations of those structure as well as the properties of the amino acids. However, there are many facts still missing.

As an example, the concept of the helix formation has been understood. Nada and Koder (2010) summarized the investigation done by many about the formation of the helix in that: if there is a sequence consists of seven amino acids where the first and the fourth amino acids are non-polar, this will induce the formation of helix (see Nada and Koser (2010) and the references within).

Rapid advances in the protein engineering related fields such as DNA isolation and purification, cloning, sub-cloning, genetic engineering, restriction enzymes, site-directed mutagenesis, gene synthesis, new expression systems, molecular biology tools, protein science, bioinformatics, instrumentation, physics, chemistry, etc., have provided the molecular biologists additional tools for modifying existing genes which are responsible for proteins and enzymes to improve their catalytic activities, stability, and selectivity.

Different results and information about protein structure/function(s) (including enzymes) have been used by different researchers to improve their design. There are many natural examples about how much the enzymes could be specific and able to do complicated processes. To understand how much the structure can affect the function of a certain protein. DNA and RNA polymerases can be taken as an example. The DNA polymerase reaction is catalysed by two-metal ion mechanism in the 3'-exonuclease reaction. In contrast, RNA polymerase does more complicated function while it works in one ribonucleic acid strand only. RNA polymerases are able to initiate RNA synthesis without requiring a primer oligonucleotide to exhibit an abortive initiation phase and they are target of host regulatory proteins (activators, inhibitors, terminators and anti-terminators) that modulate gene expression (von-Hippel *et al.,* 1984; Erie *et al.,* 1992; Ikeda *et al.,* 1986; Brautigam and Steitz. *et al.,* 1988; Freemont *et al.,* 1988; Beese and Steitz, 1991). The structure differences between DNA and RNA polymerases enable the last one to do a more complicated job.

The Logical Approach in Protein Engineering

Logical approach or Rational design enable the manipulation of the protein through its gene after understanding its 3D structure (Moss *et al.,* 2009; Costa *et al.,* 2002; Liu *et al.,* 2007; Holmwood and Schindler, 2009). Rational design has been improved by the improvement in the site directed mutagenesis methods, protein 2D and 3D, structure modelling, protein-protein interaction and their related software (Chie *et al.*, 2004; Chie *et al.*, 2005; Boeris *et al.*, 2009; Kurgan, 2008; Ludwig *et al.,* 2003; Shen *et al.*, 2007; Sugimoto *et al.*, 2004; Yan *et al.*, 2008).

The concept of protein 3D modelling is based on relating a structure to the possible expected function(s) of amino acids residues (homology modelling) and replacing them with other functions (molecular dynamics) in order to change their properties (Visegràdy *et al.,* 2001).

Conserved amino acids within a group of enzymes do the same job. This means that those amino acids could have an essential function in the catalysis. This is an easy method to specify the nucleophilic residues. Of course, the most important ones will be those, which have physicochemical properties. For this reason Rational design requires some knowledge about the basic protein principle, genetic engineering tools and good skills in mathematics and algorithms. Computing different softwares have been introduced to facilitate and reduce the steps incorporated in the PE (Du *et al.*, 2009; Quine *et al.,* 2004).

Enzyme Engineering Is a Sensitive Approach

The process of engineering a certain protein can be broken if any mistake is committed. The enzyme produced by a cloned gene should show a correct enzyme activity. The gene should be sequenced from its forward and backward sides (internal primer should also be used). Cloned gene should be sequenced more than one time before one can start to conduct protein engineering experiments. Correct sequence is very important. Some sequencing machine enables eye control to prove the sequence by enabling base by base reading. After that the overall sequence should be translated to protein. Any stop codon inside the sequence means a wrong sequence. Translation of any genes to a protein sequence should give only one stop codon at its end. Alignment in each step can be conducted to compare the sequence with other similar sequences in the database to prove that it has been correctly cloned, or with a nearly similar one for comparison. Sometimes especially after using low fidelity polymerases for DNA amplification it is essential to prove the sequence quality. Alignment then should be conducted to map the conserved amino acids which are probably essential in catalysis. The protein sequence furthermore can be aligned with different evaluable x-ray structures and a whole model can be built up (Chappell *et al.,* 2002; Gaudier *et al.,* 2002; Ozbek *et al.,* 2002; Rhem *et al.,* 2002; Vannini *et al.,* 2002; Woo *et al.,* 2002; Akarsu *et al.,* 2003; Calderone *et al.,* 2003; Feinberg *et al.,* 2003; Yun *et al.,* 2003; Ifuku *et al.,* 2004; Parker *et al.,* 2004; Timsit *et al.,* 2006; Molina *et al.,* 2009). Building a complete hypothetical model for protein that did not crystallize yet is available by using the available protein structure databases (Christendat *et al.,* 2002; Choi *et al.*, 2009; Han *et al.,* 2005; Hattori *et al.,* 2005; Holmes *et al.,* 2006; Han *et al.,* 2008; Jang *et al.,* 2009).

Different computational algorithms have been introduced to identify the amino acids sequences that have low energies for target structures. The sequence-conformation space under investigation is usually large. Software for different proteins (including enzymes) modelling have been established with different ability to detect the presence of un-natural molecules (Anfinsen, 1972; Dana *et al.,* 2006; Chen *et al.,* 2007; Cavasotto *et al.,* 2008; Bordoli *et al.,* 2009; Chen *et al.,* 2009; Chen and Shi 2009). Some of the software are able to display and manipulate the proteins 3D structures (defined by X-ray analysis).

Continuous development of different software, instruments, x-ray machines, synchrotrons etc., together with advancement in the field of molecular biology and genetic engineering brought tremendous progress to the enzyme engineering (Fieulaine *et al.,* 2001; Thore *et al.,* 2003; Ball, 2008; Herrmann *et al.,* 2002a; Herrmann *et al.,* 2002b; Yao *et al.,* 2006; Fukunishi and Nakamura 2008; Abendroth *et al.*2010; Procopiou *et al.,* 2004; Sugimoto *et al.*, 2004; Yu *et al.,* 2004; Nicolini and Pechkova 2006; Yu *et al.,* 2009).

Mutagenesis Using Molecular Tools

Change of amino acid(s) in a particular protein could happen naturally as described above. In case of human, it could lead to severe human diseases (Kao *et al.,* 2000). The mutations, which happened naturally, are happening in a very slow rate, which might not satisfy certain technical demand. Due to the space of the chapter, only two examples of the well-known tools for mutagenesis will be described. One example represents a planed mutagenesis "Site directed mutagenesis" and the other will represent a completely *in vivo* random mutagenesis. For more detailed about the different types of mutagenesis refer to Kaur and Sharma (2006).

Site Directed Mutagenesis

The use of protein engineering started in 1978 when a site directed mutagenesis was introduced in the laboratory of Michael Smith (Hutchison *et al.,* 1978). Michael Smith and his co-workers were the first to introduce synthetic oligonucleotides mediate mutations

(Hutchison *et al.,* 1978). The first modification of an enzyme, a tyrosyl-transfer RNA synthetase, using this tool was performed in 1982 (Winter *et al.,* 1982). Through site-directed mutagenesis a cysteine was replaced by a serine altering the protein's substrate binding characteristics. His revolutionary work within this field earned Michael Smith the Nobel Prize in 1993. Many alterations in a particular protein can be generated by making amino acid replacements at a specific site in the polypeptide backbone. Each protein is unique in its amino acids composition. At any position in the sequence, an amino acid can be replaced by another using site directed mutagenesis method (Flaman *et al.,* 2001; Bennett *et al.,* 2003; Ho *et al.,* 2005; Kasrayan *et al.,* 2007; Choi *et al.,* 2009; Edelheit *et al.,* 2009). As an example, pancreatic ribonuclease A is an enzyme comprising 124 amino acids, which cleaves the covalent bonds by the joining of ribonucleic acids (RNA). If at position 119 in the sequence the naturally occurring histidine is replaced by an alanine, this mutant protein is expected to have little or no biological activity, because histidine 119 is important for that activity. Other mutations have very little effect on their proteins. This is particularly true when the amino acid is substituted by other closely related amino acid(s) and when the amino acid is not conserved in simiiler proteins found in other organisms. (Branningan and Wilkinson, 2002; Lippincott-Schwartz and Patterson, 2003; Wang and Schultz, 2002).

There are many tools that can be used to specify the active amino acids residues such as: 1) through understanding the protein structure/function; 2) aligning similar proteins with same or nearly same functions to specify the conserved amino acids; 3) crystallography and x-ray analysis; 4) NMR analysis; 5) study the shift of the amino acids or their configuration after adding the substrate. This could be done by crystallizing both of the substrate and the protein using the NMR or the x-ray analysis; 6) In silico analysis or even using normal computer able to do protein substrate docking; 7) by targeting directly the amino acids with physicochemical properties, particularly those expected to react with the substrate based on their amino acids compositions and confuguration.

As another example about a story where site directed mutagenesis has been used, seven site directed mutations have been performed in *phaC*$_{Pa}$ (the gene coded for PhaC synthase the enzyme which are responsible for the polymerization of polyhydroxyalkanoates) where five conserved residues were replaced by site directed mutagenesis in order to identify the function of these amino acids in catalysis. The substitution of W398 by alanine abolished PHA_{MCL} (MCL-medium chain length) synthase activity indicating that W398 is essential for enzyme activity (Amara and Rhem, 2003). The substitution of H479 by glutamine did not affect the PHA_{MCL} activity, which indicates that H479 is not the general base catalyst that activates the nucleophilic C296 for covalent catalysis. The substitution of C296 with serine, which is the general base catalyst in lipases, did not abolish PHA_{MCL} synthase activity while still exhibiting 20% activity in comparison to the wild type. Substitution of C296 with alanine abolished PHA_{MCL} synthase activity which is a strong evidence that serine may be able to replace cysteine as catalytic nucleophile for changing substrate specificity of PHA synthase. For further investigation, another site directed mutagenesis has been done in another conserved histidine (H452), which was replaced with glutamine. The H452Q mutant was highly impaired in PHA_{MCL} activity, which indicate that H452 plays a major role as a general base catalyst instead of H479 (Amara and Rhem, 2003). Hu *et al.* (2007) reported an improve for fractions by using site directed mutagenesis. The recombinant *E. coli* harbouring plasmid pETJ1 (L65A), pETJ2 (L65V) or plasmid pETJ3 (V130A) synthesized the enhanced 3HHx fractions of PHBHHx from dodecanoate, indicating that Leu-65 and Val-130 of PhaJ(Ah) play an important role in determining the acyl chain length substrate specificity. The mutated PhaJ (Ah) (L65A, L65V, or V130A) provided higher 3HHx precursors for PHA synthase, resulting in the enhanced 3HHx fractions of PHB-co-HHx (Hu *et al.*, 2007).

Random Mutagenesis

The probability numbers that in need to change particular protein using site directed mutagenesis is very larg. Proteins, which are composed of 20 different amino acids, need significant numbers of site directed mutagenesis steps to alter its structure/functions. The random mutagenesis becomes a best choice when there is a shortage of the existed information about protein structural/function(s) and the role of active residues (Amara *et al.,* 2001, 2002; Amara, 2003). Or if there is a need for a better understand for the protein structure/function. The random mutagenesis is applied to a gene coded for a protein. The process passes through a selection protocol(s) that enable to select newly mutated genes by detecting a difference in the expressed protein behaviours after the mutagenesis steps. Gene(s) could be a subject of more than one cycle of mutagenesis (Greener *et al.,* 1997). Random mutagenesis usually seems to be time-consuming process, but alternative methods will be impossible if there is insufficient knowledge about the protein structure/functions.

Random mutagenesis mimics what could be happen naturally, that will satisfy all the criteria which lead to mutate a certain gene; even randomly but with more force and directed strategy. Random mutagenesis can be used *in vivo* using mutator strains or *in vitro* using different kinds of PCR (for random gene modification protocols). As an example Amara *et al.* (2002) have described a detailed *in vivo* random mutagenesis protocol for mutated $phaC_{Ap}$ synthase gene. The protocol has given a direction to select PhaC_{Ap} synthases with enhanced activities, change the substrate specificity and give polymers with different monomeric compositions. The *in vivo* random mutagenesis is based on the mutator strain "*E. coli* XL1 Red" that is impaired in three of its DNA repairing genes (Glickman and Radman, 1980). Interestingly the changed amino acids in the mutated PhaC synthases were not in the active site, which indicate a clear role of the structure/function(s) relationship over the enzyme active sites as reported by Amara *et al.* (2001, 2002).

Economic Prospective Value

Both of the cost and profit are crucial factors in any industrial process. Technical enzymes are one of the major biotechnological and industrial products, which had a market share of about 1 billion USD in 1999 (Schäfer *et al.,* 2005). Part of the enzymes products are the thermostable enzymes, which are well consumed in different industrial processes and constitute more than 65% of the worldwide market (Leuschner and Antranikan, 1995; Rao *et al.,* 1998). Schmid *et al.* (2001) noted: "Limiting aspects of the biocatalytic processes are improved in iterative manner, gradually leading to efficient industrial processes. In setting priorities for improvements at each process step, a detailed understanding of the costs and improvement potential of each of the partial steps in a process is vital". Technical enzymes which usually expected to be cheaper if compared with the prices of the other used enzymes (e.g. those used in the medicinal applications) put another load on the scientist and the R/D sectors in the companies to satisfy the consumer demand and to face the competitions from other possible chemical alternatives. In most cases, using cheap substrate(s) will be the solution as a first choice. Then it is the turn of the product optimization. This is usually requested in case of the first penetration to the market or when the company capital is still small. However, certain limit of quality should be maintained. Successful companies never stop improving their products. The consumers have sharp sense about what is going on. Enzymes of high quality are always preferred. It is important also to map the consumers demand. This will lead to inovate new enzymes and new products. The imagination of the researchers "even they are also consumers" could not sense everything. In some countries, the consumers have a fear of using genetically modified enzymes. They also have fear of food or products which have been manipulated with genetically modified enzymes. Some ethnic groups forbid certain products. Many aspects should be considered for the best of the productions, the consumers comfortable, the cost and the profit, the quality etc. All those aspects will be direct us to choice between wild and recombinant microbes or we need to go to the protein engineering level? Or we still have better alternatives in the nature!

References

Abendroth, J., M.S. McCormick, T.E. Edwards, B. Staker, R. Loewen, M. Gifford, J. Rifkin, C. Mayer, W. Guo, Y. Zhang, P. Myler, A. Kelley, E. Analau, S.N. Hewitt, A.J. Napuli, P. Kuhn, R.D. Ruth, L.J. Stewart 2010. X-ray structure determination of the glycine cleavage system protein H of *Mycobacterium tuberculosis* using an inverse Compton synchrotron X-ray source. *J Struct Funct Genomics*., 11: 91-100.

Akarsu, H., W.P. Burmeister, C. Petosa, I. Petit, C.W. Muller, R.W. Ruigrok and F. Baudin. 2003. Crystal structure of the M1 protein-binding domain of the influenza A virus nuclear export protein (NEP/NS2). *EMBO J*., 22: 4646-4655.

Alahuhta, M., M. Salin, M.G. Casteleijn, C. Kemmer, I. El-Sayed, K. Augustyns, P. Neubauer, R.K. Wierenga. 2008. Structure-based protein engineering efforts with a monomeric TIM variant: the importance of a single point mutation for generating an active site with suitable binding properties. *Protein Eng Des Sel*., 21: 257-266.

Amara A.A. and S.R. Salem. 2010. Logical and experimental design for phenol degradation using immobilized *Acinetobacter sp*. Culture. *IIUM Engineering J.* Vol. 11, No. 1, 2010. 98-104.

Amara, A.A. 2003. PhD. Thesis. Biochemical and Molecular Characterization of PHA synthases from *Pseudomonas aeruginosa*, *Ralstonia eutropha*, *Aeromonas punctata* as well as of the (*R*)-3-hydroxyacyl-ACP:CoA transacylase from *Pseudomonas putida*. Münster University- Schüling Verlag-(2005).Germany.

Amara, A.A. 2008. Polyhydroyalkanoates: from Basic Research and Molecular Biology to Application. *IIUM Engineering J.* 9, No. 1: 37-73.

Amara, A.A. 2011. Experimental design for simultaneous production of PHB mesophilic proteases and lipases. *IIUM Engineering J.* 12(2):155-184.

Amara, A.A. and B.H. Rehm. 2003. Replacement of the catalytic nucleophile cysteine-296 by serine in class II polyhydroxyalkanoate synthase from *Pseudomonas aeruginosa*-

mediated synthesis of a new polyester: identification of catalytic residues. *Biochem J.*, 374(2):413-421.

Amara, A.A. and B.H.A. Rehm. 2003. Replacement of the catalytic nucleophile cysteine-296 by serine in class II polyhydroxyalkanoate synthase from *Pseudomonas aeruginosa*-mediated synthesis of a new polyester: identification of catalytic residues". *Biochem. J.* vol. 1; 374(Pt 2): pp. 413-21, 2003.

Amara, A.A., A. Steinbüchel and B.H.A. Rehm. 2002. *In vivo* evolution of the *Aeromonas punctata* polyhydroxyalkanoate (PHA) synthase: Isolation and characterization of modified PHA synthases with enhanced activity. *Appl. Microbiol. Biotechnol.*, 59:477-482.

Amara, A.A., B.H.A. Rehm., A. Steinbüchel. 2001. Biopolymer overproduction by new mutants using simple methods for selection. In DAAD-Bioforum-Berlin "Grenzenlos forschen" *DAAD Biotechnologische Methoden* 231-239.

Amara, A.A., E.A. Serour. 2008. Wool quality improvement using thermophilic crude proteolytic microbial enzymes. *American-Eurasian J. Agric. Environ. Sci.,* 3 (4): 554-560.

Amara, AA. and H. Moawad. 2011. PhaC synthases and PHA depolymerases: the enzymes that produce and degrade plastic. *IIUM Engineering J.* 12(4):21-37.

Anfinsen, C. 1972. The formation and stabilization of protein structure. *Biochem. J.,* 128 (4): 737-749.

Anthea, M., J. Hopkins, C.W. McLaughlin, S.J. Maryanna, Q. Warner, D. LaHart, J.D. Wright. 1993. Human Biology and Health. Englewood Cliffs, New Jersey, USA: Prentice Hall.

Arulmuthu, E, D. Williams, H. Versteeg 2009. The arrival of genetic engineering. *IEEE Eng. Med. Biol. Mag.*, 28(1):40-54.

Bai, Y., H. Feng and Z. Zhou. 2007. Population and structure determination of hidden folding intermediates by native-state hydrogen exchange-directed protein engineering and nuclear magnetic resonance. *Methods Mol. Biol.*, 350: 69-81.

Baker, M. 2011. Protein engineering: navigating between chances and reason. *Nature Methods.* 8:623-626.

Ball, P. 2008. Complexity crystallised: Protein x-ray crystallography has come a long way from a 12 year search for the structure of a single protein. *Chemistry World* 50-56.

Baum. C., C. Kalle,, F.J.T. Staal, B. Fehse, M. Schmidt, F. Weerkamp, S. Karlsson, G. Wagemaker, D.A. Williams. 2004. Chance or necessity? Insertional Mutagenesis in Gene Therapy and Its Consequences. *Molecular Therapy.*, 9(1):5-13.

Beese, L.S. and T.A. Steitz. 1991. Structural basis for the 39-59 exonuclease activity of *Escherichia coli* DNA polymerase I: a two metal ion mechanism. *EMBO J.*, 10:25–33.

Bennett, E.J., J. Bjerregaard, J.E. Knapp, D.A. Chavous, A.M. Friedman, W.E. Royer, Jr., C.M. O'Connor. 2003. Catalytic implications from the Drosophila protein L-isoaspartyl methyltransferase structure and site-directed mutagenesis. *Biochem.,* 42:12844-12853.

Best, R.B., S.B. Fowler, J.L. Herrera, A. Steward, E. Paci, J. Clarke. 2003. Mechanical unfolding of a titin Ig domain: structure of transition state revealed by combining atomic force microscopy, protein engineering and molecular dynamics simulations. *J. Mol. Biol.,* 330: 867-877.

Boeris, V., B. Farruggia, D. Romanini, G. Pico. 2009. How flexible polymers interact with proteins and its relationship with the protein separation method by protein-polymer complex formation. *Protein J.*, 28: 233-239.

Bordoli L, F. Kiefer, K. Arnold, P. Benkert, J. Battey, T. Schwede. 2009. Protein structure homology modeling using SWISS-MODEL workspace. *Nat Protoc.*, 4: 1-13.

Branningan, J.A. and A.J. Wilkinson 2002. Protein engineering 20 years on, *Nature Rev. Mol. Cell Biol.,* 3:964-970.

Brautigam, C.A. and T.A. Steitz. 1998. Structural principles for the inhibition of the 39-59 exonuclease activity of *Escherichia coli* DNA polymerase I by phosphorothioates. *J. Mol. Biol.,* 277: 363–377.

Brode, P.F., C.R. Erwin, D.S. Rauch, B.L. Barnett, J.M. Armpriester, E.S.F. Wang, D.N. Rubingh. 1966. Subtilisin BPN' variants: increased hydrolytic activity on surface-bound substrates via decreased surface activity. *Biochem.,* 36:3162-3169.

Calderone V. 2004. Practical aspects of the integration of different software in protein structure solution. *Acta. Crystallogr. D. Biol. Crystallogr.,* 60: 2150-2155.

Calderone, V., M. Trabucco, A. Vujicic, R. Battistutta, G.M. Giacometti, F. Andreucci, R. Barbato and G. Zanotti. 2003. Crystal structure of the PsbQ protein of photosystem II from higher plants. *EMBO Rep.*, 4: 900-905

Caraglia1, M., G. Vitale., M. Marra, S. Del Prete, A. Lentini, A. Budillon, S. Beninati and A. Abbruzzese 2004. Translational and post-translational modifications of proteins as a new mechanism of action of Alpha-Interferon: Review article *Amino Acids.*, 26: 409–417.

Cavasotto, C.N., A.J. Orry, N.J. Murgolo, M.F. Czarniecki, S.A. Kocsi, B.E. Hawes, K.A. O'Neill, H. Hine, M.S. Burton, J.H. Voigt, R.A. Abagyan, M.L. Bayne, F.J. Monsma, Jr. 2008. Discovery of novel chemotypes to a G-protein-coupled receptor through ligand-steered homology modeling and structure-based virtual screening. *J. Med. Chem.,* 51: 581-588.

Chappell, J.D., A.E. Prota, T.S. Dermody, T. Stehle. 2002. Crystal structure of reovirus attachment protein sigma1 reveals evolutionary relationship to adenovirus fiber. *EMBO J.*, 21: 1-11.

Chen X., Z. Shi 2009. Sequence Analysis of the Full-length cDNA and Protein Structure Homology Modeling of FABP2 from *Paralichthys Olivaceus. Bioinform. Biol. Insights,* 3: 29-35.

Chen, Q.L., X.S. Tang, W.J. Yao, S.Q. Lu. 2009. Bioinformatics analysis of the complete sequences of cytochrome b of *Takydromus sylvaticus* and modeling the tertiary structure of encoded protein. *Int. J. Biol. Sci.,* 5: 596-602.

Chen, Y., W. Tan, X. Lu, Y. Lu, S. Qin, S. Li, Y. Zeng, H. Bu, Y. Li and J. Cheng. 2007. Full-length cDNA cloning and protein three-dimensional structure modeling of porcine prothrombin. *Blood Cells Mol. Dis.,* 38: 93-99.

Chiang, S-J. 2004. Strain improvement for fermentation and biocatalysis processes By genetic engineering technology. *J Ind. Microbiol. Biotechnol.,* 31:99–108.

Chie, L., D. Chung, M.R. Pincus. 2005. Specificity of inhibition of ras-p21 signal transduction by peptides from GTPase activating protein (GAP) and the son-of sevenless (SOS) ras-specific guanine nucleotide exchange protein. *Protein J.* 24: 253-258.

Chie, L., F.K. Friedman, T. Duncan, J.M. Chen, D. Chung, M. Pincus. 2004. Loop domain peptides from the SOS ras-guanine nucleotide exchange protein, identified from molecular dynamics calculations, strongly inhibit ras signaling. *Protein J.* 23: 229-234.

Choi, S.B., Y.M. Normi and H.A. Wahab. 2009. Why hypothetical protein KPN00728 of *Klebsiella pneumoniae* should be classified as chain C of succinate dehydrogenase? *Protein J.* 28: 415-427.

Christendat, D., V. Saridakis, Y. Kim, P.A. Kumar, X. Xu, A. Semesi, A. Joachimiak, C.H. Arrowsmith, A.M. Edwards. 2002. The crystal structure of hypothetical protein MTH1491 from *Methanobacterium thermoautotrophicum. Protein Sci.* 11: 1409-1414.

Costa, M.H., W. Quintilio, O.A. Sant'Anna, A. Faljoni-Alario and P.S. de Araujo 2002. The use of protein structure/activity relationships in the rational design of stable particulate delivery systems. *Braz. J. Med. Biol. Res.,* 35: 727-730.

Cowan, D. 1996. Industrial enzyme technology. *Trends Biotechnol.* 14 (6): 177-178.

Crameri A, Raillard SA, Bermudez E, Stemmer WP (1998. DNA shuffling of a family of genes from diverse species accelerates directed evolution. *Nature,* 391: 288-291.

Crisman, R.L. and T.W. Randolph. 2009. Refolding of proteins from inclusion bodies is favoured by a diminished hydrophobic effect at elevated pressures. *Biotechnol. Bioeng.* 102(2):483-492.

Abd-El-haleem, D., A.A. Amara, S. Zaki, A. Abuelhamd, G. Abuelreesh. 2007. Biosynthesis of biodegradable polyhydroxyalkanotes biopolymers in genetically modified yeasts. *Int. J. Environ. Sci. Tech.* 4 (4): 513-520.

Dana, C.D., D.R. Bevan, B.S. Winkel. 2006. Molecular modeling of the effects of mutant alleles on chalcone synthase protein structure. *J. Mol. Model.* 12: 905-914.

Degim, I.T. and N. Çelebi. 2007. Controlled Delivery of Peptides and Proteins *Curr. Pharm. Des.* 13: 99-117.

Du, X., J. Cheng, J. Song 2009. Improved prediction of protein binding sites from sequences using genetic algorithm. *Protein J.* 28: 273-280.

Edelheit O, Hanukoglu A, Hanukoglu I 2009. Simple and efficient site-directed mutagenesis using two single-primer reactions in parallel to generate mutants for protein structure-function studies. *BMC Biotechnol.* 9: 61.

Ellrott, K., J.T. Guo, V. Olman and Y. Xu. 2007. Improvement in protein sequence-structure alignment using insertion/deletion frequency arrays. *Comput. Syst. Bioinformatics Conf.* 6: 335-342.

Erie, D.A., T.D. Yager and P.H. von-Hippel 1992. The single-nucleotide addition cycle in transcription: A biophysical and biochemical perspective. *Annu. Rev. Biophys. Biomol. Struct.* 21: 379–415.

Ermakova-Gerdes, S., S. Shestakov and W. Vermaas. 1996. Random chemical mutagenesis of a specific psbDI region coding for a lumenal loop of the D2 protein of photosystem II in Synechocystis sp. PCC 6803. *Plant Molecular Biology.* 30:243-254.

Evdokimov, A.G., M. Mekel, K. Hutchings, L. Narasimhan, T. Holler, T. McGrath, B. Beattie, E. Fauman, C. Yan, H. Heaslet, R. Walter, B. Finzel, J. Ohren, P. McConnell, T. Braden, F. Sun, C. Spessard, C. Banotai, L. Al-Kassim, W. Ma, P. Wengender, D. Kole, N. Garceau, P. Toogood and J. Liu. 2008. Rational protein engineering in action: the first crystal structure of a phenylalanine tRNA synthetase from *Staphylococcus haemolyticus. J. Struct. Biol.* 162: 152-169.

Feinberg H, J.C. Uitdehaag, J.M. Davies, R. Wallis, K. Drickamer, W.I. Weis 2003. Crystal structure of the CUB1-EGF-CUB2 region of mannose-binding protein associated serine protease-2. *EMBO J.* 22:2348-2359.

Fieulaine S, S. Morera, S. Poncet, V. Monedero, V. Gueguen-Chaignon, A. Galinier, J. Janin, J. Deutscher, S. Nessler. 2001. X-ray structure of HPr kinase: a bacterial protein kinase with a P-loop nucleotide-binding domain. *EMBO J.* 20: 3917-3927.

Flaman, A.S., J.M. Chen, S.C. Van Iderstine, D.M. Byers. 2001. Site-directed mutagenesis of acyl carrier protein (ACP) reveals amino acid residues involved in ACP structure and acyl-ACP synthetase activity. *J. Biol. Chem.* 276: 35934-35939.

Fowler, S.B., R.B. Best, J.L. Toca Herrera, T.J. Rutherford, A. Steward, E. Paci, M. Karplus and J. Clarke. 2002. Mechanical unfolding of a titin Ig domain: structure of unfolding intermediate revealed by combining AFM, molecular dynamics simulations, NMR and protein engineering. *J. Mol. Biol.* 322: 841-849.

Freemont, P.S., J.M. Friedman, L.S. Beese, M.R. Sanderson and T.A. Steitz 1988. Cocrystal structure of an editing complex of Klenow fragment with DNA. *Proc. Natl. Acad. Sci. USA.* 85: 8924–8928.

Fukunishi, Y. and H. Nakamura. 2008. Prediction of protein-ligand complex structure by docking software guided by other complex structures. *J. Mol. Graph. Model.* 26:1030-1033.

Gaudier, M., Y. Gaudin and M. Knossow. 2002. Crystal structure of vesicular stomatitis virus matrix protein. *EMBO J.*, 21: 2886-2892.

Glickman, B.W. and Radman, M. 1980. *Escherichia coli* mutator mutants deficient in methylation-instructed DNA Mismatch correction. *Proc. Natl. Acad. Sci. USA.* 77:1063-1067.

Goodenough, P.W. 1995. A Review of Protein Engineering for the Food Industry. *Molecular Biotechnology.* 4:151-166.

Greener, A., Callahan, M., Jerpseth, B. 1997. An Efficient Random Mutagenesis Technique Using an *E. coli* Mutator Strain. *Molecular biotechnology.* 7: 189-195.

Gupta, R., Beg, Q.K., Khan, S., Chauhan, B. 2002a. An overview on fermentation, downstream processing and properties of microbial alkaline proteases. *Appl. Microbiol. Biotechnol.* 60:381-395.

Gupta, R., Q.K. Beg, Lorenz, P. 2002b. Bacterial alkaline proteases: molecular approaches and industrial applications. *Appl. Microbiol. Biotechnol.* 59:15-32.

Guzmán, F., S. Barberis and A. Illanes. 2006. Peptide synthesis: chemical or enzymatic *Electronic Journal of Biotechnology*, 0717-3458.

Han, K.D., S.J. Park, S.B. Jang and B.J. Lee. 2008. Solution structure of conserved hypothetical protein HP0892 from *Helicobacter pylori*. *Proteins.* 70: 599-602.

Han, K.D., S.J. Park, S.B. Jang, W.S. Son and B.J. Lee. 2005. Solution structure of conserved hypothetical protein HP0894 from *Helicobacter pylori*. *Proteins.* 61: 1114-1116.

Harris, A. 1992. Cystic fibrosis gene. *British Medical Bulletin.* 48:738-753

Hartely, H. 1951. Origin of the word 'Protein'. *Nature.* 168:244.

Hattori, M., E. Mizohata, M. Manzoku, Y. Bessho, K. Murayama, T. Terada, S. Kuramitsu, M. Shirouzu and S. Yokoyama. 2005. Crystal structure of the hypothetical protein TTHA1013 from *Thermus thermophilus* HB8. *Proteins.* 61: 1117-1120.

Hedstrom L 2001. Enzyme specificity and selectivity. *Encyclopedia of life science* 1-7.

Herrmann, T., P. Guntert and K. Wuthrich. 2002a. Protein NMR structure determination with automated NOE-identification in the NOESY spectra using the new software ATNOS. *J. Biomol. NMR*. 24: 171-189.

Herrmann, T., P. Guntert and K. Wuthrich. 2002b. Protein NMR structure determination with automated NOE assignment using the new software CANDID and the torsion angle dynamics algorithm DYANA. *J. Mol. Biol.* 319: 209-227.

Ho, Y., J.C. Hsiao, M.H. Yang, C.S. Chung, Y.C. Peng, T.H. Lin, W. Chang and D.L. Tzou 2005. The oligomeric structure of vaccinia viral envelope protein A27L is essential for binding to heparin and heparan sulfates on cell surfaces: a structural and functional approach using site-specific mutagenesis. *J. Mol. Biol.* 349: 1060-1071.

Hoffmann, N., A.A. Amara, Br.B. Beermann, Q. Qi, H.J. Hinz and B.H.A. Rehm. 2002. Biochemical characterization of the *Pseudomonas putida* 3-hydroxyacyl ACP:CoA transacylase which diverts intermediates of fatty acid *de novo* biosynthesis. *J. Biol. Chem.* 277: 42926-42936.

Holmes, M.A., F.S. Buckner, W.C. Van Voorhis, C. Mehlin, E. Boni, T.N. Earnest, G. DeTitta, J. Luft, A. Lauricella, L. Anderson, O. Kalyuzhniy, F. Zucker, L.W. Schoenfeld, W.G. Hol and E.A. Merritt 2006. Structure of the conserved hypothetical protein MAL13P1.257 from Plasmodium falciparum. *Acta. Crystallogr. Sect. F. Struct. Biol. Cryst. Commun.* 62: 180-185.

Holmwood, G. and M. Schindler. 2009. Protein structure based rational design of ecdysone agonists. *Bioorg. Med. Chem.* 17: 4064-4070.

Hu, F., Y. Cao, F. Xiao, J. Zhang, H. Li. 2007. Site-directed mutagenesis of *Aeromonas hydrophila* enoyl coenzyme A hydratase enhancing 3-hydroxyhexanoate fractions of poly(3-hydroxybutyrate-co-3-hydroxyhexanoate). *Curr Microbiol.* vol. 55(1) pp. 20-24, 2007.

Hutchison, C.A., S. Phillips, M.H. Edgell, S. Gillam, P. Jahnke and M. Smith. 1978. Mutagenesis at a specific position in a DNA sequence. *J. Biol. Chem.*, 253 (18): 6551-6560.

Ifuku K, Nakatsu T, Kato H, Sato F 2004. Crystal structure of the PsbP protein of photosystem II from *Nicotiana tabacum. EMBO Rep.* 5: 362-367.

Ikeda, R.A. and C.C. Richardson. 1986. Interactions of the RNA polymerase of bacteriophage T7 with its promoter during binding and initiation of transcription. *Proc. Natl. Acad. Sci. USA.*, 83: 3614–3618.

Ito, S., T. Kobayashi, K. Ara, K. Ozaki, S. Kawai and Y. Hatada. 1998. Alkaline detergent enzymes from alkaliphiles: enzymatic properties, genetics, and structures. *Extremophiles.* 2:185-190.

Jang, S.B., A.R. Kwon, W.S. Son, S.J. Park and B.J. Lee. 2009. Crystal structure of hypothetical protein HP0062 (O24902_HELPY) from Helicobacter pylori at 1.65 A resolution. *J. Biochem.* 146: 535-540.

Kan, C.C. 2002. Impact of recombinant DNA technology and protein engineering on structure-based drug design: case studies of HIV-1 and HCMV proteases. *Curr. Top. Med. Chem.* 2: 247-269.

Kao, S.L., S.S. Chong and C.G.L. Lee. 2000. The Role of Single Nucleotide Polymorphisms (SNPs) in Understanding Complex Disorders and Pharmacogenomics. *Ann. Acad. Med. Singapore.* 29:376-82.

Kasrayan, A., M. Bocola, A.G. Sandstrom, G. Laven, J.E. Backvall 2007. Prediction of the *Candida antarctica* lipase A protein structure by comparative modeling and site-directed mutagenesis. *Chembiochem.* 8: 1409-1415.

Kaur, J. and R. Sharma. 2006. Directed evolution : An approach to engineer enzymes. *Critical Review in Biotechnology.* 26:165-199.

Kendrew, J., G. Bodo, H. Dintzis, R. Parrish, H. Wyckoff and D. Phillips 1958. A three-dimensional model of the myoglobin molecule obtained by x-ray analysis. *Nature.* 181 (4610): 662-666.

Kendrew, J.C., G. Bodo, H.M. Dintzis and R.G. Parrish 1958. A three-dimensional model of the myoglobin molecule obtained by x-ray analysis. *Nature.* 181 (4610):662-666.

Kiss, R.S., P.M. Weers, V. Narayanaswami, J. Cohen, C.M. Kay and RO Ryan. 2003. Structure-guided protein engineering modulates helix bundle exchangeable apolipoprotein properties. *J. Biol. Chem.* 278: 21952-21959.

Kurgan,. L. 2008. On the relation between the predicted secondary structure and the protein size. *Protein J.* 27, 234-239.

Lai JR, Koglin A, Walsh CT 2006. Carrier protein structure and recognition in polyketide and nonribosomal peptide biosynthesis. *Biochem.* 45: 14869-14879.

Leuschner, C. and G. Antranikan. 1995. Heat stable enzymes from extremely thermophilic and hyperthermophilicmic microorganisms. *World J. Microbiol. Biotechnol.*, 11: 95-114.

Linderkofler, L.A., R.R. Barton and S.S. Rennert. 1958. Production of microbial enzymes and their applications. *Microbiological Process Report.* 6:212-221.

Lippincott-Schwartz, J. and G.H. Patterson. 2003. Development and use of fluorescent protein markers in living cells. *Science.* 300:87-91.

Liu, J., C. Li and S. Ke, S.D. Satyanarayanajois. 2007. Structure-based rational design of beta-hairpin peptides from discontinuous epitopes of cluster of differentiation 2 (CD2) protein to modulate cell adhesion interaction. *J. Med. Chem.* 50: 4038-4047.

Ludwig, K., B. Baljinnyam, A. Herrmann and C. Bottcher. 2003. The 3D structure of the fusion primed Sendai F-protein determined by electron cryomicroscopy. *EMBO J.* 22: 3761-3771.

Manning, M.C., K. Patel and R.T. Borchordt. 1989. Stability of protein pharmaceuticals. *Pharm. Res.* 6:903-918.

Michel, M.F., F. Zenklusen, D. Müller, B. Muller and D. Schumperli. 2000. Positive and negative mutant selection in the human histone hairpin-binding protein using the yeast three-hybrid system. *Nucleic Acids Research.* 1594-1603.

Milik, M., S, Szalma, K.A. Olszewski. 2003. Common Structural Cliques: a tool for protein structure and function Analysis. *Protein Engineering.* 16(8): 543-552.

Molina, R., A. Gonzalez, M. Stelter, I. Perez-Dorado, R. Kahn, M. Morales, M. Moscoso, S. Campuzano, N.E. Campillo, S. Mobashery, J.L. Garcia, P. Garcia, J.A. Hermoso. 2009. Crystal structure of CbpF, a bifunctional choline-binding protein and autolysis regulator from *Streptococcus pneumoniae*. *EMBO Rep.* 10: 246-251.

Moss, A.J., S. Sharma and N.P.J. Brindle. 2009. Bionanotechnology II: from Biomolecular Assembly to Applications Rational design and protein engineering of Growth factors for regenerative medicine and tissue engineering. *Biochem. Soc. Trans.* 37:717-721.

Muirhead, H. and M. Perutz. 1963. Structure of hemoglobin. A three-dimensional fourier synthesis of reduced human hemoglobin at 5.5 A resolution". *Nature* 199 (4894): 633-638.

Munson, M., R. O'Brien, J.M. Sturtevant and L. Regan. 1994. Redesigning the hydrophobic core of a four-helix-bundle protein. *Protein Sci.* 3 (11): 2015-2022.

Nada, V. and R.L. Koder. 2010. Designing artificial enzymes by intuition and computation. *Nature Chemistry.* 2:15-24.

Nicolini, C. and E Pechkova. 2006. Structure and growth of ultrasmall protein microcrystals by synchrotron radiation: I. microGISAXS and microdiffraction of P450scc. *J. Cell. Biochem.* 97: 544-552.

Nielsen, F.S., J. Sauer, J. Backlund, B. Voldborg, K. Gregorius, S. Mouritsen and T. Bratt. 2004. Insertion of foreign T cell epitopes in human tumor necrosis factor alpha with minimal effect on protein structure and biological activity. *J. Biol. Chem.* 279: 33593-33600.

Nishijima, K. 2005. [Attitude of pharmaceutical company toward protein structure analysis]. *Tanpakushitsu Kakusan Koso.* 50: 862-868.

O'Maille P.E., M. Bakhtina and M.D. Tsai. 2002. Structure-based combinatorial protein engineering (SCOPE) *J. Mol. Biol.* 321: 677-691

O'Maille, P.E., M.D. Tsai, B.T. Greenhagen, J. Chappell and J.P. Noel 2004. Gene library synthesis by structure-based combinatorial protein engineering. *Methods Enzymol.* 388: 75-91.

Ozbek, S., J. Engel and J. Stetefeld. 2002. Storage function of cartilage oligomeric matrix protein: the crystal structure of the coiled-coil domain in complex with vitamin D(3). *EMBO J.* 21: 5960-5968.

Parker, J.S., S.M. Roe, D. Barford. 2004. Crystal structure of a PIWI protein suggests mechanisms for siRNA recognition and slicer activity. *EMBO J.* 23: 4727-4737.

Platt, O.S. and J.F. Falcone. 1988. Membrane Protein Lesions in Erythrocytes with Heinz Bodies *J. Clin. Invest.* 82:1051-1058.

Poza, M, A.B. Sestelo, J.M. Ageitos, J.A. Vallejo, P. Veiga-Crespo, T.G. Villa. 2007. Cloning and expression of the XPR2 gene from *Yarrowia lipolytica* in *Pichia pastoris. J. Agric. Food Chem.* 55:3944-3948.

Procopiou, A, N.M. Allinson, G.R. Jones and D.T. Clarke. 2004. Estimation of protein secondary structure from synchrotron radiation circular dichroism spectra. *Conf. Proc. IEEE Eng. Med. Biol. Soc.* 4: 2893-2896.

Quine, J.R., T.A. Cross, M.S. Chapman and R. Bertram 2004. Mathematical aspects of protein structure determination with NMR orientational restraints. *Bull. Math. Biol.* 66: 1705-1730.

Rao, M., A. Tankasale, M. Ghatge and V. Desphande. 1998. Molecular and biotechnological aspects of microbial proteases. *Microbiol. Mol. Biol. Rev.* 62: 597-634.

Rehm, B.H.A., R.V. Antonio, P. Spiekermann, A.A. Amara and A. Steinbüchel 2002. Molecular characterization of the poly (3-hydroxybutyrate) (PHB) synthase from *Ralstonia eutropha: in vitro* evolution, site-specific mutagenesis and development of a PHB synthase protein model. *Biochim. Biophys. Acta.* 1594:178-190.

Sanger, F. and E.O. Thompson 1953a. The amino-acid sequence in the glycyl chain of insulin. I. The identification of lower peptides from partial hydrolysates *Biochem. J.* 53(3):353-366.

Sanger, F. and E.O. Thompson. 1953b. The amino-acid sequence in the glycyl chain of insulin. II. The investigation of peptides from enzymic hydrolysates. *Biochem. J.* 53(3):366-374.

Satyanarayana, T., C. Raghukumar and S. Shivaji. 2005. Extremophilic microbes: Diversity and perspectives. *Current Science.* 89 (1): 78-90.

Schäfer, T., O. Kirk, T.V. Borchert, C.C. Fuglsang, S. Pedersen, S. Salmon, H.S. Olsen, R. Deinhammer and H. Lund 2005. Enzymes for Technical Applications. In: Biopolymers,eds Fahnestock S.R. and A. Steinbüchel Chapter 13, pp. 377-437, Wiley VCH Editor.

Schmid, A., J.S. Dordick, B. Houer, A. Kienes, M. Wubbolts, B. Witholt. 2001. Industrial biocatalysis today and tomorrow. *Nature.* 409:258-268

Shen, S., G. Hu and J.A. Tuszynski 2007. Analysis of protein three-dimension structure using amino acids depths. *Protein J.* 26: 183-192.

Sørenson, H.P. 2010. Towards universal system for recombinant gene expression. *Microbial Cell Factories* 9:27.

Standley, D.M., A.R. Kinjo, K. Kinoshita and H. Nakamura 2008. Protein structure databases with new web services for structural biology and biomedical research. *Brief. Bioinform.* 9: 276-285.

Strausberg, S.L., P.A. Alexander, D.T. Gallagher, G.L. Gilliland, B.L. Barnett, P.N. Bryan. 1995. Directed evolution of a subtilisin with calcium-independent stability. *Bio-Technol.,* 13:669-673.

Sueda, S., M.N. Islam and H. Kondo. 2004. Protein engineering of pyruvate carboxylase: investigation on the function of acetyl-CoA and the quaternary structure. *Eur. J. Biochem.* 271: 1391-1400.

Sugimoto, I., Z, Li, S, Yoshitome, S, Ito, E, Hashimoto. 2004. Mass-spectrometric identification of binding proteins of Mr 25,000 protein, a part of vitellogenin B1, detected in particulate fraction of *Xenopus laevis oocytes. Protein J.* 23, 467-473.

Tandang, M.R., N. Atsuta, N. Maruyama, M. Adachi and S. Utsumi. 2005. Evaluation of the solubility and emulsifying property of soybean proglycinin and rapeseed procruciferin in relation to structure modified by protein engineering. *J. Agric. Food Chem.* 53: 8736-8744.

Thangam, E.B. and G.S. Rajkumar. 2002. Purification and characterization of alkaline protease from *Alcaligenes faecalis. Biotechnol. Appl. Biochem.* 35:149-154.

Thore, S. F. Mauxion, B. Seraphin and D. Suck. 2003. X-ray structure and activity of the yeast Pop2 protein: a nuclease subunit of the mRNA deadenylase complex. *EMBO Rep.* 4: 1150-1155.

Timsit, Y., F. Allemand, C. Chiaruttini and M. Springer. 2006. Coexistence of two protein folding states in the crystal structure of ribosomal protein L20. *EMBO Rep.* 7: 1013-1018.

Valer, M. 1975. Skin irritancy and sensitivity to laundry detergents containing proteolytic enzymes. Part II. Berufsdermatosen. 23:96-115.

van den Burg, B. 2003. Extremophiles as a source for novel enzymes. *Current Opinion in Microbiology.* 6:213–218.

Vannini, A., C. Volpari, C. Gargioli, E. Muraglia, R. Cortese, R. De Francesco, P. Neddermann and S.D. Marco. 2002. The crystal structure of the quorum sensing protein TraR bound to its autoinducer and target DNA. *EMBO J.* 21: 4393-4401.

Visegràdy, B., N.G. Than, F. Kilàr, B. Sümegi, G.N. Than, H. Bohn. 2001. Homology modelling and molecular dynamics studies of human placental tissue protein 13 (galectine-13). *Protein Engineering.* 14 (11):878-880.

von-Hippel, P.H., D.G. Bear. W.D. Morgan and J.A. McSwiggen. 1984. Protein-nucleic acid interactions in transcription: A molecular analysis. *Annu. Rev. Biochem.* 53:389–416.

Wang, L. and Schultz, P.G. 2002. Expanding the genetic code. *Chem. Commun.* 1:1-11.

Winter, G., A.R. Fersht, A.J. Wilkinson, M. Zoller and M. Smith 1982. Redesigning enzyme structure by site-directed mutagenesis: tyrosyl tRNA synthetase and ATP binding. *Nature.* 299 (5885): 756-758.

Woo, E.J., Marshall, J., Bauly, J., Chen, J.G., Venis, M., Napier, R.M. and Pickersgill, R.W. 2002. Crystal structure of auxin-binding protein 1 in complex with auxin. *EMBO J.* 21: 2877-2885.

Woods, V.L., Jr., Y. Hamuro. 2001. High resolution, high-throughput amide deuterium exchange-mass spectrometry (DXMS) determination of protein binding site structure and dynamics: utility in pharmaceutical design. *J. Cell. Biochem. Suppl. Suppl.* 37: 89-98.

Yan, C., F. Wu, R.L. Jernigan, D. Dobbs and V. Honavar 2008. Characterization of protein-protein interfaces. *Protein J.* 27, 59-70.

Yang, Y-R., H. Zhu, N. Fang, X. Liang, C-Q. Zhong, X-F. Tang, P. Shen and B Tang. 2008. Cold-adapted maturation of thermophilic WF146 protease by mimicking the propeptide binding interactions of psychrophilic subtilisin S41. *FEBS Letters.* 582:2620-2626.

Yao, M., Y. Zhou and I. Tanaka 2006. LAFIRE: software for automating the refinement process of protein-structure analysis. *Acta. Crystallogr. D. Biol. Crystallogr.* 62: 189-196.

Yu P, A. Jonker and M. Gruber 2009. Molecular basis of protein structure in proanthocyanidin and anthocyanin-enhanced Lc-transgenic alfalfa in relation to nutritive value using synchrotron-radiation FTIR microspectroscopy: a novel approach. *Spectrochim. Acta.. A. Mol. Biomol. Spectrosc,* 73: 846-853.

Yu, P., J.J. McKinnon, C.R. Christensen and D.A. Christensen. 2004. Using synchrotron-based FTIR microspectroscopy to reveal chemical features of feather protein secondary structure: comparison with other feed protein sources. *J. Agric. Food Chem.,* 52: 7353-7361.

Yun, M., C.E. Bronner, C.G. Park, S.S. Cha, H.W. Park and S.A. Endow. 2003. Rotation of the stalk/neck and one head in a new crystal structure of the kinesin motor protein, Ncd. *EMBO J.,* 22: 5382-5389.

In: Applications of Microbial Genes in Enzyme Technology ISBN: 978-1-62417-808-5
Editors: V.K.Gupta, M.G.Tuohy, G.D.Sharma et al.

Chapter 18

Advancement on Bacterial Enzyme Technology for Industries: Research And Application of Novel Biocatalysts

Héctor A. Cristóbal*[1], Carlos M. Abate[1,2], Alicia G. Cid[3,4] and Verónica B. Rajal[3,4]

[1]Planta de Procesos Industriales y Microbiológicos (PROIMI), CONICET, San Miguel de Tucumán, Tucumán, Argentina

[2]Facultad de Bioquímica, Química y Farmacia, Universidad Nacional de Tucumán, San Miguel de Tucumán, Tucumán, Argentina

[3]Instituto de Investigaciones para la Industria Química, Universidad Nacional de Salta (INIQUI, UNSa - CONICET), Salta, Argentina

[4]Facultad de Ingeniería, Universidad Nacional de Salta, Salta, Argentina

Abstract

A wide range of novel enzymes for biocatalysts adapted to industrial processes has been obtained from extremophile microorganisms. Marine environments possess an enormous microbial biodiversity and potential sources of many biological compounds for the development of exploitable biotechnology. The demand of biocatalysts adapted to extreme conditions (low or high temperatures, acidic or basic pH and high salt concentration) increases in the industry. The enzyme industry worldwide is valued at US $5.1 billion and it is predicted to show an annual increase in demand of 63%. Advances in biotechnology, coupled with growing scientific developments, promise technological innovations in a wide range of biotechnological applications for industries, which will be beyond estimation. Many fields of biotechnological studies need to understand the natural mechanisms in biological systems to use this information towards an integrated analysis of genes or proteins expression. In nature, as well as during industrial processes, bacteria

* Corresponding author, current affiliation: Instituto de Investigaciones para la Industria Química, Universidad Nacional de Salta (INIQUI, UNSa - CONICET), Av. Bolivia 5150. (CP. 4400) Salta, Argentina, e-mail: hacristobal@gmail.com.

are exposed to changes in environmental physico-chemical parameters, which may impair their growth or survival.

In this chapter, we focus the studies on *Shewanella* sp. G5, a psychrotolerant bacterium, which exhibits three β-glucosidases. Two of these isozymes were classified under the glycosyl hydrolase families 1 and 3, encoded by *bgl-A* (EF141823) and *bgl* (DQ136044) genes. These β-glucosidases may be of interest for winemaking and citrus juice technology processing at low temperatures. The identification of proteins or genes and its expression patterns under different growth conditions (carbon source, culture media and temperature) were studied by proteome analyses. Two-dimensional gel electrophoresis was performed and whole protein pattern of *Shewanella* sp. G5 revealed that 59 and 55 proteins spots were induced by cellobiose and glucose, respectively. Proteomic analyses showed that *Shewanella* sp. G5 re-organizes its metabolism in response to all the variables assayed, indicating expression of housekeeping and specific proteins for a particular condition. Determinate proteins spots expression showed increases, which allowed elucidating the quantitative changes relevant in the levels of gene expression. The identification of these proteins spots suggested that different master regulation schemes are involved in response to glucose and cellobiose carbon sources, and were compared with genome sequence data available for *Shewanella oneidensis*. These results allowed us to establish the optimum growth conditions for production of β-glucosidases, taking into account the greatest induction.

Introduction

Importance of Studies on Diversity of Marine Bacteria as Sources for Novel Enzymes

Marine environments have an enormous microbial biodiversity and therefore potential for the discovery of exploitable biotechnological resources. In fact, a wide range of new enzymes for biocatalytic processes has been obtained from cultured marine bacteria (Kennedy *et al.*, 2008, Kirchman, 2000). These microorganisms are important sources of various biological compounds, such as enzymes and metabolites that are useful for industrial processes. The demand of biocatalysts adapted to extreme conditions (low or high temperatures, acidic or basic pH and high salt concentration) increases in the industry (Alvarenga *et al.*, 2011, Cristóbal *et al.*, 2011a). Therefore, production of biotechnologically relevant enzymes from extremophile microorganisms has become a challenging task in recent years (Khudary *et al.*, 2010). Nowadays, many research institutes and companies have established collections of organisms from various extreme environments (e.g. soils, seawater, hot springs, Antarctic ice, alkaline lakes, etc.), yielding a variety of enzymes that catalyze reactions under normal or extreme conditions (Lee *et al.*, 2010; Groudieva *et al.*, 2004).

The extremophile life has contributed to challenge our understanding of physiology, biochemistry, biology and evolution. A great diversity of new extremophile organisms is being found by culture-dependent methods, providing a large amount of biotechnological applications. Recently, novel culturing approaches, environmental genome sequencing and whole genome sequencing have provided new opportunities for the biotechnological exploration of extremophiles (Cavichiolli *et al.*, 2002).

Cold-adapted microorganisms (psychrophilic or psychrotolerant) and ectothermic organisms constantly living in cold habitats exhibit enzymes adapted to the surrounding conditions in the environment, which often show higher catalytic activity at low and moderate temperatures and lower thermostability as opposed to their mesophilic and thermophilic counterparts (Hoyoux *et al.,* 2004, Groudieva *et al.,* 2004, Khudary *et al.,* 2010). Antarctic microorganisms may be a valuable source of cold-active enzymes. The study of their cold-active enzymes is not only of greatly biological value, but also of an important practical value due to their potential for food industry applications (Vazquez *et al.,* 2008). Indeed, cold-active enzymes have generated considerable interest, since they have potential to improve the efficiency of industrial processes and offer economic benefits through energy saving because there is no need for expensive heating steps (Gerday *et al.,* 2000, Cristobal *et al.,* 2009; 2011b). Besides, cold-active enzymes provide good reaction yields, have an elevated level of stereo specificity, minimize undesired chemical reactions that can occur at higher temperatures and can be inactivated thermally if required (Cavichiolli *et al.,* 2002).

Over the past years advances in biotechnology, coupled with growing scientific developments, have proffered promises of technological innovation in a wide array of biotechnological applications for industries, which will be beyond estimation. To maximize this potential, several researches are aimed at the search for novel biocatalysts with specific properties to be applied for the development of products. In this way, biotechnology plays a major role in several world-leading biotechnological companies, specifically covering food, pharmaceutical and chemical industries (Margesin *et al.,* 2005).

Current Use of Technology for Quantification of Gene or Protein Expression

To take advantage of the bioresources potential, several traditional methods and molecular techniques, such as cultures (-dependent and –independent), cloning and sequencing, clone libraries, 454 pyrosequencing, two-dimensional gel electrophoresis with immobilized pH gradients and mass spectrometry are employed to identify genes and proteins from various environments (Kennedy *et al.,* 2010; Görg *et al.,* 2009). Many fields in biology researches need to understand the natural mechanisms in biological systems to use this information towards an integrated analysis of genes or proteins expression and access to the biochemical pathways. Enzyme complexes and cofactors involved in the synthesis, assimilation or degradation pathways of a particular compound are regulated by induction or repression of the genes that encode them. The knowledge of these pathways is indispensable to develop models of cellular functions and physiology. Such models would be supported by quantitative information through the availability of the capture and expression of genes, proteins and metabolites. To characterize gene function on a genome-wide scale, reliable and rapid methods to quantify gene expression levels are required.

The analysis of protein or gene expression is essential to our knowledge in biological research; therefore several methods to measure proteins and transcript RNA abundance are important and frequently applied. Two-dimensional gel electrophoresis (2-DE) with immobilized pH gradients (IPGs) combined with protein identification by mass spectrometry (MS) is currently the workhorse for proteomics (Görg *et al.,* 2004, 2009). Microarrays are a powerful tool for monitoring gene expression changes under different conditions tested and have been widely used for genome-wide transcriptional analyses. Microarrays allow the parallel analysis of thousands of genes in two differential RNA populations; from this approach, and with oligonucleotides of different lengths, they are used for monitoring gene expression at a whole genome level (He *et al.,* 2005). On the other hand, real-time reverse transcription PCR (qRT-PCR) has been accepted as one of the most powerful and sensitive techniques to analyze gene expression, since it allows accurate quantitative detection of mRNA levels (Sellars *et al.,* 2007, Ellefsen *et al.,* 2008). In this case, qRT-PCR provides the simultaneous measurement of gene expression in many different conditions for a limited number of genes, and it is especially appropriate when there are a small number of cells (Sellars *et al.,* 2007, Liu *et al.,* 2009). The quantitative PCR (qPCR) has become a popular technology for quantifying gene expression levels used on both relative and absolute scales (Livak and Schmittgen, 2001, Nolan *et al.,* 2006).

Now it is possible to replace synthetic catalysts by biocatalyst in manufacturing processes to reduce costs. This is due to the interest in the search, study and capture of functional genes that encode a specific biocatalyst that catalyse a key step in an industrial process. Monitoring of gene expression changes in cell, tissue or organisms is very important to know the behaviour or plasticity of the genome under different conditions. From these approaches on transcriptional analyses we can obtain a lot of information, such as gene functions, gene interactions, and specificity in the expression of a gene, applicable to cancer studies, neuroscience, drug targets and environmental studies. From the studies of genetic expression it is expected to obtain information of the complex regulatory pathways and to identify key genes that are relevant to new biological processes or implicated in the specific metabolism of drugs, disease or environmental cases.

Biotechnological Significance

Biotechnology has experienced an important growth since scientific breakthroughs in molecular biology and genetics have occurred and continues to develop at breakneck speed. The sector is witnessing practical implementation of these scientific discoveries in virtually every aspect of human activity. Such efforts have resulted in novel products and technologies in medicine, energy, merchandise, food and environmental applications. Industrial biotechnology refers to the application of the advantages of biology and its combination with technology for industrial purposes. Thus, organisms or their products, such as bacteria, yeast, fungi, molds, animal cells, plant cells, insect cells, enzymes and metabolites from various sources, are used with the main objective of manufacturing various final products. In many of the industrial applications, the biological products are engineered with the tools of modern biotechnology (Kenedy *et al.,* 2008, 2010).

Driven by the increasing industrial demand for biocatalysts that can cope with industrial process conditions, considerable efforts have been devoted to the search for such enzymes. The enzyme industry worldwide is valued at U$S 5.1 billion and it has predicted to show an annual increase in demand of 63% and, specially enzymes used for animal feed processing and ethanol production are envisaged to have increased demand (Sarethy *et al.,* 2011). Also, enzymes show many applications, such as in detergents (34%), foods (27%), agriculture and feeds (16%), textiles (10%) and leather, chemicals and pulp and paper (10%) industries (Demain and Dana, 2007).

With all that in mind, microorganisms capable of surviving in extreme environments, such as extremophiles, constitute a valuable source of novel enzymes, and their characterization has received a great deal of attention, notwithstanding the fact that to date more than 3,000 different enzymes have been identified and many of them have found their way into biotechnological and industrial applications (Burg Van Den, 2003, Feller and Gereday, 2003). Several industrial microbial enzymes play important roles in modern biotechnology, improving or even replacing previously-existing processes (Cristóbal *et al.,* 2011a). Actually, many companies, such as Novozymes and Genencor, successfully produce native and genetically modified cold-active enzymes, like celluloses, xylanases, lipases, proteases, and other enzymes from bacteria and filamentous fungi, used in the manufacture of different products, including foods and detergents (Wang *et al.,* 2008). Current applications of cold-active enzymes are economically essential in numerous industrial processes (Cavichiolli *et al.,* 2002, Cristóbal *et al.,* 2008), including the manufacture of cheese, animal feed, leather, indigo and linen, vinegar, beer, wine and fruit juice, chemicals and biopolymers (Egorova *et al.,* 2005). All these processes relied on either enzymes produced by spontaneously growing microorganisms or enzymes present in added preparations such as calves' rumen or papaya fruit (Kirk *et al.,* 2002, Cristóbal *et al.,* 2008).

Table 1. Biotechnology applications of cold-active enzymes and metabolites*

Enzymes or Metabolites	Applications	Examples of producing organisms
Uracil-DNA-glycosylase; Alkaline phosphatase, RNA polymerase, DNA polymerase, DNA, ligase	Molecular biology	*Pseudomonas syringae*, *Cenarchaeum symbiosum*, *Pseudomonas haloplanktis*, *Gadus morthua*
Proteases	Meat industry (meat tenderizing), contact-lens cleaning solutions	*Pseudomonas strain* DYA; *Aerpyrum pernix* K1; *Pseudomonas, Shewanella, Colwellia, Psychrobacter* species
Polyunsaturated fatty acids	Food additives and dietary supplements	
β-Galactosidase	Lactose hydrolysis in milk products	*Arthrobacter* sp. SB
Amylases	Detergents and bakery	*Nocardiopsis* sp.; *Aureobasidium pullulans* N13d
Cellulases	Detergents, animal feed processing, textile industry (biopolishing and stone-washing processes), alcohol production	*Pseudoalteromonas haloplanktis*; *Pseudoalteromonas* sp. DY3; *Fibrobacter succinogenes; Teredinibacter turnerae* T7902T; *Marinobacter* sp. MSI032.
Xylanases	Food, feed, pulp, baking and paper industries, wine and juice industry (quality- and yield-improving agents)	*Cryptococcus adeliae*; *Pseudoalteromonas haloplanktis*
Chitinases	Food, health products	*Arthrobacter* sp. TAD20; *Rhodothermus marinus*
Dehydrogenases	Biosensors, biotransformations	
Lipases	Detergents and cosmetics; fermented food, cheese manufacture, beer treatment, biotransformation reactions in fine chemical processes	*Pseudoalteromonas haloplanktis* TAC 125; *Apergillus nidulans; Aureobasidium pullulans* HN2.3
Esterases	Cosmetics, pharmaceutics	*Vibrio* sp.*; Pseudoalteromonas haloplanktis, Streptomyces coelicolor* A3
Alcohol dehydrogenase	Asymmetric chemical synthesis	*Moraxella* sp. TAE 123, Psychrophilic bacterium PA-43
β-Glucosidase, α-rhamnosidase, pectinase	Wine and fruit juice industries	*Shewanella* sp. G5, *Aspergillus niger*

Table 1. (Continued)

Enzymes or Metabolites	Applications	Examples of producing organisms
Proteases, lipases, cellulases and amylases	Detergents	
Lipases and esterases	As additives in laundry detergents and as catalysts for the organic syntheses	*Moraxella* sp. strain TA144, *Pseudomonas* sp. B11-1, *Acinetobacter* sp. 6
Ice nucleating proteins	Artificial snow, ice cream, other freezing applications in the food industry	
Ice minus microorganisms	Frost protectants for sensitive plants	
Other enzymes (e.g. oxidases)	Bioremediation, environmental biosensors	*Shewanella onaedensis*
Various enzymes	Modifying flavours	
Other metabolites (e.g. bacteriocin)	Control agent against pathogenic bacteria	*Serratia proteamaculans* 136

* Data from Burg, 2003, Cavicchioli *et al.*, 2002, Satyanaraya *et al.*, 2005, Kennedy *et al.*, 2008, 2010 and Cristóbal *et al.*, 2009.

The thermostable enzymes market, especially of the cold-adapted ones, has led to an increase of their search due to the industrial processes requests. These enzymes afford significant advantages at the level of their specific activity, lower stability and unusual specificity. Some of their most common applications are shown in Table 1 (Gereday *et al.*, 2000, Satyanarana *et al.*, 2005). Cold-active enzymes are of extraordinary interest not only at the basic level to investigate the thermodynamic stability of proteins, but also to understand the relationship between stability, flexibility or plasticity and their catalytic efficiency (Pakchung *et al.*, 2006).

Microbial enzymes occupy a high up position in modern biotechnology, optimizing or even replacing processes that already existed. The majority of the industrial enzymes known to date have been obtained from bacteria and filamentous fungi. Kennedy *et al.* (2008) described marine environments as "blue biotechnology" or exploitable biotechnology that represents a widespread pool of microbial biodiversity for the discovery of new enzymes for specific biocatalysts process. At present there are a wide variety of products which are obtained from various marine organisms, such as bacteria, filamentous fungi, algae, etc. (Kennedy *et al.*, 2010).

On the other hand, an entire branch of biotechnology, referred to as "white biotechnology" (Schepens, 2003), where enzymes or microorganisms are used for the sustainable production of chemicals, biopolymers, materials and fuels from renewable resources, offers great opportunities for the chemical and pharmaceutical industries. White biotechnology has several objectives, being one of the most important the reduction of wastes, energy input and raw material to improve environmentally friendly processes (Ergova *et al.*, 2005). It also centers on the bioproduction of fuels and chemicals from renewable sources (Colin *et al.*, 2011). The continued depletion of nonrenewable fuel resources is a major problem that entangles our planet today and demand immediate solutions. Besides, economic, environmental and geopolitical issues are critical in the continued interest seen in renewable energy sources (Atsumi *et al.*, 2008). For biofuels, delicate optimization, and fine tuning of these processes to maximize productivity and yield is of particular concern, since the viability of any biofuel process is extremely sensitive to factors related to both raw material supply and production costs (Colin *et al.,* 2011).

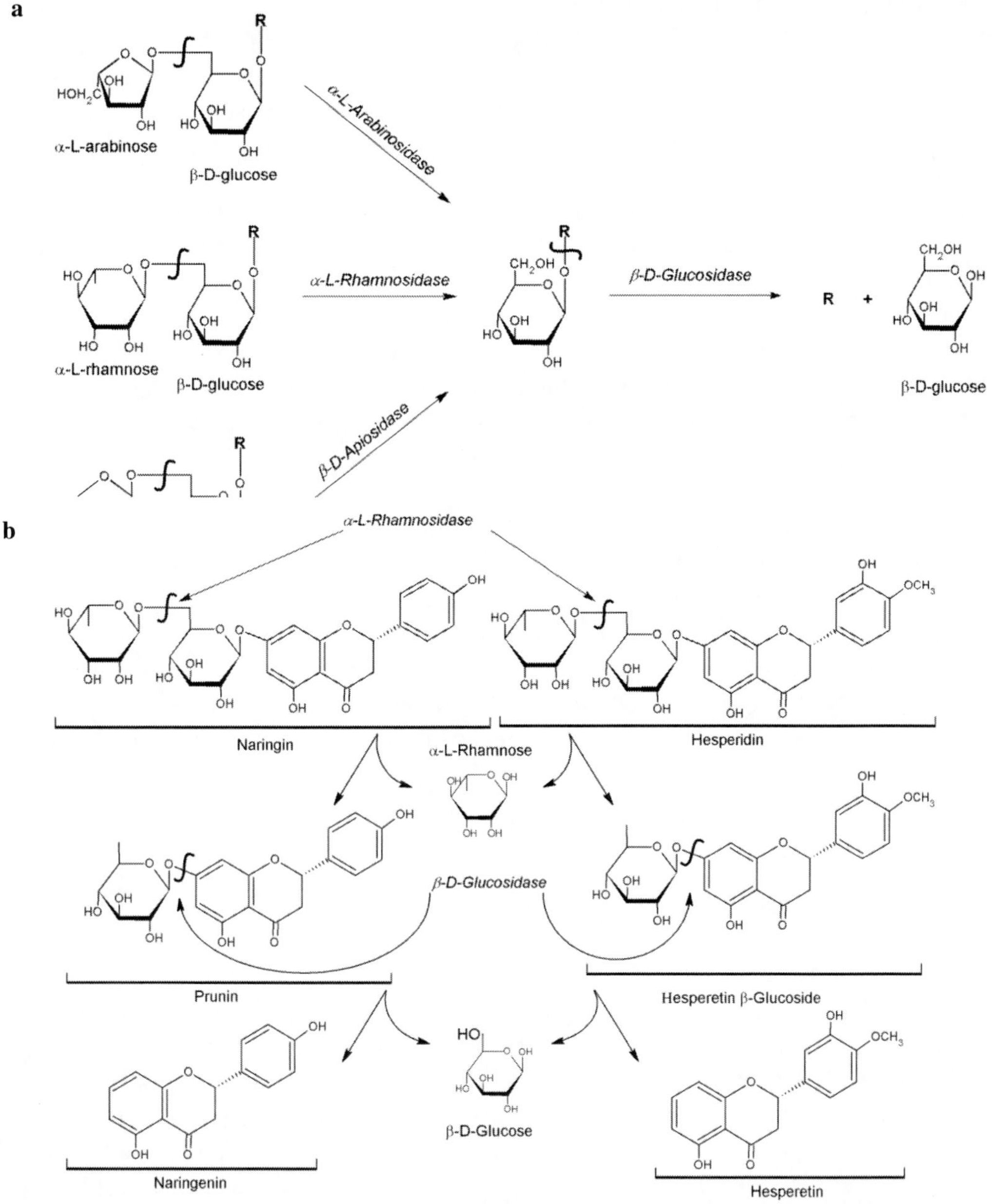

Figure 1. Sequential mechanism of glycosidases: (a) The enzymatic mechanism that releases aromatic compounds present in grapes occurs in two sequential steps: first α-L-rhamnosidase, β-D-apiosidasa or α-L-arabinosidase hydrolyzes the inter-sugar bond and then β-glucosidase releases the aglycone. R= monoterpenes, sesquiterpenes, norisoprenoids, benzene derivatives, aliphatic alcohols (Palmeri *et al.,* 2007, Conde *et al.,* 2007). (b) In citrus juices, α-L-rhamnosidas and β-glucosidase sequentially hydrolyze glycosidic flavonoids (e.g., Naringin and Hesperidin), increasing the sweet taste and releasing aglycones with antioxidant and anti-inflammatory activities (Garcia *et al.,* 1997).

Wine and Citrus Industries

Currently, food industry has shown increasing interest in enzymes, and the enological sector has especially focused its attention on pectinase and glycosidases (Bathia *et al.,* 2002, Palmieri *et al.,* 2007). Winemaking and citrus juice technology have focused its interest on glycosidases from commercial exogenous enzymes to optimize biotechnological processes. This is because glycosidases promote the release of wine aroma compounds through a hydrolysis mechanism of the aroma glycosidic precursors (e.g. terpene glycosides), that are responsible for the varietal character of many grapes (Barbagallo *et al.,* 2004). Winemaking is a biotechnological process in which the use of exogenous enzyme preparations from yeasts, filamentous fungi or bacteria helps to overcome the problem of insufficient activities of endogenous enzymes from grapes (Palmieri *et al.,* 2007). Consequently, commercial preparations of glycosidases produced by *Aspergillus niger*, which is a GRAS (generally recognized as safe) microorganism, are used to increase wine aroma (Spagna *et al.,* 2000, Palmieri *et al.,* 2007). The most important glycosides showing this aroma precursor characteristic are *O*-β-D-glucosides and the *O*-diglycosides: α-L-arabino-β-D-glucosides, α-L-rhamno-β-D-glucosides or α-D-apio-β-D-glucosides. The mechanism of enzymatic hydrolysis of glycosides occurs sequentially in two stages (Fig. 1a): in the first step, the inter-sugar bond is cleaved by α-L rhamnosidase (Rha, EC 3.2.1.40), α-L arabinosidase (Ara, EC 3.2.1.55) or β-D-apiosidase (Palmieri *et al.,* 2007). In the second stage, β-glucosidase (βG, EC 3.2.1.21) hydrolyzes the remaining glucoside releasing the aglycone, directly responsible for wine aroma (Barbagallo *et al.,* 2004). The Rha and βG combination can be also utilized in citrus-juice technology (Fig. 1b), in particular in the debittering of juices, by the way of naringin or hesperidin hydrolysis (Orillo *et al.,* 2007, Spagna *et al.,* 2005), and it can also be applied in food processing to increase the aroma of fruit juices such as those from passion fruit, apple, apricot, peach, tomato, pineapple, cherry, pear, papaya, banana, among others (Spagna *et al.,* 2000, Iwashita *et al.,* 1999).

Glycosyl Hydrolases Enzymes

The biological plasticity of glycosyl hydrolases is a consequence of the variety of β-glucosidic substrates that they can hydrolyze from disaccharides such as cellobiose up to other glycosides. Three categories of cellulases; endoglucanases, exoglucanases, and βG, are produced by living organisms for the degradation of insoluble cellulose (Salohemio *et al.,* 2002). βG plays an important role in the flavor of fruits, wine and sweet potato by the release of monoterpene alcohols such as linalool, α-terpeneol, citronellol, nerol, and geraniol (Spagna *et al.,* 2005, Barbagallo *et al.,* 2004, Iwashita *et al.,* 1999). Supplementation with βG from external sources may enhance aroma release, thus benefiting, for example, the winemaking process (Bathia *et al.,* 2002). The hydrolytic activity of βG allows its use in the medical field as antitumoral agent, in biomedical research and in the food industry.

The βGs are a constitutive homogeneous group of enzymes that occur in several organisms, performing different functions. In bacteria and filamentous fungi, βGs are part of the cellulase system catalyzing the final step in its degradation, and in xylan hydrolysis, both plant polymers (Faure, 2002, Murray *et al.,* 2004). On the basis of amino acid similarity, βGs have been divided into two Glycosyl Hydrolase Families (GHFs), 1 and 3 (Bourne *et al.,*

2001, Tsukada *et al.,* 2006), and both families hydrolyze their substrate with a net retention of configuration of the anomeric carbon (Murray *et al.,* 2004). In addition, Cournoyer *et al.* (2003) remarked that the need for biochemical and physiological studies of microbial βGs was emphasized by the prevalence of open reading frames (ORFs) homologous to genes encoding GHF 1 and 3 enzymes in the majority of genomes analyzed.

The cold-active enzymes offer potential economic benefits, as they play an important role in modern biotechnology, e.g. through substantial energy saving in large-scale processes that otherwise would require expensive heating of reactors (Cristóbal *et al.,* 2009). *Shewanella* sp. G5, a psychrotolerant and Gram negative bacterium, was isolated from the intestine of *M. subrrugosa* and two cold-active βGs produced by this microorganism (EF141823 and DQ136044) were previously characterized (Cristóbal *et al.,* 2008).

Proteomic Studies

Electrophoresis separations are widely used for identifying proteins in different chemical and biological researches. 2-DE is a method used to investigate and separate mixtures of proteins according to their isoelectric point (*pI*), molecular mass (*Mr*), solubility, and relative abundance (Molloy, 2000, Görg *et al.,* 2004, Marengo *et al.,* 2003). There is a long history of the application of 2-DE, for example in medical, clinical, biological, genetic or toxicological research, which is reflected in several publications during the last 30 years (Görg *et al.,* 2009). This approach is widely chosen since it can be routinely applied for parallel quantitative expression profiling of large sets of complex protein mixtures from samples with different treatments (Di Ciero *et al.,* 2004). Thus, the comparison of 2-DE profiles between the control and treated samples allows identifying specific proteins that are expressed and involved in complex metabolisms (Marengo *et al.,* 2003). The differences might be often due not only to the absence or presence of some proteins, but also due to subtle changes in their relative amounts (Görg *et al.,* 2004, Marengo *et al.,* 2003).

A proteome analysis of cell extracts, using any method, is technically challenging because different proteins are expressed in the range of several thousand under determined experimental or biological conditions. Moreover, current proteomic studies have revealed that the majority of identified proteins are abundant housekeeping proteins, whereas proteins such as receptor molecules that are present in much lower concentrations are usually not detected (Görg *et al.,* 2004). Therefore, 2-DE provides widespread results, which allow the resolution of hundreds of new or constitutive proteins and reveal even very small changes in the expression of different proteins patterns (Khoudoli *et al.,* 2004). Depending on the gel size and pH gradient used, 2-DE can resolve more than 5000 proteins simultaneously and detect and quantify even 1 ng of protein per spot (Görg *et al.,* 2004). Proteome analysis of soluble and whole cell proteins also represents a suitable tool to highlight variations in gene expression. This technique produces a 2-DE map that consists of a series of spots (protein) spread over the surface of the final polyacrylamide gel. Furthermore, 2-DE maps reflect changes in protein expression levels or its post-translational modifications (Marengo *et al.,* 2003). The 2-DE technology, which introduces immobilized pH gradients (IPGs) for isoelectric focusing (IEF) in the first dimension and SDS-PAGE in the second one, allows a quantitative and qualitative separation of complex protein mixtures typically found in cellular extracts from living organisms (Molloy, 2000, Görg *et al.,* 2009). Both methods, IEF and SDS-PAGE, are critically affected by the solubility of proteins prior to electrophoresis. Proteins can only be analyzed by 2-DE if they are kept in solution or solubilized during the entire process (Di Ciero *et al.,* 2004, Budin-Verneuill *et al.,* 2005). The complexity of the method arises from the expression of thousands of proteins from a cell, and the reproducibility of 2-DE gels depends on several experimental factors, such as the polymerization conditions, sample preparation, running conditions of the 2-DE gel, and the small differences which often characterize controls and treated samples (Marello *et al.,* 2003, Schmid *et al.,* 2005).

The proteome comparisons are obtained from cultures grown under different media conditions (variable factors introduced for the study of protein expression), and this analysis has become possible by high-resolution proteins electrophoresis gels. Therefore, proteins expressed in a cell with higher or lower expression can be identified giving the differential expression pattern under the assayed conditions. In addition, the identification of proteins extracted from a gel is possible for any organism, for which the entire genome encoding the proteins has been sequenced. In our studies, the combination of 2-DE gel electrophoresis and Mass Spectroscopy (ESI-MS; LCQ Deca XP, Thermo) (Lottspeich *et al.,* 1998) or MALDI-TOF (matrix-assisted laser desorption ionization time of flight) (Görg *et al.,* 2004, Wang *et al.,* 2003) was used to study the differential expression of genes from the psychrotolerant *S. oneidensis* (Kolker *et al.,* 2005), allowing the identification of proteins by similarity to those whose genome sequence is known (Chinnasamy *et al.,* 2006). The proteomic changes of *Shewanella* sp. G5 were analyzed for cultures grown at low temperature in the presence of cellobiose or glucose. The enzyme β-glucosidase was used as a marker to indicate proteome re-arrangement and to elucidate environmentally relevant expression profiles.

Sample Preparation

Shewanella sp. G5 was isolated from the benthonic organism *M. subrrugosa* collected on the coast of the Beagle Channel, Ushuaia, Argentina (Cristóbal *et al.,* 2008, 2011a). To determine the expression of different proteins by studying proteomic changes by 2-DE gel electrophoresis, *Shewanella* sp. G5 was cultivated in 1 l flasks containing 300 ml Luria-Bertani medium with 10 g/l cellobiose (LBC) or glucose (LBG) on an orbital shaker at 15°C. The main difference in the performed cultures was the carbon source, glucose (monosaccharide) or cellobiose (disaccharide), established by the β-1,4 bound in the second carbon source. Later, sub-cellular protein fractions were obtained by differential centrifugation (Kong *et al.,* 1994). After obtaining proteins in the supernatant, cells were suspended in 5 ml of distilled water and disrupted by French Press (SLM Instruments) at 25,000 psi. Cell debris was removed, and cytoplasmic proteins were separated by ultra-centrifugation into soluble cytoplasmic proteins (SCP) and membrane proteins (MP) fractions (Cristóbal *et al.,* 2009). As indicated by the different isozymes of β-glucosidase induced by cellobiose in *Shewanella* sp. G5, which are encoded by two genes *bgl-A* and *bgl* previously determined (Cristóbal *et al.,* 2008), proteome re-arrangement can be expected due to growth on different carbon sources. Both cultures were treated at the same time to avoid external changes in the proteomic profile of the cell. However, it is important to mention that our studies did not evaluate the effect of drastic changes to the cell, such as a metal bioremediation or UV exposure, which usually produce a noticeable change in the expression of different proteins. In these assays it is important to remember that each of the treatments was evaluated in the same way. In our study, the cytosolic proteins of *Shewanella* sp. G5 were precipitated (20% trichloracetic acid, 50% acetone, 20 mM dithiothreitol (DTT)) for 30 min at 20°C, then incubated for 2 h at 4°C and centrifuged at 11,000 rpm. After a two-step acetone wash the pellet was dried (SpeedVac) and re-dissolved in rehydration buffer (8 M urea, 2 M thiourea, 4% 3-[(3-cholamidopropyl) dimethyl-ammonio]-1-propane-sulfonate (CHAPS), 40 mM DTT). After ultracentrifugation at 75,000×*g*, proteins were quantified (Bradford, 1976) and then put in contact with each IEF strip in presence of the rehydration buffer (Schmidt *et al.,* 2005). Cellular protein extracts were solubilized efficiently using the rehydratation buffer, which contained two chaotropes (thiourea and urea), a reducing agent (DTT) and a detergent (CHAPS), increasing the protein spots and allowing to obtain few horizontal streaks (Fig. 2).

According to Chinnasamy *et al.* (2006), the efficiency of solubilization of the rehydratation buffer on the acidic and basic proteins extracted from samples is crucial to produce 2-DE gels with high resolution, quality and higher number of detectable proteins. Therefore, the composition of the buffer allows efficiently dissolving acidic and basic proteins. While the buffer containing two chaotropes (urea and thiourea), two detergents (CHAPS and N-decyl-N,N-dimethyl-3-ammonio-1-propanesulfonate, SB3), two reducing agents (DTT and tris-2-carboxyethyl-phosphine hydrochloride, TCEP-HCl) and two types of ampholyte carriers (BioLyte pH 4–6 and pH 3–10) solubilized acidic proteins in the pH range between 4 and 7, the buffer made up of urea, thiourea, CHAPS and DeStreak reagent solubilized basic proteins in the pH range between 6 and 11. It is important to mention that, during 2–DE, an unspecific oxidation of thiol groups from proteins can occur, especially at pH > 7. In the resulting 2-DE map this is seen as horizontal streaking and extra spots. Therefore, the transformation of the thiol-groups into a stable disulphide by a reagent (i.e. DeStreak) prevents unspecific oxidation. The preparation of Immobiline DryStrip with this reagent will result in 2–DE maps with reduced streaking between spots in the pH range from 7 to 9. It will also simplify the spot pattern as it reduces the number of spots caused by oxidation of proteins.

First Dimension (IEF)

The original IPG-Dalt or IEF protocol, based on 2-DE, was described by Görg *et al.* (1988, 2000 and 2004). The first dimension of IEF is performed in individual IPG gel strips cast on GelBond PAGfilmPAGfilm of wide pH range and length. The IPGs dry strips can be linear (L) or nonlinear (NL) (Görg *et al.,* 2000), with a wide variety of pH range between pH 2.5 and 12, and therefore it can be cast in different pH ranges: wide (e.g. IPG 3–12 or 3-10), medium (e.g. IPG 4–7) and low (e.g. IPG 4.5–5.5). Besides that, dry strips are available in different sizes, usually from 3 mm wide and up to 7 and 24 cm long. In addition, a variety of commercial IPG dry strips allow better comparison of results and have contributed to the widespread application of 2-DE in proteomics. These dry strips can now be purchased from different suppliers (Görg *et al.,* 2004). The samples can be applied either by cup-loading or by in-gel rehydration. IPG-IEF has been simplified by using an integrated IPGphor system (Görg *et al.,* 1999), where rehydration with sample solution and IEF can be performed in a one-step procedure. After IEF, the IPG strips are equilibrated with SDS buffer in the presence of urea, glycerol, DTT and iodoacetamide. This last alkylated sulfhydryl groups prevents their reoxidation, and therefore this step is highly recommended for subsequent spot identification by MS. After equilibration, the IPG strips are applied onto the surface of horizontal or vertical SDS-PAGE gels for the second-dimension (Görg *et al.,* 2009). It is important to take into account that approximately up to 20% of the proteins are lost during equilibration step, which is primarily due to adsorption of proteins to the IPG gel matrix, insufficient equilibration times and wash-off effects. These proteins probably are located near the surface of the IPG strip and are lost during the very first minutes of equilibration. The IPGs, based on 2-DE, have overcome the former limitations of ampholyte carrier in regards to reproducibility, handling, resolution, and separation of very acidic and/or basic proteins. The development of IPGs between pH 2.5–12 has enabled the analysis of very alkaline proteins and the construction of the corresponding databases (Görg *et al.,* 2004). In our study, the first dimension separation of proteins by isoelectric points was conducted with IPG Immobiline DryStrip pH 3–10 NL of 18 cm (Amersham Biosciences). IEF strips were rehydrated for 12 h at 20°C with 450 ml rehydration buffer containing 500 mg proteins and 3 ml 4% bromophenol blue for each sample. IEF was carried out in an IPGphor system (Amersham Biosciences) using the following steps: S1 300 V (15min), S2 500 V (30 min), S3 1000 V (1 h), S4 3000 V (1 h) and S5 8000 V (7 h). Afterward, the strip was equilibrated with 6 M Urea, 4% SDS (w/v), 30% glycerol (v/v), 1% DTT (w/v) and 3.3% bromophenol blue (w/v) at room temperature (RT) for 15 min. Subsequently, the strip was re-equilibrated with the same solution except for the addition of 4% iodoacetamide at RT for 15 min (Schmidt *et al.,* 2005).

Second Dimension

An optimal 2-DE gel, with the maximum number of well-resolved and detectable protein spots, is critical for obtaining a comprehensive view of a proteome. As mentioned in Sample Preparation, the proteins were efficiently solubilized in the rehydratation buffer with which we obtained better 2-DE gels with few horizontal streaks in the pH range 3–7. Previously, gels with poor resolution, few spots and horizontal bands were obtained, however eliminating sample salts and improving protein concentration and buffer composition allowed optimizing the performance of the first dimension. SDS PAGE can be carried out on horizontal or vertical systems, but the horizontal setups are ideally suitable for ready-made gels, whereas vertical systems are preferred for multiple runs in parallel, in particular for large-scale proteome analysis, which are required for simultaneous electrophoresis of batches of second dimension SDS-PAGE gels for maximal reproducibility (Görg *et al.,* 2004). To carry out our study, the second dimension SDS-PAGE (Ettan DALTsix Large Vertical System, Amersham Biosciences) was performed with strips sealed with 0.8 % agarose in the top of 1.5 mm of a 26 cm × 20 cm vertical 10% PAGE in a SE-600 system (Hoefer SE600). Electrophoresis was performed in the presence of 181.66 g Tris–HCl pH 8.8, 30 g glycine and 4 g SDS with constant voltage (600 V) followed by constant amperage (400 mA/gel) at 5°C for 16 h or until the bromophenol blue reached the bottom of the gel. Afterwards, gels were rinsed with distilled water for 5 min and fixed overnight in 10 ml 85% phosphoric acid, 20 ml methanol and 79 ml distilled water. The gels were stained with Coomassie brilliant blue (Roti-Blue

20%, Roth) for 12 h at RT and then discolored with glycine and methanol for 24 h (Schmidt *et al.*, 2005). In our study, the results showed the overall 2-DE pattern of protein extracts from cellobiose and glucose *Shewanella* sp. G5 cultures (Fig. 2). The total intra-cellular proteins extracts from *Shewanella* sp. G5 were resolved on 2-DE gels and 59 and 55 protein spots were induced by cellobiose (Fig. 2a) and glucose (Fig. 2b), respectively. Among the two conditions evaluated, taking into account the carbon source and low temperature of growth, a high number of protein spots were detected in both gels. It is important to note that determinate protein spots presented major intensity in the cellobiose culture samples; a portion of the gel images is shown in Figs. 2c and 2d. The protein spots 1 to 7 obviously regulated over expression and were selected to be identified. Finally, this identification was carried out using MS workflow methods. All results illustrated that intra-cellular proteins were significantly changed after supplementing with carbon source the cell culture (Cristobal *et al.*, 2009).

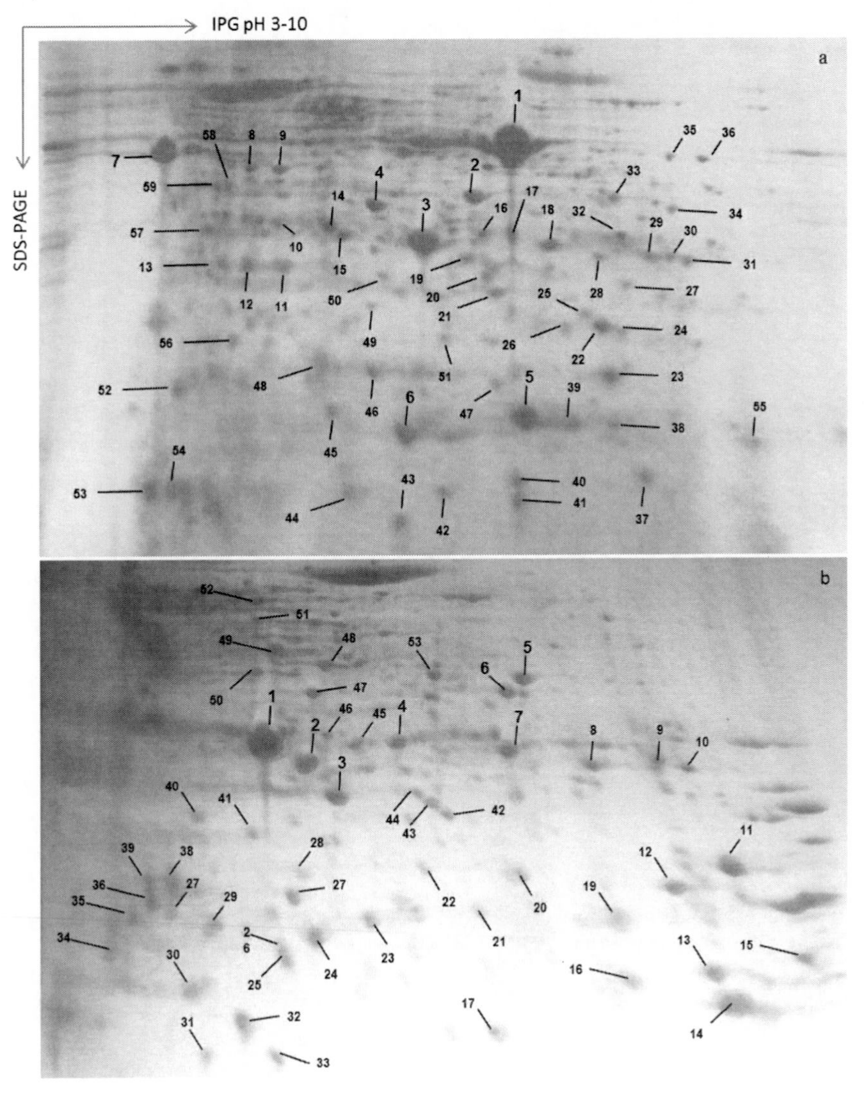

Figure 2. (Continued)

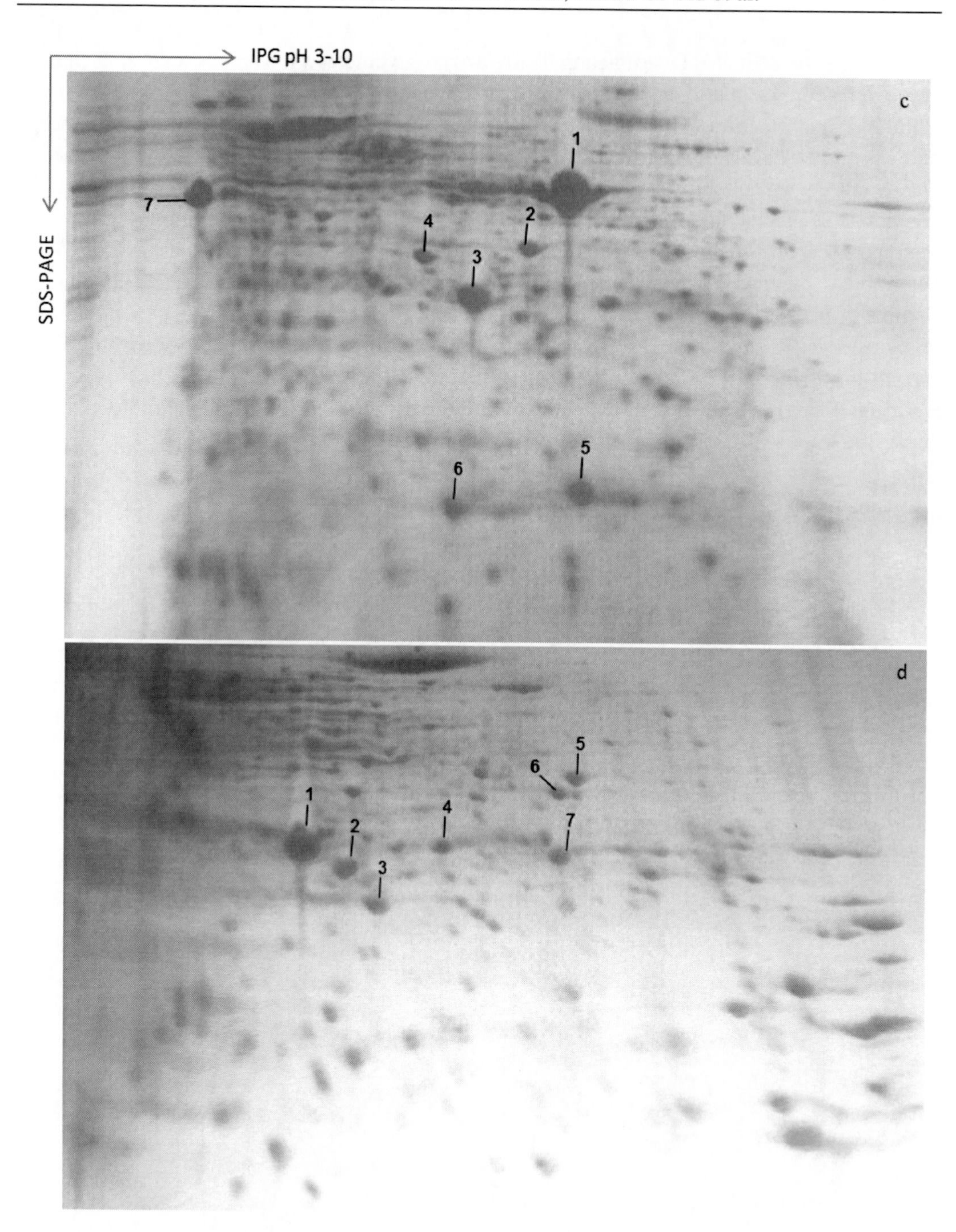

Figure 2. Two-dimensional gel electrophoresis from *Shewanella* sp G5. The protein spots selected for identification in each treatment are indicated in the 2-DE gels. (c) 2-DE gel of intracellular protein from a culture grown at 15ºC on cellobiose; called 1-Ce to 7-Ce spots proteins; (d) 2-DE gel of intracellular protein from a culture grown at 15ºC on glucose; called 1-Glu to 7-Glu protein spots (Cristóbal *et al.*, 2009).

In-Gel Digestion and Mass Spectrometry

Table 2. Role of hypothetical proteins identified in this study by ES-MS from intra-cellular fractions of *Shewanella* sp. G5 grown on cellobiose at 15°C

Putative identification [a]	Locus [b]	*Mr* [c]	*pI* [d]	Cellular Role [e]
L-allo-threonine aldolase	SO_3338	36269.28	5.378	Low-specificity threonine aldolase (TA). This family belongs to pyridoxal phosphate (PLP)-dependent aspartate aminotransferase superfamily (fold I). TA catalyzes the conversion of L-threonine or L-allo-threonine to glycine and acetaldehyde in a secondary glycine biosynthetic pathway.
Immunogenic-related protein	SO_0456	33532.42	8.617	Bacterial periplasmic transport systems use membrane-bound complexes and substrate-bound, membrane-associated, periplasmic binding proteins (PBPs) to transport a wide variety of substrates, such as amino acids, peptides, sugars, vitamins and inorganic ions. PBPs have two cell-membrane translocation functions: substrate binding and interaction with the membrane bound complex.
Conserved hypothetical protein SO4719	SO_4719	29366.60	6.978	Bacterial periplasmic transport systems use membrane-bound complexes and substrate-bound, membrane-associated, periplasmic binding proteins (PBPs) to transport a wide variety of substrates, such as amino acids, peptides, sugars, vitamins and inorganic ions.
Conserved hypothetical protein SO1190	SO_1190	29973.11	6.964	ABC-type Co^{2+} transport system, periplasmic component [Inorganic ion transport and metabolism].
Aerobic respiration control protein	SO_3988	27219.91	5.437	Effector domain of response regulator. Bacteria use two-component signal transduction systems to detect and respond to changes in the environment. The system consists of a sensor histidine kinase and a response regulator.
Ubiquinol-cytochrome c reductase	SO_0608	20904.93	7.965	Iron-sulfur protein (ISP) component of the bc (1) complex family, Rieske domain. This domain is a [2Fe-2S] cluster binding domain involved in electron transfer. The cytochromes bc (1) and b6f complexes are central components in respiration and photosynthesis.
Acetylornithine transaminase	SO_0617	43214.20	5.423	Acetyl ornithine aminotransferase family. This family belongs to pyridoxal phosphate dependent aspartate aminotransferase superfamily. The enzymes act on basic amino acids and their derivatives are involved in transamination or decarboxylation.

[a] Putative protein identified from the database (NC 004347) of *Shewanella oneidensis* MR-1 (Kolker *et al.,* 2005) incorporated into the MS.

[b] Locus of gene encoding the hypothetical protein identified. Data from the NCBI database (http://cmr.jcvi.org/cgibin/CMR/CmrHomePage.cgi).

[c] Mr: Molecular mass.

[d] pI isoelectric point.

[e] Real function of mentioned protein, cellular role in the metabolism of the cell; data from the NCBI database.

Seven prominent spots differentially expressed were analyzed by matrix solution for electron spray ionization Mass Spectroscopy (ESI-MS; LCQ Deca XP, Thermo) (Lottspeich 1998; Görg *et al.,* 2003). For identification of all peptides, the *S. oneidensis* MR-1 (NC 004347) genome was used with Sequest 3.1 (Nealson, 1999, Schmidt *et al.,* 2005, Cristobal *et al.,* 2009). In our study, we selected a total of 59 (Fig. 2a) and 53 (Fig. 2b) spots from cellobiose and glucose extracts, respectively. From NCBI (web site; http://www.ncbi.nlm.nih.gov) and CMP (Comprehensive Microbial Resource, web site; http://cmr.jcvi.org/cgibin/CMR/CmrHomePage.cgi) databases the following proteins were identified: l-allo-threonine aldolase, immunogenic-related protein, hypothetical protein SO4719, hypothetical protein SO1190, aerobic respiration control protein, ubiquinol-cytochrome c reductase, N-succinyldiaminopimelate-aminotransferase, triosephosphate isomerase, S-adenosyl-l-homocysteine hydrolase, thioldisulfide interchange protein, malate dehydrogenase, GroEL like type I chaperonin and chaperone protein DnaK. The main possible cellular roles and characteristics of these identified proteins were described previously (Cristobal *et al.*, 2009) and are shown in Tables 2 and 3.

Table 3. Role of hypothetical proteins identified in this study by ES-MS from intra-cellular fractions of *Shewanella* sp. G5 grown on glucose at 15°C

Putative identification [a]	Locus [b]	*Mr*	*pI*	Cellular Role [c]
Triosephosphate isomerase (TIM)	SO_1200	28072.9 7	5.732	TIM is a glycolytic enzyme that catalyzes the interconversion of dihydroxyacetone phosphate and D-glyceraldehyde-3-phosphate. The reaction is very efficient and requires neither cofactors nor metal ions.
Conserved hypothetical protein SO4719	SO_4719	29366.6 0	6.978	Bacterial periplasmic transport systems use membrane-bound complexes to transport a wide variety of substrates, such as, amino acids, peptides, sugars, vitamins and inorganic ions.
S-adenosyl-L-homocysteine hydrolase	SO_2776	26381.2 1	4.904	AdoHycase catalyzes the hydrolysis of S-adenosyl-L-homocysteine to form adenosine (Ado) and homocysteine (AdoHyc). AdoHycase plays a critical role in the modulation of the activity of various methyltransferases. The enzyme forms homooligomers of 45-50kDa subunits, each binding one molecule of NAD+.
Thiol:disulfide interchange protein (DsbA)	SO_0333	22303.7 0	8.209	DsbA is a monomeric thiol disulfide oxidoreductase protein containing a redox active CXXC motif imbedded in a TRX fold. It is involved in the oxidative protein folding pathway in prokaryotes, and is the strongest thiol oxidant known, due to the unusual stability of the thiolate anion form of the first cysteine in the CXXC motif. The highly unstable oxidized form of DsbA directly donates disulfide bonds to reduced proteins secreted into the bacterial periplasm.
Malate dehydrogenases (MDH)	SO_0770	32137.1 3	5.183	MDH is one of the key enzymes in the citric acid cycle, facilitating both the conversion of malate to oxaloacetate and replenishing levels of oxalacetate by reductive carboxylation of pyruvate. Members of this group are localized to the glycosome and mitochondria
GroEL_like type I chaperonin	SO_0704	57079.3 8	4.559	Chaperonins are involved in productive folding of proteins. With the aid of cochaperonin GroES, GroEL encapsulate non-native substrate proteins inside the cavity of the GroEL-ES complex and promotes folding by using energy derived from ATP hydrolysis.
Chaperone protein DnaK	SO_1126	68861.4 2	4.505	Protein fate: Protein folding and stabilization. Molecular chaperone DnaK

[a] Putative protein identified from the database (NC 004347) of *Shewanella oneidensis* MR-1 (Kolker *et al.*, 2005) incorporated into the MS.

[b] Locus of gene encoding the hypothetical protein identified. Data from the NCBI database (http://cmr.jcvi.org/cgibin/CMR/CmrHomePage.cgi).

[c] Mr: Molecular mass.

[d] pI isoelectric point.

[e] Real function of mentioned protein, cellular role in the metabolism of the cell; data from the NCBI database.

Protein spots digestion was performed in-gel according to Schmidt *et al.* (2005). This in-gel digestion of the selected protein spots was performed by trypsin treatment, which consists in washing the excised spots, air-dried and digestion with 0.02 μg modified trypsin per spot in 50 mM ammonium bicarbonate at 37°C overnight. Peptides were extracted with 60% (v/v) acetonitrile/0.1% (v/v) formic acid in water, thereafter dried in a SpeedVac (Thermo Savant, USA) and dissolved in 10 μl of 0.1% (v/v) formic acid. One μl of the digested sample was added to an equal volume of matrix ESI-MS; LCQ Deca XP.

Gao *et al.* (2006) reported that over 41% of the *S. oneidensis* ORFs encodes hypothetical proteins (Kolker *et al.,* 2005). Little information is available concerning to the impact of cold stress on cellular metabolism at the genomic level. Two published DNA microarray studies of two different cold shocked *Bacillus subtilis* strains revealed a global down-regulation of metabolically relevant proteins. This concept was in agreement with earlier proteomic studies. The available data of known protein sequences of the genome have increased the number and reliability of proteins that can be identified by proteomic studies; 560 proteins have been identified from *Methanococcoides burtonii* cells growing at 4°C, and 44 proteins have been shown to be differentially expressed from *M. burtonii* cells growing at 4 and 23ºC (Cavicchioli, 2004). In addition to being a resource for identifying proteins, the physical organization of genes in the genome sequence has provided insight into associated gene patterns and gene regulation and allowed inference of the function of expressed hypothetical proteins. Many findings from proteomic studies have shown that cold adaptation involves proteins that have an important role in transcription, protein folding, protein transport and metabolism (Goodchild *et al.,* 2004).

Conclusion

β-Glucosidase production by *Shewanella* sp. G5 was studied by proteomic analyses. It was found that the psychrotolerant *Shewanella* sp. G5 produces a substantial re-arrangement and variation of its genetic and protein expression levels. Thus, protein expression could be compared by 2-DE gels, where the alteration of intensity of protein spots in the cellobiose culture samples showed an obviously regulated over expression and these spots were selected to be identified. We determined that in our studies the β-glucosidases are induced by cellobiose, but it was observed a constitutive expression of both genes in the presence of glucose. Finally, the results of this study contribute to the knowledge of proteins expression in bacteria and could establish the basis for optimal conditions for enzyme production. Such efforts will provide avenues for high-throughput screening of new cold-active products and microbial processes with biotechnological potential.

Acknowledgments

The authors gratefully acknowledge to Dr. Erika Kothe from Friedrich-Schiller-Universität, Biologisch-Pharmazeutische Fakultät, Institut für Mikrobiologie, for her help with the proteomics studies. The proteomics assays were financially supported by SeCyT, CONICET (Argentina); and DAAD (Germany). The corresponding author gratefully acknowledge to Dr. Carlos M. Abate for his generosity and unconditional support.

References

Alvarenga, A.E., Cristóba,l H.A. and Abate, C.M. 2011. Cold-Active Enzymes: Potential Use in Biotechnology. *In Advances in Medicine and Biology*, ed. by Berhardt LV, Nova Science Publishers, Inc New York ISBN 978-1-62100-937-5. Vol. 45. *In press*.

Atsumi, S. and J.C. Liao. 2008. Metabolic engineering for advanced biofuels production from *Escherichia coli*. *Curr. Opin. Biotechnol.* 19:414–419.

Barbagallo, R.N., G. Spagna, R. Palmeri, C. Restuccia and P. Giudici. 2004. Selection, characterization and comparison of β-glucosidase from mould and yeasts employable for enological applications. *Enzyme Microb. Technol.* 35:58–66.

Bhatia, Y., S. Mishra and V.S. Bisaria. 2002. Microbial β-glucosidases: cloning, properties, and applications. *Crit. Rev. Biotechnol.* 22:375–407.

Bradford, M. 1976. A rapid and sensitive method for the quantitation of microgram quantities of protein utilizing the principle of protein-dye binding. *Anal. Biochem.* 72:248–254.

Budin-Verneuill, A., V. Pichereau, Y. Auffray, D.S. Ehrlich and E. Maguin. 2005. Proteomic characterization of the acid tolerance response in *Lactococcus lactis* MG1363. *Proteomics* 4794–4807.

Burg Van Den. 2003. Extremophiles as a source for novel enzymes. *Curr. Opin. Microb.* 6:213–218.

Cavicchioli, R., K.S. Siddiqui, D. Andrews, K.R. Sowers. 2002. Low-temperature extremophiles and their applications. *Curr. Opin. Biotechnol.* 13:253–261.

Cavicchioli, R. 2004. A proteomic de termination of cold adaptation in the Antarctic archaeon, *Methanococcoides burtonii*. *Mol. Microbiol.* 53:309-321.

Colin, V.L., A. Rodrıguez and H.A. Cristóbal. 2011. The role of synthetic biology in the design of microbial cell factories for biofuel production. *J. Biomed. Biotechnol.* ID 601834, 9 doi:10.1155/2011/601834.

Cristóbal, H.A., A.E. Alvarenga and C.M. Abate C.M. 2011a. Isolation and molecular characterization of marine bacteria isolated from the Beagle Channel, Argentina. *The Marine Environment: Ecology, Management and Conservation*, ed. by Nova Science Publishers, Inc New York ISBN 978-1-61209-265-2. pp 87-118.

Conde, C., P. Silva, N. Fontes, A.C. Dias, R.M. Tavares, M.J. Sousa, A. Agasse, S. Delrot, H. Gerós. 2007. *Food - Global Science Books.* Biochemical changes throughout grape berry development and fruit and wine quality. pp 1-22.

Cristóbal, H.A., A.M. López, E. Khote and C.M. Abate. 2011b. Diversity of protease-producing marine bacteria from sub-Antarctic environments. *J. Basic Microbiol.* 51:590-600.

Cristóbal, H.A., A. Schmidt, E. Kote, J. Breccia and C.M. Abate. 2009. Characterization of inducible cold-active β-glucosidases from the psychrotolerant bacterium *Shewanella* sp. G5 isolated from a sub-Antarctic ecosystem. *Enzyme Microb. Technol.* 45:498–506.

Cristóbal, H.A., J.D. Breccia and C.M. Abate. 2008. Isolation and molecular characterization of *Shewanella* sp. G5 a producer of cold-active β-D-glucosidases. *J. Basic Microbiol.* 48:16-25.

Chinnasamy, G. and C. Rampitsch. 2006. Efficient solubilization buffers for two-dimensional gel electrophoresis of acidic and basic proteins extracted from wheat seeds. *Bioch. Biop. Acta*. 1764: 641–644.

Demain, A.L. and C.A. Dana. 2007. *The business of biotechnology* Vol. 3 N° 3 Gen Publishing Inc 269-283.

Deming, J.D. 2002. Psycrophiles and polar regions. *Curr. Opin. Microb.* 5:301–309.

Di Ciero, L., C.M. Bellato, L.W. Meinhardt, F. Ferrari and J.C. Novello. 2004. Assessment of four different detergents used to extract membrane proteins from *Xylella fastidiosa* by two-dimensional electrophoresis. *Braz. J. Microbiol.* 35:269-274.

Egorova, K. and G. Antranikian. 2005. Industrial relevance of thermophilic *Archaea. Curr. Opin. Microbiol.* 8:649–655.

Ellefsen, S., K. Stenslokken, G. Sandvik, T. Kristensen, E. Nilsson. 2008. Improved normalization of real-time reverse transcriptase polymerase chain reaction data using an external RNA control. *Anal. Biochem.* 376:83–93.

Faure, D. 2002. The family-3 glycoside hydrolases: from housekeeping functions to host-microbe interactions. *Appl. Environ. Microbiol.* 68:1485–1490.

Feller, G. and C. Gerday. 2003. Psychrophilic enzymes: hot topics in cold adaptation. *Microbiology* 1: 200-208.

Gerday, C., M. Aittaleb, M. Bentahir, J.P. Chessa, P. Claverie, T. Collins, S. D'Amico, J. Dumont, G. Garsoux and D. Georlette. 2000. Cold-adapted enzymes: from fundamentals to biotechnology. *Trends Biotechnol.* 18:103-107.

Goodchild, A., N.F. Saunders, H. Ertan, M. Raftery, M. Guilhaus, P.M. Curmi, R. Cavicchioli. 2004. A proteomic determination of cold adaptation in the Antarctic Archea on, *Methanococcoides burtonii. Mol. Microbiol.* 53:309–321.

Gao, H., Z.K. Yang, L. Wu, D.K. Thompson and Z. Zhou. 2006. Global transcriptome analysis of the cold shock response of *Shewanella oneidensis* MR-1 and mutational analysis of its classical cold shock proteins. *J. Bacteriol.* 188:4560–4569.

Garcia, B.O., J. Castillo, F.R. Marin, A. Ortuno, J.A. Del Rio. 1997. Uses and properties of Citrus flavonoids. *J. Agric. Food Chem.* 45:4505-4515.

Görg, A., O. Drews, C. Luck, F. Weiland, W. Weiss. 2009. 2-DE with IPGs. *Electrophoresis* 30:1–11.

Görg, A., W. Weiss and M.J. Dunn. 2004. Current two-dimensional electrophoresis technology for proteomics. *Proteomics* 4:3665–3685.

Görg, A., C. Obermaier, G. Boguth, A. Harder. 2000. The current state of two-dimensional electrophoresis with immobilized pH gradients. *Electrophoresis* 21:1037–1053.

Görg, A., C. Obermaier, G. Boguth, W. Weiss. 1999. Recent developments in two-dimensional gel electrophoresis with immobilized pH gradients: Wide pH gradients up to pH 12, longer separation distances and simplified procedures. *Electrophoresis* 20:712–717.

Görg, A., W. Postel, S. Günther. 1988. Two-dimensional electrophoresis. *Electrophoresis* 9:531–546.

Groudieva, T., M. Kambourova, H. Yusef, M. Royter, H. Grote and G. Antranikian. 2004. Diversity and cold-active hydrolytic enzymes of culturable bacteria associated with Artic sea ice, Spitzbergen. *Extremophiles* 8:475-488.

He, Z., L. Wu, M. Fields and Zhou. 2005. Use of microarrays with different probe sizes for monitoring gene expression. *Appl. Environm. Microb.* 71:5154–5162.

Hoyoux, A., V. Blaise, T. Collins, S. D`Amico and C. Gereday. 2004. Extreme catalysts from low-temperature environments. *J. Biosci. Bioeng*. 5:317-330.

Iwashita, K., T. Nadahara, H. Kimura, M. Takono, H. Shimol and K. Ito. 1999. The *bglA* gene of *Aspergillus kawachii* encodes both extracellular and cell wall-bound β-glucosidases. *Appl. Environ. Microbiol.* 65:5546–5553.

Kennedy, J., B. Flemer, S.A. Jackson, D.P. Lejon, J.P. Morrissey, F.O. Gara and A.D. Dobson. 2010. Marine metagenomics: new tools for the study and exploitation of marine microbial metabolism. *Mar. Drugs* 8:608-628; doi:10.3390/md8030608.

Kennedy, J., R. Marchesi and D. Dobson. 2008. Marine metagenomics: strategies for the discovery of novel enzymes with biotechnological applications from marine environments. *Microb. Cell. Fact.* 7:27doi10.1186/1475-2859-7-27.

Khoudoli, G.A., I.M. Porter, J.J. Blo and J.R. Sedlo. 2004. Optimization of the two-dimensional gel electrophoresis proteocol using the Taguchi approach. *Prot. Scie.* 2, doi;10.1186/1477-5956-2-6

Khudary, R.A., R. Venkatachalam, M. Katzer, S. Elleuche and G. Antranikian. 2010. A cold-adapted esterase of a novel marine isolate, *Pseudoalteromonas arctica*: gene cloning, enzyme purification and characterization. *Extremophiles* 14:273-285, DOI: 10.1007/s00792-010-0306-7.

Kirchman, D.L. 2000. *Microbial Ecology of the Oceans*. Wiley-Liss, Inc. pág. 4-16.

Kolker, E.P., M. Galperin, M. Romine, R. Higdon, K. Makarova. 2005. Global profiling of *Shewanella oneidensis* MR-1: expression of hypothetical genes and improved functional annotations. *Proc. Natl. Acad. Sci. U.S.A.* 102:2099–2104.

Kong, S., D.L. Johnstone, D.R. Yonge, J.N. Persen and T.M. Brouns. 1994. Long-term intracellular chromium partitioning with subsurface bacteria. *Appl. Microbiol. Biotechnol*. 42:403-407.

Kirk, O., T.V. Borchert and C.C. Fuglsang. 2002. Industrial enzyme applications. *Curr. Opin. Biotechnol*. 13:345–351.

Lee, H.S., K.K. Kwon, S.G. Kang, S.S. Cha, S.J. Kim and J.H. Lee JH. 2010. Approaches for novel enzymes discovery from marine environments. *Curr. Opin. Biotechnol.* 21:353-357.

León, J., F. Pellón, V. Unda, J. David, C. Anaya and V. Mendoza. 2000. Producción de enzimas extracelulares por bacterias aisladas de invertebrados marinos. *Rev. Peru Biol.* 7:202-210.

Livak, K.J. and T.D. Schmittgen. 2001. Analysis of relative gene expression data using real-time quantitative PCR and the $2^{-\Delta\Delta Ct}$ Method. *Methods* 25:402–408.

Liu, Z.L., D.E. Palmquist, M. Ma, J. Liu, N.J. Alexander. 2009. Application of a master equation for quantitative mRNA analysis using qRT-PCR. *J. Biotechnol*. 143:10–16.

Lottspeich, F. and H. Zorbas. 1998. *Bioanalytical*. Spektrum Verlag, Heidelberg.

Marengo, E., E. Robotti, V. Gianotti, P.G. Righetti, D. Cecconi and E. Domenici. 2003. A new integrated statistical approach to the diagnostic use of tow-dimensional maps. *Electrophoresis* 24:225-236

Margesin, R., V. Fauster and P.A. Fonteyne. 2005. Characterization of cold-active pectate lyases from psychrophilic *Mrakia frigida*. *Lett. Appl. Microbiol*. 6:453–459.

Molloy, M.P. 2000. Two-dimensional electrophoresis of membrane proteins using immobilized pH gradients. *Anal. Biochem*. 280:1-10.

Murray, P., N. Arob, C. Collins, A. Grassick, M. Penttilä, M. Saloheimo, M. Tuohy. 2004. Expression in *Trichoderma reesei* and characterization of a thermostable family 3 β-glucosidase from the moderately thermophilic fungus *Talaromyces emersonii. Protein Expr. Purif.* 38:248–257.

Nealson, K.H. 1999. Polyphasic taxonomy of the genus *Shewanella* and description of *Shewanella oneidensis* sp nov. *Int. J. Syst. Bacteriol.* 49:705–724.

Nolan, T., R.E. Hands, S.A. Bustin. 2006. Quantification of mRNA using real-time RT-PCR. *Nat. Protoc.* 1:1559–1582.

Olivera, N.L., C. Sequeiros, M.L. Nievas. 2007. Diversity and enzyme properties of protease-producing bacteria isolated from sub-Antarctic sediments of Isla de Los Estados, Argentina. *Extremophiles* 11:517-526.

Orrillo, A.G., P. Ledesma, O.D. Delgado, G. Spagna, J.D. Breccia. 2007. Cold-active α-L-rhamnosidase from psychrotolerant bacteria isolated from a sub-Antarctic ecosystem. *Enzyme Microb. Technol.* 40:236–241.

Pakchung, A.H., P.J. Simpson and R. Codd. 2006. Life on earth. Extremophiles continue to move the goal posts. *Environ. Chem.* 3: 77–93.

Palmeri, T. and G. Spagna. 2007. β-Glucosidase in cellular and acellular form for winemaking application. *Enzyme Microb. Technol.* 40:382–389.

Salohemio, M., J. Kuja-Panula, E. Yosmaki, M. Ward and M. Penttila. 2002. Enzymatic proprieties and intracellular localization of the novel *Trichoderma reesei* β-glucosidase BGLII (cel1A). *Appl. Environ. Microbiol.* 68:4546–4553.

Sarethy, I.P., Y. Saxena, A. Kapoor, M. Sharma, S.K. Sharma, V. Gupa and S. Gupa. 2011. Alkaliphilic bacteria: applications in industrial biotechnology. *J. Ind. Microbiol. Biotechnol.* 38:769-790.

Satyanarayana, T., C. Raghukumar and S. Shivaji. 2005. Extremophilic microbes. *Curr. Sci.* 89:78-90.

Schepens, H. 2003. White biotechnology: gateway to a more sustainable future *EuropaBio*, Lyon, France.

Schmidt, A., G. Haferburg, M. Siñeriz, M. Merten, G. Buchel and E. Kothe. 2005. Heavy metal resistance mechanisms in actinobacteria for survival in AMD contaminated soils. *Chemie der Erde.* 65:131–144.

Sellars, M.J., T. Vuocolo, L.A. Leeton, G.J. Comana, B.M. Degnan, N.P. Preston. 2007. Real-time RT-PCR quantification of Kuruma shrimp transcripts: A comparison of relative and absolute quantification procedures. *J. Biotechnol.* 129:391–399.

Spagna, G., R. Barbagallo, A. Martino, P. Pifferi. 2000. A simple method for purifying glycosidases: α-l-rhamnopyranosidase of *Aspergillus niger* to increase the aroma of Moscato wine. *Enzyme Microb. Technol.* 27:522–30.

Tsukada, T., K. Igarashi, M. Yoshida and M. Samejima. 2006. Molecular cloning and characterization of two intracellular β-glucosidases belonging to glycoside hydrolase family 1 from the basidiomycete *Phanerochaete chrysosporium. Appl. Microbiol. Biotechnol.* 73:807–814.

Vázquez, S. C., E. Hernández and W.P. Mac Cormack. 2008. Extracellular proteases from the Antarctic marine Pseudoalteromonas sp. P96-47 strain. *Rev. Argent. Microbiol.* 40:63-71.

Wang, Q.F., Y.H. Hou, Z. Xua, J.L. Miao and G.Y. Li. 2008. Purification and properties of an extracellular cold-active protease from the psychrophilic bacterium *Pseudoalteromonas* sp. NJ276. *Biochem. Eng. J.* 38:362–368.

Wang, W., J. Sun, M. Nimtz, W. Deckwer and A. Zeng. 2003. Protein identification from two-dimensional gel electrophoresis analysis of *Klebsiella pneumoniae* by combined use of mass spectrometry data and raw genome sequences. *Proteome Sci*; 1:6 doi:10.1186/1477-5956-1-6.

In: Applications of Microbial Genes in Enzyme Technology ISBN: 978-1-62417-808-5
Editors: V.K.Gupta, M.G.Tuohy, G.D.Sharma et al.

Chapter 19

Biotechnology of *Trichoderma*: An Overview

Vijai Kumar Gupta[*1], *Gauri Dutt Sharma*[2] *and Maria G. Tuohy*[1]
[1]Molecular Glycobiotechnology Group,
Department of Biochemistry, School of Natural Sciences,
National University of Ireland Galway, Galway, Ireland
[2]Department of Life Sciences, Assam University, Silchar, Assam, India

Abstract

Microorganisms are the main producers of a variety of enzymes, including proteases, chitinases, amylases, cellulases, and hemicellulases. These enzymes degrade organic biological substrates, providing nutrients for growth and contributing to carbon recycling in nature. *Trichoderma* is one of the most important filamentous fungi producing a number of valuable compounds along with production of many beneficial enzymes widely used in the food and feed industries, textile, pulp and paper, and biofuels and biorefinery industries. Biotechnological applications of *Trichoderma* species play an important role in various industries where its genes and function related to production of protein synthesis and secretory capability are widely exploited.

Introduction

Trichoderma strains are considered to be one of the most useful fungi in industrial enzyme production, agriculture, and are environment friendly. *Trichoderma* is a fungal genus including anamorphic fungi isolated primarily from soil and decomposing organic matter. Strains within this genus include a wide spectrum of evolutionary history (Papavizas, 1985; Misra and Gupta, 2009). The growing importance of many *Trichoderma* strains has made

[*] Corresponding author e-mail: vijaifzd@gmail.com; vijai.gupta@nuigalway.ie; Phone: +353 91 49 3693.

their identification and distinction from other *Trichoderma* isolates crucial. This is particularly true in relation to the commercialization of strains where the distinction of these strains from all other *Trichoderma* strains is essential for the purpose of patenting. However, as with the molecular techniques, the information gained is reliable and the technique is easily repeated. Sequence analysis, RAPD marker and microsatellite marker analysis and ***in situ*** diversity studies using a taxon-specific metagenomic approach provides characters that could easily be obtained and recognized by researchers, as well as to resolve isolates to a level greater than that achievable with morphological and cultural characters alone (Gupta, 2010; Friedl and Druzhinina, 2012). The variety of activities displayed by the *Trichoderma* strains *viz.* the antagonistic potential to effective control of a wide set of phytopathogenic fungi (Samuels, 1996) and the biodegradative capacity of produced enzymes system in different industrial sectors (Harman and Kubicek 1998; Schuster and Schmoll, 2010; Harman *et al.,* 2012). In this review we have discussed the biology of *Trichoderma* with respect to recent updates on its important genes and functions in production of valuable enzymes.

Characteristics of *Trichoderma* SPP

Species of the fungal genus *Trichoderma* are typically soil dwellers, existing as anamorphs belonging to the sub-division Deuteromycotina (fungi imperfecti) (Hawksworth *et al.,* 1983). *Trichoderma* species are fast growing fungi, which are commonly found in a variety of soil types, such as, agricultural, prairie, forest, salt marsh, and desert soils in all climatic zones (Domsch *et al.,* 1980). Rifai (1969) and Bissett (1991) have discussed morphological characters they employed to characterize and differentiate species of Trichoderma. Both authors emphasized the difficulties inherent in defining morphological species of Trichoderma. Samuels (1996) also provided detailed observations and comments on the utility of morphological characters to define species in Trichoderma. Characters useful for characterization and identification in other Hyphomycete genera frequently are not as useful in differentiating Trichoderma species, usually because of the narrow range of variation of the simplified morphology in Trichoderma, or because descriptive terms to describe variation in colour or pattern are not sufficiently precise to define differences between species. Nonetheless, careful morphological observations often are sufficient for identification of species and strains of Trichoderma, at least to the extent that taxa have been adequately differentiated morphologically and described in the existing literature. Morphological characters remain the primary method for identification and verification of species in Trichoderma *(http://www.isth.info/morphology.php)*.

Trichoderma strains often can readily be identified by a distinctive morphology that includes rapid growth, bright green or white conidial pigments, and a repetitively branched, but otherwise poorly defined conidiophore structure. Bissett (1991) proposed to include all the anamorphs of Hypocrea in the genus Trichoderma. If this concept is accepted, then a clear morphological definition for the genus Trichoderma would be problematic (Samuels, 1996), since the conidiophore branching structure is highly variable, and in many cases superficially resembles to unrelated genera such as Verticillium and Gliocladium. In most of these cases, the Trichoderma anamorphs of Hypocrea can be differentiated into a less regular pattern of branching at an indefinite number of levels - as opposed to the more regular verticillate or biverticillate branching in Verticillium, and the production of a terminal penicillate arrangement of branches and more regularly aculeate phialides on a relatively well-defined stipe in Gliocladium *(http://www.isth.info/morphology.php)*. Morphologically *Trichoderma* somewhat resembles *Verticillium* and *Gliocladium.* In *Trichoderma* the branching pattern is less regular as compared to *Verticillium*, where branching is more regular verticillate or bicilliate, whereas in *Gliocladium* branching arrangement is terminal. The colonies can easily be identified by their rapid growth, white, yellow green or bright green, dull reddish colour; matted wooly with strong or faint odour (Bisett, 1991).

Many *Trichoderma* isolates are of great economic importance, producing hydrolytic enzymes (e.g. chitinases, cellulases and xylanases) (Schirmbock *et al.,* 1994), biochemicals and antibiotics (Ghisalberti and Sivasithampamm, 1991; Ghisalberti, 2002; Baker et al., 2012; Mukherjee et al., 2012) and products which have been applied to fields, such as food processing and pulp bleaching (Nigam, 1994). In addition, some species produce heterologous proteins (Nevalainen *et al.,* 1980; Peterson and Nevalainen, 2012; Saloheimo and Pakula, 2012) and others have been successfully used as biological control agents against a range of phytopathogens (Chet and Inbar 1994; Ryder et al., 2012).

Biotechnology of *Trichoderma*

Industrially useful *Trichoderma* strains have received much attention due to production of homologous and heterologous bio-molecules at significant levels. Several enzymes from *Trichoderma* strains have been engineered to function better in industrial processes. These include proteinases, lipases, cellulases, α-amylases and glucoamylases. Xylanases and glucanase are good examples of an industrial enzyme that needs to be stable in high temperatures and active in physiological temperature and pH when used as feed additive, and in alkaline conditions when it is used for bleaching in pulp and paper industry. By designed mutagenesis its thermal stability has been increased many-fold. The known structure of an enzyme is used to design and simulate mutations. The most successful strategies to improve the stability of the *Trichoderma* enzymes include the stabilization of the alpha-helix region and the N-terminus (Dashtban, 2009). So, cellulases and hemicellulases are among the important enzymes produced by these organisms, and have shown potential for use in a variety of industrial processes and applications, especially for the degradation of biomass. Systematic improvement of characterized *Trichoderma* strains by mutagenesis and screening has resulted in strains producing reported levels of extracellular protein. The proteins produced mainly consist of cellulase, cellobiohydrolase I (CBHI) (Durand *et al.,* 1988; Buchert and Heikinheimo, 1998). The relative proportions of the different hydrolases can be influenced only to some extent by varying the growth media and cultivation conditions. With genetic engineering techniques such as gene inactivation and overproduction under the control of the strong cbh1 promoter, it has been possible to construct *Trichoderma* strains with novel cellulase profiles (Harkki *et al.,* 1991), and enzyme mixtures highly enriched in certain activities such as that of xylanase (Saarelainen *et al.,* 1993). The expressions of fungal hydrolytic genes are generally repressed by glucose; the promoters of these genes would allow production of a certain protein essentially free of most contaminating activities. The use of the promoters of the gene encoding translation elongation factor 1a, tef1, and of a still-unidentified gene for cDNA1 in the construction of strains that secrete as model proteins active CBHI and the catalytic core domain of endoglucanase I (EGI) into the culture medium when *T. reesei* is grown on glucose-containing medium (Nakari-Setala and Penttila, 1995).

Some recent results of the molecular mechanisms of cellulose gene regulation and protein secretion in *Trichoderma* could possibly be utilized to increase the production levels of cellulases. The suitability of the cellulases in efficient conversion of biomass to sugars that can be fermented to ethanol should also be investigated. Cellobiohydrolases are the key components of the redesigned, highly synergistic cellulase mixtures required for such processes. *Trichoderma* cellulases are useful in denim finishing imparting a certain type of stonewashed appearance, but they have disadvantages such as a tendency to promote back staining and weakening of fabrics. The application of techniques for protoplast isolation and fusion and gene cloning will result in further development of new technologies for genetic manipulation of fungi. With the help of latest tools of biotechnology, attempts should be made to develop Genetically Modified (GM) *Trichoderma* spp. (Schuster and Schmoll, 2010; Peterson and Nevalainen, 2012).

Enhanced Enzyme Production by *Trichoderma*

Members of the fungal genus *Trichoderma* have been extensively studied, particularly due to their ability to secrete cellulose degrading enzymes or to act as biocontrol agents. Most of the work has been carried out on strains of *T. viride, T. reesei, T. harzianum.* These strains have been extensively studied in their ability to produce extracellular cellulolytic enzymes, namely endoglucanases, exoglucanases, and cellobiase, which act synergistically in the conversion of cellulose to glucose (Eveleigh, 1987). The strains have been mutagenized and genetically modified to obtain an organism capable of producing high levels of cellulases (Szengyel *et al.,* 2000; Peterson and Nevalainen, 2012; Saloheimo and Pakula, 2012). Furthermore, members of the genus *Trichoderma* have also been reported as biocontrol agents (Hermosa *et al.,* 2000) due to its ability to successfully antagonize other fungi including plant pathogenic species. Because the skeleton of filamentous fungi cell walls contains chitin, glucan and proteins, enzymes that hydrolyze these components have to be present in a successful antagonist in order to play a significant role in cell wall lysis of the pathogen (Carsolio *et al.,* 1999). Several distinct chitinolytic enzymes have been reported in *T. harzianum* (Haran *et al.,* 1996; Ryder *et al.,* 2012). These include endochitinases, exochitinases and 1,4-ß-N-acetylglucosaminidases, which are induced during growth of *T. harzianum* in liquid medium containing chitin as carbon source. Another enzymatic system that is involved in cell wall degradation by an antagonistic organism is ß-glucan degrading enzymes. Two mechanisms of glucan degradation have been reported: exo- and endoglucanases, both of which act synergistically in glucan degradation. ß-glucan degrading enzymes are classified according to the type of ß-glucosidic linkages: 1,4-ß-glucanases (including cellulases), 1,3-ß-glucanases, and 1,6-ß-glucanases (Pitson *et al.,* 1993). Because 1,3-ß-glucan is a structural component of fungal cell walls, the production of extracellular 1,3-ß-glucanases has been reported as an important enzymatic activity in biocontrol microorganisms. In addition to chitin and glucans, filamentous fungi cell walls contain proteins. Thus, the production of proteases may play a role in antagonism (Sivan and Chet, 1989; Flores *et al.,* 1997).

Trichoderma in Industries

The genus *Trichoderma* comprises a group of filamentous ascomycetes that are widely used in industrial applications because of their ability to produce extracellular lignocellulose-degrading hydrolases in large amounts. Enzymes secreted by *Trichoderma* have received widespread industrial interest, leading to commercial applications in the various industries including textile (Cavaco- Paulo and Gübitz, 2003), foods and feed industries, pulp and paper industries (Galante *et al.,* 1998) and biofuels and biorefineries industries (Gusakov, 2011; Gupta *et al.,* 2012). *Trichoderma reesei* is a biotechnically important filamentous fungus commercially used in enzyme production. *T. reesei* is one of the best known cellulolytic organisms, producing readily and in large quantities a complete set of extracellular cellulases for the degradation of crystalline cellulose. Cellulases originating from various organisms and having different characteristics are used industrially in many applications, such as in the textile industry and in biofinishing of cotton. *T. reesei* can be used as an industrial host for homologous and heterologous enzyme production (Penttilä *et al.,* 2004; Peterson and Nevalainen, 2012). Cellulases are industrially important enzymes with a current market value of about US$190 million (Schülein, 2000). Cellulase enzymes are used for fabric and garment finishing to produce higher value products, as cellulases clean fuzz and prevent formation of pills on the surface of cotton garments. Cellulases can also be used in denim finishing creating a fashionable stonewashed appearance in denim in a process called biostoning. About 10 % of textile finishing of cellulose materials is estimated to be performed by cellulases and approximately 80 % of the 1.8 mrd pairs of denim jeans produced annually are finished with cellulases as an alternative to pumice stones (Buchert and Heikinheimo, 1998). In the detergent industry cellulases are used to clean cotton garments or to brighten faded coloured garments by removing fuzz. In animal feed applications cellulases are utilized together with other hydrolases in the degradation of non-starch polysaccharides to improve feed conversion rates (Galante *et al.,* 1998). The food industry uses cellulases together with other plant cell wall-degrading enzymes in fruit and vegetable processing (Urlaub, 2002). Cellulases also have potential in the pulp and paper industry, e.g. in de-inking, releasing ink from fibre surfaces and in improving pulp drainage (Suurnäkki *et al.,* 2004). Within the forest industry cellulases have been shown to be effective in decreasing the energy consumption of mechanical pulping (Pere *et al.,* 2002). Cellulases have been found to increase the alkali solubility of treated pulp and directly alkali soluble cellulose has been obtained with specific cellulase compositions (Rahkamo *et al.,* 1996). This property can be utilized in developing new environmentally beginning processes for manufacturing cellulosic articles such as films and fibers. In recent years, enzymatic hydrolysis of biomass to sugars for subsequent ethanol production has also been a major research area.

Trichoderma is a cellulose-degrading fungus and it secretes large amount of cellulases (Jiang *et al.,* 2011). Bioconversion of biomass to bio-fuels has been the subject of intense research efforts and gained significant political and scientific momentum, owing to concerns about energy security and the emission of greenhouse gases (Bayer *et al.,* 2004; Antoni *et al.,* 2007; Service, 2007). The on-site production of cellulases is an important strategy for the development of sustainable second generation ethanol production processes. Cellulases are glycosyl hydrolases (GH) that play an important role in the bioconversion of cellulosic materials into biofuels. The major bottleneck for a wider application of cellulases in second generation ethanol production is their cost, especially because large quantities of the enzymes are required (Zhang *et al.,* 2006). Filamentous fungi, typically *Trichoderma* (Mandels *et al.,* 1976), have an excellent capacity for extracellular protein production. *Trichoderma* produces the cellobiohydrolase (CBH) and endoglucanase (EG) components of cellulolytic enzyme complex in large quantities. Therefore, it as an ideal cellulolytic enzyme producer for industrial exploitation, and biotechnological applications using gene expression systems are currently in process to develop *Trichoderma* strains that are efficient microbial factories for cellulolytic enzyme complex production with applications in second generation biofuel production and bioenergy research (Ghand *et al.,* 2005; Asdul *et al.,* 2007; Gusakov 2011).

Trichoderma as a Source of Genes and Their Function

Trichoderma is a filamentous fungus and is a potential agent for the production of industrial enzymes (Dalboge, 1997). Potential industrial applications of *Trichoderma* strains have recently been demonstrated, and it is now clear that hundreds of separate genes and gene products are involved in the processes of enzyme production (Monte, 2001). Some of these genes have been identified, cloned from *Trichoderma* spp., and offer great promise for producing higher levels of valuable enzymes for various biotechnological processes (Table 1). These enzymes have been extensively studied at the biochemical, molecular, and structural levels for several years (Figure 1). Cloning of regulatory genes involved in the expression of extracellular enzymes is very important. Numerous cellulase and hemicellulase encoding genes have been cloned from *T. reesei* and other *Trichoderma* spp., but only a few (*cbh*1, *cbh*2, *xyn*1 and *xyn*2) have been investigated in detail concerning their expression and regulation (Stangl *et al.,* 1993a, b; Zeilinger *et al.,* 2000; Aro *et al.,* 2001). There is a need to understand the mechanism by which negative regulatory factors repress the expression of xylanolytic and cellulolytic enzymes, and which reduce the cost effective industrial production of xylanases and glucanases (Schmoll and Kubicek, 2003; Saadia *et al.,* 2008). The production of cell wall degrading enzymes such as chitinases, glucanases, and proteases is an important mechanism that has been implicated in *Trichoderma*. These hydrolytic enzymes are thought to be involved in the degradation of cell wall (Zeilinger *et al.,* 1999, 2000). Chitin polymers are an essential structural component in the fungi kingdom, as well as in some members of the animal kingdom (Kendrick, 2000). In fact, chitin is one of the most abundant polysaccharides found in nature, second to cellulose. The degradation of chitin is catalyzed by chitinolytic enzymes, called chitinases. They consist of a group of hydrolytic enzymes that are able to break down polymeric chitin into simple monomers of N-acetyleglucosamine (Sahai and Manocha, 1993). Exochitinases and chitobiosidases are responsible for cleaving the chitin to produce dimers of GlcNAc units (Harman *et al.,* 1993). The *Trichoderma* chitinolytic enzyme system is both complicated and not fully understood.

Differences between these enzymes might occur between the different fungal strains that vary in their habitats, nutritional, and antagonistic behavior. Several endochitinases have been isolated from *T. harzianum*, such as the endochitinases. The chitinase Ech42 gene is involved in the mycoparasitic action of *Trichoderma* on three levels, including cell wall hydrolysis, spore germination inhibition, and the inhibition of the elongation of germ tubes of several filamentous fungi (Lorito *et al.,* 1993, 1994, 1996; Schirmbock *et al.,* 1994). It has been reported that the ech42 enzyme is over expressed during the interaction between *T. atroviride* and *R. solani* (Kulling *et al.,* 2000).

Table 1. Genes and functions in production of enzymes for selected *Trichoderma* spp.

S. no.	Gene name	Function	*Trichoderma* spp.	Reference
1	*cbh II*	Cellobiohydrolase II	*T. reesei*	Chen *et al.,* 1987
2	*prb1*	alkaline proteinase	*T. harzianum*	Geremia *et al.,* 1994
3	*bg11*	β-D-glucoside glucohydrolase	*T. reesei*	Mach, 1994
4	*ech-42*	chitinase	*T. harzianum*	Hayes *et al.,* 1994; Carsolio *et al.,* 1994
5	*cbh1*	Cellulose1,4- β-cellobiosidase/ Cellobiohydrolase I	*T. koningii*	Wey *et al.,* 1994
6	*egIII*	endoglucanase III	*T. reesei*	Saloheimo *et al.,* 1988
7	*eg15*	endo-1-4- β-glucanase V	*T. reesei*	Saloheimo *et al.,* 1994
8	*eg11*	cellulase	*T. longibrachiatum*	Perz-Gonzalez, 1993
9	*b16-2*	glucan endo-1,6- β-glucosidase	*T. harzianum*	Lora *et al.,* 1995
10	*chi42,pc1ch1*	endochitinase	*T. harzianum*	Draborg *et al.,* 1996
11	*bng3.1*	endo-1,3(4)- β-glucanase	*T. harzianum*	de la Cruz *et al.*, 1995
12	*cbh2*	cellobiohydraseII	*T. reesei*	Stangl *et al.,* 1993b
13	*endo51*	endoglucanaseI	*T. reesei*	Penttila *et al.*, 1986
14	*xy11*	arabinofuranosidase/ β-xylosidase	*T. koningii*	Huang *et al.,* 1991
15	*cre154*	Cre1	*T. reesei*	Strauss *et al.*, 1995; Saadia *et al.,* 2008
16	*xln2*	endoxylanaseII	*T. reesei*	Saarelainen *et al.,* 1993
17	*tham-ch*	endochitinase	*T.hamatum*	Fekete *et al.*, 1996
18	*cell1*	1,4- β-D-glucan cellobiohydrolase	*T.viride*	Cheng *et al.*, 1990
19	*xyn1*	endo- β-1,-4-xylanase I	*T.reesei*	Torronen *et al.*, 1992
20	*xyn2*	endo- β-1,-4-xylanase I	*T.reesei*	Torronen *et al.*, 1992
21	Chitinases gene	N- acetylglucosaminidase	*T.reesei*	Haran *et al.,* 1995
22	exc2	N- acetylglucosaminidase	*T.reesei*	Draborg *et al.,* 1996
23	excl/nag1	N-acetylglucosaminidase	*T.reesei*	Peterbauer *et al.,* 1996
24	Chitinases gene	N-acetylglucosaminidase	*T.reesei*	Deane *et al.,* 1998
25	Chitinases gene	endochitinase	*T.reesei*	Haran *et al.*, 1996
26	ech42	endochitinase	*T.reesei*	Carsolio *et al.*, 1994
27	chit42	endochitinase	*T.reesei*	Garcia *et al.*, 1994
28	cht42	endochitinase	*T.reesei*	Baek *et al.*, 1999
29	ThEn42	endochitinase	*T.reesei*	Lorito *et al.,* 1998
30	Chitinases gene	chitoblosidase	*T.reesei*	Harman *et al.*, 1993

Table 1. (Continued)

S. no.	Gene name	Function	*Trichoderma* spp.	Reference
31	chit33	endochitinase	*T.reesei*	de la Cruz *et al.*,1992
32	chit36	endochitinase	*T.reesei*	Vilerbo *et al.*, 2002
33	bgn13.1	β -1,3-endoglucanase	*T.reesei*	El-Katatny *et al.*, 2001
34	Glucanases	β -1,3-endoglucanase	*T.reesei*	Lorito *et al.*, 1994
35	kan1.3	β -1,3-exo glucanase	*T.reesei*	Cohen-Kupiec *et al.*, 1999
36	Glucanases	β -1,3-exo glucanase	*T.reesei*	Ramot *et al.*, 2000
37	egII	β -1,4-endoglucanase	*T.reesei*	Migheli *et al.*, 1998; 2009
38	prb1	alkaline protease	*T.reesei*	Flores *et al.*, 1997
39	*cbh1/cel7a*	Cellobiohydrolase	*T.reesei*	Shoemaker *et al.*, 1983
40	*cbh2/cel6a*	Cellobiohydrolase	*T.reesei*	Teeri *et al.*, 1987
41	*egl1/cel7b*	Endo-1,4-glucanase	*T.reesei*	Penttila *et al.*, 1986
42	*egl2/cel5a*	Endo-1,4-glucanase	*T.reesei*	Saloheimao *et al.*, 1988
43	*egl3/cel12a*	Endo-1,4-glucanase	*T.reesei*	Okada *et al.*, 1998
44	*egl4/cel61a*	Endo-1,4-glucanase	*T.reesei*	Saloheimao *et al.*, 1997
45	*egl5/cel45a*	Endo-1,4-glucanase	*T.reesei*	Saloheimao *et al.*, 1994
46	*cel74a*	Endo-1,4-glucanase	*T.reesei*	Foreman *et al.*, 2003
47	*cel61b*	Endo-1,4-glucanase	*T.reesei*	Foreman *et al.*, 2003
48	*cel5b*	Endo-1,4-glucanase	*T.reesei*	Foreman *et al.*, 2003
49	*bgl1/cel3a*	β -Glucosidase	*T.reesei*	Barnett *et al.*, 1991; Mach, 1993
50	*bgl2/cel1a*	β -Glucosidase	*T.reesei*	Takashima *et al.*, 1999
51	*cel3b*	β -Glucosidase	*T.reesei*	Foreman *et al.*, 2003
52	*cel3c*	β -Glucosidase	*T.reesei*	Foreman *et al.*, 2003
53	*cel1b*	β -Glucosidase	*T.reesei*	Foreman *et al.*, 2003
54	*cel3d*	β -Glucosidase	*T.reesei*	Foreman *et al.*, 2003
55	*cel3e*	β -Glucosidase	*T.reesei*	Foreman *et al.*, 2003
56	*xyn1*	Xylanase	*T.reesei*	Torronen *et al.*, 1992; Saarelainen *et al.*, 1993
57	*xyn2*	Xylanase	*T.reesei*	Saarelainen *et al.*, 1993
58	*xyn3*	Xylanase	*T.reesei*	Nogawa *et al., 2001*
59	*xyn4*	Xylanase	*T.reesei*	Saloheimao *et al.*, 2001
60	*bxl1*	β -Xylosidase	*T.reesei*	Margolles-Clark *et al.*, 1996a
61	*axe1*	Acetyl xylan esterase	*T.reesei*	Margolles-Clark *et al.*, 1996d
62	*axe2*	Acetyl xylan esterase	*T.reesei*	Foreman *et al.*, 2003
63	*abf1*	Arabinofuranosidase	*T.reesei*	Margolles-Clark *et al.*, 1996a

S. no.	Gene name	Function	*Trichoderma* spp.	Reference
64	*abf2*	Arabinofuranosidase	*T.reesei*	Foreman *et al.,* 2003
65	*man1*	Mannanase	*T.reesei*	Stalbrand *et al.,* 1995
66	*agl1*	α-Galactosidase	*T.reesei*	Margolles-Clark *et al.,* 1996b
67	*agl2*	α-Galactosidase	*T.reesei*	Margolles-Clark *et al.,* 1996b
68	*agl3*	α-Galactosidase	*T.reesei*	Margolles-Clark *et al.,* 1996b
69	*glr1*	α-Glucuronidase	*T.reesei*	Margolles-Clark *et al.,* 1996c
70	*bgal*	α-Galactosidase	*T.reesei*	Kubicek, 1987
71	*swo1*	Unknown	*T.reesei*	Saloheimao *et al.,* 2002
72	Cellulases	Cellulases (CMCase, CBH, BGL),	*T. reesei*	Chahal, 1985
73	tub*1*	Beta tubulin	*T. viride, T. virens*	Goldman *et al.,* 1993; Mukherjee *et al.,* 2003
74	tub*2*	Beta tubulin	*T. viride, T. virens*	Goldman *et al.,* 1993; Mukherjee *et al.,* 2003
75	Xylanase	Hemicellulase (xylanase)	*T. reesei*	Kurzatkowski 1996
76	Cellulases	Cellulases (CMCase, CBH), β-1,3-glucanases	*T. harzianum*	Sivan, 1984; Khan, 2007
77	Glucanases, Family 55	b-1,3-glucanase	*T. virens*	Dong-Jin, 2002
78	*cip1*	Unknown	*T.reesei*	Foreman *et al.,* 2003
79	*cip2*	Unknown	*T.reesei*	Foreman *et al.,* 2003
80	Glucanases, Family 5	b-1,6-glucanase,	*T. virens*	Dong-Jin, 2002

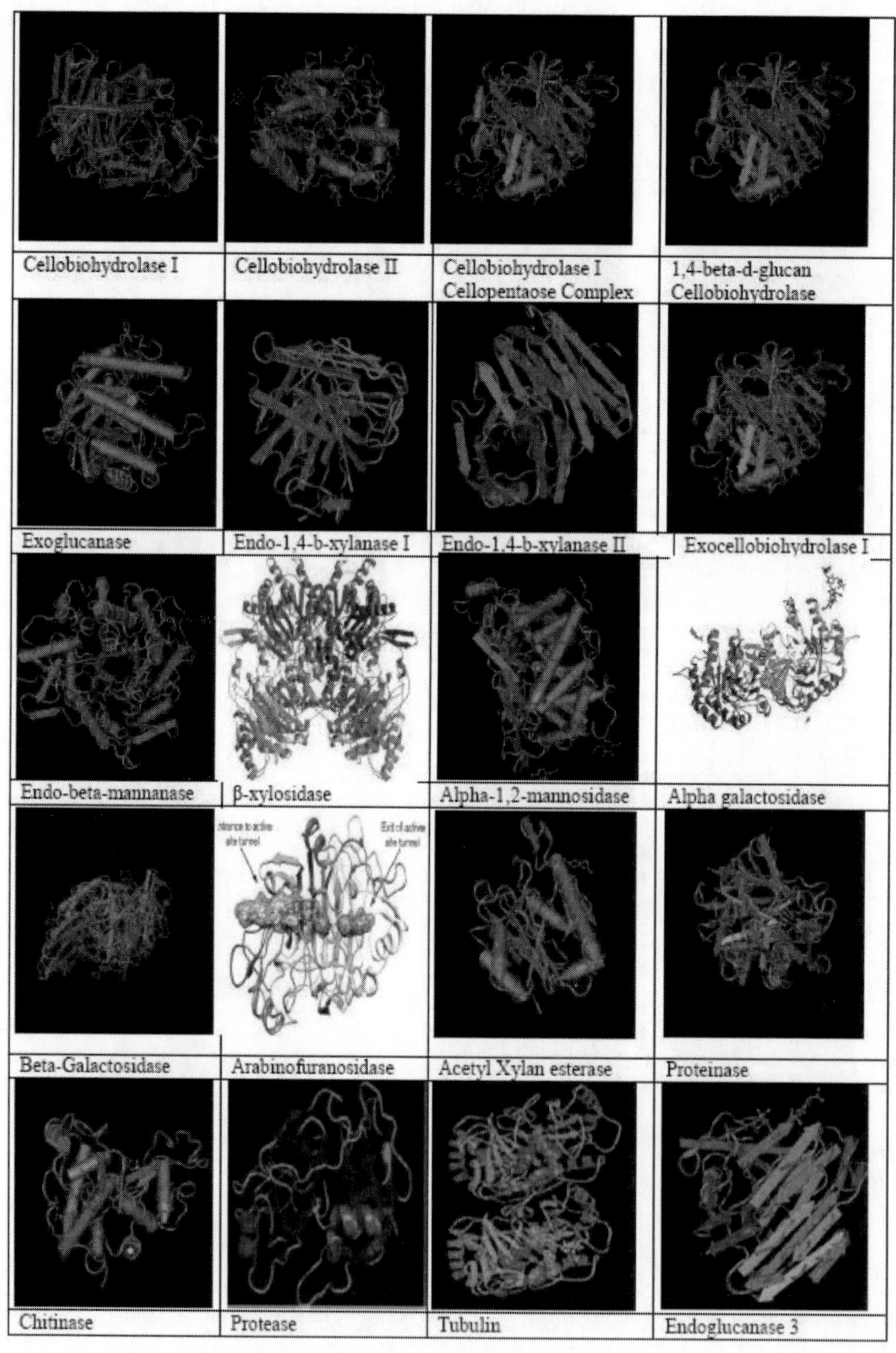

Source: www.ncbi.nlm.nih.gov/structure/?term=*Trichoderma*.

Figure 1. Structures of Important *Trichoderma* genes.

The second important group of enzymes from *Trichoderma* spp. are the glucanases. The fungal cell wall is composed mainly, along with chitin, of β-1,3-glucan (laminarin) and 1,4-D-glucan (cellulose). Glucan is a major component in fungal cell walls and its primary role is to provide structure, rigidity, and protection (Kollar *et al.,* 1995). The synthesis of glucan-degrading enzymes is a shared characteristic between many organisms, although fungi are the principal producers (de la Cruz and Llobell, 1999). Fungal plant polysaccharide-hydrolyzing enzymes, cellulases and hemicellulases, are industrially important enzymes with a wide spectrum of well-established applications.

Members of the fungal genus *Trichoderma* have been extensively studied, particularly due to their ability to secrete cellulose degrading enzymes. Most of the work has been carried out on strains of *T. viride, T. reesei, T. harzianum*, being extensively studied in their ability to produce extracellular cellulolytic enzymes, namely endoglucanases, xylo-glucanases and cellobiase, which act synergistically in the conversion of cellulose to glucose (Eveleigh, 1987). The enzyme activity specific to cellulose activity produced by *Trichoderma* is composed of a complement of endoglucanases (EGI/Cel7B, EGII/Cel5A, EGIII/ Cel12A, EGIV/Cel61A, and EGV/Cel45A) and exoglucanases (the cellobiohydrolases, CBHI/Cel7A, and CBHII/Cel6A) that act synergistically to break down cellulose to cellobiose (glycosyl β-1,4-glucose) (Okada *et al.,* 1998; Saloheimo *et al.,* 1994). Two β-glucosidases (BGLI/Cel3A and BGLII/Cel1A) have been identified that are implicated in hydrolyzing cellobiose to glucose (Barnett *et al.,* 1991; Takashima *et al.,* 1999). Expression of many of the genes encoding hemicellulase, with the notable exception of man1, is induced by xylans. Sugars such as sophorose, arabitol, xylobiose, cellobiose, and galactose also induce expression to varying extents, particularly of enzymes that degrade substrates related to these sugars (Margolles-Clark *et al.,* 1997).

The molecular mechanisms by which *Trichoderma* senses the composition of the extracellular expression of these enzymes is the area of current research around the world. Therefore, mechanisms by which the cellulose and hemicellulase genes are regulated are likely to influence the ecological niches that *Trichoderma* occupies and are of interest in the commercial production of these enzymes (Foreman *et al.,* 2003). So, *Trichoderma* strains are required to be mutagenized and genetically modified to obtain an organism capable of producing high levels of cellulases (Mandels and Andreotti, 1978; Nevalainen *et al.* 1980; Durand *et al.* 1988; Szengyel *et al.* 2000; Adav *et al.,* 2012).

Conclusion

Trichoderma spp. is one of the best sources for the production of industrially important enzymes because of excellent secretion capacity, alongside cheap and easy cultivation. Specific applications for hydrolysis and controlled modification of plant polysaccharides have to be developed using *Trichoderma* enzymes. These applications may require highly specific enzyme preparations, even preparations with only one individual hydrolytic enzyme-producing *Trichoderma* strain. Purification of the desired activities is costly for large scale applications, and it is desirable to use the whole enzyme mixture produced by *Trichoderma* strains. New production strategies are needed in order to obtain specific enzyme preparations for future applications. To date, many important genes from *Trichoderma* spp. have been isolated and characterized. Their DNA sequences have revealed the presence of a number of common sequence elements that might be important in the expression of genes of interest responsible for encoding valuable enzymes.

References

Adav, S.S., L. T. Chao and S. K. Sze. 2012. Quantitative secretomic analysis of *Trichoderma reesei* strains reveals enzymatic composition for lignocellulosic biomass degradation. *Mol. Cellu. Prot.* (in press; M111.012419).

Alexander V. G. 2011. Alternatives to *Trichoderma reesei* in biofuel production. *Trends Biotechnol.* 29: 419-425.

Antoni, D., V. V. Zverlov and W. H. Schwarz. 2007. Biofuels from microbes. *Appl. Microbiol. Biotechnol.* 77: 23–35.

Aro, N., A. Saloheimo, M. Ilmen and M. Penttilla. 2001. ACEII, a novel transcriptional activator involved in regulation of cellulase and xylanase genes of *Trichoderma reesei. J. Biol. Chem.* 276: 24309-24314.

Asdul, M. G., K. B. Bastawde, A. J. and D. V. Varmaand Gokhale. 2007. Strain improvement of *Penicillium janthinellum* NCIM 1171 for increased cellulase production. *Bioresour. Technol.* 98: 1467–1473.

Baek, J.M., C.R. Howell, and C.M. Kelerney. 1999. The role of extracellular chitinase from *Trichoderma virens* Gv29-8 in the biocontrol of *Rhizoctonia solani. Curr. Genet.* 35: 41-50.

Baker, S. E., G. Perrone, N. M. Richardson, A. Gallo, and C. P. Kubicek. 2012**.** Phylogenetic analysis and evolution of polyketide synthase-encoding genes in *Trichoderma. Microbiol.* 158*:* 147–154.

Barnett, C. C., R. M. Berka, and T. Fowler. 1991. Cloning and amplification of the gene encoding an extracellular beta-glucosidase from *Trichoderma reesei*: evidence for improved rates of saccharification of cellulosic substrates. *Biotechnol.* 9: 562–567.

Bayer, E. A., J. P. Belaich, Y. Shoham, and R. Lamed. 2004. The cellulosomes: multienzyme machines for degradation of plant cell wall polysaccharides. *Annu. Rev. Microbiol.* 58: 521–554.

Bissett, J. 1991. A revision of the genus *Trichoderma*: Section Longibrachiatum new section. *Can. J.Bot.* 69: 924-931.

Buchert, J. and L. Heikinheimo. 1998. New cellulase processes for the textile industry. EU-project. report. C*arbohydrate Eur.* 22:32–34.

Carsolio, C., A. Gutierrez, B. Jimenez, M. Van Montagu, and A. HerreraEstrella. 1994. Characterization of ech-42, a *Trichoderma harzianum* endochitinase gene expressed during mycoparasitism. *Proc. Natl. Acad. Sci. USA* 91: 10903–10907.

Carsolio, C., N. Benhamou, S. Haran, C. Cortés, A. Gutiérrez, I. Chet, and A. Herrera-Estrella. 1999. Role of the *Trichoderma harzianum* endochitinase Gene ech2 in mycoparasitism. *Appl.Environ. Microbiol.* 65:929-935.

Cavaco-Paulo, A. and G. Gübitz, 2003. Catalysis and processing. In: Textile processing with enzymes. (eds. A.Cavaco- Paulo and G.Gübitz), Woodhead Publishing Ltd., England. pp. 86-119.

Chahal, D. S. 1985. Solid-State Fermentation with *Trichoderma reesei* for cellulase production. *Appl. Environ. Microbiol.* 49:205-210.

Chen, C.M., M. Gritzali, and D.W. Stafford. 1987. Nucleotide sequence and deduced primary structure of cellobiohydrolase II from *Trichoderma reesei. Biotechnol.* 5:274– 278.

Cheng, C., N. Tsukagoshi, and S. Udaka. 1990. Nucleotide sequence of the cellobiohydrolase gene from *Trichoderma viride. Nucl. Acids Res.* 18:5559.

Chet, I. and J. Inbar. 1994. Biological control of fungal pathogens. *Appl. Biochem. Biotechnol.* 48:37-43.

Cohen-Kupiec, R., K.E. Broglie, D. Friesem, R.M. Broglie, and I. Chet. 1999. Molecular characterization of a novel b-1, 3-exoglucanase related to mycoparasitism of *Trichoderma harzianum. Gene* 226:147–154.

Dalboge, H. 1997. Expression cloning of fungal enzyme genes; a novel approach for efficient isolation of enzyme genes of industrial relevance. FEMS. *Microbiol. Rev.* 21: 29-42.

Dashtban, M., H. Schraft and Q. Wensheng, 2009. Fungal Bioconversion of Lignocellulosic Residues; Opportunities and Perspectives. *Int. J. Biol. Sci.* 2009; 5(6):578-595.

De La Cruz, J., A. Hidalgo-Gallego, J.M. Lora, T. Benitez, J.A. Pintor-Toro and A. Llobell, 1992. Isolation and characterization of three chitinases from *Trichoderma harzianum. Eur. J. Biochem.* 206: 859–867.

De La Cruz, J., and A. Llobell. 1999. Purification and properties of a basic endo-b-1, 6-glucanase (BGN16.1) from the antagonistic fungus *Trichoderma harzianum. Eur. J. Biochem.* 265: 145-151.

De la Cruz, J., J.A. Pintor-Toro, T. Benıtez, A. Llobell, L.C. Romero. 1995. A novel endo-beta-1,3-glucanase, BGN13.1, involved in the mycoparasitism of *Trichoderma harzianum. J. Bacteriol.* 177: 6937–6945.

Deane, E.E., J.M. Whipps, J.M. Lynch, and J.F. Peberdy. 1998. The purification and characterization of a *Trichoderma harzianum* exochitinase. *Biochimica et Biophysica Acta.* 1383: 101-110.

Domsch, K. H., W. Gams, and T. H. Anderson. 1980. Compendium of Soil Fungi. Vol I, Academic Press, London, UK.

Dong-Jin Kim, Jong-Min Baek, P. Uribe, C. M. Kenerley and D. R. Cook. 2002. Cloning and characterization of multiple glycosyl hydrolase genes from *Trichoderma virens. Curr Genet.* 40: 374–384.

Draborg H., S. Christgau, T. Halkier, G. Rasmussen, H. Dalbøge and S. Kauminen.1996. Secretion of an enzymatically active *Trichoderma harzianum* endochitinase by Saccharomyces cerevisiae. *Curr. Genet.* 29:404–409.

Durand, H., M. Clanet, and G. Tiraby. 1988. Genetic improvement of *Trichoderma reesei* for large scale cellulase production. *Enzyme. Microb. Technol.* 10:341–345.

Durand, H., M. Clanet, and G. Tiraby. 1988. Genetic improvement of *Trichoderma reesei* for large scale cellulase production. *Enz. Microbial Technol.* 10:341-346.

El-Katatny M.H., M. Gudelj, K.H. Robra, M.A. Elnaghy and G.M. Gubitz. 2001. Characterization of a chitinase and an endo-β-1, 3-glucanase from *Trichoderma harzianum*, Rifai T24 involved in control of the phytopathogen *Sclerotium rolfsii. Appl. Microbiol. Biotechnol.* 56:137–143.

Eveleigh, D.E. 1987. Cellulase: a perspective. Philosophical Transanctions of the Royal Society of London, Series B-Biological Sciences 321:435-447.

Fekete, C., T. Weszely and L. Hornok. 1996. Assignment of a PCR-amplified chitinase sequence cloned from *Trichoderma hamatum* to resolved chromosomes of potential biocontrol species of *Trichoderma. FEMS Microbiol. Lett.* 145: 385–391.

Flores, A., I. Chet and A. Herrera-Estrella. 1997. Improved biocontrol activity of *Trichoderma harzianum* by overexpression of the proteinase-encoding gene prb1. *Curr. Genet.* 31:30-37.

Foreman P.K., D. Brown, L. Dankmeyer, R. Dean, S. Diener, N.S. Dunn-Coleman, F. Goedegebuur, T.D. Houfek, G.J. England, A.S. Kelley, H.J. Meerman, T. Mitchell, C. Mitchinson, H.A. Olivares, P.J. Teunissen, J. Yao and M. Ward. 2003. Transcriptional regulation of biomass-degrading enzymes in the filamentous fungus *Trichoderma reesei. J. Biol. Chem.* 278:31988-31997.

Friedl M. A. and I. S. Druzhinina. (2012**).** Taxon-specific metagenomics of *Trichoderma* reveals a narrow community of opportunistic species that regulate each other's development. *Microbiol.* 158*:* 69–83.

Galante, Y., A. De Conti, and R. Monteverdi. 1998. Application of *Trichoderma* enzymes in the food and feed industries. In: (eds. G. Harman and C.Kubicek.) *Trichoderma* and *Gliocladium*, Enzymes, *biological control and commercial applications,* Vol. 2. pp. 327-342.

Garcia, I., J. M. Lora, J. de la Cruz, T. Benitez, A. Llobell and J. A. PintorToro. 1994. Cloning and characterization of a chitinase (chit42) cDNA from the mycoparasitic fungus *Trichoderma harzianum. Curr. Genet.* 27, 83–89.

Geremia R.A., G.H. Goldman, D. Jacobs, W. Ardiles, S.B. Vila, M. Van Montagu and A. Herrera-Estrella. 1994. Molecular characterization of the proteinase encoding gene, prb1, related to mycoparasitism by *Trichoderma harzianum. Mol. Microbiol.* 8:603–613.

Ghand, A., A. Aruna, A. M. Maqsood and L. V. Rao. 2005. Novel mutation method for increased cellulase production. *J. Appl. Microbiol.* 98: 318–323.

Ghisalberti, E.L. and K. Sivasithamparam, 1991. Antifungal antibiotics produced by *Trichoderma* spp. *Soil Biol. Biochem.* 23: 1011-1020.

Ghisalberti, E.L. 2002. Anti-infective agents produced by the hyphomycetes general *Trichoderma* and Glioclaudium. *Curr. Med. Chem.* 1:343–374.

Goldman, G.H., W. Temmerman, D. Jacobs, R. Contreras, M. Van Montagu, and A. Herrera-Estrella. 1993. A nucleotide substitution in one of the beta-tubulin genes of *Trichoderma viride* confers resistance to the antimitotic drug methyl benzimidazole-2-yl-carbamate. *Mol. Gen. Genet.* 240: 73–80.

Gupta, V. K., M. Tuohy and G.D. Sharma. 2012. Isolation and Screening of Cellulolytic fungal species from soil. MBT-32. In: *International Conference on "Mycology and Plant Pathology: Biotechnological Approaches* (ICMPBA-2012)", 27-29th Feb., Banaras Hindu University, Varanasi, India. pp.201.

Gupta, V.K., A.K. Misra, A. Gupta, B.K. Pandey and R. K. Gaur. 2010. RAPD-PCR of *Trichoderma* isolates and in vitro antagonism against *Fusarium* wilt pathogens of *Psidium guajava* L. J.Pl. *Protec. Res.* 50: 256-262.

Gusakov, A.V. 2011. Alternatives to *Trichoderma reesei* in biofuel production. *Trends. Biotechnol.* 29:419–425.

Haran, S., H. Schickler, A. Oppenheim and I. Chet. 1995. New components of the chitinolytic system of *Trichoderma harzianum. Mycol. Res.* 99: 441-446.

Haran, S., H. Schikler, A. Oppenheim and I. Chet. 1996. Differential Expression of *Trichoderma harzianum* chitinases. *Phytopathol.* 86:981-985.

Harkki, A., A. Mantyla, M. Penttila, S. Muttilainen, R. Buhler, P. Suominen, J. Knowles and H. Nevalainen. 1991. Genetic engineering of *Trichoderma* to produce strains with novel cellulase profiles. *Enzyme Microb. Technol.* 13:227–233.

Harman, G. E. and C. P. Kubicek. 1998. *Trichoderma and Gliocladium*, Vol. 2, Enzymes, Biological Control and Commercial Applications. Taylor and Francis, London. 393 pp.

Harman, G. E., A. H. Herrera-Estrella, B. A. Horwitz and M. Lorito. 2012. Special issue: *Trichoderma* – from Basic Biology to Biotechnology. *Microbiol.* 158: 1-2.

Harman, G. E., C.K. Hayes, M. Lorito, R.M. Broadway, A. Di Pietro, C. Peterbauer, A. Tronsmo. 1993. Chitinolytic enzymes of *Trichoderma harzianum*: Purification of chitobiosidase and endochitinase. *Phyopathol.* 83:313-318.

Hawksworth, D.L., B.C. Sutton and G.C. Ainsworth. 1983. Ainsworth and Bisby's Dictionary of Fungi. Seventh Edition. Commonwealth Mycological Institute, Kew, Surry, UK.

Hayes, C.K., S. Klemsdal, M. Lorito, A. Di Pietro, C. Peterbauer, J.P. Nakas, A. Tronsmo, G.E. Harman. 1994. Isolation and sequence of an endochitinase-encoding gene from a cDNA library of *Trichoderma harzianum*. *Gene* 138:143–148.

Hermosa, M.R., I. Grondona, E.A. Iturriaga, J.M. Diaz-Minguez, C. Castro, E. Monte and I. Garcia-Acha. 2000. Molecular characterization and identification of biocontrol isolates of *Trichoderma* spp. *Appl. Environ. Microbiol.* 66: 1890–1898.

Huang, L., T.H. Hseu and T.T. Wey. 1991. Purification and characterization of an endoxylanase from *Trichoderma koningii* G-39. *Biochem. J.* 278:329-333.

Jiang, X., Geng, A., He, N., and Li, Q. 2011. New isolate of *Trichoderma viride* strain for enhanced cellulolytic enzyme complex production. *J. Biosci. Bioengg.* 111: 121-127.

Kendrick, B. 1992 The Fifth Kingdom, Mycologue Publications, Waterloo, Ontario, Canada, Mycologue Publications.

Khan, M.H., S. Ali, A. Fakhrul-Razi and Z. Alam, 2007. Use of fungi for the bioconversion of rice straw into cellulase enzyme. *J. Environ. Sci. Health.* B 42:381-386.

Kollar, A., V. Thole, T. Dalmay, and E. Balazs. 1993. Efficient coat protein mediated cross protection induced by integrated potato virus Y coat protein gene in tobacco. *Biochemie* 75: 623–629.

Kubicek, C. P. 1987. Involvement of a conidial endoglucanase and a plasma-membrane-bound beta-glucosidase in the induction of endoglucanase synthesis by cellulose in *Trichoderma reesei*. J. *Gen. Microbiol.* 133: 1481–1487.

Kulling, C.M., G. Szakacs, C.P. Kubicek. 2000. Molecular identification of *Trichoderma* species from Russia, Siberia and the Himalaya. *Mycol. Res.* 104: 1117-1125.

Kurzatkowski, W., A. Torronen, J. Filipek, R.L. Mach, P. Herzog, S. Sowka, C.P. Kubicek. 1996. Glucose-induced secretion of *Trichoderma reesei* xylanases. *Appl. Environ. Microbiol.* 62:2859-2865.

Lora, J.M., J. De La Cruz, T. Benitez and J.A. Pintor-Toro. 1995. A putative catabolite-repressed cell wall protein from the mycoparasitic fungus *Trichoderma harzianum*, *Mol. Gen. Genet.* 247: 639-645.

Lorito, M., C.K. Hayes, A. Di Pietro, S.L Woo and G.E. Harman. 1994. Purification, characterizationa and synergistic activity of a glucan 1, 3-ß-glucosidase and N-acetyl-ß-glucosaminidase from *Trichoderma harzianum*. *Phytopathol.* 84:398-405.

Lorito, M., G.E. Harman, C.K. Hayes, R.M. Broadway, A. Tronsmo, S. L Woo and A. Di Pietro. 1993. Chitinolytic enzymes produced by *Trichoderma harzianum*: antifungal activity of purified endochitinase and chitobiosidase. *Phytopathol.* 83: 302–307.

Lorito, M., V. Farkas, S. Rebuffat, B. Bodo, C. P. Kubieck. 1996. Cell wall synthesis is a major target of mycoparasitic antagonism by *Trichoderma harzianum*. *J. Bact.* 178:6382-6385.

Loritto, M. 1998. Chitinolytic enzymes and their genes. In: *Trichoderma* and *Gliocladium*, vol 2. (eds. C.P. Kubicek, G.E. Harman). Taylor and Francis, London, pp 73-99.

Mach, R. L. 1993. Mikrobielle Biochemie. Ph.D. thesis, Institute of Biochemistry and Technology, Vienna, Austria.

Mach, R.L. 1994. Direct submission EMBL accession number U09580.

Mandels, M. and R.E. Andreotti. 1978. Problems and challenges in the cellulose to cellulase fermentation. *Process Biochem.* 13:6-13.

Mandels, M., R. Andreotti, and C. Roche. 1976. Measurement of saccharifying cellulose. Biotechnol. Bioeng. Symp. 6: 21–33.

Margolles-Clark, E., M. Saloheimo, M. Siika-aho and M. Penttila. 1996c. The a-glucuronidase-encoding gene of *Trichoderma reesei*. *Gene* 172:171–172.

Margolles-Clark, E., M. Tenkanen, E. Luonteri, and M. Penttila. 1996b. Three α-galactosidase genes of *Trichoderma reesei* cloned by expression in yeast. *Eur. J. Biochem.* 240: 104–111.

Margolles-Clark, E., M. Tenkanen, H. Soderlund and M. Penttila. 1996d. Acetyl xylan esterase from *Trichoderma reesei* contains an active-site serine residue and a cellulose-binding domain. *Eur. J. Biochem.* 237: 553–560.

Margolles-Clark, E., M. Tenkanen, T. Nakari-Setala and M. Penttila. 1996a. Cloning of genes encoding alpha-L-arabinofuranosidase and beta-xylosidase from *Trichoderma reesei* by expression in Saccharomyces cerevisiae. *Appl. Environ. Microbiol.* 62, 3840–3846.

Margolles-Clark, M., M. Ilmen, and M. Penttila. 1997. Expression patterns of 10 hemicellulase genes from filamentous fungus *Trichoderma reesei* on various carbon sources. *J. Biotechnol.* 57: 167–179.

Migheli, Q., L. GonzalezCandelas, L. Dealessi, A. Camponogara and D. RamonVidal. 1998. Transformants of *Trichoderma longibrachiatum* overexpressing the β-1,4-endoglucanase gene egl1 show enhanced biocontrol of *Pythium ultimum* on cucumber. *Biol. Control.* 88: 673-67.

Misra A.K. and V.K. Gupta. 2009. *Trichoderma*: Biology, Biodiversity and Biotechnology. *J. Eco-friendly Agri.* 4:99-117.

Monte, E. 2001. Understanding *Trichoderma*: Between biotechnology and microbial ecology. *Int. Microbiol.* 4: 1-4.

Mukherjee P. K., N. Buensanteai, M. E. Moran-Diez, I. S. Druzhinina C. M. Kenerley. 2012. Functional analysis of non-ribosomal peptide synthetases (NRPSs) in *Trichoderma virens* reveals a polyketide synthase (PKS)/NRPS hybrid enzyme involved in the induced systemic resistance response in maize. *Microbiol.* 158: 155–165.

Mukherjee, M., R. Hadar, P.K. Mukherjee and B.A. Horwitz. 2003. Homologous expression of a mutated beta-tubulin gene does not confer benomyl resistance on *Trichoderma virens*. *J. Appl. Microbiol.* 95: 861–867.

Nakari-Setala, T and M. Penttila. 1995. Production of *Trichoderma reesei* cellulases on glucose-containing media. *Appl. Environ. Microbiol.* 61:3650–3655.

Nevalainen, K.M.H., E.T. Palva and M.J. Bailey. 1980. A high cellulase producing mutant strain of *Trichoderma reesei*. *Enz. Microbial Technol*. 2:59-60.

Nigam, P. 1994. Processing of sugar beet pulp in simultaneous saccharification and fermentation for the production of a protein-enriched product. *Process Biochem*. 29:331-336.

Nogawa, M., M. Goto, H. Okada and Y. Morikawa. 2001. L-sorbose induces cellulase gene transcription in the cellulolytic fungus *Trichoderma reesei.Curr. Genet*. 38: 329–334.

Okada, H., K. Tada, T. Sekiya, K. Yokoyama, A. Takahashi, H. Tohda, H. Kumagai and Y. Morikawa. 1998. Molecular characterization and heterologous expression of the gene encoding a low-molecular-mass endoglucanase from *Trichoderma reesei* QM9414. *Appl. Environ. Microbiol*. 64: 555–563.

Papavizas, G. C. 1985. *Trichoderma* and *Gliocladium*: Biology and potential for biocontrol. *Ann. Rev. Phytopathol*. 23: 23-54.

Penttila, M., P. Lehtovaara, H. Nevalainen, R. Bhikhabhai, and J. Knowles. 1986. Homology between cellulase genes of *Trichoderma reesei*: complete nucleotide sequence of the endoglucanase I gene. *Gene* 45:253–263.

Penttilä, M., C. Limon, and H. Nevalainen. 2004. Molecular biology *Trichoderma* and biotechnological applications. In: *Handbook of fungal biotechnology*, (Ed. Arora, D). Marcel Dekker, Inc. pp. 413.427.

Pere, J., J. Ellmen, J. Honkasalo, P. Taipalus, and T. Tienvieri. 2002. Enhancement of TMP rejects refining by enzymatic modification of pulp carbohydrates. A mill study. In: *Biotechnology in the Pulp and Paper Industry: 8th ICBPPI Meeting, Progress in Biotechnology* (eds. L. Viikari, and R.Lantto), Elsevier Science B.V. Vol. 21. pp. 281-290.

Peterbauer, C. K., M. Lorito, C. K. Hayes, G. E. Harman and C. P. Kubicek. 1996. Molecular cloning and expression of the nag1 gene (N-acetyl-b-D-glucosaminidase-encoding gene) from *Trichoderma harzianum* P1. *Curr. Genet*. 30: 325–331.

Peterson R. and H. Nevalainen. 2012. *Trichoderma reesei* RUT-C30 – thirty years of strain improvement. *Microbiol*. 158*:* 58–68.

Pitson, S.M., R.J. Seviour and B.M. McDougall. 1993. Non cellulolytic fungal ß-glucanases: their physiology and regulation. *Enz. Microbial Technol*. 15:178-192.

Rahkamo, L., M. Siika-Aho, M. Vehviläinen, M. Dolk, L. Viikari, P. Nousiainen and J. Buchert. 1996. Modification of hardwood dissolving pulp with purified *Trichoderma reesei* cellulases. *Cellulose 3*:153.163.

Ramot, O., R. Cohen-Kupiec and I. Chet. 2000. Regulation of b-1,3-glucanase by carbon starvation in the mycoparasite *Trichoderma harzianum*. *Mycol. Res*. 104, 415-420.

Rifai, M.A., 1969. A revision of the genus *Trichoderma*. Commonwealth Mycological Institute. *Mycological Papers* 116: 1-56.

Ryder L. S., B. D. Harris, D. M. Soanes, M. J. Kershaw, N. J. Talbot, C. R. Thornton. 2012. Saprotrophic competitiveness and biocontrol fitness of a genetically modified strain of the plant-growth-promoting fungus *Trichoderma hamatum* GD12. *Microbiol*. 158*:* 84–97.

Saadia, M., S. Ahmed and A. Jamil. 2008. Isolation and cloning of cre1 gene from a filamentous fungus *Trichoderma harzianum*. *Pak. J.* Bot. 40: 421-426.

Saarelainen, R., M. Paloheimo, R. Fagerstro¨m, P. L. Suominen, and K. M. H. Nevalainen. 1993. Cloning, sequencing and enhanced expression of the *Trichoderma reesei* endoxylanase II (pI9) gene xln2. *Mol. Gen. Genet.* 241:497–503.

Sahai, A.S. and M.S. Manocha. 1993. Chitinases of fungi and plants: their involvement in morphogenesis and host-parasite interaction. *FEMS Microbiol. Rev.* 11:317–338.

Saloheimo, A., B. Henrissat, A. M. Hoffren, O. Teleman, and M. Penttila. 1994. A novel, small endoglucanase gene, egl5, from *Trichoderma reesei* isolated by expression in yeast. *Mol. Microbiol.* 13:219–228.

Saloheimo, M. L. A., M. Siika-aho, M. Tenkanen, M. Penttila, B. S. Bower and K. Clarkson. 2001. World Intellectual Property Organization, Genencor International, Inc., Palo Alto, CA.

Saloheimo, M., M. Paloheimo, S. Hakola, J. Pere, B. Swanson, E. Nyyssonen, A. Bhatia, M. Ward, and M. Penttila. 2002. Swollenin, a *Trichoderma reesei* protein with sequence similarity to the plant expansins, exhibits disruption activity on cellulosic materials. *Eur. J. Biochem.* 269: 4202–4211.

Saloheimo, M., P. Lehtovaara, M. Penttila, T. T. Teeri, J. Stahlberg, G. Johansson, G. Pettersson, M. Claeyssens, P. Tomme, and J. K. Knowles. 1988. EGIII, a new endoglucanase from *Trichoderma reesei*: The characterization of both gene and enzyme. *Gene* 63:11–22.

Saloheimo, M., T. Nakari-Setala, M. Tenkanen, and M. Penttila. 1997. cDNA cloning of a Trichoderma reesei cellulase and demonstration of endoglucanase activity by expression in yeast. *Eur.J. Biochem.* 249: 584–591.

Saloheimo, M., and T. M. Pakula. 2012**.** The cargo and the transport system: secreted proteins and protein secretion in *Trichoderma reesei* (*Hypocrea jecorina*). *Microbiol.* 158*:* 46–57.

Samuels, G.J. 1996. *Trichoderma*: a review of biology and systematics of the genus. *Mycol. Res.* 100:923-935.

Schirmbock, M., M. Lorito, Y. Wang, C.K. Hayes, I. Arisan-Atac, F. Scala, G. E. Harman, and C.P. Kubicek. 1994. Parallel formataion and synergism of hydrolytic enzymes and peptaibol antibiotics, molecular mechanisms involved in the antagonistic action of *Trichoderma harzianum* against phytopathogenic fungi. *Appl.Environ. Microbiol.* 60:4364-4370.

Schmoll, M and C.P. Kubicek. 2003. Regulation of *Trichoderma* cellulase formation: Lessons in molecular biology from an industrial fungus. A review. *Acta. Microbiol. Immunol. Hung*. 50:125-145.

Schülein, M. 2000. Protein engineering of cellulases. *Biochimica* et *Biophysica Acta* 1543 : 239-252.

Schuster, A. and M. Schmoll. 2010 Biology and biotechnology of *Trichoderma*. A*ppl Microbiol Biotechnol.* 87:787-99.

Service, R. F. 2007. Cellulosic ethanol: biofuel researchers prepare to reap a new harvest. *Science* 315: 1488–1491.

Shoemaker, S., V. Schweickart, M. Ladner, D. Gelfand, S. Kwok, and K. A. I. M. Myambo, 1983. Molecular cloning of exo-cellobiohydrolase derived from Trichoderma reesei strain L27. *Biotechnol*. 1: 691–696.

Sivan, A. and I. Chet. 1989. The possible role of competition between *Trichoderma harzianum* and *Fusarium oxysporum* on rhizosphere colonization. *Phytopathol.* 79: 198-203.

Sivan, A., Y. Elad and I. Chet. 1984. Biological control effects of a new isolate of *Trichoderma harzianum* on *Pythium aphanidermatum*. *Phytopathol.* 74:498-501.

Stalbrand, H., A. Saloheimo, J. Vehmaanpera, B. Henrissat, and M. Penttila. 1995. Cloning and expression in *Saccharomyces cerevisiae* of a *Trichoderma reesei* beta-mannanase gene containing a cellulose binding domain. *Appl. Environ. Microbiol.* 61: 1090–10977.

Stangl, H., F. Gruber and C.P. Kubicek. 1993. Characterization of the *Trichoderma reesei* by sophorose. *J. Bacteriol.* 139: 761-767.

Stangl, H., F. Gruber, and C.P. Kubicek. 1993. Characterization of the *Trichoderma reesei* cbh2 promoter. *Curr. Genet.* 23:115–122.

Strauss, J., R.L. Mach, S. Zeilinger, G. Hartler, G. Stoffler, M. Wolschek, and C.P. Kubicek. 1995. Cre1, the carbon catabolite represser protein from *Trichoderma reesei*. *FEBS Lett.* 376:103–107.

Suurnäkki, A., M.L. Niku-Paavola, J. Buchert, and L. Viikari. 2004. Enzymes in pulp and paper processing. In: Enzymes in industry (ed. W.Aehle), Weinheim, Wiley-VCH. pp. 437-439.

Szengyel, Z., G. Zacchi, A. Varga, and K. Reczey. 2000. Cellulase production of *Trichoderma reesei* RUT C30 using steam- pretreated spruce. Hydrolytic potential of cellulases on differnt substrate. *Appl. Biochem. Biotechnol.* 84-86:679-691.

Takashima, S., A. Nakamura, M. Hidaka, H. Masaki, and T. Uozumi. 1999 *J. Biochem.* (Tokyo) 125: 728–736.

Teeri, T. T., P. Lehtovaara, S. Kauppinen, I. Salovuori, and J. Knowles. 1987. Homologous domains in Trichoderma reesei cellulolytic enzymes—gene sequence and expression of cellobiohydrolase-II. Gene 51: 43–52.

Torronen, A., R. L. Mach, R. Messner, R. Gonzalez, N. Kalkkinen, A. Harkki, and C. P. Kubicek. 1992. The two major xylanases from *Trichoderma reesei*: characterization of both enzymes and genes. *Biotechnol.* 10: 1461–1465.

Urlaub, R. 2002. Enzymes in fruit and vegetable juice extraction. In: Enzymes in food technology. (eds. R. Whitehurst and B.Law) Sheffield, Academic Press, CRC Press. USA. pp. 145-183.

Viterbo, A., M. Montero, O. Ramot, D. Friesem, E. Monte, A. Llobell and I. Chet. 2002. Expression regulation of the endochitinase chit36 from *Trichoderma asperellum* (T. *harzianum* T-203). *Curr. Genet.* 42: 114–122.

Wey, T.T., T.H. Hseu and L. Huang. 1994. Molecular cloning and sequence analysis of the cellobiohydrolase I gene from *Trichoderma* koningii G-39. *Curr. Microbiol.* 28: 31–39.

Zeilinger, S., C. Galhaup, K. Payer, S.L. Woo, R.L. Mach, C. Feket, M. Lorito and C.P. Kubicek. 1999. Chitinase gene expression during mycoparasitic interaction of *Trichoderma harzianum* with its host. *Fungal Genet. Biol.* 26: 131-140.

Zeilinger, S., M. Haller, R. Mach and C.P. Kubicek. 2000. Molecular characterization of a cellulose negative mutant of *Hypocrea jecorina*. *Biochem. Biophys. Res. Commun.*, 277: 581-588.

Zhang, Y.-H.P., M.E. Himmel, J.R. Mielenz. 2006. Outlook for cellulose improvement: screening and selection strategies. *Biotechnol. Adv.* 24: 452–481.

http://www.isth.info/morphology.php.

Index

B

D

E

F

G

H

I

J

K

L

M

N

O

P

Q

R

S

V

W

X

Y

Z